ALIAS MACALIAS

By the same author

Elegies for the Dead in Cyrenaica (1948)

Gramsci's Prison Letters: a selection translated and introduced by Hamish Henderson (1988)

Pipes, Goatskin & Bones: the Songs and Poems of Hamish Henderson (1992)

The Obscure Voice: translations of Italian Poets (1994)

The Armstrong Nose: Selected letters of Hamish Henderson ed. Alec Finlay (1995)

Freedom Come-All-Ye: Poems and Songs of Hamish Henderson (1999)

Collected Poems and Songs (2000)

Alias MacAlias

Writings on Songs, Folk and Literature

HAMISH HENDERSON

Edited by Alec Finlay

Second edition first published in Great Britain in 2004 by
Polygon, an imprint of Birlinn Ltd
West Newington House
10 Newington Road
Edinburgh
EH9 1QS

First published in 1992 by Polygon

www.birlinn.co.uk

ISBN 1 904598 21 8

The publishers acknowledge subsidy from

Scottish
Arts Council

towards the publication of this volume

British Library Cataloguing-in-Publication Data
A catalogue record for this book is available on request
from the British Library

Typeset by Koinonia, Bury, Lancashire
Printed and bound in Great Britain by
Antony Rowe Ltd, Chippenham, Wiltshire

To Peter Kravitz and Eck Finlay

Contents

LITERATURE AND POLITICS

Editor's Preface

These essays span some fifty years, from the first, 'Germany in Defeat', which Hamish wrote when he was 27 and sent home to be published by Hugh MacDiarmid in *The Voice of Scotland* in June of 1947, to the late episodes in autobiography that he gave to his friend Ray Ross for *Cencrastus* magazine. The first predates his *Elegies for the Dead in Cyrenaica*, the work which won him his first literary recognition, while the last date from his years of retirement from academic life.

Most of the essays were published during Hamish's years at the School of Scottish Studies, Edinburgh University, which he joined in 1952 – he was never a conventional academic and as many appeared in the fugitive pages of little magazines as did in scholarly periodicals. Hamish devoted himself to the living folk traditions of Scotland and the Revival that he campaigned for has been an important contribution to the wider growth in national consciousness. The essays descry a constant faith in the possibilities of renewal and offer an illuminating commentary on our national character, its vicissitudes and virtues.

As Hamish describes, the folk tradition proceeds by a series of revivals, as each generation rediscovers and recreates the culture of the past. His essays were one of the ways in which he sought to guide the movement, setting up the finest performers and material as examples to the new generation of singers, musicians and collectors. As well as actively contributing to the Revival, his writings form a critical history of the movement, one authored by its principal strategist. Particular attention is paid to the early years of the movement, including the arrival of Alan Lomax, the 'discovery' of Jeannie Robertson, and the People's Festival Ceilidhs of 1951, 1952 and 1953, which Hamish referred to as 'epoch making'.

The essays range in style from amusing autobiographical reminiscences, chatty reviews, flytings and scholarly analyses of songs and tales. They form a rich commentary on a folk culture that is now commonly available on radio, television, video and DVD, recordings and live performances. This expanded edition benefits from the inclusion of Hamish's long essay on Antonio Gramsci, first published in the Zwan edition of his translation of the *Prison Letters*.

As Hamish makes clear, some of the greatest riches of folk arts are preserved on the fringes of Scotland, geographically and socially. In his case, it was the North-East that he returned to, again and again, and especially the tinker-gypsies, whose contribution to contemporary folk culture is given full and rightful recognition. He lived to see one of the singers nourished within the Revival, Sheena Wellington, sing a Burns song unaccompanied at the opening of the Scottish parliament, and, as much as Donald Dewar, it was Hamish who made this possible.

My own friendship with Hamish was dear to me and he exerted a strong influence on my vision, not so much in terms of folk culture or poetry, though he taught me a great deal about both, but more in the way that he allowed a new sense of my social world. Hamish taught all of his friends the art of sharing our common humanity. I am glad to hear that another close friend of Hamish's, Tim Neat, is embarking on a biography, for the story of that singular adventurous life needs to be told and there is no one better equipped for the task.

I first ordered a copy of *Alias MacAlias* from Polygon's catalogue when I was living in a freezing cottage outside Dunblane. Shortly afterwards I moved to Edinburgh and met Hamish for the first time. We were neighbours, and I often bumped into him when he was ambling across the Meadows to his University office or his other 'office' in Sandy Bell's. I was still waiting for the book to arrive from Polygon. One day Hamish asked me to pop over for lunch – always a *dolce latte* roll for him – and revealed that the 'book' I had ordered was sitting in its raw state in a cardboard box in the corner of his kitchen. That was how I got the job of editor. When I first met my new boss, Marion Sinclair, in the tiny attic room that Polygon squatted in upstairs from the offices of Edinburgh University Press, I agreed to take on the job if she would first return the cheque that I sent in payment for the book.

There followed many many lunches in Hamish's chaotic kitchen, with the twin bars of the electric fire blazing. The fees were not what you would call royal, but my involvement with the man was one of the great joys of my life. It has been an eerie experience to return to this material a dozen or more years later, with Hamish now departed and myself living in Newcastle, over the border I had not expected to cross. If I feel less certain of my relationship to the Scotland of today, re-encountering Hamish's idealistic vision returns me to the yellow on the broom and the sharp beauty of Jeannie Robertson's voice. No doubt other readers will encounter a gulf of some kind between the vision that Hamish describes and the Scotland of their day-to-day lives, for the essays are a key political interrogation of this post-devolution nation.

I would like to thank the new incarnation of Polygon for inviting me to make this journey into the past, especially Neville Moir and Alison Rae. I would also like to take this chance to thank Peter Kravitz, Murdo MacDonald, Marion Sinclair and Alison Bowden, all of whom were involved in the cultural adventure that was Polygon and the *Edinburgh Review*, for, along with Hamish, they helped to shape a culture.

Alec Finlay
June 2004

Introduction to the First Edition

'You spend too much time', growled, genially, a distinguished Scots academic long domiciled in the South, 'talking to little poets in Sandy Bell's.' 'Oh but', I replied, 'there are *big* poets in Sandy Bell's.'

I remembered a day in 1981 when I dropped into Bell's for a half pint before lunch and came out dizzy seven hours later. Hamish Henderson had presided over an impromptu colloquium involving Tom Leonard, Cathal the flautist from the Boys of the Lough, and a schoolteacher from Glasgow called Lorna never seen by any of us before nor, by me, since. She and I mostly nodded and smiled while Cathal played, Tom recited stanza after stanza of 'B. V.' Thomson from memory, and Hamish reminisced, sang, and reminisced more. There was no kitschy, self-conscious posturing, no beery flirtation – it was all serious pleasure, a communion on some high frontier of culture to which Hamish had led us, from which every Scottish century could be surveyed, but also green Ireland, the townships of South Africa, Brittany, Italy, Germany, Lorca's Andalusia ... even England. '*Little* poets'?

Yet I didn't put together in my head quite how big Hamish has been till I had the chance to inspect the matter gathered in this book. At one moment he's impinged as a great scholarly song collector – as the late Ewan MacColl said, 'worthy of being ranked with Gavin Greig and David Herd'. At another as the writer of songs himself – above all of 'Ye Banks of Sicily' and the 'Freedom Come All Ye' – and also a fine poet, regrettably scant in output, whose *Elegies for the Dead in Cyrenaica* are uniquely ambitious among poems in English from World War II and indeed are unlike anything else in the language. In another connection still, one has seen Hamish as a serious political fighter - the first British translator of Gramsci, back in the Forties; the man who threw Thatcher's offer of a decoration back in her face.

But in fact all these remarkable persons have been present in Hamish at once, whenever one's noticed him. Like David Lindsay and David Hume, he can't be contained within any of the categories which the bureaucratised culture of the industrial west has insisted we use. He skips wavelengths. Is he Radio 4 or Radio 2? He's certainly too outgoing for Radio 3. Today's world politics and a renaissance sonnet, a bairn's rhyme and the history of religion, matter equally to him, and he can relate them all to each other. Straitlaced theoretical Marxists are likely to shake their heads as hard as fashionable Social Marketeers over the small-c communism which provides Hamish with his perspective on human life. He fought Fascism in person, at risk. He wrote songs about it. He studies songs. Ideas and action haven't been separate.

Hamish has called this book *Alias MacAlias* in tribute to Hugh Mac-Diarmid, so named by him in an article here informed by exasperation as well as affection. The first time I ever saw either man was at a public Edinburgh Festival debate in the 1960s. Hamish protested when MacDiarmid denounced folk-song as 'the ignorant drivellings of swinish shepherds'. Valda Grieve riposted with sandblasting invective – does my memory trick me or did she really say 'Ye lie in your black heart, Hamish Henderson'? Yet as every fiction writer and opera composer in Russia was once proud to have come out from under Gogol's overcoat, so Hamish joins the extremely diverse assemblage of distinguished artists and thinkers who have saluted Grieve-MacAlias's diffuse yet definitive influence on our culture.

Hamish was early in touch with another great Grievite. His article on Sorley MacLean's poetry in the *Daily Worker,* published in 1949 when only a very few Anglophones knew of Sorley's work, and anticipating by two decades its international impact, is one of the sharpest pleasures in this book. His comparison of MacLean with Neruda points us to his own capacity to achieve a synthesis distinct from, yet complementing, MacDiarmid's.

Neruda – like Brecht, like Picasso, like MacDiarmid himself – exemplifies one element in Hamish's synthesis. All these men were large-C communists. But any twittering liberal or gallus Thatcherite rottan who believes that their influence on our lives has lapsed with the coming down of the Berlin Wall is pissing into a hurricane. Hamish has drawn great strengths from the movement with which they, and he, associated, which promoted working-class internationalism. Before long, considered verdicts will begin to separate such strengths from the vices of Stalinist bureaucracy.

But Neruda also relates – as the others named do – as MacLean does, and as Henderson does – to another international movement, Modernism. Hamish was happy, in 1966, to acknowledge the influence on him of T. S. Eliot, and of Yeats's *Last Poems* which he carried to war with him. That film *Play Me Something* in which we can savour Hamish's appearance was constructed by its writer, John Berger, and director Tim Neat, in the late Eighties in terms of continuing modernist experiment. As with Communism, negative aspects of Modernism have to be acknowledged. The elitism of leading Modernists is well documented – not least, that, on occasion, of MacDiarmid.

And that is where a third element in Hamish's synthesis, the one best represented in this book, is so important. Like Bartók, like Copland, he recognised the power of folk tradition. More clearly, perhaps, than either, he saw its potential political significance. This tradition is a basis for the Scottish political autonomy which Hamish wants – it is also a nursery of forms for living protest song, and celebration, in our industrialised, now perhaps 'post-industrial', Scotland.

Enough can be found in this book, and elsewhere, to establish, without much further marvelling from me, the truly epochal significance of Hamish's meeting with Jeannie Robertson in Aberdeen in 1953. Insofar as Hamish had already inspired the Edinburgh People's Festival, launched by Norman Buchan and others in 1951, with his own delight in traditional music, the 'Folk-song Revival' was already under way. The existence of the School of Scottish Studies already guaranteed that tradition would be recorded and conserved. But the austere classic power of Jeannie's singing of the great ballads gave the causes of popularisation and preservation the stimulus of association with artistry of international calibre, with language as powerful as any in literature. If it's almost impossible to talk with Hamish for long on any subject whatever without hearing him refer to 'Jeannie', well, that is his proud right, and no more than her due.

However, nostalgia for unaccompanied singing like Jeannie's, when she rose up like the Middle Ages in person, is not in Hamish's character. When, in a note of 1987 printed here, he praises Freddy Anderson for belonging to 'a long line of courageous radical poets whose most famous members include Byron and Burns – not forgetting Woody Guthrie', he identifies himself completely with the work of modern, urban song writers. In his 'MacAlias' essay on MacDiarmid, he refers, as so often, to the 'constant fruitful interaction of folk song and art literature in our tradition ... the sort of set-up in which no one can say for sure where MacAlias ends and anon begins'. All the major Scottish writers since before Dunbar and Lindsay, through Burns and Scott and Hogg, down to Grassic Gibbon, MacDiarmid and MacLean, can be heard as distinctive voices arising within, not separate from, a continuous strong flow of language and music in which labourers and scholars have swum together.

Hamish has quoted the American folklorist Alan Lomax, with whom he collaborated for several years, to the effect that 'the Scots have the liveliest folk tradition of the British Isles, but, paradoxically, it is the most bookish.' Hamish himself, his head stored with Gramsci and Hölderlin, chatting with the Stewart family of travelling folk musicians amid the berryfields of his native Perthshire, exemplifies as no one else among us does a particular mode of the 'democratic intellect'. If Donnie Munro of RunRig gets elected Rector of Edinburgh University – and takes his job very seriously – this can be seen as a tribute to the way in which Hamish, above all, has sustained the most distinctively Scottish of our traditions. When Communicado marched into the Tramway arena at the opening of Glasgow's 1990 'European City of Culture' festival, singing, to start their Burns-play *Jock Tamson's Bairns*, Hamish's 'Flyting o' Life and Daith' that, justly, produced him as representative:

> Quo life, the world is mine
> Though ye bigg preesons o' marble stane
> Hert's luve ye cannae preeson in
> Quo life, the world is mine.

Or, as Neruda wrote:

> Salgo ahora
> En este día lleno de volcanes
> Hacia la multitud, hacia la vida...

> I am going out now
> On this day of volcanoes
> Towards the multitude, towards life.

Angus Calder, 1992

A River That Flows On[1]

Hamish Henderson: a man whose stature may stand compared to that of Nelson Mandela, as Tim Neat suggested in his funeral oration. What are we to make of such a claim? Standing among the throng in St Mary's Cathedral, our shared feelings allowed the comparison, for each of us recalled the spirit of the man we all knew simply as *Hamish*.

His funeral was fittingly an occasion that blended state ceremony and the common people: when Essie Stewart came forward in her buttoned Mac, stepping past the pews in which Hamish's dear family sat, past the small figure of the First Minister, to sing 'Jock Stewart', our voices rose in unison to the chorus, *a man you won't meet every day*. In that profane song that ebbed through the nave there was the epitome of the man. Like so many people who were there that day, Hamish's life touched and changed mine, and I believe there is no-one in modern Scotland who affected as many people's lives.

From his wartime exploits with the Highland Div., to his achievements as a poet, song-maker, folklorist, translator and political activist, Hamish made an unquantifiable contribution to the renewal of Scottish culture. He figures alongside Robert Burns and Hugh MacDiarmid: like Burns his lifework bridges the gap between the 'heich' and 'laich' arts, renewing the carrying stream of traditional culture through a popular folksong Revival; and with MacDiarmid he shaped a renewal of national consciousness.

This expanded edition of *Alias MacAlias* includes his late autobiographical essays, the introduction to Gramsci's *Prison Letters* and a few earlier pieces that slipped through the net of the first edition. Hamish's creativity cannot be measured in terms of bibliography alone, for we have first to account for the influence of his informal pedagogy and the manner in which his natural conviviality was in itself a cultural force.

* * *

The Folk Revival is the crucial bridge between the Scottish Renaissance of the 1920s and 1930s, conceived and inspired by MacDiarmid, and contemporary Scottish culture. Writing in 1948 Hamish gave a high estimate of MacDiarmid's achievements :

> Rescuing the Scots tongue from the slough of havering provincialism ... Mac-Diarmid demonstrated incontrovertibly ... that it was still capable of becoming art poetry ... [his] stand in defence of these ideas against every kind of defam-

ation and calumny has been little short of heroic. Now, having won through, he towers in rugged monolithic eminence above the contemporary Scottish scene.[2]

The Folk Revival widened the scope of its predecessor and, in Hamish's view, was a counter-balance to the sequestered characteristics of the Renaissance. Straightways we confront the tension between the two men that would spark and take flame in their flytings. Hamish's complex relationship to the Langholm byspale was played out over three decades. In a poem that he began in 1945 but only published in 1967, he speirs: '*I try to make sense of your tortured logomachy* ... / *Amidst all the posturings tantrums and rages* ... / *Just what do you stand for MacDiarmid? / I'm still not certain*'.[3] The lengthy reminiscences that he published in *Cencrastus* magazine in the mid-1990s are a late digging over of this dark matter.

Hamish suggested that their flytings were inevitable, that MacDiarmid '*had* to have them', and so, over the course of a decade (1959–69), they matched one another blow-for-blow. Flyting is shadow play, with all the exaggerations and distortions that entail and, given their intimate knowledge of each other's strengths and weaknesses, as the disputes grew in intensity they tended to project aspects of Scotland's riven consciousness onto one another. The portrait of MacDiarmid that emerges here does reveal the worst of his faults: a life-denying isolationism and an intellectual fascism. Their disputes also illuminate Hamish's complex psyche and it becomes impossible to avoid an Oedipal interpretation.

*   *   *

The period of Hamish's close alliance with MacDiarmid in the aftermath of the war saw his most direct political statements in terms of Marxism and Nationalism. As a handsome young Highlander newly returned from illustrious service in the anti-fascist struggle, he was the natural successor, and, with the publication of his great poetic epic *The Elegies for the Dead of Cyrenaica* (1948), he laid down his claim.

The 'Tenth Elegy' describes the task Hamish had taken on:

> So I turn aside in the benighted deadland
> to perform a duty, noting an outlying
> grave, or restoring a fallen cross-piece.
> Remembrancer ...[4]

The *Elegies* were begun in the desert (1942), worked over in the Lochboisdale Hotel, South Uist (1946), and completed during a visit to Naomi Mitchison in Kintyre (1947). They stand as one of the great poetic responses to World War II, an attempt to discern a wider philosophical significance in this 'human civil war'.

Hamish went to war with copies of *A Drunk Man Looks at the Thistle*, and Sorley MacLean and Robert Garioch's *17 Poems for 6d.* tucked in his battledress, and then embarked on his own contemporary bardic history. This uncanny landscape of failure and dream, in which 'roles seem constantly to shift and vary',[5] was prescient of his lifelong examination of the ambiguities of identity. The bare wasteland recalls the desolation wreaked by Calvinism: '*the wilderness of your white corries, Kythairon* ...', the '*treeless machair*' and '*circled kirkyard*'. Nor was Hamish shy of mythic identities as a day's leave becomes a quest through the Valley of the Kings searching for Rilke's single column, *'die eine im Karnak'*.[6]

Hamish sought to forge an art which could resist the political chasm of Fascism and proclaim the warring aspects of the psyche reconciled:

> We'll mak siccar!
> ... mak siccar against the monkish adepts
> of total war against the oppressed oppressors
> ... against the worked out systems of sick perversion
> mak siccar
> against the executioner
> against the tyrannous myth and the real terror.
> *mak siccar*[7]

MacDiarmid praised *The Elegies* as comparable with the war poetry of Brooke, Sassoon and Owen':[8] generous though this is, it obscures the poems' range of intellectual concerns. More convincing comparisons are with Eliot, Pound and Auden, who cast a spell over his generation at Cambridge, and with his peers, Nicholas Moore and John Cornford (martyr of an earlier episode in the anti-fascist struggle). Most remarkable of all is the influence of Heine, Goethe, Hölderlin and Rilke,[9] poets who reconcile 'our own and the others'. This love of German poetry stayed with Hamish, and I can remember an afternoon in Melville Terrace when he recited Rilke's *Tenth Elegy* to me in German entirely from memory.

The *TLS*'s reviewer described *The Elegies* as a 'Teutonic oversimplification';[10] yet Hamish understood Germany well from his stay in Göttingen (1939), where he wrote some songs in German that remain unpublished to this day. His translations of European poetry place him in a great tradition of Scottish translators. MacDiarmid had translated Rilke as early as 1930 and, in 'Vestigia Nulla Retrorsum', identified his 'stone world' of Shetland with Duino:

> A naked stone from the castle wall
> Of Duino itself riven might be brought here to serve!
> And yet no different from many another stone
> Of this small island incredibly grey and lone.[11]

Relatively few years separate their very different 'desert' poems. In 'The War with England' MacDiarmid admits '*I was better with the voices of the sea / Than with the voices of men / And in desolate and desert places / I found myself again*'. Although Hamish understood something of the desperate poverty MacDiarmid and his family endured on Whalsay, he was repelled by these chill emotions. The vehemence of the Flytings can, in part, be traced back to the emotive associations between MacDiarmid's isolationism and the deathly tyranny Hamish confronted in the desert.

Despite the dangers of wartime Hamish loved the comradeship of battle, especially his time with the *Resistenza*, and his political vision was inspired by these experiences. They also explain why the poetic epic was not finally enough and why he chose to turn instead towards the popular art of song, choosing a 'fusion of my two greatest loves: the anonymous song poetry of Scotland ... and the comradely solidarity of the anti-fascist struggle which dominated my early manhood'.[12]

In the aftermath of the war Hamish was a loyal supporter to MacDiarmid and Valda.

While he was in Belfast working with the W.E.A. (1948–49) he edited *Selected Poems*, though this fell foul of the ups-and-downs in the relationship between MacDiarmid and his printer patrons. He also proselytised for MacDiarmidism in essays such as 'Flower of Iron and Truth' (1946), an overview of contemporary Scottish literature which distinguishes between two schools, The Lallans Makars, who 'desire to extend and enrich the capacities of the revitalised Scots tongue as a vehicle for literature', are an 'unofficial Academy', and the Clyde Group, who follow MacDiarmid but are:

> ... not primarily interested in the language question ... They are resolved ... to produce work which will interpret more immediately the reality of the ... commons of Alba, the industrial proletariat ... [and the] Highland remnant. In a word they have comprehended the need for a literature of presentification. Reacting strongly against the seeming archaism of the Makars – an archaism more of subject matter than language ... The poets of the 'Clyde Group' ... fear that [Lallans] may turn into a mere academic exercise, a field of Alexandrian virtuosity – a 'pluralism of superstructures' above a life with which it has lost all contact.[13]

The Clyde Group, John Kincaid, Thurso Berwick (Maurice Blythman), George Todd and Freddie Anderson,[14] were all good friends of Hamish's. Criticism of the Makars became marked in a companion essay, 'Lallans and all that' (1949), where these 'bourgeois nationalists' are described as 'hopelessly hobbled from the start by their political gormlessness'.

Although Hamish is now associated with Edinburgh, in the 1940s he allied himself with the more progressive Glasgow. The Clyde Group has faded from view but its characteristics can be recognised in that broad Glaswegian tradition of working-class art: Unity Theatre; 7:84 and The Citizens; Workers' City; writers such as Tom Leonard, James Kelman and Gerry Loose; artists such as Ken Currie, Ross Sinclair and Ross Birrell.

Hamish's political philosophy refined when he embarked on a close reading of Gramsci and his rhetoric softened when he began collecting folk-song in the early 1950s. He had the collecting habit long before, making forays as a teenager on long cycle tours over the back roads of the Mearns. In the war his notebooks were filled with the songs, stories and bawdy verses of British soldiers, POWs and partisans, and letters home peppered with fragments of folk-song and poetry. The soldiers' songs, including his own 'D-Day Dodgers' and 'The Banks of Sicily', appeared in his first published book, *Ballads of World War 2* (1947), a clandestine publication sanctioned by the fictitious Lili Marlene Club, anticipating 'O, What a Lovely War' by some two decades.

When Hamish returned to Cambridge to complete his degree in Modern Languages at Downing College (1945) he found a circle of friends and mentors, including E. P. Thompson and Raymond Williams, who shared his interest in popular culture. This was a generation for whom wartime experiences allied radicalism with pragmatism.

One of the most perceptive reviews of *The Elegies* was by Thompson, though his praise did not preclude some critical questioning:

> He desires to speak directly, out of his experiences, to his fellow men. But he is all the time aware that the audience he is most likely to reach is circumscribed by

the coteries and sophisticated reviews. If he can only cast off this censor and assert his confidence, not in an impersonal dialectic but in the people who make their own history, he will find in himself an unusual ability to speak their most mature thoughts and sing them on the way to victory.[15]

Thompson understands that at the heart of Hamish's creativity was a complex attitude to *voice* and perceptively suggests the resolution that would follow, *song*. In the 'Prologue' of *The Elegies* Hamish admitted as much in his description of poetry: '... *a bit/That sets on song a discipline,/A sensuous austerity*'. A personal letter from Thompson pinpoints what was at stake:

> I greet you with humility campagno, for you are that rare man, a poet. You have achieved poems out of our dead century ... and you must never let yourself ... be driven into the arms of the 'culture boys' ... They would kill your writing, because you, more than any other poet I know, are an instrument through which thousands of others can become articulate. And you must not forget that your songs and ballads are not trivialities – they are quite as important as the *Elegies*. (10 February 1949)[16]

Hamish was never in any danger of forgetting his songs, but he did find himself unable to complete another poem of such deep philosophical substance as *The Elegies*. He recognised that he would always be frustrated in his search for a poetic subject of equivalent intensity and historical drama to the war. Although he attempted other long poems – the never completed political poem 'Freedom Becomes People', the autobiographical 'Journey to a Kingdom', the bawdy 'Auld Reekie's Roses' and the published poems, 'The Cell' parts I and II, which appeared in *Lines Review* in the late 1950s – his energies were increasingly taken up with the Revival. Hamish not only lacked the will to take on the 'bit' of poetry he was also reticent about revealing the fullness of his emotional life.

Temperamentally Hamish was drawn to folksong out of sheer love for the conviviality and sentiment of the idiom and, in his only in-depth interview (1966), he quotes from the Wilde of *De Profundis*:

> The object of love is to love ... to feel itself in the joy of its own being ... one shouldn't divide it between the moment of creation and the created thing. Its joy is the joy of itself, to feel itself in being ... this has always with me taken the shape of direct communication ...[18]

In the spring of 1950, travelling on the prize money he received from the Somerset Maugham Award for *The Elegies*, he went back to his beloved Italy. His reason for returning is described in a friendly letter to MacDiarmid: 'I am working hard [translating] Antonio Gramsci's *Letters from Prison*, a book of the first importance. G. was certainly the most important Marxist thinker outside Russia in the period 1920– 35.'[19] Hamish first heard of Gramsci from his comrades in the *Resistenza*, and he met the Sicilian's friend, the political economist Piero Sraffa during his second period of study at Cambridge. Hamish was therefore one of the first people outside Italy to recognise Gramsci's importance and the influence on his thinking was immediate. This intellectual wellspring inspired Hamish's entire vision of the Revival, justifying his love of folksong as 'an alternative to official bourgeois culture'.[20]

It is fascinating to consider Hamish in his early thirties, measuring his creative nature and resolving his attitude towards poetry and song; absorbing currents of contemporary European thought; and forging such an ambitious strategic choice, for he conceived a project that was nothing less than the reconciliation of Scottish culture.

The Revival was consciously planned, however, its beginnings can be traced to a chance encounter signalled in a letter he received in February 1951 from his friend Ewan MacColl warning of an imminent arrival:

> There is a character wandering about this sceptred isle at the moment ... Alan Lomax. He is a Texan and the none the worse for that, he is also about the most important name in American folksong circles ... The idea is that he will record the folk-singers of a group of countries ... He is not interested in trained singers or refined versions of the folk songs ... This is important, Hamish. It is vital that Scotland is well represented in this collection.[21]

With the synchronicity of this meeting all of the elements that would gel into the modern Folksong Revival fell into place.

*   *   *

After the success of this first collecting trip to the North-East the newly formed School of Scottish Studies financed Hamish for further tours – 'God's own job' as he described it. On one of these he recorded Willie Mathieson, John McDonald, John Strachan and then, in 1953, Jeannie Robertson.

The importance of meeting Jeannie was clear. He had already predicted that there would be someone with such a rich repertoire – probably a woman, possibly a traveller – the only surprise was that he expected to find her in the country. The short walk between the Library in King's College, Aberdeen, where he would study Gavin Greig's great folksong collection, to Jeannie's house in nearby Causewayend where he would often enough walk into an impromptu ceilidh or story-telling session, was symbolic of the gulf between academicism and the living tradition. It was this cultural apartheid that Hamish set about to remove once and for all.

In 1954 he was finally appointed as a full-time research fellow by Edinburgh University and, the following summer, returned on a collecting trip to his home town, Blairgowrie, where Maurice Fleming had informed him there was a wealth of traditional material to be gathered amongst the travellers at the berry picking. Hamish was:

> ... overwhelmed by the wealth of song, story and lore which flowed from the travelling people at the berry picking. Never had it been so clear to him that this was not a question of isolated survivors preserving old fragments of balladry; this was an alternative culture shared by the whole gathering, old and young.[22]

Collecting took him back to the emotional landscape of childhood, to his native Perthshire and the great hinterland of Fyvie. Reading Hamish's essays and letters and recalling his conversation, the love he felt for this period of his life is unmistakable: free to play the intellectual vagabond, he was attempting to renew the political reconciliation idealised in his 'John Maclean March', where Neil the Highland teuchter joins hands with Clydeside's Jock and Jimmy and 'the red and the green are worn side by side'.

When McCarthyism forced Lomax to quit America, he brought with him a piece of machinery already in common use amongst collectors Stateside: a tape recorder.[23] The fidelity to the oral tradition this technology allowed would make possible a new kind of Folk Revival in which the oral arts rather than print would predominate, and the ballads need no longer be separated from their tunes. With the emphasis on interpretation the greatness of a figure like Jeannie Robertson shone clear.

The urgent need as Hamish saw it was: '... that of placing examples of authentic native singing-styles, and – wherever possible – actual performances of good traditional artists within the reach of the young apprentice singers of the Revival ...'[24] So many people have stories of long afternoons spent listening to reel-to-reels in Hamish's office perched over George Square and the richness of the collection he amassed is still only beginning to be absorbed. Ewan MacColl acknowledged it as 'one of the great Scots collections, worthy of being ranked with those of Gavin Greig and David Herd'.[25]

The role of collector was one for which Hamish was phenomenally suited. I have never met anyone who had his ability to cut through people's differences. This gift was born of his unique interweaving of the social fabric of Europe: illegitimate son of a Highland serving woman and an Irish soldier; taken under the wing of the Duke of Atholl as a boy; educated in two of the finest public schools in England; distinguished service in the Intelligence Corps; and wanderings through the cultures of pre- and post-war Europe. Hamish thrived on crossing and recrossing borders of all kinds. The tale of how he escaped Nazi Germany on one of the last trains to leave before war was declared, spiriting away a young Jewish lad, Karl Heinz Gerson, was one I heard him tell many times. The leitmotif was repeated when he found himself on a motorbike riding through Sicily, the first Allied soldier on occupied European soil.

In the mid-1950s Hamish made another crucial crossing, entering into the tight-knit clannish world of the Scottish travellers or 'summer walkers', who had preserved the finest examples of the traditional arts. His affinity for their way of life allowed him to win their respect, as Ailie Munro records: 'Hamish took time to fraternise, to win confidence and trust, to sleep in rough tents. In the early fifties, to be on such friendly equal terms with social outcasts was hardly the way to win friends and influence people of the Establishment, academic or otherwise'.[26] He carried a steady flow of songs and stories back to the archives of the School, passing them on to the young apprentice singers in the cities through folk clubs, records and radio programmes. Norman Buchan summed up the importance of this:

> It's difficult for me to imagine how the Folk Revival could have taken off without Hamish and Hamish's work. First, there was the keel of the School of Scottish Studies, which said: This is important; this matters; this must be collected! Then, curiously enough, you had a collector who was interested in the living thing, that also songs had to be made, who wrote songs himself. This is a great distinction, that he recognised it wasn't an archaic, an antiquarian ploy that he was on. It was something that was living ... He knew the task of collecting was to dredge, was to trawl, and you took everything up ... whether they mattered a good deal or not, the body was incomplete without them ... He had both the quality approach, as it were, understanding the importance of a big ballad,

understanding the importance of a living tradition, but also knowing that the squibs were part of the process. He understood the process as well. And this, I think, was quite remarkable.[27]

Hamish's faith in the value of live performance shines through in the sleeve notes he wrote for the LPs *The Muckle Sangs* and *The Berry-Fields of Blair*.

To succeed the Revival needed an urban platform, so he set about organising The People's Festival Ceilidhs of the early 1950s. In his program notes for the 1952 Festival Hamish made his aims clear:

> If the Ceilidh succeeds in its purpose, it will perform something of tremendous cultural significance for Scotland. In our cities the folk tradition has never completely disappeared, in spite of all the inroads made upon it, and it is still possible to graft these flowering branches from the North and West upon a living tree. We are convinced that it is possible to restore Scottish folksong to the ordinary people in Scotland, not merely as a bobbysoxer vogue, but deeply and integrally.[28]

This project was as far-reaching as that proposed by MacDiarmid in the 1920s. And what of the relationship with MacDiarmid? They remained ostensibly on good terms, and, although Hamish's work for the School prevented him offering as much practical help as before, he did take an early opportunity to pay homage, dedicating the 1952 Ceilidh in honour of MacDiarmid' sixtieth birthday. MacDiarmid rose to propose a vote of thanks:

> Our tremendous treasury of folksong in Scotland, whether in Lallans or Gaelic ... has been occluded, very largely for political reasons, from the majority of our people. The Edinburgh People's Festival, and the movements in which my friends on the platform and others in the audience are concerned, is a reassertion of that tradition ...[29]

Hamish desired to unite forces, insisting that MacDiarmid's poetry exemplified the 'best features of the marriage between folksong and art song ...' Retrospectively he admitted their strategies were parallel:

> And if it is objected that this is a 'forced' development due mainly to the efforts of those concerned with the current Folksong Revival, I would counter by claiming that the tradition as it exists today is in large part the heritage of many similar revivals in the past: for example, those which we associate with the names of Gavin Greig, Robert Burns and Allan Ramsay. It is an honourable list, and one that Scotland can be proud of.[30]

Burns remained the crucial precedent for this process for, after all, hadn't he 'set up a folk-song workshop of his own, and transformed, without seeming effort, our whole conception of the meaning of traditional art for society ...'[31] As the Revival became more confident Hamish began to prod at the Lallans 'Academy' again, suggesting that if the Renaissance was to be carried further then 'our poets and writers could maybe do no worse than go to school once again with the folk-singers.'[32] His radicalism remained focused on the MacDiarmidian issue of 'voice', as he championed the 'natural' folk-singer and a heterogeneous blend of ballads, protest songs, skiffle and music hall. His darts against the 'art' singer also brought him into conflict with the BBC, who remained stiflingly conservative on such matters. There is no doubt that his virtual ban from radio was something Hamish greatly regretted and he rightly castigated the corporation's treatment of Jeannie Robertson.

In 1955 Hamish went on the offensive in an essay with the stark title 'Enemies of Folksong'. Folksong threw down

> a challenge to the culture of the elite, [because] it expressed with power and élan the communal creativeness of the people against a book-song and art-poetry increasingly contracted and withdrawn from the life of the common people ... Young singers in Glasgow are learning old songs from the tapes, and making new ones on the old tunes ... The national consciousness is stirring; if we act promptly and boldly we can make the folksong Revival a powerful component part of the Scottish Renaissance.

Hamish talked of alliances but portrayed the oral tradition as unfairly trodden upon by its brother in the Muses – only the wild vitality of the 'despised' folk tradition would wrestle the worn-out debates over the national voice free of art-poets clinging too tightly to their lexographs.

Presiding over the first modern Revival in which print did not predominate, Hamish's approach was both archaic and contemporary. He understood that the oral tradition prospered when it drew on festivals and fairs, days set apart from the governance of state or throne; his collecting tutored him in the popular idioms of the barracks, farm and travelling hawker, the dissident commentaries of their time, *'Dear Lady Astor, you think you know a lot,/standing on a platform talking bloody rot.'* Songs were the common people's alternatives to the disputations of Court, Kirk and Law Court, and Hamish loved hanging ballads and outlaw tales, songs like 'MacPherson's Rant', in which the dispossessed told their own stories in their own ways.

The desire for communality lies at the root of Hamish's commitment to the Revival, though, paradoxically, it is a movement in which he became a larger-than-life presence. This explains his prejudice against print and reluctance to record his own songs, preferring them to be transmitted within the carrying stream. Maurice Fleming tells an amusing story from one of the collecting tours: Hamish is sitting in Mona Stewart's kitchen in Galloway when she turns to him and says

> Put on your tape recorder again. I'll sing you a song you'll really like.' Hamish switched it on and she began to sing. To his amazement it was his own 'Freedom Come-All-Ye'! The tune had 'developed' considerably, and so had the words, but it was his song all right. When she had finished Hamish didn't know what to say ... Should he tell her he had written it? ... In the end he took his courage in his hands and told her. Mrs Stewart had learned the song two years before from a Glasgow singer now in the USA. Where he had learned it from is anyone's guess.[33]

* * *

Jeannie Robertson and Lizzie Higgins' seminal interpretations of 'the muckle sangs' formed a 'classical' model, a living connection with the voices of the past. Hamish loved the way Jeannie talked of the battle of Harlaw as if it was an event still alive in our consciousness. By the same measure, while he despised Orangeism, the folk-culture of Ulster always held a fascination, and I can remember one party at my house where he gave a bold rendition of 'The Sash' followed immediately by a Rebel Song. He loved that borderland that Yeats describes: 'a vivid speech that has no laws except that it must not exorcise the ghostly voice ... my moment of revelation, self-possessed in self-surrender'.[34]

Folk-song has consistently been identified with a golden age in Scottish culture, as that wild and savage garden that flourished before the linguistic dichotomy of the seventeenth and eighteenth centuries. MacDiarmid railed against this cultural schizo-phrenia, embarking on a linguo-archaeological dig, excavating the Scots spoken in his Langholm childhood and literary precedents, Ramsay, Fergusson and Burns; the great Border Ballads; back to more ancient forms of Scotland's languages, the Makars, the great Gaelic poets; and then finally, through his readings in linguistics and anthro-pology, unearthing Celtic roots in his own idiosyncratic manner in *In Memoriam James Joyce* and the Introduction of *Golden Treasury of Scottish Poetry* (1940). The *Golden Treasury* presents a radical new canon, allying Latin and Gaelic poets and the anonymous ballads and folk-songs with the Makars and the modern Renaissance in a redoubt against Anglification. This determination to establish a literary tradition entirely separate from English prompted some of MacDiarmid's most controversial remarks about the 'true racial life'' – inspired by Kuno Meyer – as he proposes Gaelic as the dominant national language of Scotland's future.

The Folk Revival broadened this linguistic project by presenting the gallus brogue of Jimmy MacBeath; the classic ballad style of Jeannie Robertson; Matt McGinn's 'wee cock sparra' Glaswegian; and Hamish's own songs such as the 'Freedom Come-All-Ye', written in Perthshire ballad-Scots, with a vocabulary every bit as subtle and wide-ranging as MacDiarmid's finest lyrics. Rather than tidy song into the orthodoxy of print, Hamish revelled in this polyglot oral tradition, which made such a nonsense of the ascendancy of any single tongue. He took delight in demonstrating that all languages are, as Gavin Douglas has it, 'bastard' affairs.[35] The Folk movement kept on friendly terms with English comrades, and Hamish had no time for Anglophobia: after all, he had been schooled in England. A political divergence with MacDiarmid was always likely.

Politically the ballads remained at the heart of Hamish's political vision and, in his extended retrospective essays on the folk tradition 'At the Foot o' yon Excellin' Brae' (1983), he returns to his favourable comparison of the folk-song tradition over and against Scottish art-poetry. His arguments in favour of ballad-Scots demonstrate that 'a curious "bilingualism in one language" has always been a characteristic of Scots folksong'. Literary Scots is criticised as a 'self-conscious ... and sad case of arrested development ...', while the ballad-makers operate 'in a zone which ignored national and political boundaries'. The Scottish ballad tradition is 'a flexible formulaic language which grazes ballad-English along the whole of its length, and yet remains clearly identifiable as a distinct folk-literary lingo ... [Thus] in the folk field as well as in the less agile literary Lallans, Scots may be said to include English and go beyond it.' This claim is the highpoint in his championing of folksong as a politico-cultural identity for Scotland. It is in many ways a pragmatic definition, one that reflects the post-1978 consensus of a country that is both *included within* and *going beyond*. He insists there is to be no standard language; no orthography should ever become a question of race or blood; even the orthodoxy of a single homogeneous nation is repudiated.

Of course, the Revival itself was nationalist in character and provided an invaluable source of propaganda for left-wing political causes – the reiving of the 'wee magic stane', 'Ding-Dong-Dollar' anti-Polaris songs and Hamish's great political anthems, 'Rivonia' and 'The Freedom Come-All-Ye' – but the Revival's chief political theorist chose to identify with marginalised communities and ally himself to Gramsci's vision of a vibrant international folk culture:

> That which distinguishes folk song in the framework of a nation and its culture is neither the artistic fact nor the historic origin; it is a separate and distinct way of perceiving life and the world, as opposed to that of official society.[37]

Hamish recognised that the flower of traditional song is 'never purely "colloquial"; it is formal, even stylised ... It is in the great songs, licked into shape like pebbles by the waves of countless tongues, that this sense of formality is most marked.'[38]

Just as MacDiarmid had done before him, Hamish embarked on a journey through the spiral intaglio of the ear, listening in on undercurrents of Scottish consciousness that were concealed in the unrivalled interpretations of the source-singers. This ancient timbre reached a peak in the songs of the travellers and of the waulking board. Hamish revered the singers' abilities to reveal unconscious realms of emotion: 'elements have become locked together, and have disengaged, some changes probably occurring in the free-flow of improvisation – the result perhaps of the momentary whim of some long-dead soloist – and others (one senses) corresponding to a deep underlying aesthetic pattern.'[39]

*   *   *

The idealised territory of song that Hamish imagined returns us once again to the play of identity. In a number of essays he points to the tendency among many of Scotland's greatest authors to adopt the folk tradition and he fastens on to the bastard children of this, the pseudonym, alias or byname. 'Alias MacAlias' (1969) outs MacDiarmid as the most fascinating example, analysing his playful and sometimes rashly inconsistent attitudes to authorship. Hamish delighted in the literary detective work that poems such as 'Perfect' invited, as when he deduces that 'this acquisitive attitude to material from all sorts of sources' is 'strongly reminiscent of the folk poet, who frequently appropriates lines or even whole stanzas from other poems or songs'.[40]

Try as he might though, Hamish could only draw MacDiarmid so far towards his position. A telling point of comparison of their differing attitudes to authorship is the chapter on 'Ossian' MacPherson that MacDiarmid published in *Scottish Eccentrics* (1936).[10] MacDiarmid exonerates MacPherson, arguing that the 'true nature' of the 'Scottish genius' lies in 'the play of personality ... the act of absorbing the mask of another personality into our own'. The poet who is capable of shape-shifting consciousness is the ultimate embodiment of these irrational forces, a Nietzschean figure of genius.

Against this diabelerie of the self, Hamish is drawn towards shifts of identity that are experienced through the direct emotional contact of song, above all the gritty magical realism of the ballads. These transition states of consciousness are always identified with the carrying stream which cleanses and slakes the poetic muse. He douses MacDiarmidian Modernism in these folk models of authorship, washing away at the boundaries of the creative intelligence as if they were marked in chalk. The poet is described as a symbol of 'craggy' remoteness; an isolated 'standing stone'; a Faustian changeling – wherever he can Hamish draws him down into the tides of communality, where the redeeming waters of song wash away at the rocky eyrie of genius.

The depth of Hamish's criticisms lay in the tyrannical history of their 'dead century'. These clashes of violent will and metaphysical strife are the crux of the Flytings, even if they were clothed in arguments over the respective merits of folk-song and art-poetry.

By the end of the 1950s the alliance of their respective movements had been forged but their personal relationship was about to descend into bitter dispute. MacDiarmid's criticisms of the Folk Revival follow on from his savaging of the Burns cult. In 'Robert Fergusson: Direct Poetry and the Scottish Genius' (1952),[42] published in the same year as his speech of praise at the People's Festival Ceilidh, he accused Burns of sentimentality and political wavering, and castigated the 'dangerous' popularity of folksong, which encourages 'maudlin sentiment' and 'permanent juvenility'. His later repudiation of the Revival, published in'The Scotsman in January 1960, was equally stark: 'Mr Henderson seems ... to wish to scrap all learning and all literature as hitherto defined in favour of the boring doggerel of analphabetic and ineducable farm-labourers, tinkers and the like.'

MacDiarmid passionately believed that great poetry served heights to which only the greatest spirit could aspire. Folk-song was the kailyaird, inimicable to the avant-garde. George Davie discusses the intellectual background to the disputes in *The Crisis of the Democratic Intellect*:

> The starting point of [MacDiarmid's] argument ... is the historic ... struggle between the elite, the intellectual few who do the discovering, and make possible the progress, and the anti-elitist many, who are not equal to participating in the general argument, and who seek, often successfully, to bring to an end '*The insatiable thocht, the beautiful violent will,/The restless spirit of man*' by imposing egalitarianism, of which the Burns International is [for MacDiarmid] the great example.[43]

In his turn Hamish unmasked, teased and assailed 'MacAlias', accusing his outmoded Stalinism and dredging up his early interest in Fascism: 'MacDiarmid ... throws into sharpest relief the reasons for the murderous alienation of the poet in contemporary society.'[44] And, from their second Flyting (1964): '[He] has come to despise and reject the 'people of his country's past' with all the ardour of a seventeenth-century 'saint' outlawing the folksinging and dancing damned to outer darkness ... the apostle of a kind of spiritual apartheid.'[45] He paints MacDiarmid as the elect *pater familias* crying down judgement on the damned. If, in hindsight, these Oedipal rivalries appear to be a foolish waste of their creative energy, they were at least being truthful to their personae and they reflect in an uncanny way deep-set patterns in the Scottish psyche.

George Davie's analysis of the Enlightenment provides a wider philosophical context, when he describes the dangers of: '… an intellectual atomisation in which the learned and conversable, as Hume calls them … get out of contact with one another, losing in the process the sobering sense of the common origin of their respective modes of culture in what Hume refers to as the animality of the vulgar …'[47] Certainly Hamish – like Burns – celebrated the lusty comedy of the sexes, and he would often enliven a ceilidh with a performance of 'The Banks o' Ross', or another favourite bawdy song.

*   *   *

In these essays Hamish celebrates transgressive aspects of Scottish folk culture in terms of gender and sexuality, redefining the consensus of the Revival project and echoing radical continental philosophical thought of the 1960s and 1970s. He turns back toward *bios*, to songs: 'where the surge and beat of the [women's] song often reaches a pitch which one can only call ecstatic … in uninhibited self-expression, desire, scorn, reproach, desolation – all the sexual joys and agonies of the women come pouring out like a burn in spate'.[48] Emotionally Hamish was always attuned to the feminine, in much the same way as Burns who composed so many beautiful love songs from a woman's point of view. He grew up with the songs of his mother and grandmother and gravitated back towards these maternal voices. One of his most beautiful ballad imitations is 'The Ballad of the Speaking Heart', in which a son cuts out his mother's heart and carries it off to his wicked lover. When he falls and drops the heart it cries out, *'Are you hurt my son, are you hurt ava.'*

Women have always been to the fore in the Scottish folk tradition, from Mrs Brown of Falkland to 'Big Mary of the Songs'. Hamish's personal credo was multiplicity and he habitually undermined such masculine institutions as Cambridge University, Modernism, the British Army and the Renaissance in its smoky pubs. Where MacDiarmid determined that ideas must clash and collide Hamish extolled symbiosis.

'The Women of the Glen' (1982), for example, is a manifesto of sexual liberation and a piece of disguised autobiography. There are telling echoes between the male love-bond in Celtic warrior society and his own memories of wartime. This theme is developed further in the dedication to androgyny, one of the wellsprings of his creative muse, in his translations from Campana and Cavafy (1985), representing heterosexual and homosexual love, and in the attraction towards ambiguous emotional relationships expressed in *The Elegies* and poems such as 'Janus'.[49] Hamish also acutely analyses the sado-masochistic gay culture of Nazi Germany, and joys in the emotional openness of his beloved Italy.

Finally though, in the manner of a Pasolini or a Lorca, Hamish chose to identify himself deeply with the most dispossessed clan of all, the travellers or 'tinker gypsies' who, by the very nature of their nomadic existence, would never be confined within the conventional borders of society or politics. Their ancient counter-culture was 'profoundly alien to most industrialised society'[50] and they embodied his lifelong disdain for materialism. He left home and academe to return to the world of the gypsies time and again, searching out some new variant of a story or song.

Their secret languages and codes of behaviour attracted him, for, despite his democratic spirit, clandestine orders always held a fascination – Army Intelligence, the *Resistenza*, gay subculture, the Orange Order and the Horseman's Word.

Hamish delights in the parallel with Lorca, noting proudly that 'the Scots travelling people have an expression "conyach" (from the Gaelic caoineach, weeping or "keening") which corresponds with the *duende*'.[51] Lorca traced the 'cante jondo' back to ancient India and 'the mysterious colour of primordial ages'.[52] Hamish describes how, mixing amongst the travellers in the berry fields of Blair, 'you could hear a rare 'Child' ballad, or the high flamenco-like cadences of a Gaelic love lament',[53] and encounter 'ancient Ossianic hero-tales, whose content reflects the life of primitive hunter tribesmen'.[54]

In an Arthurian mood he describes an extraordinary incident in the summer of 1955, when he encountered blind Alec Stewart, 'Ali Dall':

> This amazing old hero had a version of 'Am Bron Binn' (The Sweet Sorrow), an heroic lay now very rare, and stories of Oisean and the Feinne, as well as a vast store of wonder tales and other Marchen … he had learned most of his stories from [his mother] Old Susie … Old Susie died in 1938 aged 91; this means she was born 13 years before the publication of the first volumes of Campbell of Islay's *Popular Tales of the West Highlands*, and must have learned many of her stories orally in the mid-nineteenth century from relations born before the end of the eighteenth century – from folk, therefore, who in all likelihood were travelling the roads while 'Ossian' MacPherson was still alive …[55]

These essays are a Scottish companion to the radical experimental anthologies and archaeologies of Michel Foucault; the American poets Jerome Rothenberg and George Quasha, who anthologised ancient poetry in *Technicians of the Sacred* and *Shaking the Pumpkin*; John Berger, a friend and admirer, author of the peasant novel trilogy, *Into Their Labours*; and the Friuliano poet and film-maker, Pier Paolo Pasolini, who identified with archaic society in films such as *Medea* and *The Arabian Nights*.

*   *   *

By the 1960s the achievements of the Revival were clear to see. At festivals and clubs new interpreters of the classic ballads emerged. The Revival also inspired the demotic vitality of the new poetry and Hamish became a talismanic figure amongst the bohemian clanjamfrie at the Traverse Theatre, mixing with pop singers, theatre folk, the Mersey Beat poets, and young Scots poets such as Alan Riddell and Alan Jackson.

MacDiarmid's curmudgeonly ability to jumble together folk-song, skiffle, the beats and Concrete Poetry and place them all on one proscribed list, only served to solidify the alliance between the folkies and their bohemian poet friends. An amusing episode in these skirmishes was the McGonagall factor, as the Dundonian bard became a satirical club to whap MacDiarmid with. Edwin Morgan, the spokesman for the new poets, and Hamish wrote important essays on the McGonagall phenomenon. Morgan's 'The Beatnik in the Kailyard'[56] (1962) admits McGonagall seems to represent 'some deep-rooted human feelings … some need of the Scottish soul …'; while Hamish's later study 'McGonagall the What' (1965) overlays these 'mixed-up geniuses' in a virtuoso display that was calculated to infuriate MacDiarmid. Their pleas for a more honest appraisal of the Scottish character, including its sentimentality, were part of the struggle for a new openness in emotional and political terms.

*   *   *

Gathered together these essays represent an outstanding achievement but we must bear in mind that the greater part of Hamish's work lay in collecting and transmitting the songs themselves. The sum of the task he set himself as a young man amounted to a healing of Scottish culture – a life project then, and one born of his own need to renew the moment of direct and open communication between people, whether in the spontaneous applause of the masses at a political rally, a young partisan reciting Dante in memory of a lost comrade, or two lovers kissing in the Meadows. Such moments Lorca describes as 'the delicate bridge uniting the five senses with that core made living flesh, living cloud, living sea, of Love freed from Time.'[57] There is no doubting that contemporary Scotland remains firmly tied to its greyness and that process of renewal is by no means complete; but, if we listen, something of the song of Hamish remains, for so many people have a clear memory of his spontaneous infectious joy.

For Hamish this was 'the moment of resolve, of transformation, of insurrection',[58] and it could occur whenever a song is shared, for in the sharing the song is reborn. This moment is a proving ground for all emotional and political truths. It gifts us our common humanity, or insurrectionary awareness that 'freedom becomes people', for as his own song foretells, *'all the roses and geans will turn to bloom'*.

Alec Finlay

Notes

1 This Introduction is a revised shortened version of the Afterword first published in *The Armstrong Nose* (1996). The title is taken from a letter of Pier Paolo Pasolini's: 'As a man lives beyond his temporal death in his good works so a language lives beyond its temporal death in its good poems. As for the temporal death, it is inevitable – there is nothing to be done about it: language, says Savi Lopez ... is a river that flows on: its life is a continual act of dying.' Letter to Luigi Cerceri, 29 January 1953, from *The Letters of Pier Paolo Pasolini*, vol. I, 1940–54, translated by Stuart Hood, Quartet Books, London, 1992, 409.

2 HH, 'Flower and Iron of the Truth', *Our Time*, 10 September 1948, 305.

3 An early draft of this poem was written in 1945, a year before his first meeting with MacDiarmid. It was not published until Henderson contributed to *Poems Addressed to Hugh MacDiarmid: Poems Addressed to Hugh MacDiarmid and Presented to him on the occasion of his seventy-fifth Birthday*, edited by Duncan Glen, Akros Publications, Preston, 11 August 1967.

4 HH, *Elegies for the Dead in Cyrenaica*, John Lehmann, London, 1948.

5 HH, *Elegies*, 'Foreword', 11.

6 'Synthesis is implicit/in Rilke's single column, (die eine) ...', *Elegies*, 'Eighth Elegy: Karnak', 43. 'Rilke refers in his *Sonnets to Orpheus* to "die eine in Karnak", the one in Karnak; the single pillar which survives to live beyond the near eternal temples. I walked for hours all over Karnak to see if I could find a definite pillar.' Henderson, 'For Our Own and the Others', an interview with Colin Nicholson, in *Poem, Purpose and Place: Shaping Identity in Contemporary Scottish Verse*, Edinburgh University Press, 1992, 148.

7 HH, *Elegies*, 'Interlude', 32.

8 *National Weekly*, 9 April 1949, l.3.

9 HH heard Ruth Speirs read from her translations of Rilke in Cairo in 1942; see Letter 4, *The Armstrong Nose*. He acknowledged the influence of German poetry on the *Elegies*, noting especially the influence of Hölderlin's later poems; '... the poems of his madness. In a time of tremendous suffering and war, small wonder that poems of a poet's personal suffering, horror, ecstasy,

and extreme agony should influence [me].' From an interview with Peter Orr, *The Poet Speaks*, Routledge & Kegan Paul, London, 1966 (reprinted in *Alias MacAlias*, Polygon, Edinburgh, 1992, 322).

10 See Raymond Ross's essay 'Hamish Henderson: In the Midst of Things', *Chapman* 42, VIII.5, Winter 1985, VIII.5, 12.

11 Hugh MacDiarmid, *Complete Poems*, 417.

12 HH, sleeve notes to *Pipes, Goatskin & Bones: the Songs and Poems of Hamish Henderson*, Grampian Television: Aberdeen, 1992 (GPN 3001).

13 The title of the essay is a quotation from MacDiarmid's *First Hymn to Lenin*; MacDiarmid was himself quoting from a speech of Stalin's, *Our Time*, 10 September 1948, 304–6. The contents of the issue are listed in Letter 23, *The Armstrong Nose*.

14 HH, *Conflict*, the magazine of Glasgow University Socialist Club, edited by Norman Buchan, March 1949, 5–9.

15 E P Thompson,–'A New Poet', *Our Time*, June 1949, 156, 158–9.

16 HH, *The Armstrong Nose*, Letter 25, 28–9.

17 Ibid, Henderson, Letter X.

18 Colin Nicolson, 'For Our Own and the Others', *Poem, Purpose, Place: Shaping Identity in Contemporary Scottish Verse*, 134.

19 HH, *The Armstrong Nose*, Letter 37, 42–3.

20 HH, Introduction to Gramsci's *Prison Letters*, Zwan Publications, London, 1988, 14.

21 HH, *The Armstrong Nose*, Letter 42, 46–7.

22 Adam MacNaughtan,–'Hamish Henderson', *Tocher* 43, 1991, 2.

23 The use of modern technology in the Folk Revival is one defence against the accusations of archaism levelled against it. For example, Ewan MacColl's 'Radio Ballads', and later, the television documentaries and film collaborations between Timothy Neat and HH, such as *The Summer Walkers* and *Play Me Something* (with John Berger).

24 HH, 'It Was In You That It A' Began: Some Thoughts on the Folk Conference', *The People's Past*, edited by Edward J Cowan, Polygon, Edinburgh, 1980, 13–14.

25 Ewan MacColl, 'Hamish Henderson', *Tocher* 43, 1991, 14.

26 Ailie Munro, *The Folk Music Revival in Scotland*, 215.

27 'Norman Buchan on Hamish', *Tocher* 43, 1991, 21.

28 Reprinted in *Chapbook*, III.6, 1967.

29 Ibid., 9.

30 HH, 'At the Foot o' yon Excellin' Brae'. See also Henderson's remarks to Tom Scott, rebuking him for his comments in the Introduction to'*The Penguin Book of Scottish Verse* about 'pseudo folksongs': '"Banks of Sicily" has circulated as freely and anonymously as Besom Jimmy [MacBeath]'s "Tramps and Hawkers"'; Letter 166, *The Armstrong Nose*, 195–6.

31 HH, sleeve notes to *The Muckle Sangs* (TGNM 119/D, 2).

32 HH, 'Programme Notes for the 1952 People's Festival Ceilidh'; reprinted in *Chapbook*, III.6, 1967, 27.

33 Maurice Fleming, 'Seumas Mór', *Chapbook*, III.6, 1967, 6.

34 See the discussion of the Scottish voice in 'The Oral Ballads of Mrs Brown', *The Ballad and the Folk*, David Buchan, Routledge & Kegan Paul, London, 1972, 68.

35 Roderick Watson, 'Alien Voices from the Street: Demotic Modernism in Modern Scots Writing', 141.

36 HH, *The Armstrong Nose*, Letter 57, 63.

37 HH, 'At the Foot o' yon Excellin' Brae'.

38 HH, 'Scottish Songs at Work', a review of *Hebridean Folk Songs: A Collection of Waulking Songs*, Donald MacCormick, Clarendon Press, Oxford, 1970, in

Times Literary Supplement, 29 May 1970.

39   Antonio Gramsci, *Letteratura e Vita Nazionale*, quoted in Glen, 'Hamish Henderson: Poetry Becomes People' (Inter Arts 1.7, 1988).

40   HH, 'Hugh MacDiarmid: The Langholm Byspale', *Edinburgh City Lynx*, No. 35, 21 (September 1978).

41   Hugh MacDiarmid, *Scottish Eccentrics*, Routledge: London, 1936 (reprinted by Carcanet Press: Manchester, 1993).

42   Hugh MacDiarmid, 'Robert Fergusson: Direct Poetry and the Scottish Genius', *Selected Essays of Hugh MacDiarmid*, edited by Duncan Glen, Jonathan Cape, London, 1969. A contradictory point is made by MacDiarmid in another essay of the period, 'The Scottish Renaissance: The Next Step' (1950), where he recommends to younger Scottish writers, 'the acute analysis based on a thorough knowledge of popular types, local dialects, slang, and the profound love of the streets and all sorts and conditions of people'; he then goes on to state that 'the great task confronting Scottish poetry today' is to 'reachieve a body of popular Scottish song ...', *Selected Essays of Hugh MacDiarmid*, 107.

43   George Elder Davie, *The Crisis of the Democratic Intellect*, Polygon, Edinburgh, 1986, 111.

44   HH, 'Freedom Becomes People', Chapman 42, VIII.5, Winter 1985, 1.

45   HH, *The Armstrong Nose*, Letter 113, 132.

46   George Elder Davie, 'The Social Significance of the Scottish Philosophy of Common Sense', the Dow Lecture, delivered at the University of Dundee, 30 November 1972; reprinted in *The Scottish Enlightenment and Other Essays*, Polygon, Edinburgh, 1991, 58.

47   Ibid, 43.

48   HH, 'Scottish Songs at Work', op. cit.

49   Translations first published in *Chapman* 42, VIII.5, Winter 1985, 19–20.

50   HH, 'Folksongs and Music from the Berry Fields of Blair', sleeve notes to the album of the same title (Prestige International 25016, 1962).

51   HH, 'Lorca and Canto Jondo', *Cencrastus,* No. 26, Summer 1987.

52   Ibid.

53   HH, 'Folksongs and Music from the Berry Fields of Blair', 102.

54   Ibid.

55   HH, *Tocher* 28, 267–8.

56   Edwin Morgan, 'The Beatnik in the Kailyard', *New Saltire Review*, No. 3, Spring 1962.

57   Frederico Garcia Lorca, 'Theory and Function of the Duende', *Penguin Poet Series: Lorca*, (Penguin: 1960, 136).

58   HH, 'Freedom Becomes People', *Chapman* 42, VIII.5, 1.

59   HH, from his song 'Freedom Come-All-Ye'.

FOLK-SONGS

The Voice of the People

> Eighteenth-century Scotland, there is no doubt at all, was a nation of ballad singers and ballad lovers. How much earlier it had been so, no one knows; but it is a fact that what we today know as British balladry at its best is a mass of texts taken down by interested persons from living Scottish tradition in the latter half of the eighteenth century, or learned then and transmitted to print or manuscript early in the following century.

These words of the distinguished American scholar Bertrand H. Bronson describe a flourishing 'folk scene' in post-1707 Scotland, and there can be little doubt that the years leading up to and including Robert Burns's short lifetime were a golden age in Scottish culture. Some of the finest versions of the great classical ballads were put on record at this time, and collections such as David Herd's provide ample evidence of an exceedingly lively and creative popular culture, which crossed class boundaries, and which displayed a muscular capacity for dealing poetically with the most diverse human moods and conditions.

Victorian Scotland presents a startlingly different picture. The hegemony of the Kirk was more or less absolute, and the elements of Scottish life that Burns had glorified in his anarchic cantata *Love and Liberty* – in Thomas Crawford's words, 'a world-upside-down celebration of energy and instinct' – were well and truly battened down. This was an era when many Scots were devoting themselves to empire-building, and the numerous songbooks that were produced became repositories of the 'refined', the mawkishly sentimental and the braggadocio-patriotic, helping to create an image of Scotland outwith our borders that no nation on earth could possibly covet. These sad songbooks put into circulation 'cleaned-up' versions, by poets such as Lyle and Tannahill, of the old 'high-kilted' songs that were such a glorious feature of the older, rumbustious Scottish tradition.

It was not until the beginning of the twentieth century, with the dedicated collecting work of the Aberdeenshire dominie Gavin Greig and the Revd James Duncan of Lynturk, that the sheer size of the old 'underground' song culture became apparent. Together, these two amassed one of the largest and most impressive folk-song collections in the world.

It was not until 1981 that the massive Greig-Duncan collection began to see the light of day in published form; for years it had lain dormant in a strongroom in the Aberdeen University Library. However, its existence was known to enthusiasts and amateur folklorists, and when the American collector Alan Lomax visited Scotland in 1951 to make recordings for a Scottish LP in his Columbia Records folk-song series, he naturally expressed an interest in that same north-east corner.

Singers recorded by Lomax came to Edinburgh later in 1951 to take part in the first Edinburgh People's Festival (a series of 'alternative' events, organised by the Labour movement, which aimed to cover the areas the official Edinburgh International Festival did not bother to address).

There were, in all, five People's Festivals in successive years. The third, in 1953, witnessed the Edinburgh debut of the newly discovered Jeannie Robertson, whom A. L. Lloyd called 'a singer sweet and heroic', and there is no doubt that these People's Festivals supplied much of the dynamism behind the rapidly developing folk-song revival. However, an even more potent weapon in the revivalist armoury was soon brought into action. Schools in the Glasgow area were lucky to have as teachers some notable folk-song enthusiasts; the first to invite country singers to perform in his school club was the late Morris Blythman, who brought the bothy ballad singer Jimmy MacBeath and Jeannie Robertson herself to perform at Allan Glen's School. Closely following on the same trail was Norman Buchan – the former Labour MP – who invited these and other singers to Rutherglen Academy.

The result of their proselytising endeavours among the young was a veritable cultural explosion in Scottish cities, and it was not long before the repercussions of this were felt in the rural areas from which the traditional singers had come.

Folk clubs began to spring up in various places in the late 1950s, the earliest being the Edinburgh University Folk Song Society, organised by the poet and novelist Stuart MacGregor, but the most significant event in the history of the revival was undoubtedly the foundation in 1965 of the Traditional Music and Song Association of Scotland (TMSA). In 1966 this body organised a traditional folk-music festival in the little Perthshire town of Blairgowrie. 'Blair' was chosen because it already hosted a huge informal get-together in the berryfields at the height of summer, when pickers from all over Scotland came to pick raspberries and to have a good time. Also, it was the home of the 'Stewarts of Blair' – Alec and Belle Stewart and their daughters Sheila and Cathie – one of Scotland's foremost folk-singing families. Last but not least, Blair was in berry-time the temporary home of hundreds of gifted traveller musicians and singers from as far away as the north Highlands and Ireland. Collecting in the berryfields – songs as well as berries – often seemed like holding a tin can under the Niagara Falls.

The TMSA's policy of taking the revival to the source paid off handsomely, and when 'Blairgowrie' moved to Kinross, and then to Kirriemuir, there were already two more traditional festivals of the sort on the go, catering for ever more passionate *aficionados*: one in the Borders, at Newcastleton, and the other at Keith in the heart of the north-east bothy country. To these festivals the revival singers came as apprentices; the invited guests were mainly authentic traditional singers such as Jane Turriff, Stanley Robertson, Betsy Whyte and the veteran Border shepherd Willie Scott.

Alongside the more strictly traditional festivals there grew up a number of others, which pulled in all the various strands that contributed to the revival. A photograph taken at the Inverness Folk Festival of 1969 shows how widely the net could be cast.

Along with the brilliant 'folk comedian' Billy Connolly and his one-time Humblebums mate Gerry Rafferty, the group includes the three McCalmans and the three members of Bitter Withy; Aly Bain (the notable Shetland fiddler, then very young); Jean Redpath (widely regarded as the successor to Jeannie Robertson); Arthur Argo (Greig's great-grandson, and himself a most accomplished singer); Mike Whellans (a multi-instrumental virtuoso from the Borders); and Archie Fisher (senior member of an outstanding folk family, and a key figure of the revival). Kneeling at the front, and holding his pint with pensive dignity, is an honoured guest, the renowned English folk-singer Cyril Tawney.

As in the eighteenth century, political events have continued to stimulate vigorous, and usually satiric, ballad-making. The 'reiving' of the Stone of Destiny from Westminster Abbey on Christmas Day 1950 inspired a host of celebratory songs. Most were ephemeral, but one – Johnnie McEvoy's 'The Wee Magic Stane' – has survived to join the present-day corpus of Scots folk-song.

The event that spawned the greatest output of protest songs for a very long time was the arrival in 1961 of the American depot ship *Proteus* in the Holy Loch, carrying its lethal load of Polaris missiles. The ballad-makers immediately got to work, and when a series of massive anti-nuclear demonstrations began, there were dozens of songs circulating to encourage the marchers. Among the most popular was 'Ding Dong Dollar'; this excellent song reminded the world that 'Ye canny spend a dollar when ye're deid.' Other favourites were 'Ban Polaris Hallelujah' (to the tune of 'John Brown's Body'), 'Ye'll No Sit Here' (to 'Hey, Jock McCuddy') and 'We Dinna Want Polaris' (to 'Three Craws Sat Upon a Wa'').

The unrivalled chief and brigade-major of the anti-Polaris balladeers was Morris Blythman, who was also well known as a literary poet (his 'MacAlias' was 'Thurso Berwick'). Indeed, one of the most striking features of Scottish literary history has been the cross-fertilisation between 'high art' and the native demotic tradition. The twentieth-century folk revival has thrown up some masterly poet-songmakers. The best known is undoubtedly the singer-playwright Ewan MacColl, whose radio ballads (written with Charles Parker) broke fresh ground in broadcasting. Songs such as 'Freeborn Man' and 'Shoals of Herring' are still frequently heard in folk clubs. Other noteworthy names are Adam MacNaughtan ('Skyscraper Wean' and 'They're Tearin' Doon the Building Next tae Oors'), Eric Bogle ('The Band Played Waltzing Matilda'), Andy Hunter ('Up and Awa wi' the Laverock') and Robin Laing ('The Union Canal').

In a class of his own was Matt McGinn, a rasp-voiced Glaswegian of genius, whose main inspiration was the Glasgow music hall. Matt wrote some superb comic songs such as 'The Dundee Ghost' and 'The Foreman O'Rourke', but he also wrote songs conveying immense tenderness and compassion: an example is 'Coorie Doon' ('The Miner's Lullaby'). Anyone listening to his hard-hitting political songs – and Matt could take on and demolish anything that smelled of toffee-nosed pretension – will readily understand what Pete Seeger meant when he called him 'the Scottish Woody Guthrie'.

The lines between tradition and revival, and between 'art' and 'folk', become steadily more blurred with the songs of Matt McGinn, and even more in the work of some younger writers. The progression has actually been remarkably similar to that in the eighteenth century. As Tom Crawford succinctly put it: 'Each resurgence of the creative spirit in Scotland since 1707 has been associated with renewed interest in popular culture, and with something of a folk revival: each has felt the need to tap the popular tradition, which is, perhaps, the most abidingly *national* part of our culture.'

Sunday Mail 'Story of Scotland', vol. 4, part 48, 1989.

Folk-singing in Auld Reekie

'Edina, Scotia's darling seat' … maybe truer to life is the brutal Hogarthian folk-taunt 'city of pride, pox and poverty'. So let's start with a dram in honour of Auld Reekie's folk-singers and musicians of the past, who quite often suffered their share of at least two of the three. James Boswell, for example, when he was in Corsica in 1765, played 'Gilderoy' and 'Corn Rigs are Bonny' on the German flute for an appreciative audience of the locals. He wrote in his *Journal of a Tour to Corsica*: 'It was quite a joyous riot.' This is by no means a bad description of many Scottish folk occasions before, during and since, whether at home or away. Ten years later, as though to show that Scots have no petty chauvinism, Boswell led the occupants of an Edinburgh-to-London stage-coach in 'Hearts of Oak', 'Gee Ho Dobbin' and 'The Roast Beef of Old England'. He wrote afterwards: 'We made a prodigious jovial noise going through Welwyn, and other villages.'

In Edinburgh in 1776 there was published the second edition of David Herd's *Ancient and Modern Scottish Songs, Heroic Ballads, etc.* Davie Herd (byname: 'Greysteil') was weel kent in the howffs of the Canongate, in the company of such men as 'Saint' David Hume, the 'infidel'; he left us one of the finest collections of folk texts of the eighteenth century. A toast to him, then – and while we're at it another to poor Robert Fergusson ('Sir Precentor'), Burns's 'elder brother in the Muses', who wrote ribald drinking songs for the Cape Club (of which Herd was a member), and died at the age of twenty-four in the Edinburgh Bedlam – just across the road from what is now Sandy Bell's bar.

Burns never met Fergusson, but he raised 200 songs in his honour another ten years later … it was the 'Crochallan Fencibles', then; as we might say, the 'Coorie-dooners' or 'The Jug of Punch Grenadiers'. The Crochallan Fencibles met in Dawney Douglas's tavern in Anchor Close. They got their name from the landlord's favourite party piece, which was Crodh Chailein (Colin's Cattle), a popular Gaelic number. Burns mentioned the club in his 'Rattlin' Roarin' Willie':

> As I cam by Crochallan,
> I cannily keekit ben;
> Rattlin' roarin' Willie
> Was sittin' at yon board-en'.
> Sittin' at yon board-en',
> And amang guid companie …

One of the songs in Herd's collection is the 'Dreg Song': nonsense verses forming a lengthy version of the half-traditional, half-improvised rowing song of the oyster-fishers of the Firth of Forth. When they were out at sea, the fishers took compass bearings on landmarks along the coast:

> Fleemin's inkworks tae the gasworks,
> Dodge your wheel and fill your creel-a.
> Katie Bairdie's got a wee lairdie
> That they ca' the skipper o' the Row-a ...

The *New Statistical Account* (1845) tells us that 'long before dawn, in the bleakest season of the year, their dredging song may be heard afar off'. In the grey-shrouded mornings, a mile or two from the coast, the fishers could make out in the distance the huddled contour of Arthur's Seat, with the Newhaven lighthouse blinking nearby.

> There's an auld carle sits by the sea.
> Wi' a white caun'le on his knee ...

The oyster-fishing is over now, but the 'Dreg Song' lives on; in Newhaven, Leith, Portobello, Fisherrow and Musselburgh, detached fragments of it are still spinning like tops among the bairns, in the singing street.

Bob Bertram, who is in his thirties, works in the Grassmarket at Scott's the wholesale ironmongers, where he is a costing clerk. When Bob was a kid, he used to see the Newhaven fishwives selling cockles and mussels in the Lawnmarket, outside Deacon Brodie's pub ...

> Wi' a creel o her back, and a strap tae her broo;
> In each hand a tin pitcher o' mussels quite fu'.

One of the many fine songs Bob has written recently is called 'The Buckie Wife':

> Her red-strippit dress was sae bonny an' braw,
> Up frae Newhaven, or far Fisherraw.
> Her bright buckled shuin, and her wares fae the sea,
> And followed by bairnies a' jumpin' wi' glee.
> Fine buckies
> Fine buckies
> Noo that wis her cry.
> Fresh mussels the day O
> Please come an' buy.

Bob is an excellent satirical song-writer; the best and wittiest squibs about the Profumo affair are by him. And he has written so many songs in the last year or so that he would bid fair to rival Matt McGinn ... if Matt McGinn would stop writing for perhaps five years.

Salute to the makars! We still have plenty. In 1948 Jimmy Miller, alias Ewan MacColl, returned to Scotland with Theatre Workshop: Joan Littlewood and Ewan were the original Fringe of the Edinburgh International Festival, and folk-song ceilidhs were the fringe of Theatre Workshop. One year we even had a pipers' flyting, or battle royal, between exponents of traditional pibroch style, and Donald Main, a bold experimentalist (as it turned out, he needed to be). The makar Robert Garioch immortalised the scene in his poem 'Embro Tae the Ploy':

> The Epworth Hall wi' wonder did
> behold a pipers' bicker;
> Wi' hadarid and hindarid
> the air gat thick an' thicker.
> *Cumha na Cloinne* set for strings
> inflames a piper quicker,
> tae get his dander up, by jings,
> than thirty u.p. liquor
> we thocht
> at Embro tae the ploy.

Cumha na Cloinne (Lament for the Children) is one of the great MacCrimmon pibrochs; you can hear it on John Burgess's Folk-Lyric LP, 'The Art of the Bagpipe', which was produced in collaboration with the School of Scottish Studies. This department of Edinburgh University came into existence in 1951, and it at once set about the urgent task of collecting Scottish folk traditions all over the country. When men such as the late Dr Calum MacLean returned from collecting tours, students came thronging round to hear his finds, and the folk revival received a powerful new impetus because of this. Songs learned from our tapes began to be heard at the ceilidhs of the University Highland Society. Thanks to the tape-recorder, unknown waulking songs with beautiful tunes and splendid texts, recorded on Hebridean islands or in the remotest fastnesses of Wester Ross and Sutherland, were being sung by young folk in the capital only a matter of weeks after being taped.

(It was only a matter of time before some smart alec would try to start copyrighting them, but we decided to cope with that problem if and when it arose. However, we thought it sensible to explore the legal position, and – if necessary – take appropriate action.)

That same year, 1951, saw the formation of the Edinburgh People's Festival Committee; during the 'big' Festival of that year, it ran a marvellous ceilidh of traditional singers and musicians which was recorded in its entirety by Alan Lomax.

II

'Peat-fire flame of heart's desire' … the vulgarisation of Scottish folk-tradition was (and is) a flourishing industry. And it didn't start in London recording studios. Like most attempts to make money out of 'folk', it started at the old home-fire itself, whether that happened to be peat or the best anthracite.

Kennedy and Fraser are two good Scots names. Put them together double-barrelled, and you get that extra subliminal guarantee of 'authenticity'. When Mrs Kennedy-Fraser arrived on the folk scene, in the early years of this century, she found that the Irish had got in ahead of her with a really profitable Celtic Twilight racket, which was fast ripening into a boom. It says much for her artistic virtuosity as well as for her business acumen that by the time she rested from her labours, for every person in Muswell Hill or South Kensington who associated fairy-knolls and lovelorn cattle-croons with Killarney, Donegal or Ballybunion, there were at least ten who associated these same phenomena with the misty islands of the Highlands. However, the cultural price was heavy – nothing less than the distortion of an entire folk-tradition.

Others had done their bit too, such as 'Fiona MacLeod' (William Sharp). But it was the name Kennedy Fraser which became synonymous with the most vapid Celtic moonshine, and when, in the 1930s, students such as Calum MacLean began to reassess our folk-heritage, it was her name which became a symbol of kitsch, an obstacle which had to be lifted at all costs, and set aside.

Looking back on it now, one can give Mrs Kennedy-Fraser her due – she was an assiduous collector, as well as a flamboyantly successful arranger. But her work had a built-in datedness – this was an Anglo-Scots bourgeois use of pre-bourgeois Celtic folk-tradition, which would soon cease to satisfy. By the time Calum MacLean was an Edinburgh student, the 'in' names were not Kennedy Fraser but Frances Tolmie and Gavin Greig.

Earlier on I referred to the influence on Edinburgh folk-song enthusiasts of Calum's own collecting work. Here is a prose version of one of the songs which, in the early 1950s, fired the imagination of student folk-singers. It is the 'Taladh Dhòmhnaill Ghuirm (Lullaby of Blue Donald), in which a baby is thought of by his nurse as already a mature warrior:

> The strength of the moon, the strength of the sun, the strength of corn shoots in May time, the strength of the heavy, mighty waves, the strength of the swiftly leaping salmon, the strength of Cuchulainn in full armour ... the strength of the great whale blowing, the strength of the elements and of heaven's children – may each one of these, and the strength of the Son of God, lie between Donald Gorm and his armour.

At that time, Calum and I were working in a corner of an old warehouse in Chambers Street transcribing and annotating our tapes by day, and playing tapes to all who would listen by night. I remember the pleas to play it again from Highland students when Calum played the magnificent version of this same song which he had recorded from 'Bean Airchie' (Mrs Archie MacDonald) of South Uist.

It wasn't only the recorded texts or tunes – glorious though many of these were – that caused a sort of qualitative change in the response to folk-music when Calum came back with his finds. What leapt from the tape, and made instant contact, was the native singing-style of the folk-artist concerned, blowing to oblivion the genteel accents and tinkly piano accompaniments of the Kennedy Fraser school of deformers. The new response brought it home to us that the whole point about oral transmission is that it is *oral* – and if that is a truism, it is surely one that is in need of constant repetition from year to year, and from decade to decade. As Chesterton's Father Brown observed, in one story after another, the obvious tends to be overlooked, precisely because it *is* obvious.

We were far from being anti-print latter-day Luddites, but our experiences convinced us that the printed text – and, even more, the printed tune – deserved to be given a rest in Scotland. All over Scotland, the shelves of libraries, public and private, were groaning with folk-song and folk-music collections, but nobody (or practically nobody) was using them. If the BBC in the 1930s wanted to present folk-song, whether Gaelic or North-East bothy, it enlisted art-singers prepared to do a bit of slumming –

'mucking the byre in white tie and tails'. In our cities, the young aped Yanks ('fake Yankee snuffling of denatured Scots', as the poet Robert Garioch put it). And yet, all round us, it took only the most perfunctory researching to find the living article.

Owing, at that time, to the occlusion of the Scots literary tradition from Scottish schools, youngsters seeing song-texts in Scots tended to associate them with the 'blether-r-r in the heather-r-r' tradition of our city music-halls – a tradition which, while racy and vigorous enough, was only one small part of the Lallan song-heritage. A sense of revelation may sound a corny phrase, but it is accurate enough if you wish to describe the feelings of hundreds of young folk introduced to our tape-recordings 'in the spring of the year'.

After listening to the ballad-recordings made in Aberdeenshire, it was possible as never before to appreciate the lean subtle grace of the ballad-Scots – its ability to deal with themes as varied as the great tragic narratives (Sir Patrick Spens and the Four Maries, for example) as well as the grotesque randiness of comic Child ballads like The Wee Toon Clerk. And (as Alan Lomax was quick to sense) these recordings gave a valuable fresh insight into the way the Scots literary and folk traditions through the centuries have been constantly and inextricably intertwined.

Soon after the launching of the first Edinburgh International Festival, the idea began to be canvassed of a native popular festival, based on the Scottish working-class movement which would undertake the sort of cultural activity which the 'big' Festival seemed likely to ignore. In 1951 a committee was formed, on which were represented the Edinburgh City Labour Party, the Trades Council and other bodies. In many ways this People's Festival Committee was a sort of forerunner of Arnold Wesker's Centre 42. The organiser was a Communist, Martin Milligan, a man of great brilliance; he had returned a short time before from Oxford, where he had studied philosophy, although his philosophy was hardly of the Establishment kind. As it turned out, the first folk-song ceilidh run by the People's Festival was to be a landmark in the history of the 'folk' revival in Scotland, and its consequences are still with us.

The Barra singers Flora MacNeil and Calum Johnston presented Hebridean folk-song, stripped of its Kennedy Fraser mummy-wrappings. Jimmy MacBeath sang 'Come A' ye Tramps and Hawkers' for the first time on any stage (as opposed to the reeling road, or the booths of Porter Fair). John Burgess, master piper, played us marches, jigs, strathspeys and reels with all the expertise of Auld Nick at Kirk Alloway. John Strachan, the Fyvie farmer, and Jessie Murray, the Buckie fishwife, sang versions of classic ballads such as 'Johnnie o' Breadisley' (Child 114) and 'Lord Thomas and Fair Ellen' (Child 73) which convinced even the most sceptical that a noble oral tradition was still with us. After the Theatre Workshop show was over, Ewan MacColl and Isla Cameron joined us to sing 'Eppie Morrie' and 'Can Ye Sew Cushions?'. Then the pipes sounded again, and the dancing started.

Later that night – or was it that morning – Jimmy MacBeath stopped in York Place, shook himself loose from the friends who were supporting him home, and lifting his mottled face to the moon, sang 'The Bleacher Lassie o' Kelvinhaugh'.

All over Auld Reekie the ceilidh was continuing. In a sense, it is continuing still.

III

Private faces in public places
Are wiser and nicer
Than public faces in private places

W. H. Auden

Folk-song has, as its natural habitat, almost every imaginable set-up of human loneliness or togetherness *except* the concert-hall – or, indeed, the regular planned entertainment. It was during the interval of one of the most successful of our People's Festival ceilidhs – that of 1952, at which Kitty MacLeod and her sister Marietta gave superb renderings of traditional Lewis songs, and Arthur Argo, great-grandson of Gavin Greig, delighted the audience by singing earthy bothy ballads in a boyish treble – that an Inverness friend of mine enunciated his partly sober opinion on the subject. The only justification for a public ceilidh, he said, was the private ceilidh (or ceilidhs) which it spawned. If it didn't spawn any, it was a phoney. And even if it did, it was probably a phoney, anyway.

By and large, I agreed with him. However, the Auden quote (above) came into my mind, and I pointed out that we had a five-star array of private faces in that public place ... Anyway, just to show that there was no ill-feeling, I told him where he could find some of them afterwards.

Luckily, Auld Reekie has plenty of hospitable ceilidh houses where the private ceilidh, once spawned, can go its dinger. At that time, for example, there was the Queen Street flat of Sorley MacLean (Calum's schoolmaster brother) which saw plenty of magnanimous sessions. It was there we made the rendezvous for Alan Lomax to meet the singers Calum Johnston and the then nineteen year-old Flora MacNeil; there, too, that John Burgess played for Alan's tapes a stately pibroch, 'MacIntosh's Lament', part of which had found its way, via the folk process, into Dvořák's Symphony No 9 'From the New World'.

Sorley MacLean is a renowned Gaelic poet – by general consent our best since the eighteenth century – so it was appropriate that such confrontations should take place under his roof. His poetry draws much of its sinewy strength, as well as its passionate intensity, from the anonymous Gaelic song-poetry, much of the best of which goes back to the seventeenth century, and earlier. The following is a prose version of his poem to the Skye bard William Ross (1762–90):

> William Ross, what would we say, meeting beyond death? I should mention your *Oran Eile*. What would you say about the poems I let loose art-bridled, a wild Cavalry for bards?

Sorley also addressed a poem to the folklorist Alexander Carmichael, who, while working as an exciseman in the Hebrides, assembled the wonderful collection of hymns and invocations known as 'Carmina Gadelica'. Here's the first verse:

> Carmichael, I often think of each treasure you chanced on, and of your wealth every day without bitter wrestling and delirium; that you got the grace and happiness of the muse without struggle against loneliness and terror, and that very different it will be for us against the venomous howl to windward.

I first read these lines quite a while before the 'cash nexus' began to take the modern folk-song revival by the throat; but as the grip tightened – with effects on conduct and artistic performance which were distressing, even where predictable – it often came back into my mind, with a new layer of meaning distinctly audible.

Like Calum, Sorley is very much part of his own clan's tradition. Here is a poem of his about the MacLeans which suggested to me the punch-line for a song. He refers first to those of his clan who died in battle resisting the Cromwellian invasion of Scotland, and then to a Socialist thinker, man of action and martyr of the First World War period:

> Not they who died
>   in the hauteur of Inverkeithing,
> in spite of valour and pride,
>   the high head of our story;
> but he who was in Glasgow
>   the battle-post of the poor –
> great John Maclean,
>   the top and hem of our story.

The second big landmark in the history of the modern revival in Scotland was undoubtedly the discovery of Jeannie Robertson in 1953. When Jeannie came to Edinburgh to sing at the People's Festival ceilidh that year, she stayed with Simon and Ella Ward at their flat in Bernard Terrace – another happy confrontation of tradition and creative opportunity. Ella, born in Scotland, was brought up in Uruguay, and sings Spanish songs with rare *élan*; also an important ethnic distinction, she still laughs in Spanish. Simon, her husband, a Corkman brought up in the North of Ireland, is a hard-working civil servant who has done a lot for Scottish agriculture; however, he has an alter ego, 'Sean Sweeney', Irish poet, whose poems are meant for declamation and not for the printed page.

When Jeannie first raised 'Harlaw' and 'Lord Lovat' in the Wards' kitchen, there were two young, attentive listeners – daughter Pat and son Colin. Born in Edinburgh, the children had the luck to come into contact at the most impressionable age with the high Aberdeenshire ballad tradition, and the even greater luck that nobody tried to chivvy them into liking it or disliking it, or indeed paying any attention to it at all, if they didn't want to. The result was that, ten years later, Pat blossomed into one of the finest young ballad-singers in Scotland. She sings unaccompanied in a style which has completely assimilated Jeannie's, and is not a mere pastiche of it (as some other essays in the Jeannie style have been).

Of hundreds of memorable occasions at Ella's, I have space to mention only two – one, in July 1952, with Sorley and Pat Darling (who were helping to organise that year's People's Festival) and Seamus Ennis; a night which seemed suffused through and through with the strains of the uillean pipes. And, second, the fabulous ceilidh in honour of Sean O'Casey, when Sean came to Edinburgh for the première of his play *Purple Dust*; everyone was on top form, and the rich voice of Angus MacLeod, singing Duncan Bàn MacIntyre's 'Praise of Ben Dorain', resonates in the mind. (The next day was the Scottish Miners' gala day, and Sean sent a special message of greetings to the miners' pipe-bands competing for the annual trophy; he recalled that when a young fellow he had himself played in a Dublin pipe-band.)

The Porch Philosophical Club in Doune Terrace was, while it lasted, the scene of some unusual folk events. In the summer of 1953, ceilidhs featuring Jeannie Robertson and Jimmy MacBeath alternated with a cabaret starring Fenella Fielding, who never seemed to get rid of the dark suspicion that the Porch was Auld Reekie's 'House of the Rising Sun'. We had roulette on the ground floor, and philosophical studies upstairs. It couldn't last, of course – the police had little difficulty in infiltrating, and, after a couple of raids, the place was closed down.

I shall never forget the look on Jean Ritchie's face when she arrived back late one night from a field trip in the North-East and saw the inmates of the Porch being taken away in vans. Laugh? She nearly cried. It was the only place in the city she could be sure of getting a decent meal at 2.30 a.m.

The oldest unofficial folk club in Scotland is undoubtedly the Forrest Hill Bar, better known as Sandy Bell's. This was our local during all the early Festival ceilidhs, and is still the local of the School of Scottish Studies. Dozens of songs which are now the common currency of the folk clubs had their 'revival première' at Sandy Bell's. In April 1952, old Willie Mathieson, source-singer of 'I'm a Rover and Seldom Sober', gave spirited renderings of this and other songs for an audience which included Johnny MacEvoy (author of 'The Wee Magic Stane') and two professors of the 'Toon's College'.

Sandy's first theme-song was my own version of the 'D-Day Dodgers', but it soon acquired songs of its own – for example, 'Old Bell's Bar' and 'I've been wronged by a Sandy Bell's man', written by Stuart MacGregor (founder of the University Folk-song Society). Both these songs have crossed the Atlantic, and Scots travellers have reported hearing them sung in American folk-song clubs. Stuart was tickled to learn that, thanks to him, Sandy's had become (for singers in Texas and the Yukon) a kind of fabled 'badman's bar' in darkest Caledonia.

By the late 1950s it was becoming obvious that the ruthless commercialism of the American folk scene, and its increasing onslaught on the sensibilities, would soon be our problem too. Headlines of the 'Pop goes Folk' variety began to appear in the London jazz and pop press. Our feeling was that although the British promoters were probably over-reaching themselves, it was necessary to formulate a definite defensive policy. There could be no question of a retreat into a private folk-song redoubt (which in any case doesn't exist). On the other hand, there were certain debasements we felt bound to attack.

We've had some bad moments, but on the whole we've been successful – more or less. We had to endure at least one major breach of trust, but this hasn't stopped us giving help to hundreds of visitors and contacts, just as before. The School has received some pleasant and much-appreciated tributes to its work, but none nicer than the following from Professor Richard M. Dorson of Indiana, dated 21 March 1965:

> For an itinerant folklorist, The School of Scottish Studies is surely a paradise. All kinds of resources abound: valuable files, indexes, books, journals, tapes, beau-teous Skye maidens, friendly earth-youths, learned dons are scattered about to furnish help. When one becomes intoxicated with folklore, he can sober up at Sandy Bell's around the corner.

The good things of life (folk-life) all converge at 27 George Square.

IV

'So if ever ye come on a stane wi' a ring ...' Earlier on I mentioned Johnnie MacEvoy's 'Wee Magic Stane', almost the only song of the many written after the reiving of the Stone of Destiny to gain a secure foothold among songs likely to last. It was first published in the *National Weekly* on 17 March 1951, and was shortly afterwards included in the Scottish Secretariat anthology *Sangs o' the Stane*. Printers, in both cases, were the Argyle Street teuchters Calum and Kenny Campbell, who a year or two previously had brought out my *Ballads of World War II* (unexpurgated texts, privately printed for the Lili Marlene Club of Glasgow).

As Leslie Shepard has pointed out, commenting on the poster offering £2000 reward for information leading to the identification of Elizabeth I of Scotland DEAD OR ALIVE, this was all in the direct line of descent from an earlier broadside and chapbook tradition.

In 1953 came a popular successor, *The Rebels' Ceilidh Song Book*; this brought together nearly all the songs, such as 'The Men of Knoydart', which had sprung from events like the crofters' land seizures in Wester Ross, and the Home Rule agitation of the previous years. Tunes were indicated by their most familiar titles, with the addition 'as sung by Jimmy MacBeath', 'as sung by Hugh MacDonald', etc. Also circulating at this time were songs which reflected the current party line, such as Ewan MacColl's 'Ballad of Stalin', a very curious document of the 'personality cult' aberration. (The Communist Party, being pursued through the petrified forest of Stalinism by nightmarish trolls like the 'Doctors' Plot', it was itself the perfect subject for a satirical song, but I'm not sure if it ever managed to get written.)

A decade later, the great anti-Polaris demonstrations at the Holy Loch inspired a spate of CND songs with a Scottish slant. These were published in successive editions of *Ding Dong Dollar*, and were later included on a Folkways LP with the same title. The 'Freedom Come-All-Ye' belongs to this period.

Throughout the 1950s, Sandy Bell's Bar was a congenial rendezvous for student folk-singers, and the University Folk-Song Society existed 'de facto' for some time before it was formally constituted. The prime mover in getting it organised on a proper footing was Stuart MacGregor, then a fifth-year medical student. The first secretary was a Scotland-oriented Geordie called Donald Bowers; Calum MacLean and I were elected honorary Vice-Presidents. At the inaugural meeting, held on 18 April 1958, Jeannie Robertson was guest of honour, for the Society wanted to encourage its members to learn direct from the best traditional singers. Jeannie gave several of her already famous classic-ballad versions. Among the other singers were two young Americans, Christopher S. Wren and Danny Botkin, who had both done a certain amount of field collecting in the States. Also present was Norman Buchan, who played a tape made by Rutherglen schoolchildren, and described his work of folk-song popularisation among them.

The theme of the second meeting was 'The Love Song'; examples were provided by singers from Japan, Hungary, Canada, the USA and the Isle of Lewis. The third was devoted in its entirety to North American folk-song. The fourth was a jubilant ceilidh, at which Calum MacLean acted as *fear an tighe* (compère); the guest singer was his clansman Norman MacLean, a Celtic student from Glasgow University, who had done a good deal of song-collecting among his mother's people in South Uist and Lochaber.

These details of the first term's activities are given to show how widely the Society was resolved to throw its net. During the presidency of Dolina Maclennan, there was an International Night which included most everything from Icelandic folk-song to a Jamaican steel band. However, the central emphasis has always been, wherever possible, on 'the wine of the country' – the native Scottish product. Dolina and Robin Gray ranged from the Hebrides to Aberdeenshire, taking in the bothan and the bothy. Isabel Sutherland was an early visitor to the Society, giving ballads big and braw in a voice to match. John Watt leaped the Forth from time to time. Another Fifer, Jean Redpath, who succeeded Robin Gray as president in October 1960, left nobody in any doubt that Scotland came first, whoever came second. Jean's mother is a traditional singer, and her father plays an old dulcimer, so she starts off with rich natural advantages, but it is the verve and panache of her personality which makes immediate impact. When I went along to the Society one evening, and heard Jean raising the family version of 'The Overgate' in her stunning soprano voice, I felt that the Scottish revival was really getting somewhere.

The Society has also undertaken field-collecting. Under the resourceful and energetic leadership of Jim Closs, an ex-draughtsman now studying psychology, a team from the Society spent part of the summer of 1963 in the Strathdon and Corgarff areas, financed by a grant from the University. This expedition was documented on film as well as on tape. The same year, a Folk Festival was organised by the Society; traditional singers such as Jeannie, Jimmy MacBeath and Willie Scott shared a platform with Matt McGinn, Josh MacRae, Ray and Archie Fisher, Colin Ross, the Tregullion, Hamish Imlach, the Corrie Folk Trio and Paddy Bell, Bobby Campbell, Gordon McCulloch and the local 'tramps and hawkers'.

A staunch supporter of the Society almost from its inception until she got married and emigrated to the States in 1964 was a Belfast lassie, Maggie Kerr. Ed 'Memphis' Marshall sings Woody Guthrie and Tom Paxton songs. 'Pav' Verity, an architecture student who plays guitar, five-string banjo, mandoline and autoharp, has recently constructed for himself a 'Pav'-style mountain dulcimer. Dave Hamilton (President, 1963–4) has a wide repertoire, ranging from the 'Scarborough Fair' version of 'The Elfin Knight' to contemporary songs in the folk idiom.

The Society now has clubrooms of its own at 3 Potterrow; these house an extensive disc and tape library, including twenty hours of field recordings. The members who come there are by no means all students; the Society has always welcomed adherents from outside the student body, and has benefited accordingly.

In January 1965 the Society ran a concert, 'Folksong 65', which was taped in its entirety, and two LP records were produced on a non-commercial basis for individual subscribers. In the notes to these records, Jim Closs writes: 'The concert brought together performers from leading folk-song clubs in Scotland; all amateurs who sing regularly at the clubs they represented. From Aberdeen, Glasgow, Dunfermline, St Andrews and Edinburgh, they included engineers, teachers, clerks, typists, draughtsmen, shop assistants, schoolgirls, miners, journalists and students ... In many other fields of music the amateur is only a poor substitute for the professional ... this is not the case with folk-music – at least not in 1965. The performances given by those you will hear on records – and by those who, for lack of space, you won't hear – was, without any doubt, as good as, if not better than, that commonly given by the current professionals.'

After hearing the LPs, I'd go a bit further and say that there is a freshness and bloom on most of these performances which leaves the bulk of the folk professionals very much in the background. One outstanding track on two excellent discs is the performance of 'The Dowie Dens o' Yarrow' by Isla MacDonald, then the twelve-year-old daughter of Zetta MacDonald, Aberdeen singer and song-writer. On the strength of this alone, it would be possible to forecast a great future for this young ballad-singer. (She became better known, a few years later, as Isla St Clair.)

Just over a year ago, the Perthshire collector Maurice Fleming wrote an angry and eloquent piece about the other side of the picture – the fatty degeneration of the commercialised folk scene. Writing in *Horus*, a Dundee student magazine, he called the Scottish folk-song clubs 'frosted blooms in the garden of the Scottish Folk-song Revival', and added: 'A lover of folk-song, I often feel starved of it. This despite the fact that I attend, fairly regularly, a folk-song club. The sad truth is that I could, on these evenings, probably hear more folk-song if I passed the club and turned into the first backyard where kids were playing, dropped into a backroom in a downtown pub, or sat on a late-night bus going home to one of the Corporation Housing Estates.' After describing the richness of traditional song as it is still to be found in Scotland, he asked: 'Of all these ripe riches, how much spills over on to the platforms of the folk-song club? An occasional gleaming plum. A few shrivelled damsons ... Most of what one hears in a Scots folk-song club is only remotely connected with folk-song, the singing is only vaguely related to folk-singing. The clubs have chosen to adopt the Tin Pan Alley standards of Television Light Entertainment. Faced with the choice – folk-song or entertainment – they have bowed three times to the music publishers, the record companies and the artist's agents, and chosen entertainment.'

What Maurice Fleming is suggesting is that many promising newcomers may have been put off folk-song altogether by their first experience of folk-song clubs. What is anyone of intuitive sensibility and intelligence going to think and feel when he hears a song that has achieved beauty and character on the lips of a singer such as Jeannie Robertson, or John Strachan of Fyvie, being pop-folked up by some boneheaded sod whose ideas are centred exclusively on the spondulicks? His reaction will probably be – and I am indebted for the phrase to John Marshall – that the entire folk-song revival must be 'the biggest confidence trick since the Sermon on the Mount'.

Earlier in the article already quoted, Maurice Fleming wrote: 'In my view, the functions of a folk-song club ought to be to encourage folk-singing at its best; to provide a platform for singers of quality, no matter who or what they may be: to promote the collecting of songs, particularly songs native to the locality in which the club is situated.' This sets a very high standard, and I'd never claim that The Edinburgh University Folk-song Society has always measured up to it, but the record shows that it has not done too badly. By and large, it has had a reasonable shot at fulfilling these functions, and giving rising talent a square deal, at the same time. My guess is that it will be continuing to do this long after the present 'boom' is a thing of the past.

Folk Scene, 1965: I, Feb; II, March; III, May; IV, June.

Scottish Folk-song and the Labour Movement

The present flourishing folk-song revival in Scotland has its roots in a number of different historical events and accidents: one of the latter was the decision in 1947 to found a large-scale International Festival of the Arts in Edinburgh. (The founding father Rudolf Bing later admitted that it had been a toss-up between Bath and Edinburgh.) Bing and his pals were not interested in the splendid, vigorous tradition of Scots folk-song which has been described as the most truly 'national' part of our cultural heritage; their aim was to make Edinburgh a showcase for the finest 'art music' of Europe, and in this they undoubtedly succeeded. However, it was not long before the point was being made – by Hugh MacDiarmid, among others – that our native riches seemed likely to remain unexploited by the Festival bosses. This realisation led within a year or two to the formation of an Edinburgh Labour Festival Committee, based solidly on the labour movement and the trade unions.

The second 'accident' was that this momentous coming together of people on the left who were interested in the arts in Scotland coincided with the appearance in Britain of the distinguished American collector Alan Lomax. Alan – son of John A. Lomax, the first major collector in the English-speaking world to devote his attention to 'contemporary' folk-song, as opposed to survivals coming down to us from the past – had been a member during the Second World War of a Music Committee formed under the auspices of various US left-wing groupings. This committee had fostered and encouraged the work of Woody Guthrie, Pete Seeger, and The Weavers, but with the advent of the Cold War its activities had become more and more suspect in the eyes of the authorities; finally, when full-scale McCarthyism came into operation, many of its members felt that the US was becoming too hot to hold them.

It was this ugly right-wing reaction to the 'liberalism' of the war years which led Alan Lomax to accept a job which would keep him outside the States for several years – namely, a commission from Columbia Records to edit a series of LPs, covering the 'folk and primitive music' of the world. Scotland was to be Vol. VI in the series. And so it came about that when the Edinburgh Labour Festival Committee organised and brought into being the first People's Festival (1951), Alan Lomax was there to record it on tape.

The activities of the People's Festival included, among other things, poetry readings, plays and art exhibitions, but it was generally agreed by critics and punters alike that the most notable event, and the one most likely to bear fruit in the future, was the ceilidh: this was an amazing, indeed epoch-making folk-song concert which brought together some of the 'greats' of the traditional folk-scene: outstanding tradition-bearers from the Gaelic-speaking Hebrides, and ballad-singers from Aberdeenshire, heartland of the great Scots ballad tradition.

What made this inaugural People's Festival ceilidh so important was the fact that this was the first time such a masterly group of authentic traditional musicians and ballad-singers from rural Scotland had sung together to a city audience; the result was a veritable cultural explosion, for a number of the 'folk' virtuosi of the future were present in the audience. It is no exaggeration to say, therefore, that this powerful 'shot in the arm', given by veterans to the apprentice revival, was directly due to the far-sighted and imaginative initiative taken by the Scottish labour and trades union movement.

Subsequent years saw the consolidation and strengthening of this side of People's Festival activities. In 1952 Lewis gave of its best with the singing of sisters Kitty and Marietta MacLeod; Frank Steele, from Banff, sang some exquisite lyric love songs; and – most impressive of all – Arthur Argo – reminded everyone in the act of performance that traditional folk-song is by no means the exclusive property of old people; many in the audience thought he was the star of the evening.

The high point in this exciting development was without doubt the appearance at the third ceilidh (1953) of the 'traveller' ballad-singer Jeannie Robertson, discovered in Aberdeen a couple of months previously. In many ways the parallel course of field-collecting and 'ploughing back' had been leading up to just such a discovery; ballad-scholars all over the world were thrilled when they heard recordings of songs like Jeannie's 'Son David' (her version of the classic ballad usually known as 'Edward'), and at the same time the young apprentice ballad-singers who crowded in to hear her realised that at last they had a model of the highest excellence.

It is regrettable to have to add that not long after the 1953 Festival there was an outbreak of ludicrous McCarthyism in the Labour Party itself, and the People's Festival was banned. In spite of continued support from some unions, it soon became impossible to organise festivals on anything like the same scale.

Nevertheless, the basic work was already accomplished, and when the nuclear submarine depot ship *Proteus* sailed up the Holy Loch in 1961, there was a lively and vociferous corps of anti-Polaris protest singers ready to greet her; these owed their musical education to the People's Festivals – and to the valiant efforts of schoolmaster enthusiasts like Morris Blythman and Norman Buchan, who (building on the achievements of the People's Festival) brought traditional singers and musicians to schools in Glasgow and the central belt, thus educating a rising generation of creative youngsters.

Mention should also be made of the work of Ewan MacColl, partner with Joan Littlewood in the founding and running of the original Theatre Workshop; many of Ewan's songs were – and are – inspired by the international labour movement and working-class struggle. His superb radio ballad *Singing the Fishing* – co-authored with Charles Parker – popularised one of the very best songs to come out of the modern folk-song revival, 'Shoals of Herring'.

I hope it will not seem out of place if I add that one of my own songs, now in the repertoire of Dick Gaughan, was directly inspired by – and indeed eventually spon-sored by – a trade union. This was 'The Gillie More' (Gaelic *Gille Mór*, the Big Fellow), which I wrote after hearing that among the messages of fraternal good wishes exchanged during Scottish-Soviet Friendship Week, at the height of the Cold War, was one 'From the Blacksmiths of Leith to the Blacksmiths of Kiev'.

The man who was responsible for the dispatch of this resonant greeting was the late Jimmy Jarvie, secretary of the Leith branch of what was then the Associated Black-smiths' Forge and Smithy Workers' Society. Hearing this, I went down to Leith to talk to him about it and see him and his mates at work. They were marine or ships' blacksmiths, and I wanted to learn something of the terminology of the trade. In the song, my aim was to express the reality of Scottish-Soviet 'solidarity', and to do this I decided to conjure up the figure of the 'Big Fellow', familiar in the folklore of many trades – the superhuman individual who is really the sum total of the men who make up the union and give it its communal strength. Here are the two final verses:

> O horo the Gillie More
> Noo's the time, the haimmer's ready.
> Haud the tangs – ay, haud them steady
> O horo the Gillie More
> Gar the iron ring, avallich!
> Gar it ring frae shore tae shore
> Leith tae Kiev – Don tae Gairloch
> O horo the Gillie More

> O horo the Gillie More
> Here's a weld'll wear for ever,
> Oor grup they canna sever
> O horo the Gillie More.
> Ane's the wish yokes us thegither –
> Ane's the darg that lies afore.
> You an' me: the man, the brither!
> Me an' you: the Gillie More.

Writing in the *Melody Maker*, Eric Winter commented: 'The "Gillie More" deals with the legendary fellow, larger than life and strong as John Henry or as the elements themselves … Henderson explicitly poses the ability of men acting collectively to transcend human frailty, and the power of human brotherhood to over-reach frontiers.'

The Associated Blacksmiths' Forge and Smithy Workers' Society published 'The Gillie More' as a song-sheet in 1953 to commemorate the greeting sent a year or two earlier to the Soviet Union, and it was later to republish it as a 'song-sheet hardback' with an attractive tartan cover. The inscription inside reads:

> Presented by the Leith Branch of the Society to the Delegation from the Kiev Trades Council on the occasion of their visit to Edinburgh Trades Council in September 1962.

Dick Gaughan, who often sings the song, is himself a working-class Leither. A fine performance of the song can be heard on his LP *Gaughan*.

Scottish Trade Union Review, no 41, Spring 1989.

Rock and Reel

I'll sell my rock, I'll sell my reel
I'll sell my grannie's spinning wheel ...

Folk-song is on the way back, these days, both north and south of the Border. Bothy Ballads have been featured on TV, and teenager skiffle groups in Glasgow have started to sing the breezy vivacious street songs of their native city. It's only too easy, in many cases, to write all this off as a bobby-soxer vogue which will fall off when something new is thought up by the backroom boys of popular entertainment, but it is an undeniable fact that folk-songs in Scotland have a wider and more enthusiastic audience today than at any time in the last fifty years.

Will this wave of interest in folk-song subside? And can those of us who are interested in safeguarding the Scottish cultural heritage do anything to direct the enthusiasm of younger folk into channels which will lead to the reinforcing and strengthening of a genuine native tradition?

Before attempting to answer these questions, let's take a look at the state of folk-song in this country – and by folk-song, here, I do not only mean the splendid traditional song of Scotland, flowing down the hillsides of our history from generation to generation, but also the songs and ballads continually being composed in the folk idiom, songs which adapt traditional motifs, and share expressions, phrases and sometimes whole verses with older songs which are the common property of the community. Is this tradition in decay, or is its condition healthy?

As a folk-song collector who has spent much of the last decade going about the country picking up the 'unconsidered trifles' of town and countryside, I think we are entitled to take a much brighter view of the position than many previous folklorists have done. The collectors who in the early years of this century devoted their energies to salvaging classical ballad versions in Aberdeenshire and heroic lays in the Western Isles, were, on the whole, pretty pessimistic and solemn about the whole thing. They regarded the commodity they were presenting to the public as strictly perishable. They shared with nearly every generation of collectors since the eighteenth century the view that they were the very last elegiac remembrances of a way of life and a tradition which had gone forever, and that after them would come the deluge which was bound inevitably to sweep all the old magnificence away. Yeats described this attitude very well when he talked of 'That high horse riderless' ...

Though mounted in that saddle, Homer rode
where the swan drifts upon a darkening flood.

It is not to decry the collectors of earlier years, who did work of tremendous value, to
suggest that their attitudes were based on a fundamentally mistaken idea of the nature
of folk-song. They thought of it as something lingering on into the present, tolerated
barely in the changed conditions of modern society. They did not conceive of it as (in
my view) it actually is: a permanent aspect of human culture, which will go on
persisting whatever social and technological changes take place, and will certainly
adapt itself, as it has always done, to changing circumstances.

Let us take a few concrete instances. The shire which for 150 years has provided the
best versions of Lowland Scots classical ballads is Aberdeenshire. The great American
ballad editor, F. J. Child, gave it as his opinion, towards the end of the last century, that
the best Scots ballads were 'undoubtedly from the north'. Early in this century, the
Buchan schoolmaster, Gavin Greig, did wonderful work collecting classical ballads in
the North-East, and he did what many previous collectors had not done – he wrote
down the tunes as well as the words of the songs he collected. But when part of Greig's
balladry was published after his death – and Alexander Keith's edition of it is one of the
most important books in the entire history of ballad literature – the name given to it
was *Last Leaves of Traditional Ballads in the North-East*.

Well, after Greig came the radio and the cinema and long-playing records, but the
people of the North-East are *still* singing the 'muckle sangs' of Scotland, as the
thousands of records in the archives of the School of Scottish Studies prove beyond a
shadow of doubt. And not only the old people, but young folk, too. I know several
youthful ballad singers in various parts of Scotland who sing great songs like 'The
Dowie Dens of Yarrow', 'The False Knight upon the Road', 'Lord Randall', 'Son
David' (better known as 'Edward'), 'The Twa Brothers' and many more, and who sing
them as their parents or grandparents sang them.

Almost invariably the same singers have 'collected' folk-songs from the wireless
and gramophone records too, but the versions taken from these sources begin to get
modified and transformed in exactly the same way as many of the old broadsheet
ballads did which entered folk currency from printed copies hawked at fairs or feeing
markets. The native folk-song in Scotland is still a carrying stream

Not all folk-singers are of equal merit. In this, folk-song is no different from any
other branch of human culture. But a living folk-song or story-telling tradition is
always throwing up the occasional 'champion' or 'virtuoso', freely recognised as such
by the rest of the folk; and of these we have in Scotland many dozens – perhaps a
hundred, perhaps more. Among Gaelic story-tellers, for example, we have blind Alec
Stewart of Lairg, from whom I have recorded many *sgialachdan* (folk-tales) in Gaelic,
some of them about Oisein and the ancient Fenian heroes. Among Gaelic singers there
is Alan Macdonald of Skye, whose repertoire and singing style have been admired by
folklorists from all over the world. The two finest Scots-speaking 'first-raters' are both
from Aberdeenshire, and it may be of interest to describe them and their background
in some detail.

John Strachan of Crichie, near Fyvie, is by profession a farmer, but by nature a poet
and chronicler who occupies much the same sort of position in the agricultural

community of the North-East as the old time *seanchaidh* used to in the clan society of
the North and West. When he was a boy, he began to learn songs, ballads and stories
from the farm servants on his father's farm, and all through his life he has been given a
natural precedence among singers – from the singabout at the meal and ales of earlier
times to the rollicking country concerts where he is still a popular figure.

I shall always remember old John Strachan as he was when I first heard him sing
'The Laird o' Drum', 'Glenlogie' and 'Lang Johnnie More'. It was early July, and from
the veranda of the farmhouse we could see the lush fields of Fyvie drenched with
summer and swimming in a sunshine haze. Not far away lay Bethelnie, mentioned in
the last verse of 'Glenlogie':

> O Bethelnie, O Bethelnie, ye shine faur ye stand,
> And the heather bells on ye shines o'er Fyvie's land.

Old John handed me a great dram, laced his own with a splash of ginger wine, and
raised his powerful resonant voice in the ballad of the young Scots giant 'Lang Johnnie
More', who goes to England to be standard-bearer to the King, but earns the court's
displeasure by falling in love with the Princess, 'Lady Jean'.

> But the English dogs are cunning rogues
>   And roond him they did creep –
> And they gave him drams of laudamy
>   'Til he fell fast asleep.

Between ballads, John will tell stories of the 'gay Gordons' and the 'stately
Williamsons' (the last named farmed Crichie before his own family got it), and describe
the old-style country dances, when the farm servants would put on their bonnets
before the last reel and then rush across to claim their 'ain lassies'. One can't help
feeling, talking to him, that if ever a fierce stubborn tradition manifested itself in a
single individual, it is the North-East tradition which speaks and sings with the voice
of old John Strachan.

The other 'champion' mentioned is Jeannie Robertson, of whom the American
folklorist Marguerite Olney has said: 'Here is the finest ballad-singing I've ever heard.
It's as near as you can get to the high ballad style. There's nothing like it in the States –
no trained singer could possibly imitate it. It has to be inherited.'

Jeannie comes of 'travelling folk' stock, but she has spent most of her life in the town
of Aberdeen. The bulk of her vast repertoire of songs and stories she seems to have got
from her mother, who kept a shop in the Gallowgate; nowadays her little house in
Causewayend is a recognised 'ceilidh house' for the singers, story-tellers and pipers of
the district. Just down the road from her lives Albert Stewart, one of the finest
traditional fiddlers in Scotland. There are many notable folk artists among Jeannie's
visitors, but she is freely acknowledged by them to be in a class by herself – and indeed,
when she lifts up her voice, Jeannie can keep a ceilidh going for a whole night without
assistance.

'Yes,' the objection may likely be heard at this point, 'that's the countryside. What
about the towns?'

Until quite recently, it was the fashion to affirm that the industrialisation of the
nineteenth century had overwhelmed and smothered such urban folk culture as existed

in Scotland. One reason for this was that very few collectors were familiar with the Scots working class, and the majority of folklorists regarded folk-song as strictly a rural thing – the billy goat tethered to the village green.

But in the early years of this century a movement, starting in America, revolution-ised the approach to folk-song; collectors like John Lomax and his son Alan began to look for folklore among the cowboys and railroad construction labourers of the opened-up West, and people began to shed the sort of prejudices which made Bishop Percy refer to the classical ballads as 'Reliques' at a time when he might quite likely have heard most of them sung at the nearest inn.

Eventually, people got around to looking for folk-songs in the great cities them-selves, and, needless to say, they found them; indeed, several of the most beautiful traditional songs which have ever been recorded in Scotland bear clear traces of their urban origin – for example, 'The Bleacher Lassie o' Kelvinhaugh'. Scores of songs reflecting Glasgow life in all its raucle virr and vitality have been recorded in recent years by the School of Scottish Studies.

And what about the influence on the tradition of radio and TV? Well, here again, I think, the tendency has been to be too pessimistic by half. The coming of print and the broadsheet did not kill folk-song; it merely meant that another and less assimilable strain entered it, leaving gobbets of material which might take decades and even centuries to dissolve. Radio and TV are by comparison much more fluent media – they are (or can be) a powerful ally of oral culture, and offer immense possibilities for the diffusion of the very best and most virile in our national culture.

Needless to say, people wishing to use them for this purpose will have to fight a lot of vested interests and old fogeyisms. But that they will win through in the end I have no doubt whatsoever.

Scotland, November 1958.

The Ballads

There was never ane o my sangs prentit till ye prentit them yoursel, and ye hae spoilt them awthegither. They were made for singing an no for readin: but ye hae broken the charm noo, and they'll never be sung mair.

This rebuke was administered by Margaret Laidlaw, the mother of the Ettrick Shepherd, to Sir Walter Scott, through whose agency the most familiar versions of the Scots classic ballads were to become known to the world: so much so that 'Border ballad' and 'Scots ballad' have become for people at large almost synonymous terms. Like Burns before him, Scott set up what was virtually a personal folk-song workshop – William Motherwell referred to it somewhat caustically as 'the alembic established at Abbotsford for the purification of Ancient Song' – and the ballads that passed through it were almost invariably 'improved', not always to their advantage. Scott's work in the field of ballad editing played – like his novels – a significant part in the growth of European Romanticism, and at home generations of Scottish schoolchildren have been introduced to their country's ballad heritage through his *Minstrelsy*, or anthologies based on it. Nevertheless, Scott's role in our convoluted ballad history is a much more complex one than might appear at first sight; it is necessary to get it into focus, and to do this we must examine Margaret Laidlaw's remark, quoted above, in a little more detail.

Her forthright words serve to remind us that the ballads are essentially folk-*songs*, linked by countless ties to others of the species, and that without the reshapings and recreations of oral tradition they would not possess their characteristic qualities and identity. Not a few are living and evolving folk-songs, and some excellent specimens of these have been collected from singers young and old in the last two or three decades. The most prolific ballad-zone of Britain is and seems always to have been not the Borders but the North-East – Aberdeenshire, Banff, Moray and the Mearns – and at the beginning of this century the Buchan dominie Gavin Greig (in collaboration with the Rev Duncan of Lynturk) gathered a harvest there that can well be called a 'burstin' kirn': about 3050 folk-song texts and 3100 records of tunes, one of the largest and most important folk-song collections in the world. This included hundreds of versions of classic ballads, eighty-four of which came from a single informant, Bell Robertson (who was, however, not a singer and could recite only what she had heard). The ballads in the Greig/Duncan collection were edited by Alexander Keith, and published by the Buchan Club in 1925.

And what, it may be asked, do we actually mean by ballad? Although the word has often been used to denote a fairly wide range of song-poetry, ballad, for present purposes, means a song-poem belonging to the high 'caste' of narrative folk-song which Professor Francis James Child admitted to his great thesaurus *English and Scottish Popular Ballads*; it means the 'big ballad' or (*Scotice*) 'muckle sang', which has often been regarded as the aristocrat of the folk-song world – more by scholars, needless to say, than by the egalitarian clan of ordinary folk-singers. In his excellent short study *The Ballads,* M. J. C. Hodgart warns us that the 'Child' ballads

> are as hard to define as they are easy to recognise. They are anonymous, narrative poems, nearly always written down in short stanzas of two or four lines. They are distinguished from all other types of narrative poetry by a peculiar and effective way of telling their stories. They deal with one single situation and deal with it dramatically, beginning 'in the fifth act'*; and there is a high proportion of dialogue to stage-direction. They are not only anonymous but also impersonal: the story-teller does not intrude his personality, and there is no moralising or didacticism.

To this we may add Professor Gordon H. Gerould's admirably concise definition: 'a ballad is a folk-song that tells a story with stress on the crucial situation, tells it by letting the action unfold itself in event and speech, and tells it objectively with little comment or intrusion of personal bias'.

After the foundation of the School of Scottish Studies, systematic collecting with tape-recorders began in the North-East; the School's research-workers were looking for everything that came under the general heading of oral tradition, but priority was naturally given to these same classic or 'Child' ballads. This led in 1953 to the discovery in Aberdeen of the great Jeannie Robertson (1908–75). Jeannie was, however, only one of a sizeable company of singers who turned out to have good versions of classic ballads. Others were found all over the Lowlands, and even in parts of the still Gaelic-speaking Highlands. We can claim with confidence, therefore, that the great stream of Scots traditional balladry is still flowing strongly, and that Hogg's mother was luckily wrong when she averred that they would 'never be sung mair'.

She was also wrong, of course, when she thought of the ballads as never having been printed before. Ever since the invention of cheap printing, broadside versions of the ballads had been travelling all over the country, and many of the variants current among non-literate singers had undoubtedly reached them from printed sources. Not only the sometimes gormless reworkings of hack writers employed by the broadside printers but even the sophisticated (if not always felicitous) re-touchings and tintings of learned antiquarian poet-editors became tributaries of the main stream of oral tradition. The result was a situation aptly described by Alan Lomax when he was assembling documentation for the Scottish album (Vol. VI) of the Columbia World Library of Folk and Primitive Music:

> The Scots have the liveliest folk tradition of the British Isles, but paradoxically it is the most bookish. Everywhere in Scotland I collected songs of written or

---

* The reference is to Thomas Gray's celebrated remark about Child Maurice that 'it begins in the fifth act of the play'. It was this ballad which had earlier given John Home the idea for his play *Douglas.*

bookish origin from country singers, and, on the other hand, I constantly encountered bookish Scotsmen who had good traditional versions of the finest folk-songs. For this reason I have published songs which show every degree and kind of literary influence.

The most famous single figure in Scotland's ballad history was a bookish lady who read Ossian and wrote verses – this was Anna Gordon, better known as Mrs Brown of Falkland (1747–1810). Anna was the daughter of the Professor of Humanity at King's College, Aberdeen, and the wife of a Kirk of Scotland minister, and also the source-singer of priceless oral versions of classic ballads. Child gave every ballad version preserved by her a place in his canon; twenty of her versions are his A or primary texts, and four his B texts. It has lately been argued by Dr David Buchan in *The Ballad and the Folk* (1972) that Mrs Brown was able to recreate her ballads at every singing, using techniques similar to those employed by the Yugoslav epic singers investigated by Milman Parry and Albert Lord. A discussion of this still highly controversial subject formed the basis of my contribution 'The Ballad, the Folk and the Oral Tradition' in *The People's Past*, a symposium edited by Edward J. Cowan (1980). Suffice it to say here that Mrs Brown does not seem to me by any means a unique figure, in spite of the excellence of the ballad versions she preserved; she is rather an outstanding exemplar of a *type* of creative literate folk-singer which is one of the most characteristic types of folk-singer on the Scottish scene, and one which certainly did not die out during the course of the nineteenth century.

The first traditional singer to record his entire repertoire for the School of Scottish Studies was Willie Mathieson, a septuagenarian retired farm servant who had devoted much spare time throughout his life to collecting songs. In his kist, which he transported from farm to farm when he got a new fee, were three large ledger books full to overflowing with songs of all kinds, from classic ballads through lyric-lovesongs to place-name rhymes and bairn songs. Willie had either collected songs on the spot from his fellow ploughmen, or had diligently followed up his informants by correspondence. He had also tried his hand at versifying, and one of the poems which he wrote down alongside ballads and bothy songs was a moving elegy for his dead wife. Willie Mathieson was quite capable of discoursing knowledgeably about different 'weys' of a ballad, and he would often quote 'what Gavin thocht aboot it' – giving the great collector his first name, in familiar Scots style – but the ballads, especially the tragic love ballads, were closer to him (and 'truer') than they could possibly be to the mere scholar; when he referred to Barbara Allen's callous cruelty to her luckless lover on his death-bed, he would shed tears.

Willie was one of a long and distinguished line of Aberdeenshire singer-collectors. In a letter to the Aberdeen antiquary William Walker, written in 1895, Professor Child expressed the opinion: 'The original derivation of many of the ballads cannot be determined, but that the best Scottish ballads are from the North, there can be no doubt.' As recent collecting amply confirms, the North-East continues to maintain its supremacy, but in recent years a great deal of fascinating material has come to light in East Central Scotland: the Dunkeld-Blairgowrie area, and Strathmore. Quite apart from geographical locations, however, intensive and highly productive research has been conducted among social groups hardly, if at all, investigated by earlier collectors, and concentrated fieldwork has succeeded in revealing part at least of the treasure that had previously lain unworked among the camps and on the stamping grounds of the Scots tinkers (or 'travellers').

It should be stressed that many of the ballads which we have been brought up to regard as distinctively Scottish have relatives in many other countries. Gavin Greig put it well when he remarked of the Aberdeenshire balladry that 'it connects at every point with the world beyond "the bonnie Buchan borders". Our folk-song like our language has endless affinities, and together they become the twin handmaidens of ethnology.' Of the international ballads with worldwide ramifications, the best known is 'Lord Randal' (No 12 in Child's great thesaurus), the ballad of the false 'true-love' who poisons her lover with 'eels boiled in broo':

> I've been awa courtin'; mither, mak my bed soon,
> For I'm sick at the heart, and I fain wad lie doon.

Scott's much anthologised version is the most familiar to us, but the ballad has been reported in communities all over Europe; it first appears in Italy in 1629, and it may well have spread to the North from the Mediterranean world. (Other ballads have crossed and re-crossed the seas lying between Scotland and Scandinavia.) Versions of 'Lord Randal' collected in many different languages exhibit the most striking correspondences of stanza to stanza, the sequence of questions and answers being often virtually identical, and this means that the ballad – which has obviously struck a deep shaft into human consciousness everywhere – has travelled and crossed language-boundaries not just as a narrative story-line (folk-tale fashion) but as a structured poetic artefact. This phenomenon is surely not the least among the many mysteries of human artistic creation.

The Scots ballads have relations, therefore, which in some cases can be traced quite literally to the ends of the earth, but there has been – and still is – a notable consensus of opinion among folklorists and literary critics that Scottish produce 'bears the gree'. I have space for only one quotation, which must stand for many. In the *Kenyon Review* of Winter 1954, in an article on 'The Language of Scottish Poetry', the American critic Stanley Hyman referred to

> a folk literature unsurpassed by any in the world, the Scottish popular ballads ... If we seek language that is simple, sensuous, and passionate, a corpus of more than a dozen tragic Scottish ballad texts constitutes almost a classic tradition. I think of 'The Wife of Usher's Well', 'The Twa Sisters', 'Edward', 'Clerk Saunders', 'Sir Patrick Spens', 'Johnie Cock', 'Mary Hamilton', 'The Bonny Earl of Murray', 'Child Maurice', 'Young Waters', 'The Baron of Brackley', 'Lamkin', 'The Cruel Mother', 'The Twa Corbies', and 'The Daemon Lover'. Alongside these there is a body of Scottish folk-song and rhyme in other forms that adds up to as rich a poetic heritage as any we know.

If we accept these golden opinions, we are still left with the question, 'Why *are* the Scots ballads so good?' – and this brings us curvetting back to Sir Walter Scott, that canny heritor of a highly idiosyncratic national-cultural patrimony. In the same article already quoted, Hyman speaks more harshly of Scott's smoky 'alembic' than Motherwell cared to do – 'the worst fouler of the nest was certainly Scott' – but in retrospect

Scott's services seem vastly to outweigh his demerits; he is, with Mrs Brown of Falkland, one of the two most interesting practitioners of that singular folk-literary collaboration which has been such a constant feature of Scots song tradition. If we are to press for an answer to the question at the beginning of the paragraph, part of it must surely lie in this recurrent fruitful cross-fertilisation, which has operated at every stage of ballad creation and re-creation.

Another part of the answer to the question undoubtedly resides in the nature of 'ballad-Scots', the idiom in which these song-makers were operating – a flexible formulaic language which grazes ballad-English along the whole of its length, and yet is clearly identifiable as a distinct folk-literary lingo. Gavin Greig paid tribute to the 'simple, clear and dignified' language of the older classic ballads found in Aberdeenshire, and the curious 'bilingualism in one language' which greatly extends its range and demonstrably makes it a much suppler instrument than the often rather wooden 'ballad-English'. Yet one of the major influences in the shaping of ballad-Scots, as we know it in the finest eighteenth- and nineteenth-century texts, undoubtedly came to us from the South. It was the coming of the New Testament 'in Inglis tung', and then the mighty power and authority of King James VI's Bible, which played a vital part in stabilising ballad-Scots, and facilitating a resourceful creative 'togetherness': a sort of chemical fusion of two distinct but related ballad languages. In the folk field, as well as in the less sure-footed literary Lallans, Scots may be said to 'include English, and go beyond it'.

A Companion to Scottish Culture, 1981.

Come Gie's a Sang

Unlike the peasantry of most other European nations, the Scots countryfolk do not decorate and paint their homes much. The interior of an old-style Highland cottage is austere, the predominant colours black and white, or else seedily dingy. People have sometimes mistakenly put this down to Calvinism; however, the same thing is true of the Catholic areas of Scotland, and indeed of the Irish domestic landscape. It looks as if in Scotland and in Ireland all the urge of the people towards artistic self-expression has flowed into the oral folk-arts, into song and story. These we have, and galore.

People who know Scots song only from the battered lyric gems which adorn concert platforms would be surprised to hear the old stately tragic – or wanton and ribald – balladry as it still persists. The classical or 'Child' ballads, condemned to death by successive generations of collectors, continue to be sung up and down Scotland by folk-singers of all ages. Travelling with a tape- recorder, I have collected 'The Dowie Dens of Yarrow' from a girl of nineteen, and 'The False Knight upon the Road' from a boy of the same age. In Aberdeenshire (the shire, incidentally, which provided Child with no less than a third of his principal text), the vigorous balladry about farm life which was sung into shape in the ploughmen's bothies during the nineteenth century has gone on reproducing itself up to the present day; in Fife and Lanarkshire the miners have a folk-song of their own, commemorating the disasters of the past, the heroism of rescue squads, the struggles for better living conditions. Edinburgh itself, whose adult citizens do not always look as if they regard life as a singing matter, has a children's folk-song rich and strange beyond measure, a kind of childish bulwark against the harshness and rigidity of the old theocracy.

Scottish folk-song is part of the submerged resistance movement which reacted against the tyranny of John Knox's Kirk at a time when the Kirk was making a bid for absolute rule in Scotland. This explains why, in the whole range of our folk-song, there is hardly a reference to ministers or to religion – apart from the most formal – which is not hostile or satiric. All the best passages of social criticism in Burns leapt directly out of this movement, which in turn was fortified and encouraged by his intransigence.

In a world which divided mankind with a clean cut into the elect and the damned – a division which not infrequently coincided with socially privileged and underprivileged – folk-song became uncompromisingly the cult of the damned. Scotland, a country in which the pendulum always swings half an inch farther than anywhere else (between action and quietism, puritanism and bawdry, gargantuan riotousness and anchorite self-mortification), was soon full of the smoke from burning faggots; the antagonisms implicit in the theocracy's political ambitions became sharpened to a point of mortal hostility. The witch cult, which had begun to wither away, received a fresh lease of life from the intensity of this conflict.

Not that the balladeers fought a losing battle. The dances, stories and songs which were outlawed in the seventeenth century were not long in coming back on the rebound. Burns took them, re-created and glorified them; and it has taken all the strenuous straining of the 'Unco Guid and Rigidly Righteous', operating through Burns Clubs and other sanctifying agencies, to neutralise the effect he had on Scotland.

The anonymous singers who preceded him even succeeded, in the interests of Scotland's honour, in rewriting history. The other day, in the window of an Edinburgh bookseller, I saw a ragged chapbook, printed at Stirling in the early nineteenth century and embellished with a woodcut showing two swordsmen in action; it bore the legend, 'The Haughs of Crumdel, giving a full account of that memorable battle fought by the Great Montrose and the Clans against Oliver Cromwell.'

> The Gordons boldly did advance,
> The Frasers fought with sword and lance;
> The Grahams they made the heads to dance
>   Upon the Haughs of Cromdale.
>
> The Royal Stewarts, with Montrose,
> So boldly as they faced their foes,
> They laid them low with Highland blows
>   Upon the Haughs of Cromdale.
>
> Of twice ten thousand Englishmen,
> Five hundred fled to Aberdeen;
> The rest of them lie on the green
>   Or on the Haughs of Cromdale.

Few people reading or hearing this ballad would realise that Montrose never fought a battle at Cromdale; the only battle ever fought there was one in 1690 between a Williamite army under Sir Thomas Livingstone and a Jacobite army under Colonel Buchan. Livingstone surprised the Highlanders while they were still in their beds recovering from the previous night's revels, and completely routed them – a defeat as decisive in its way as the Battle of the Boyne fought in the same year. Now, thanks to the old song, with its fiery words and haughty tune, it is generally accepted throughout the North of Scotland that the battle fought on the Haughs of Cromdale was a famous victory for the clans. If history, as Ernst Toller said, is the propaganda of the victors, balladry is very often the propaganda of the defeated.

Over from the reiving border of Liddesdale to the wild frontier of Tennessee. 'That phoney folklore figure' Davy Crockett has put the match to a genuine folk-song bonfire among the children of Britain; kids are singing rhymes which alter from day to day and from street to street:

> Born in a tenement in Gorbals Cross,
> Of all the teddy boys he was the boss.
> His razor sharp and four feet wide,

> He threw it into the deep, deep Clyde.
> Davy ... Davy Crewcut,
> King of the teddy boys.

The Razor King's doxy in *No Mean City* had a song which prefigures this. But the native Edinburgh product is a success story:

> Born in a cave of the Pentland Hills,
> Cleaned his mother's window sills.
> Then he got a job in the rubber mills –
> But now he's a traveller for Beecham's Pills.

Sci-fi, needless to say, can hardly be left out:

> Born on an asteroid in outer space,
> Met his girlfriend face to face –
> But his braces were caught in a rocket
> And that was the end of Davy Crockett.

In many of these rhymes, one comes across not only the reflexes of old mythologies, but also the authentic ring of old Scots idioms and expressions – artfully assimilated into demotic Scoto-American speech. When Davy Hume boozed in the High Street – how homely Scots, incidentally, seems the name Davy Crockett in this city – the ancestors of many of the present bairnsangs were undoubtedly on the go. But whereas Davy Hume, that perfervid Scot, had to purge his prose of Scotticisms, the modern makars are trying to purge their poetry of Englishisms. Perversity and foolishness, then as now, go gallivanting through the world.

The English, who are coming north in considerable numbers to take managerial and executive positions in a country rapidly losing its 'heids of depairtments', are not slow, of course, to dismiss all this nationalist nonsense – history and legend, exploit and dream – as kitsch beneath their notice. The trouble is that these incoming English (most regrettably non-U) seem to think that non-U English is superior to U Scots; which is ridiculous.

Clearly some action is necessary. U (it stands for 'Unblended' or 'Undiluted') Scots is the language of many makars, survives lustily on the lips of fisher-wives, ploughboys and playboys, and cannot be pronounced by Miss Nancy Mitford. In spite of these advantages, it urgently needs championing in the right quarters.

I wonder, would an article in *Neuphilologische Mitteilungen* do the trick?

Spectator, 25 May 1956.

The Underground of Song

It was early 1946, and I was only a month or two out of the Army. Having a drink in the Café Royal in Edinburgh, I got into conversation with a gentleman who claimed to be interested in the Scottish Renaissance and 'What these Lallans boys are doing'. After discussing recent developments in Scots poetry, I mentioned that I was interested in folk-song, and thought that systematic collection of our folk heritage ought to be part and parcel of the general cultural revival.

'You surprise me,' he replied, 'I thought all that had died out years ago.'

I told him that there were several folk-singers of my acquaintance who would be as puzzled by his remark as he had been by my own statements.

This appeared to astonish him even more. He thought it over, took a lengthy swig at his pint, and then came away with a crack which fairly shook me. 'Well, if they were any good, somebody would have put them on the radio.'

This was one of those remarks which either put paid to a conversation, or start hours-long discussion. As it happened, it finished the conversation, for my companion had to leave – but not before I had tried to point out that ethnic song seemed to be rather low on the BBC's list of priorities, and that in any case that organisation had to consider the 'popular taste' which it was itself largely helping to create.

Since then, the latter-day folk-song revival has swept Europe and America, and the BBC has devoted hours and hours of sound radio and TV time to what (for want of a better word) is usually styled 'folk-song'. However – in Scotland, at any rate – the genuine native singers have about as much of a look-in these days as they had before. Where previously folk-song programmes meant concert-hall performances by trained singers, they nowadays conjure up a vision of youthful guitar-strumming revivalists whose concern is usually, and quite understandably, more for the appealing gimmick than for authenticity.

Where does the native folk-song tradition stand in the face of all this?

The answer is that it goes on stubbornly existing, although there are still many people – and not least in such institutions as the BBC – who think, like my Café Royal companion, that it is a thing of the past. The idea that folk-song is dying, if not dead, is as old as the hills, and is a direct result of the attitude of many ballad-scholars of the past who tended to regard their particular collection as the final and ultimate full stop. After them, the public was given to understand, there would be no use prospecting for hidden gold; they had it in the bag already. As we shall see, this pessimistic view has happily proved to be quite unjustified.

Now, why should people be so keen to erect a gravestone for traditional song? Maybe the best comment on the psychological background of this 'folk-song is dead' nonsense was given in the wise words of the great folklorist John Francis Campbell, of Islay, who (commenting on the view held by many Highlanders in 1859 that Gaelic folk-tales had become extinct in their own areas) wrote in his introduction to *Popular Tales of the West Highlands*:

> In the Highlands, as elsewhere, society is arranged in layers, like the climates of the world. The dweller on an Indian plain little dreams that there is a region of perpetual frost in the air above him; the Eskimo does not suspect the slumbering volcano under his feet; and the dwellers in the upper and lower strata of society, everywhere, know as little of each other's ways of life, as the men of the plain know of the mountaineers in the snow.

Early in 1952 I was staying in Turriff in Aberdeenshire, and was recording the extensive repertoire of a retired farm servant called Willie Mathieson, who was born near Ellon. Willie had spent his life in the North-East, and everywhere he had gone, he had collected songs, and written them down in a large ledger book. He started his collecting while still a laddie at the school, but told neither his father nor the dominie for fear of getting a thrashing.

By the time I made his acquaintance he had three ledger books filled with nearly 600 songs, and he could supply the tunes for well over half of his collection. In April 1952 he accompanied me to Edinburgh – the first time he had ever been further South than Stonehaven – in order that his manuscript books (which he did not wish to let out of his sight) should be photostatted in the University Library. While he was in Auld Reekie a reception in his honour was held in the house of a leading member of the university staff and – in Willie's own words – 'Professors were buzzin' roon' me like horseflies.'

Not long before our departure for the South I met the doctor who had attended Willie for many years. He looked incredulously at the recording gear strewn all over the cottage floor, and freely admitted that until he had seen the fact mentioned in the papers he had never realised that Willie was a singer.

Usually on the day of the Miners' Gala, early in May, I go to the Queen's Park to see if I can run across old friends from Fife or West Lothian – and also, naturally, in the hope of coming across something of interest in the folk-song or folklore line. Once I had a piece of rare luck – the sort of luck which the collector regards as a kind of bonus, over and above the normal returns of his trade. There were two or three lads from Bathgate watching the piping contest – I remember they were all keen Shotts and Dykehead supporters – and they made a rendezvous with me for a sing-song at a bar near the Lawnmarket. I knew what that sort of sing-song usually implies – fulsome Edwardian ditties, battered lyric gems from bygone concert halls, the occasional 'Scotch' item deriving from Harry Lauder or Will Fyffe – and frankly I didn't look forward to the evening with any particular pleasure. However, I didn't want to let the lads down, and I turned up quite early at the appointed place.

The sing-song was a well-conducted affair, with a cheerful master of ceremonies in full control, and it didn't seem at all likely that anything of even middling interest would turn up to ruffle the pleasant, blowsy camaraderie of the evening. Nor did it – till an elderly man sitting quietly in the corner was asked to give a song. (I rather think the

MC expected to draw a blank, and was quite prepared to move on to the next singer.) After a moment's hesitation the miner he had called on rose to his feet, and the next instant I realised I was listening to a real folk-singer. And not only that – the song he was singing was a Jacobite song about the Battle of Prestonpans which I'd never heard before:

'The Lothian Hairst'
(Text taken from the MS collection of the late Willie Mathieson)
On August twelth from Aberdeen we sailed on the Prince
And landed safe on Cliffords fields oor harvest to commence
    For six lang weeks and better frae toon tae toon we went
    And I took richt weel wi' the Lothian fare and aye was weel
content.

Oor maister William Mathieson from sweet Deeside he came
Oor foreman cam fae the same place and Logan was his name
    I followed Logan on the point sae weels he laid it doon
    And sae boldly as he led oor squad o'er mony's the thistly
toon.

My mate and I could get nae chance for Logan's watchful eye
And wi' the lad we got nae sport for Logan was sae sly
    He cleared oor bothy every nicht before he went to sleep
    And never left him one behind but strict the rules did
keep.

And when we come to Aberdeen he weel deserves a spree
For the herding o' us a' sae weel for the Lothian lads
we're free
    Fare-weel McKenzie Reid and Ross and all your jovial crew
    And Logan Jock and Chapman Pratt and the Royal Stewart,
too.

We'll fill a glass and drink it roon afore the boat will
start
And may we safely reach the shore and all in friendship
part
    And I mysell a Highland lass could wish nae better cheer
    Than a Lothian lad in a Deeside bed and a nicht as lang as
a year.

A few days later I had my first extended recording session with this outstanding singer – Jock Cameron by name – and began listing his repertoire of songs, which included over a dozen items of first-rate interest. Needless to say, it was only the first of a series of such recording sessions.

    Another time at the Queen's Park I looked around for 'kent faces' on a Miners' Gala Day. I wandered in vain by the amusement stalls, the brass band contest, the crowning of the Beauty Queen, and even drew a blank at the piping contest; so by the end of the afternoon I was quite despondent, the weather being none too good, into the bargain.

I decided that the road home up the Canongate was the thing for me, and on the way
I went into the Blue Blanket for a quiet pint. A few minutes later I heard the sound of
pipes outside in the street.

Now, travelling or stravaiging pipers can be interesting enough, but many of them
are a dead loss. Their piping is, in any case, usually the least noteworthy thing about
them. However, I decided to try my luck. I went out, leaving my pint, and gave the lad
sixpence to play 'The Hills of Glenorchy'.

He was short, sallow, black-haired, and the set of pipes he had looked like an ill-
natured caricature of the gangrel player's instrument – a dingy, tattered tartan bag and
two drones, one of which was plainly out of commission. Nevertheless, he played the
tune not badly, and when he had finished I asked him where he came from. He told me
he belonged to a branch of the notable gaberlunzie tribe bearing the name of Stewart,
and that the glens and the straths, the highways and byways of Perthshire were his
native place.

Not long before, I had been recording folk-tales, legends, droll stories, and wonder
tales in and around Blairgowrie, so I asked Davie – that was his first name – if he had
heard one about the three brothers who went out to seek their fortune. Needless to say,
he had – this is an opening which leads into umpteen folk-tales – and I decided to bring
him back to the School of Scottish Studies to record him. The first tale he recorded for
me was a version of 'The Girl as Helper in the Hero's Flight' – the Jason and Medea tale
– which contained a vital detail absent from a version recorded in Aberdeenshire which
I was then editing. And before the night was out I had on tape a version of a very
strange tale, 'The Maiden without Hands', a tale which up to that time had never been
recorded in a Scots version.

A few months later I received a request for versions of 'The Maiden without Hands'
from a scholar writing a thesis in Canada, and Davie's version went out to Quebec,
where it proved to be of great interest.

After the recording session was over I arranged to meet him the following day in
order to stand him a drink and a meal. It turned out that the owner of the café we went
to had seen Davie before – was, in fact, on quite familiar terms with him but he was very
puzzled when he heard that Davie had been making some recordings for me which I
thought highly of. 'Good heavens, he wouldnae hae onythin' for ye, would he?'

The truth is that the world of authentic traditional art – and particularly the world
of folk-song and story – forms a kind of underground which those 'not in the know'
very often have considerable difficulty in contacting, let alone penetrating. There are a
number of reasons for this. First and foremost, the authentic story-teller or folk-singer
represents a tradition which in our day and age feels itself very much on the defensive.
It is a sort of 'anti-culture' and embodies ideas, predilections and values which are not
those of learned culture, and which in the sterner Puritan societies of the past were
ruthlessly put to the horn. Today such genuine folk culture as survives coexists
uneasily with the majority 'art-culture' and it is quite possible to live right in the middle
of it and never to apprehend its existence.

There are many accounts of the mixed feelings with which the traditional singer
views the activities of the man 'from the other side' who takes an interest in his art. The
great English collector, Cecil Sharp, paid a visit in September 1903 to the vicarage of a
friend, the Revd Charles L. Marson, in Somerset, and he collected 'The Seeds of Love'

from John England, the vicar's gardener. A. H. Fox Strangways and Maud Karpeles describe what happened as follows:

> Sharp whipped out his notebook, took down the tune, and afterwards persuaded John to give him the words. He went off and harmonised the song, and that same evening it was sung at a choir supper by Mattie Kay, Sharp accompanying. The audience was delighted; as one said, it was the first time that the song had been put into evening dress. John was proud, but doubtful about the evening dress; there had been no piano to *his* song.

Nowhere are the characteristic attitudes of our folk culture more obvious than in the sphere of sex. Folk-song has no use for the conventional hypocrisies and taboos of respectable society. It handles the joys, miseries, and above all the comedy of sex with medieval directness. Needless to say, this has never endeared it to the Holy Willies of Scottish life.

Our folk-song, therefore, from the great tragic ballads to the lightest of ribald mouth tunes, is a world of its own; but it is a splendid, eloquent, and poetic world, fully deserving of the attention and indeed of the love of all Scots interested in their country's culture. In the past, and especially in the hundred-odd years between 1720 and 1830 it certainly received this attention and love in full measure; among the collectors and editors of that wonderful epoch can be numbered some of the most famous men in our literary history – Ramsay, Burns, Scott, Hogg, Buchan, Mother-well.

It was a period when the grip of Calvinism had been loosened, and when cultivated men felt free to go in search of the older Scotland which had been driven underground by religious fanaticism. They were conscious of the fact that in earlier centuries the literary and the folk cultures of Scotland had constantly interacted, and they wished to resume and enlarge that fruitful tradition.

With what triumph they achieved their objective would be familiar to every child in every Scottish school – if the Scots literary tradition were taught to them in Scottish schools. The poets and folk-song collectors of the late eighteenth and early nineteenth centuries made it possible, once again, for the people of Scotland to come to terms with their own folk-tradition, and although the Holy Willies and Groaning Jonahs are still with us, no amount of sanctimonious double-talk since then has been able totally to obscure this fact. The best of our literature is impregnated through and through with the despised folk tradition.

The search into surviving balladry has gone hand in hand with investigation of the folk-tale. Both songs and tales are to be found in large numbers among the Scots travelling folk – nomadic clans such as the Stewarts, Whytes, and MacPhees. For that reason a considerable amount of our collecting time in recent years has been spent among these folk, who possess an enormous treasure of oral lore of all descriptions.

Indeed, so much fresh ground has been broken in the study of the tinkers that a project was initiated in 1955 which aimed at surveying 'traveller' communities from an anthropological as well as from a folk-cultural point of view. This project, in which several scholars have collaborated, has provided an opportunity for the various depart-ments in the School of Scottish Studies to work as a team, and the School intends to do a great deal of additional research in this fascinating field.

As recorded material comes into the School, it must be indexed, classified, and annotated. This means that a considerable amount of time is spent on the play-back of material tape-recorded by the School's field workers, or by the local collectors mentioned above. Transcription of texts and music must be undertaken. This means that the digesting of material collected often takes much longer than the collecting tour itself.

Scots Magazine, Feb. 1963.

Scots Folk-song Today

In November 1788, Robert Burns wrote in a letter to his friend, James Johnson, an Edinburgh music engraver:

> I see every day a new Musical Publications advertised; but what are they? Gaudy hunted butterflies of a day, and then vanish for ever: but your Work will outlive the momentary neglects of idle Fashion, and defy the teeth of Time.

The work Burns was referring to was the *Scots Musical Museum*, the great collection to which the bard devoted so much of his time and genius. It has been suggested – by J. C. Dick – that Burns himself chose the title *Musical Museum*, but the evidence points the other way, and the idea seems in itself unlikely. There are over 200 songs in the collection which Burns either wrote, or re-fashioned to a greater or lesser extent, and the word *Museum* (defined by Dr Johnson, 1755, as 'a repository of learned curiosities') must surely strike one as itself gey curious when one thinks of Burns's enthusiastic creative labours, and indeed of the many shrewd comments on Scots folk-song which one finds in his letters.

However, James Johnson – if it was he who chose the word – was merely echoing the generally accepted ideas of his day about the fate of traditional song. Until comparatively recently – as Peter Opie has pointed out – the great majority of collectors and editors have regarded their finds as 'museum pieces', and laid them out as such – often with due funereal solemnity. Collection after collection has appeared bedecked with elegiac ribbons, like the ceremonial last sheaf from the harvest field.

Modern ballad scholarship, especially in America, has virtually put paid to this backward-looking antiquarian approach to the folk-arts – an approach which has stultified so much 'literary' criticism of the products of the folk-process. In his fine work, *The Ballad of Tradition* (1932), the late Professor Gordon Hall Gerould rounded off a study of the classical or 'Child' ballads with an appendix containing a dozen American folk-songs; these included 'The Wreck of the C. and O.', 'The Buffalo Skinners', 'The Old Chisholm Trail', 'John Henry' and 'Jesse James'. The pioneering work of John Lomax and others among lumberjacks and cowboys had found acceptance on the douce campus of Princeton, and the way was cleared for some very necessary revaluations.

Of the Aberdeenshire ballad versions collected in the early years of this century by Gavin Greig, and edited after his death by Alexander Keith, Gerould says, 'It is perhaps the most valuable single volume of texts collected since Child's day.' I do not

myself have the honour to be an Aberdonian, so I think I can say without chauvinism
that few ballad scholars on either side of the border – or on either side of the Atlantic,
for that matter – would be likely to dispute this statement. The Greig/Keith volume,
Last Leaves of Traditional Ballads and Ballad Airs, is one of the monuments of modern
ballad scholarship, and alone would be enough to make Aberdeen hallowed ground for
the students of these great songs everywhere. However, the 'Last Leaves' of the title
have happily proved to be only – so to speak – the last leaves of a season, and that there
are fresh leaves on the old branches, you will in a moment have incontrovertible proof.

The great standard reference work for the ballad is Professor Child's monumental
compilation *English and Scottish Popular Ballads* – or *Scottish and English Popular
Ballads*, as Dr William Montgomerie has suggested that in justice it should have been
called. In Child's massive five volumes, no less than a third of the texts from Scottish
sources belong to Aberdeenshire, and these include some of the most famous ballad
texts in the world. Today, Aberdeenshire still bears the gree, as the unchallenged ballad
shire of Scotland; of the classical ballad variants on tape in the archives of the School of
Scottish Studies, well over two-thirds were collected in the North-East. Of these, some
of the finest were recorded by the Aberdeen ballad singer, Jeannie Robertson.

Jeannie was born in Aberdeen and has spent most of her life in this city. When I first
met her, in 1953, she was living within quite easy walking distance of King's College
Library, where Gavin Greig's great manuscript collection is preserved. In that first
summer, when I was working with her, and starting to put on tape her magnificent
personal repertoire of folk-songs, learnt from her mother and from her own people, I
often used to walk from her house to the Library and back, and it was a strange
sensation to make that short journey, in space and time; to move from the home of a
wonderful Aberdeen folk-singer, a house which was always ringing with pipe music
and fiddle music, and in which a casual guest might come away with a Robin Hood
ballad, or a song in the folk-idiom composed a week or a day before; a house in which
Jeannie told the bairns international folk-tales which she had heard round the camp
fires of her own people; to move from that house, and in a quarter of an hour be sitting
in the Library strongroom, among Gavin Greig's manuscript notebooks, which some
– if not all – visiting scholars assumed to be the relics of a regional folk-culture as dead
as a door-nail.

Sometimes, I would return from the Library, after reading a ballad or a song written
out in Greig's beautiful handwriting, and ask Jeannie if she had ever heard it. If she
hadn't herself, she spared no pains to find someone in the area who had; her aunt,
Maggie, for example, had a beautiful variant of 'Little Sir Hugh and The Jew's
Daughter' (Child 155), and a young fellow had a variant of 'Johnnie Cock' (Child 114),
which he had heard in a school playground in Angus. But Jeannie was herself the
likeliest person to provide a song, a tale or a tune, and I'd like to call on her now to sing
her version of 'The Laird o' Drum' (Child 236) – which is a 'true ballad', in every sense
of the word, and a local one, for Drum is only nine or ten miles away down the Deeside
road. In 1681 Alexander Irvine, Laird of Drum, who had come through the troubled
times of the Civil War and the Cromwellian invasion with very depleted worldly
fortunes because of his fidelity to the house of Stuart, married as his second wife a
sixteen-year-old girl called Margaret Coutts, much to the dudgeon of his relatives
because she came of a poor family. Also the Laird was sixty-three, so no doubt they

thought he should have known better. The common folk, however, were on the Laird's side, as the popularity of this ballad testifies.

When Edwin Muir, towards the end of his life, used to come to the School of Scottish Studies to hear Jeannie's ballad recordings, it was 'The Laird o' Drum' which was his favourite – and after hearing Jeannie sing it, I don't think anyone here will be surprised.

In a moment, I am going to call on Jeannie to sing another Aberdeenshire ballad, perhaps the most famous of all – 'The Battle of Harlaw'. But I think she ought to rest for a moment, so before I do, let us hear a border ballad 'The Dowie Dens o' Yarrow' (Child 214), which is very popular still all over the country (we have twenty-four recordings of it on tape in the School). Most of these variants were recorded North of the Forth – although the name 'Yarrow' is to be found in every version, even in one recorded in the Northern Highlands. Here, however, it is sung by Willie Scott, a border shepherd from Canonbie, in Dumfriesshire.

The big ballads have not survived in the Borders to anything like the same extent as in the North-East – maybe they were never so thick on the ground there as has been popularly supposed – so I think you will agree it is a great experience to hear a real Border voice singing that famous ballad.

Now we return to Aberdeenshire. In 1411, the burghers and feudal barons of the North-East fought the Highland army of Donald, Lord of the Isles, to a standstill – at Harlaw, near Inverurie, less than twenty miles from here. However, at the end of the day the flower of the Lowland chivalry lay dead on the field – including, incidentally, an earlier Irvine of Drum:

> Gude Sir Alexander Irvine,
> The much renownit Laird of Drum.

Both sides eventually claimed that they had won the day, but the Irish Annals of Loch Ce are undoubtedly right in logging the battle as a victory of the Gael over the Gall (Gael is to Gall as Deutscher is to Welscher). The Lord of the Isles did not, however, follow up his victory, and Aberdeen was spared the sacking it was to receive two and a half centuries later at the hands of Montrose's Irish and Hielandmen.

In 1549, the anonymous author of *The Complaint of Scotland* listed 'The Battle of Hayrlau' among the songs and dances known to the peasantry of Scotland. Has this ballad survived? – or is 'The Battle of Harlaw', first printed by Alexander Laing in *The Thistle of Scotland* in 1823, an eighteenth-century production? I know Alec Keith inclines to think it is; he has suggested that the 'Hellenic enthusiasm' of one Robert Forbes, Gent (who wrote *Ajax's Speech to the Grecian Knabbs*, published in 1742), may have been responsible for the Homeric proportions of the battle-scene. Furthermore, the Forbeses, who play such a notable part in the folk-ballad, were not, it seems, at Harlaw at all.

However that may be – and the weight of critical opinion seems to be against the antiquity of Harlaw as we now hear it sung – there can be no doubt that when Jeannie sings it, it fully deserves to be styled a traditional ballad, and questions of historical accuracy are in abeyance, at any rate for the moment.

I should maybe add that my own opinion about 'Harlaw' – my present opinion, anyway – is that there is a very old core of ballad in the stanzas which describe the onset of the battle ('ilka sword gaed clash for clash'), but that a lot of re-writing and re-shaping may well have taken place in the eighteenth century. Also, I should think that the tune, which is a wonderful pentatonic ballad-tune, could well be exceedingly old; my guess would be that it has carried this ballad, in one shape or another, for three or four centuries – and even if that is not the case, you'll agree that 1800 to the mid-twentieth century is quite a respectable length of time for a ballad to become 'traditional'.

Before we leave the great ballads, I'd like to play you a few verses of 'Clerk Saunders' sung by a young Fife lassie, Jean Redpath. Jean was for a year President of the Edinburgh University Folk-song Society, and to the songs she learnt from her mother in Leven, she added songs learnt from our tapes, and from the great collections of the past. I suggested to her that she should learn 'Clerk Saunders', showed her the texts in Child, and sang her Kinloch's tune. Consequently, we have here a song from the modern folk-song revival – also a part, and an important part, of the folk-song scene.

The School of Scottish Studies has done a good deal of work with social groups such as the coal miners who have not in the past received much attention from collectors. In 1954 I recorded a Jacobite song, 'King Fareweel', from a Fife miner, Jock Cameron, who now lives in Edinburgh. He learnt it from his father, and it is of considerable historical interest – the first verse sounds like a rather grim comment on the Jacobite nobility from the point of view of a trooper in the field:

> Oh you've feather beds and carpet rooms –
> Could you no' pit doon a wee German lairdie?

In Ayrshire, the cult of Robert Burns has by no means obliterated the native folk-song which he sought out and edited.

Up and down Scotland the dance tunes, the horn-pipes, jigs, strathspeys and reels, which auld Hornie played in Kirk-Alloway are the carrying stream on which the old songs are borne forward, and on which new songs try their luck to float or sink. When you hear the old ribald mouth tunes, the best-loved offsprings of the Merry Muses, you get as near as you ever get to the heart of our song tradition.

The new songs I referred to are springing up everywhere, and most of them are products of the present-day folk-song revival. They are sung in folk-song clubs, mostly by young people, and the best of them catch on and get adapted and altered in the time-honoured fashion. A programme called 'The Crow and the Cradle', broadcast on radio on 18 August 1963, was about this development, and a paragraph in the *Radio Times* for that week contains an admirable short description of this particular development:

> Folk-songs, unexpurgated, deal honestly with love, work, war. Young people in folk-song clubs are discovering this heritage, and, within the tradition, are making new songs of a type the commercial media don't provide: serious and satirical songs about contemporary affairs, including, of course, the Bomb.

Short statements about folk-song are chancy things – as Professor Child tacitly admitted, by never writing an introduction to *English and Scottish Popular Ballads*. Nevertheless, I am prepared – at any rate, for the purposes of the discussion which follows – to support this short statement which I have just quoted. We have a number of fairly gifted folk-poets in present-day Scotland, and I'd like to display for you specimens of the work of two of them – Matt McGinn of Glasgow, and Bob Bertram of Edinburgh.

First of all, a song by Bob Bertram about a Pakistani bus-conductor. According to my information, there have only been Pakistani bus-conductors on Edinburgh buses for about two months, and Bob's song was composed three or four weeks ago. The tune is a well-known folk-tune, usually called 'The Dundee Weaver'.

Well, I don't want to make any exaggerated claims for this little song, although I should think it stands a reasonable chance of getting picked up and sung. However, I think it is worth noting how tellingly it makes its point against racialism – and it makes it quite without rhetoric, or undue stridency.

Matt McGinn is even more prolific, and nearly all his songs have merit, as well as high entertainment value. He was born in the Gallowgate district of Glasgow, of Catholic-Irish parentage; his songs have the gallus sardonic verve of that area, and I'd back at least half a dozen of them to 'bide' – for a while, at least. One notable thing about Matt is that he nearly always makes up his own tunes; he may start, either consciously or subconsciously with a folk-tune, in the time-honoured fashion, but by the time he has made the song, he has usually made a new tune into the bargain.

The first song of his I'd like to play to you is topical enough, in all conscience, for it deals with the grandeurs and miseries – or at any rate, the illusions of grandeur – bound up with hire-purchase; indeed it's a sort of anthem for a society affluent on the never-never. Matt leads into it himself with characteristic dead-pan humour.

It is not hard to see, behind some of Matt's songs, the honourable influence of the Glasgow music-hall. However, it would be a very withdrawn folklorist, it seems to me, who failed to include the Glasgow music-hall within his terms of reference.

One of the few things Matt hasn't been in his life is a miner – and yet he has succeeded in writing a song which has become popular among Fife and Lothian miners, and shows every sign of catching on. In the same way, the anti-Polaris songs sung at the Holy Loch have been taken up, adapted and altered, and have sprouted fresh variants in time-honoured style.

Since he began to write these songs, Matt has been across in the USA and has shared a Carnegie Hall concert in New York with Pete Seeger. He has also become a successful commercial folk-singer, performing at clubs and concerts up and down the country for money (occasionally). I'd like to comment briefly about the commercial aspects of the folk-song revival, in the hope that it might engender a little healthy controversy.

There is at present a so-called folk boom in the USA, so an article in the *Melody Maker* of 23 August 1963 assures us:

> You can throw out the bossa nova, the twist, the hully gully, surf music and a flock of other dance-based musical fads. Forget them.
>
> The 'in' words in the United States this summer include 'Hoote-nanny' (more familiarly known as 'Hoot'), five-string banjo, twelve-string guitar, and most of all, 'folkniks' because the folkniks have given the record and music business here its biggest boost in many years.

At the end of the article the *Melody Maker* scribe risks a cautious explanation for this development:

The message of the music may have something to do with its growing acceptance; if indeed its youthful followers are actually aware of what the songs are
saying.

The news that a folk-boom after the American model may possibly hit our shores as
well will undoubtedly be greeted with mixed feelings by many people interested in the
present subject. In the *New Statesman* of 26 July 1963, there appeared an article by
Francis Newton called 'Two Cheers for Folk-Song'. Mr Newton does not mince
words about the dangers inherent in every commercially promoted vogue, especially
among young people:

> There is no doubt that commercialism must distort, corrupt and transform folk-
> music, and may well destroy it by sheer over-stimulation, as has recently
> happened to traditional jazz, which is a sub-department of the folk thing.

On the other hand, Mr Newton advises against retreat into a private folk-song redoubt.
Independence of business, he says, may merely hide that much more doubtful thing,
hostility to popularity. And he goes on:

> It will not do to confine folk-song to a morally and socially pure archaeological
> museum, even one visited by a lot of people. This is merely another way back to
> greensleevery, and the embalming of songs in classrooms, and minority breasts.

The moral of Mr Newton's article is that the 'folkniks' should have the courage of their
convictions and be prepared to enter the commercial arena – realising that if *they* don't,
the vacuum will be filled by a motley crew of Tin Pan Alley corrupters and exploiters.

Here, it seems to me, is a theme on which discussion can usefully centre. May I
hazard an opinion, and a prediction, to set the ball rolling? The pessimists who foresee
doom in the boom, and lament folk-song drowned in an ill-favoured commercial
flood, are merely the latest in that very long line of premature mourners, to which I
referred earlier. If we haven't learned by now that folk-song has enormous resilience,
and that after the late-night final there is always a final night edition, and so on into the
dawn, we shall never learn.

A certain stream of the folk-song revival may well go commercial, and become a
new type of pop-song – in which case it will probably do the pop-song world a lot of
good – but new generations of Bob Bertrams and Matt McGinns will come forward, to
make new songs, and adapt the old ones, whether they are invited to go commercial, or
not. And good luck to them, if they are! The paid professional is no new thing in folk-
song. As Charles L. Seeger remarked in his essay, 'Professionalism and Amateurism in
the Study of Folk Music':

> Folk singers and players are not uncommon who have earned portions of their
> living through their art … There is a difference between the outstanding per-
> formers of a local community and the rank-and-file of the population. And it is
> generally recognised in the community. We should not ignore it, even though
> the music performed by the outstanding performers is virtually the same as that
> performed by the rank-and-file. We must admit, I feel, that the outstanding
> performers have about them the essential qualities we have customarily found in
> the 'professional' in scholarly life, and upon various levels of music activity. In

relation to these, the rank-and-file of the community where a folk-culture can be said to thrive have similarly the essential qualities of those we have called 'amateurs'. *We cannot, therefore, class folk music, as a whole, as an amateur idiom. (The Critics and the Ballad*, ed. M. Leach and T. P. Coffin)

That is what Seeger says. And you need look no further than Jeannie Robertson, who has sung at folk-song clubs all over Britain, and who has a number of LPs to her credit, to see an excellent example of the outstanding traditional *professional*.

Further on in the same article I have just quoted, Seeger observes (referring to the American folk-scene in 1949):

There will be some awfully sweet prettifying for city people, a lot of slicking down of good folk stuff in radio stations, and some terrible folk symphonies.

Well, there has been a lot of sweet prettifying and slicking down of folk-song in the past – it goes rather further back with us than it does in the States – and no doubt we are in for plenty more in the immediate future. A great deal of tholing – of spartan enduring – will certainly be necessary. But the manifest vitality of Scots folk-song emboldens me to say with confidence that we will survive the boom – and the doom – and come through singing on the other side. I know that it would be over-sanguine for me to expect every folklorist and musicologist present to take the same optimistic view, but I can assure you that many young Scots folk-singers of today, who have respect for their art, and have taken the trouble to learn something about it, do share this view with ardent enthusiasm. And that, I submit, is what will count in the long run.

Folklore, Vol. 75, Spring 1964.
(Text of a talk given at the 125th meeting of the British Association of the Advancement of Science, Aberdeen, 1963)

A Plea for the Sung Ballad

Since around the middle of the eighteenth century, the ballads of Scotland have been intensively collected. Once the religious fanaticism that had stultified so much of Scottish life during the seventeenth century had subsided, intellectuals of one sort and another felt themselves liberated from the theocratic tyranny, and free to investigate our folk culture, which had been driven underground by the harsh puritanism of the zealots.

The same sort of thing happened in England, too, but to a much lesser extent. The reason why the Scots ballad texts recovered from oral tradition are so superior to those found in England may be due partly to a more fiery imagination among the Scots, but also to the fact that England simply lacked collectors as assiduous and devoted as, for example, David Herd and George Ritchie Kinloch.

Another reason is that so many of our eighteenth- and nineteenth-century collectors were themselves accomplished poets. Nearly all these poets and collectors were more interested in the texts of the ballads than in the tunes. They presented their finds as if they were poems, not songs. Ballad scholarship in Scotland consequently has had – until this century – a very strong literary – as opposed to musical – bias. This has led to some strange aberrations in criticism, and at its worst has obfuscated the nature of the ballads. It also accounts for the odd fact that all the ballads that have been heard up to now in this broadcast series have been spoken, not sung. How did these wonderful narrative songs come into existence? Whatever their ultimate origin, they are not, *in the form in which we now have them*, the work of one person.

It is true that quite a number of ballads, such as 'Sir Patrick Spens' and 'The Twa Corbies' do make admirable poems for declamation. Other ballads most emphatically do not. Now if it is conceded that the ballad should be *sung*, who is to sing it – the trained singer, or the natural folk-singer? There is no doubt in my mind that the latter is infinitely preferable. The techniques of the trained art-singer also almost invariably force folk-song into a contorted and incongruous mould; 'ludicrous' is not too strong a word to describe the end-result of some ill-advised attempts to mate folk-song and art-song.

Nevertheless, the idea still seems to linger on in some quarters that folk-singers cannot sing their own songs because they have poor, cracked, croaky voices, and are mostly older than the allotted span. This – in Scotland, at any rate – is happily not the case. We have some excellent young singers who are continuing the tradition in its integrity.

BBC Scottish Home Service, 1963.

Enemies of Folk-song

J. F. Campbell of Islay (Iain Og Ile), the great collector of Gaelic song, relates that when he began to enlist help from schoolmasters and other 'lettered' contacts in various parts of Scotland, he soon found out that there were many Gaelic-speaking Highlanders who believed, until they searched at his request, that folk-tales had become extinct in their respective districts. It was only gradually, and in some cases probably with reluctance, that they came to acknowledge the existence of a living folk-art at the hearths of the very people among whom they were living and working. Iain Og's experience could be paralleled by nearly every other collector, before and after. Folk culture may well excite – to quote H. Davenson – 'la curiosité permanente de l'élite', but the élite has a habit of imagining, in every century, that it is barely treading, and no more, on a thin small sliver of the ultimate tail-end of it. (Embarrassing, indeed, for the patronising armchair critic to find that after the late-night final there comes an unexpected final extra!)

If what Campbell wrote was true of the Gaidhealtachd a hundred years ago, who will wonder when he hears that the demise of the classical Scots ballads has been announced over and over again from the days of Scott onwards? The idea that they were still living on the lips of the people seems almost to have been repugnant to certain critics, who in any case were contemptuous of folk-song and tried to claim the ballads for book-song in defiance of nearly all ascertainable facts about them. Gavin Greig summarised the position as follows:

> It has always been taken for granted that the true and authentic minstrelsy of the Scottish people is all recorded, and is to be found in the so-called collections of Scottish song – folk-song, if taken into account at all, being looked on as the negligible fringe of this authentic minstrelsy – a kind of rag-tag selvidge. It has been our pride as a nation to think of Scottish swain and maid singing the songs of Ramsay, Burns, Tannahill and Hogg as they moved about the field or sat by the fireside, or courted in the courtyard. It may be a pity to destroy this pleasing picture; but we can't help it. The idea is largely a pious delusion. As far at least as the North-East is concerned, research has convinced us that in the main our peasantry do *not* sing the songs of the books – but that their minstrelsy has been in the main just this hitherto unrecorded kind of thing which we are calling folk-song.

The same misconceptions and the same prejudices have existed in many other countries besides Scotland. The élite, especially in countries with a sharply stratified class-structure, invariably have their work cut out when trying to come to terms with their own folk-culture. The trouble here in Scotland has been, and still is, that the élite are to a big extent also the elect, and consequently have a vested interest in keeping the songs of the damned well battened down under hatches. Firmly entrenched in all key positions of administration, religion and the organisation of culture, the elect deny just as long as they are able that anything so vulgar as popular culture exists. (It is an extraordinary fact that until the School of Scottish Studies of Edinburgh University came into existence, no single academic body in Scotland had given more than the most trifling attention to the urgent work of recording, preserving and safeguarding the native traditions of the people, both Scots and Gaelic.)

Almost worse, however, than the studied ignoring of popular culture has been the attempt of the elect – once the existence of folk-song and folk-art could no longer be denied – to take possession of them, at the same time bowdlerising them and emasculating them. Realising that folk-song threw down a challenge to the culture of the élite, that it expressed with power and *élan* the communal creativeness of the people as against a book-song and an art-poetry increasingly contracted and withdrawn from the life of the common people, the mandarins of official taste did their utmost to purvey a diluted spirit to the public. Scottish folk-song has been bedevilled by professional beautifiers whose antics rather resemble those of the beauty-parlour morticians in Evelyn Waugh's satire *The Loved One*. For folk-song is an elusive thing, and captivity is hateful to it. Those who wish to coat it with rouge and greasepaint find inevitably that they must first turn it into a cadaver. The history of Scottish folksongism has been chiefly a determined attempt to take all the guts and spunk, all the ardour, verve and raucle randiness out of the song of the people, and reduce it to the level of a kirk social.

Burns himself foresaw the way things were likely to go. Anticipating the rougeing and bedizening operations of later collectors and anthologists, he wrote in April 1793, to Thomson:

> Another hint you will forgive. Whatever Mr Pleyel does, let him not alter one *iota* of the original Scotts Air; I mean, in the Song department; but let our National Music preserve its native features. They are, I own, frequently wild and unreducible to the more modern rules; but on that very eccentricity, perhaps, depends a great part of their effect.

These words, which one wishes could have rung for ever in the lugs of Dean Christie and Marjory Kennedy-Fraser, not to mention George Thomson himself, bring us to another ground for disputation – and one which the retreating hostile critics of the anti-folk-song camp have lately chosen to make a stand on. Was not Burns himself a recreator and reshaper, as well as a collector? Where does one draw the line between 'folk-song' and the productions of the individual bard? What is the difference, if any, between Burns adding stanzas to old anonymous fragments, and Mrs Kennedy-Fraser turning a Barra waulking song into her 'Kishmul's Galley'?

To answer this, let us look for a moment at one of the songs where Burns was not successful. Usually, when re-patching his fragments, he was able with marvellous sureness to counterfeit the anonymous folk voice – so expertly, that in many cases it is impossible to tell where the old song ends and the poet's work begins. Not infrequently his versions were in their turn taken up and remoulded by the people, so that they can today be collected as real folk-songs. But in the case of the old Banff song 'MacPherson's Rant', he produced a version which has moved far enough away from traditional song to be recognised at once as the production of an individual poet, losing in the process the homely directness of the folk-song without gaining anything to speak of in shapeliness or dignity.

The Burns version is readily available in any collected edition of his works. Here is a traditional version (from the singing of Jimmy MacBeath of Elgin and Davie Stewart of Dundee):

Fare ye weel ye dark and lonely hills
   Away beneath the sky.
MacPherson's Rant will nae be long
   Below the gallows tree.

Sae rantinly, sae wantonly,
   Sae dauntily gaed he –
He played a tune and danced it roun'
   Below the gallows tree.

'Twas by a woman's treacherous hand
   That I was condemned to dee.
Abune a ledge, at a window she stood,
   And a blanket she threw ow'r me.

The Laird o' Grant, that Highland saunt
   That first laid hands on me.
He pled the cause on Peter Broon
   To let MacPherson dee.

There's some come here to see me hanged
   And some to buy my fiddle –
But afore that I would part wi' her
   I'd brak her through the middle.

Fare ye weel my ain dear Highland hame –
   Fare ye weel, my wife and bairns.
There was nae repentance at my hert
   While the fiddle was in my airms.

He took the fiddle into baith o's hands
   And he broke it ower a stone.
Says, there's nae anither hand sall play on thee
   When I am deid and gone.

The reprieve was comin' ow'r the brig o' Banff
   To set MacPherson free,
But they pit the clock a quarter afore
   And hanged him to the tree.

The old Rant is tied fast to time and place and circumstance; in spite of this (or maybe because of this) it transcends these and speaks proudly with a universal tongue for the outlaws and dispossessed of the world. By comparison, Burns's poem, which general-ises and inflates the sentiment of the folk-song, appears as operatic braggadocio.

Although attempts to delimit the frontiers of folk-song with pencil and compass are inept to the nth degree, one begins to pick out here the outlines of two distinct and very different aesthetic worlds. Burns has retrieved a folk-song and carried it back into the world of the individual man of letters; the Rant, as I have transcribed it above, is an example of high artistic achievement through communal reshaping. This does not mean to say that a folk-song may not come off print and enter the oral tradition; on the contrary, many folk-songs now being collected in Scotland can be traced back to broadsides. Of these, however, the 'first' or broadside versions are seldom the best; later versions are often immeasurably superior, because communal recreation has given them a new shape and idiom.

Mention of the inept brings to mind Maurice Lindsay's recent book on Robert Burns, in which, as one might have expected, the demise of folk-song is hailed with the familiar elegiac droop:

> Nowadays in Scotland there are no peasants; and ours is not a singing age. The tradition in which Burns wrought died out in the Lowlands during the latter part of the nineteenth century, lingered out a brief decadence in the form of the Bothy Ballad in the relative seclusion of the North-East, and is now gone for ever. We cannot make folk-songs any more:
>
> > The laurels are all cut
> > The bowers are full of bay
> > That once the Muses wore.

This passage reminds me of a certain amiable doctor in the North of Scotland, who attended one of my principal informants for over forty years and did not know that he was a singer. God save the mark! That folk-song in Scotland, both Highland and Lowland, is still a going concern is attested by the 3,000-odd records made from living singers in the archives of the School of Scottish Studies: these include excellent versions of classical ballads such as 'The Battle of Harlaw', 'Clyde's Water', 'Johnnie Cock', 'Lord Lovat', 'The Laird o' Drum', 'Lang Johnnie More', 'Lord Thomas and Fair Ellen', 'The False Knight upon the Road' and scores of others. There are many singers in their teens in Scotland who have classical balladry by oral transmission, and the making up of 'novice' folk-songs proceeds apace, in our cities as well as in the countryside. So much for all this lamentable wailing at the windy walls. However, Lindsay's statement that 'we cannot make folk-songs any more' brings me to one of the last charges of the enemies of folk-song, namely, that it is by definition archaic and a thing of the past. 'Conditions are different now, they just don't favour it.' As a rider to this, one still sometimes hears (especially from the purist-presbyter school of critics) the statement, 'That song can't be a folk-song, it's got a known author, and quite modern too.' Let us take the second of these first.

Amateurs of the 'decadent' bothy ballad tradition to which Maurice Lindsay refers will know the name of 'The Hairst o' Rettie', a familiar cornkister. Many readers may well have heard it on the air, because versions of it, sung by John Strachan and John Mearns, have quite frequently been broadcast. It is about the introduction of the back delivery reaper at the end of the nineteenth century, and how it revolutionised the harvest; it's a grand robust song, glorifying in the completion of the hairst in record time, almost as if it were – as in a sense it was – a victory in the field:

> I hae seen the hairst o' Rettie,
>   Ay, an' twa-three off the throne:
> I've heard for sax or seyvin weeks
>   The hairsters girn an' groan –
> But a covie Willie Rae
>   In a monthie an' a day
> Gars a' the jolly hairster lads
>   Gae singin' doon the brae.
>
> A monthie an' a day, my lads,
>   The like was never seen!
> It beats to sticks the fastest strips
>   O' victory's best machine.
> A Speedwell now brings up the rear,
>   A Victory clears the way –
> An' twenty acres daily yields
>   Nor stands to Willie Rae.

It goes on to describe the expertise with which Willie handles the new reaper:

> He whittles aff at corners
>   And maks crookit bitties straucht,
> An' sees that man an' beast alike
>   Are equal in the draucht –
> An' a' the sheevies lyin' straucht
>   An' neen o' them agley,
> For he'll coont wi' ony dominie
>   Frae the Deveron tae the Spey.

This song was composed, by William Park, blacksmith on the farm of Rettie near Banff, in the last years of the nineteenth century. (Rettie was a huge farm, and had its own blacksmith. This century an aerodrome has been carved out of it, and still left it big.) The song hit the mood of the people so well that it spread like wildfire, and within a few years innumerable variants had sprouted from its text. It is possible today to record different versions of it all over the North-East.

Now this is a song which is quite definitely not 'anon'. Not only is its author known, but there are people still alive who remember Willie Rae, and tell anecdotes about him. Furthermore, the song has appeared in print and these printed versions may well have influenced singers who got the song by oral transmission. Indeed, the song may in certain parts have entered the oral tradition from Greig's *Buchan Observer* articles.

And not only that. The song has been broadcast, and it is by no means out of the question that some of the folk-singers who have 'The Hairst o' Rettie' may have been influenced by, for example, John Strachan's rendering – which has itself, I am pretty sure, been influenced by Ord's printed version.

So here we have – to use a phrase dear to the armchair critics of folk-song (and folk-song collectors) – a clear case of 'contamination'. Maybe the 'Hairst o' Rettie' isn't a folk-song at all! Let me ask, then – does this sad piece of tampered-with goods I have been exhibiting constitute a folk-song within the meaning of the act? My own answer, for what it is worth, is – certainly! And why? Because the people have taken it, possessed themselves of it, gloried in it, recreated it, loved it. That is the only test worth a docken.

The same is true of the modern workers' songs to which Maurice Lindsay alludes contemptuously in a footnote. Some of these are mighty good now: in a decade they will likely be even better. For (to come to the first heading of the charge) folk-songs can be made today much the same as they always were. I have recently collected splendid satirical songs from the Korean battle-fronts which bear all the marks of developed folk-songs – a campaign is always a powerful incubator of song. And ballads can grow in Clydeside factories as well as in Ross-shire glens and Buchan bothies.

'But what on earth are you going to do with all this stuff once you've collected it?' comes a parting shot from the opposite camp. The answer is: give it back to the Scottish people who made it. I dare say there are still people in academic circles in Scotland who think that collected folk-songs should be allowed to gather dust in the archives, but their point of view has been expressed (better maybe than they could express it) by Ogden Nash in his 'Private Dining Room':

> At midnight in the vasty hall,
> The fossils gathered for a ball ...
> Pterodactyls and brontosauruses
> Sang ghostly prehistoric choruses.
> Above the megalosauric wassail
> I caught the eye of one small fossil.
> Cheer up, old man, he said, and winked –
> It's kind of fun to be extinct.

Well, that is one way of looking at it. I would venture a more sanguine hope. The arts of the people display an amazing resilience – one thinks of the commons of Scotland who rallied to Wallace when the Scottish nobility were treacherously deserting him. I mentioned earlier J. F. Campbell's experiences with some of his collaborators who doubted a hundred years ago if there were any *sgialachdan* still in circulation: in July 1955, I recorded near Bettyhill in Sutherland fine versions of folk-tales about Oisein and the Feinne, versions which Iain Og himself might have been proud of.

Young singers in Glasgow are learning old songs from the tapes, and making new ones on the old tunes. Play the traditional music in schools, as I have done, and the effect is electric. The national consciousness is stirring; if we act promptly and boldly, we can make the folk-song revival a powerful component part of the Scottish Renaissance.

Saltire Review, Autumn 1955.

At the Foot o' yon Excellin' Brae': The Language of Scots Folk-song

> If Platitude should claim a place
> Do not denounce his humble face;
> His sentiments are well intentioned
> He has a place in the larger legend.
>
> PATRICK KAVANAGH

In his foreword to Superintendent John Ord's collection of bothy ballads,[1] Robert A. Rait, Principal of Glasgow University, wrote in April 1930:

> We have here the real thing – the songs as actually sung in the bothies of the farms in the north. Their text may be evidence of the invasion of the vernacular by southern influence (though many words conventionally printed in English were, and are, pronounced as Scots), but their substance provides a living picture of Scottish rural life, absolutely sincere and free from any form of affection.

Open Ord's collection at random, and one finds (for example) the following:

> Love's hottest glow is kindled in my breast,
>   And, oh, but it beats so sairly;
> There is none in this world can bring me comfort and rest
>   But my handsome ploughman laddie.[2]

And again:

> Like midges on a summer's day the French around us lie,
> But with our British bayonets we'll make them fight or fly;
> We'll make them fight or fly, he says, and drive them out of Spain,
> That war may cease and bring us peace, and send us home again.[3]

And again:

> And if the thistle it be strong,
> I fear 'twill jag thy milk-white hand,
> But with my hook I'll cut it down,
>   When we join yon band o' shearers.[4]

When Rait wrote the above quoted passage, collection of folk-song with mechanical appliances – the primitive ancestors of present-day tape-recorders – had already been going on for more than two decades, but so firmly was scholarship thirled to the printed or written word that he could not be expected to think of invoking the authority of such mechanically recorded song and speech. One could indeed compile quite a sizeable anthology of similar comments on the language of Scots folk-song, as it appears in printed collections. The purpose of the present essay is to demonstrate that a curious 'bilingualism in one language' has been a characteristic of Scots folk-song at least since the beginning of the seventeenth century; meaning, in effect, since the arrival on the Lowland scene of that magisterial influence on Scottish hearts and minds, the King James VI Bible.

However, important though the advent of the Word of God 'in Inglis tung' undoubtedly was – from the earliest smuggled imports to the momentous appearance of the great Authorised Version itself – it would be quite wrong to attribute the galloping anglicisation of the seventeenth and later centuries to the Bible alone. As Stanley Hyman put it in a masterly essay in 1954:

> The finest Scottish poetry has always been bilingual in a curious fashion. Douglas the translator, Dunbar using Latin refrains, Boyd writing in Scottish and Latin, Burns writing in Scottish and English, are all poets for whom Lowland Scots was one of the world's tongues, not the language in which God and Adam held converse.[5]

To this thought-provoking list he might have added the name of George Buchanan, who was capable of writing prose in trenchant Scots and elegant English as well as poetry in justly eulogised Latin, and who throughout his life was probably thinking off and on in what seems to have been his mother tongue – Gaelic.

And when referring to 'Douglas the translator', Hyman might well have made the point that the Bishop of Dunkeld, if he wrote any of his *Eneados* in Dunkeld, was composing in a language he called 'Scottis' in the middle of a Gaelic-speaking population. (Professor Kenneth Jackson and Fred Macaulay were still able to record Perthshire Gaelic from a native speaker in the Dunkeld area as late as 1952.)

Put simply, this means that Scotland – like Switzerland – is (and always has been) a multi-lingual community, and that the language problems of Scottish poets go back at least as far as the Flyting of Dunbar and Kennedy:

> Thow lufis nane Irische, elf, I understand,
> Bot it suld be all trew Scottis mennis lede.[6]

and probably a lot further.

It is by no means strange, therefore, that the literary language of the great makars, which Dunbar called Inglis and Gavin Douglas (on one occasion, at least) Scottis, should exhibit signs of linguistic tension rather more complex than is often assumed. The makars were writing 'Inglis', but they were also Scotsmen, members of a nation with a fierce precocious national pride: it would not be strange, therefore, if their attitude to their own linguistic medium were in some sense ambivalent. They were not Chaucerians, but they were writing under Chaucer's shadow: like all Scottish poets ever since, they knew they were writing 'over against' another and closely related literature, which they could not have ignored even if they had wished to do so.

In the article already quoted, Hyman had some hard things to say about the Lallans poets of the 1940s, suggesting that they had not come within a mile of comprehending their own historic linguistic predicament; at the end of the essay he referred, somewhat disdainfully, to 'the quixotic effort to write in an artificial and resurrected literary language requiring a glossary in each volume'. Now and then he took a canny pot-shot at Hugh MacDiarmid's bristling carnaptious redoubt, but he also paid tribute to 'The Seamless Garment', which was for him MacDiarmid's 'most impressive poem', and one in which he found 'something like Henryson's or Dunbar's perfectly achieved linguistic balance':[7]

> And as for me in my fricative work
>   I ken fu' weel
> Sic an integrity's what I maun hae,
>   Indivisible, real,
> Woven owre close for the point o' a pin
> Onywhere to win in.[8]

Hyman's praise was reserved, however, for 'a folk literature unsurpassed by any in the world, the Scottish popular ballads'.

If prose and poetry in a self-conscious literary Scots came increasingly to seem documentations of a sad case of arrested development, the anonymous ballad-makers continued on their way, knowing little and caring less of the niceties of hyperborean lingo and prosody. They were, in any case, operating in a zone which ignored national and political boundaries. The themes of the great tragic ballads to which Hyman refers are elemental folk motifs – and many of these cross national language boundaries. Take 'Lord Randal' for example. This is the ballad of 'the false true love' who poisons her lover; it has been found in innumerable guises right across Europe, but the identity of the ballad remains remarkably stable – even the exact sequence of stanzas being often the same. Why then have the Scottish versions, from Scott's onwards, received such universal acclaim? (Again, it would be possible to list a whole battery of eulogies.) There are no doubt several feasible answers to this question but I here put forward the proposition that one of the reasons for the unchallenged excellence of many of our ballad versions resides in the actual nature of the language in which they are couched – in what we may term 'ballad-Scots'.

This, the idiom in which the virtuoso song-makers were operating, is a flexible formulaic language which grazes ballad-English along the whole of its length, and yet remains clearly identifiable as a distinct folk-literary lingo. Gavin Greig paid tribute to the 'simple, clear and dignified' language of the older classic ballads found in Aberdeenshire; and the strange 'bilingualism in one language', which greatly extends its range, demonstrably makes it a much suppler instrument than the often rather wooden ballad-English. We have already noticed the importance of the arrival of the King James Bible, and there can certainly be no doubt that it played a vital part in stabilising ballad-Scots, and facilitating a resourceful creative togetherness: a sort of chemical fusion of two distinct but related ballad languages. In the folk field, as well as in the less agile literary Lallans, Scots may be said to include English and go beyond it.

The tape-recordings of Scots classic ballads in the archives of the School of Scottish Studies add a new dimension to the study of the 'muckle sangs' as they existed – and still exist – in oral currency in Scotland. Their importance from both a textual and musical point of view can hardly be exaggerated. Just as the traditional manner of singing the older modal tunes often defies orthodox musical notation, so numerous linguistic and phonetic points (which in print and in manuscript collections are more often than not hopelessly blurred and fuzzed over) leap out at one from the tape-recording with a freshness and immediacy which amount in some cases to positive revelation.

The most striking thing which emerges is that the bilingualism referred to by Stanley Hyman is a reality. The tape-recording enables one to look behind and through the records of David Herd and Gavin Greig to what the North-East folk-singers actually said and sang.

The Buchan folk-singer does not sing in the same way in which he speaks. Or, to put it rather differently (and possibly more accurately), he is liable to speak and sing in at least two and sometimes more ways. But here we can easily run into misunderstandings at several levels. Let me clear the ground by making one or two points about folksong in general which would not, I think, be challenged nowadays except by the most incorrigible of armchair romanticists.

The language of the older folk-song is never purely 'colloquial'; it is formal, even stylised, bearing much the same relation to the normal speech of the singer that the literary language of Augustan art-poetry, say, bore to the everyday speech of the poets concerned. It is in the great songs, licked into shape like pebbles by the waves of countless tongues, that this sense of formality is most marked.

The technique of singing the traditional ballads involves a number of definite linguistic conventions which are still to be heard on the lips of traditional singers from Cornwall to Macduff, and from County Cork to Suffolk. (The most characteristic of these is the 'wrenched accent'; when a trochaic dissyllable occurs at the end of a line, the accent is shifted to the last syllable – e.g. 'The King has written a braid lettér.')

As Hodgart puts it in his study The Ballads: 'The rhythms of folk-song do not always correspond to speech-rhythms: the English language is used almost as if it were French, in that full value may be given to normally unstressed syllables.'[9]

The modifications caused in the 'Child' ballads by oral transmission are infinitely various, but they remain amazingly constant in mood, personality and development. Consequently the changes which they undergo when passing from one folk-song community to another (I do not refer only to linguistic changes) are of extraordinary ethnological interest.

All this is as true of the English ballad-singer as it is of the Scots. A Dorset labourer singing 'Lord Lovel' is singing ballad-English, not Dorset dialect – although there may well be an intrusion of Dorset localisms here and there.

Now move to North-East Scotland, and the situation becomes a good deal more complicated. In Aberdeenshire, the native speech of the ballad-singer is a very marked idiosyncratic dialect of Scots, very different in intonation, and to a considerable extent in vocabulary, from the south-country Doric. This dialect bears a definite relation to the old (vanished) Metropolitan Scots of the pre-Reformation court, and to the English of the King James Bible which has been since the seventeenth century very much the prestige speech over a great part of Scotland.

When he is singing the classical ballads, the Buchan ballad-singer usually tends instinctively to avoid the characteristic Aberdeenshire localisms, e.g. 'fa' for 'wha', 'fit' for 'what' etc. He employs a clear braid Scots, which turns out on examination to be a

'folk-literary' language of great subtlety and sophistication as well as of massy
strength:

> Johnnie rose up on a May morning,
>   Ca'd for water to wash his hands.
> Says, gae lowse to me my twa grey dogs
>   That lie bound in iron chains, chains,
>   That lie bound in iron chains.
>
> When Johnnie's mither she heard o' this
>   Her hands wi' dule she wrang.
> Says, Johnnie, for your venison
>   To the green woods dinna gang, gang
>   To the green woods dinna gang.
>
> It's we hae plenty o' guid white bread
>   And plenty o' guid red wine
> So, Johnnie, for your venison
>   To the green woods dinna gang, gang,
>   To the green woods dinna gang.
>
> But Johnnie has breskit his guid benbow,
>   His arrows one by one,
> And he's awa to the gay green woods
>   To pull the dun deer doon, doon,
> To pull the dun deer doon.[10]

These are the opening verses, as I now sing them, of 'Johnnie Cock' (Child 114), the
archetypal ballad of the 'bold poacher'. To make my version I drew on those of John
Strachan (recorded in 1951) and of Jeannie Robertson (recorded in 1953); I also drew
on the version which appears in Gavin Greig's *Last Leaves* (p. 93) – it was collected
from Alex Mackay, a butcher in Alford – and which is included by Bertrand H.
Bronson among the versions of Child 114 in Volume III of *The Traditional Tunes of
the Child Ballads*. The tune I use is an amalgam of those mentioned. Before this version
gelled I moved across from one text to another, and an inspection of the various
versions would show why this process is comparatively easy for anyone familiar with
'ballad-Scots': all the variants concerned are from oral tradition, and have had time to
settle into what we may truly call a classic mould. Indeed, when Child called 'Johnnie
Cock' 'this precious specimen of the unspoiled traditional ballad' he was paying a
compliment as much to the language as to the story-line.

The language is obviously that of the native Scots ballad-singer, but there is little
that would not be immediately comprehensible to a singer in Durham or in Dorset.

Even closer to ballad-English is the following stanza of a beautiful fragment of
'Sweet William's Ghost' (or, it could be, of 'Clerk Saunders') recorded in Fraserburgh
in 1954 from an old illiterate tinker woman who hailed originally from the Perthshire
Highlands:

> My mouth it is full of mould, Maggie,
>   And my breath it is wonderful strong;

And if I was to kiss your sweet ruby lips
Your time would nae be long.[11]

Old Betsy's natural speech was that of her clan, which draws on both Deeside and
Perthshire elements, as well as on fragmentary Gaelic and luxuriant travellers' cant; but
this verse (which I reproduce exactly as she sang it) has one distinctively Scots locution
in it. But it should be noted that that single 'nae' means that the whole verse has to be
read and pronounced *more Boreali*, and ca's the ground from under the feet of anyone
who tries to read it in refined Suddroun.

If it seems strange that a Scots folk-singer who never spoke English in conversation
could nevertheless sing in a lingo so close to ballad-English, one need only point out –
as Gavin Greig pointed out – that the language of distinctively English folk-songs like
'The Foggy Dew' presents no difficulty to singers who are familiar with the metrical
psalms and paraphrases.

The swing of the pendulum between ballad-Scots and ballad-English in the language of the classic ballads is sometimes capricious, but it more often corresponds to
deep instinctive aesthetic patterns. Where the Scots ballad-singer (following countless
singer-ancestors) feels that 'dead' sounds better than 'deid' in a particular verse of 'The
Battle of Harlaw', he comes right out and sings 'dead'. But if you asked him which he
had sung, he would probably have to sing the verse again to find out.

The same oscillation between Scots and English can be seen in the language of the
Scots folk-tales recorded on tape from Jeannie Robertson, Belle Stewart, Duncan
Williamson and many others since the foundation of the School of Scottish Studies. It
is interesting to compare the language of these stories with that of the versions collected
and retold by Peter Buchan in *Ancient Scottish Tales* (1829; reprinted 1908 by the
Buchan Field Club). Buchan's tales are somewhat wooden anglicised recensions which
reproduce neither the language nor the flavour of his originals; furthermore, the
incidental trappings bear witness to the florid self-indulgent imagination of the editor
(e.g. the opening of 'The Cruel Stepmother', which is number 706 in the Aarne/
Thompson Type Index):

> About the year 800, there lived a rich nobleman in a sequestered place in
> Scotland, where he wished to conceal his name, birth, and parentage, as he had
> fled from the hands of justice to save his life for an action he had been guilty of
> committing in his early years. It was supposed, and not without some good show
> of reason, that his name was Malcolm, brother to Fingal, King of Morven.[12]

Nevertheless, Peter's collection does consist almost entirely of identifiable international folk-tales (e.g. Aarne/Thompson numbers 300, 303, 313, 325, 326, 425, 510A,
706, 851 and 955); and it is undoubtedly the first repository we have – and the only one
until this century – of tales circulating in the Scots-speaking areas of the North-East.

Peter Buchan's version of Aarne/Thompson 313 – 'The Girl as Helper in the Hero's
Flight', for which his own name is 'Green Sleeves' – contains the swan-maiden motif
often found throughout the world in variants of this tale (cf. my note to 'The Green
Man of Knowledge', *Scottish Studies* vol. 2, pp. 61–85). This is how Peter presents the
encounter between his hero and the girl who will eventually assist him to overcome his
adversary (her father, the Green Man):

The prince went as directed, and hid himself behind the sloe-thorn hedge, when he saw three of the most beautiful swans come and hover over the river for a little time, at length alighted and threw off their swan-skins, when he snatched up the one with the blue wing. After they had continued for some time in the water, they prepared to proceed directly home; but as the one who had the skin with the blue wing could not find hers, she was at a loss what to do, more particularly as the other two told her they would not wait, but go home without her. On looking wistfully around her, she spied the prince, whom she knew, and asked him if he had her swan-skin. He acknowledged the theft, and said, if she would tell him where Green Sleeves stayed he would deliver unto her the skin. This she said she durst not venture to do, but upon his immediately giving it up, she would teach him how to discover the place of his retreat if he would follow her directions. He then gave her the skin, and she directed as follows.[13]

Here is the same sequence of events, as recounted by a young traveller called Geordie Stewart in Jeannie Robertson's house in 1954:

He lands at the banks o the river. And now, as the blacksmith telt him to hide hissel, so Jack hides hissel … just aside the bridge, and he sees this three lovely maidens comin ower, and they were bonnie lassies. But the littlest one was the slenderest, and the most graceful o lot, you would have thought, you know? So they come trippin ower the bridge and undress, and into the water. And whenever they touch the water, the two oldest ones turned til a black swan, and they swum fast an away. And this youngest one undresses; and he watches where she pits her clothes, and ye ken what like Jack, I mean a fairm servant, never seen a woman in his life hardly, says, 'Lord, this is fine!' They're into the water, and they're away swimming. So he's awa up wi her claes, up every stitch o claes she had, everything, even the very ribbons, and hides them.

So the two oldest ones comes out and dresses, and across the bridge and away. And she's up and doon this side, and she says, 'Where are you, Jack?'

He says, 'I'm here.'

She says, 'My clothes, please, Jack.'

'Ah na na, I'm nae giein ye nae claes,' he says. 'I was weel warned aboot ye.'

She says, 'Jack, please, my clothes, Are you a gentleman?'

'Na na,' he says, 'I'm just Jack the Feel. I'm nae gentleman.'

She says, 'What have I to do, Jack?'

'Well,' he says, 'it's a cruel thing to ask, but you must help me across this river on your back.'

She says, 'Oh Jack, you'd break my slender back.'

'Ah,' he says, 'the old smith's nae feel. Ye're nae sae slender.' He says, 'Ye'll take me across the river.'

She says, 'Well Jack, step on my back, but whatever you do, on the peril of my life and your life, don't tell how ye got across.'

He says, 'Okay'.

So he jumps on her back, and she takes him across, an he steps up on the bank.[14]

Another very revealing comparison can be drawn between the stilted high-falutin English of Peter Buchan's recensions, and modern translations into workmanlike 'carpentered Scots' of these same tales (which were taken down – according to Peter – from 'aged Sybils in the North Countrie'). Here is the opening of 'The History of Mr Greenwood', which is Peter's version of the international 'Bluebeard' Tale (Aarne/ Thompson 955):

> In the Western Isles of Scotland there lived a very rich man, of the name of Gregory, who had two beautiful daughters, to whom he was inordinately attached, but being vastly rich, he would not suffer either of them to go for an hour out of his presence without a strong detachment of the inmates of his house accompanying them wherever they went and for the purpose of defending them from violent attacks that might be made upon them, or being carried off by the lawless banditti who at that time infested that part of the country. It happened, however, one day when they were at their usual walk and recreation, a little distance from their house, there came up to them a gentleman with his servant on horseback, who accosted them in a rather familiar way, asking them if those men they saw at a little distance were attendants of theirs? They answered in the affirmative. He also put some other questions to them which they did not choose to answer. One of the ladies then wished to know how he was so impertinent; when he replied that, being much attached to the elder of the two, her beauty being so enchanting, he broke through the rules of good breeding.[15]

In a recent number of *Lallans* there is a version of the tale entitled 'The Storie o Caermoulis' contributed by David Purves. This is a recension of Peter's recension, 'pitten intil his ain Scots' by the translator. The opening goes as follows:

> Ae tyme in the Western Isles, thare bade a walthie man bi name o Gregorie that had twa braw dochters. He loued thaim baith that weill, he wadna allou thaim ti gang outby the houss athout a strang gaird, for in thae days, the kintrasyde wes thrang wi outlaws an ketterins.
>
> Houanevir, it fell that ae day whan thai warna fer frae the houss, a gentilman an his sairvant rade up ti thaim an spiered at thaim anent the gairds that was staunan tae neirhaund. Says he,
>
> 'Ma leddies, is aw yon your men staunan owre thare.'
>
> The auldest dochter, whas name wes Mysie, wesna verra weill pleised at this an answered him,
>
> 'Ay, thai ir that, but what's that ti you, Sir. A'm thinkan ye ir a wee thing forritsum, sae ye ir. We dinna even ken yeir name.'
>
> Says he, 'Ma name is Caermoulis, an it's no lyke me ti be forritsum, but A wes that taen up wi yeir bewtie, A juist coudna help addressan ye.'[16]

David Purves has turned out a solid serviceable piece of work which is certainly a vast improvement on Peter's bleached pallid artefact; nevertheless, the difference in idiom between his 'colloquial-literary' Scots and the language of Scots tales collected from oral tradition is (quite understandably) very marked.

One of the best told tales in the archive of the School of Scottish Studies is 'The Cat and the Hard Cheese', which was recorded in Montrose from Bessie Whyte by Peter

Cooke and Linda Headlee in 1975.[17] The first part of this story – printed in *Tocher* in 1976 – is the familiar fraternal exodus 'to seek their fortune' which is the lead-in to hundreds of Jack tales. The elder brother is offered the wee bannock with a blessing or the big bannock with a curse, and he chooses wrongly: very shortly his head is on a spike on the tyrant bossman's gates. However, when the younger brother is due to set off on his travels, he chooses rightly (i.e. unselfishly) – 'Ach, the wee yin'll dae fine' – and his mother take him at his word:

> So she baked him this wee bannick an she fried this wee callop tae him, an she tied it up in a hankie, an he's away, an he's hi tae the road and ho tae the road, through sheep's parks and bullocks' parks an all the high an the low mountains o Yarrow, an there was no rest for poor Jeck, till the birds were makin nests in his heid an the stones were makin holes in his feet … no rest fir him.

This passage – from 'he's hi tae the road' – is immediately identifiable as a 'run' very similar to the lyrically-intensified stereotyped passages well-known in Gaelic folktales – but it also closely resembles those formulaic passages of conventional rhetoric in the ballads which enable the narrator to 'leap and linger', and thus invigorate and sustain the action. The language of the Lallans folktales, in fact, does quite frequently bear a clear resemblance to ballad-Scots, and is in any event nearly always closer to the oscillating bilingual language of folk-song we have been describing than to what has been termed 'punterspeak'.

One more example from the wonder tales: here is Jeannie Robertson's version of this same run, which she employed in several of the Jack tales she used to tell:

> He's hey the road, ho the road, doon the road; the tods ging to their holes, and the wee birdies flee awa hame to their nests – but there's nae rest for Silly Jack.[18]

If I may be allowed a personal reminiscence – when my children were small, Jeannie used to tell them her wonder tales, and I well remember how this verbal magic lodged in their minds, and would be reproduced with Jeannie's own incantatory cadences when the children told the same stories to their friends – and to me.

If the language of Jeannie's folktales was comparatively easy for Edinburgh children to understand and reproduce, even easier was the language of her version of the great ballads. Here is the text of her now world-famous version of 'Son David' (= 'Edward', Child 13):

> 'Oh, what's the blood 'its on your sword,
> My son, David, ho son David?
> What's that blood 'its on your sword?
> Come, promise, tell me true'
>
> 'Oh, that's the blood of my grey meir,
> Hey, lady Mother, ho, lady Mother,
> That's the blood of my grey meir,
> Because it wadnae rule by me.'
>
> 'Oh, that blood it is owre clear,
> My son David, ho, son David,

That blood it is owre clear,
Come, promise, tell me true.'

'Oh, that's the blood of my greyhound,
Hey, lady Mother, ho, lady Mother,
That's the blood of my greyhound,
Because it wadnae rule by me.'

'Oh, that blood it is owre clear,
My son David, ho, son David,
That blood it is owre clear,
Come, promise, tell me true.'

'Oh, that's the blood of my huntin hawk,
Hey, lady Mother, ho, lady Mother,
That's the blood of my huntin hawk,
Because it wadnae rule by me.'

'Oh, that blood it is owre clear,
My son David, ho, son David,
That blood it is owre clear,
Come, promise, tell me true.'

'For that's the blood of my brother, John,
Hey, lady Mother, ho, lady Mother,
That's the blood of my brother, John
Because he wadnae rule by me.

'Oh, I'm gaun awa in a bottomless boat,
In a bottomless boat, in a bottomless boat,
For I'm gaun awa in a bottomless boat,
An I'll never return again.'

'Oh, whan will you come back again,
My son David, ho son David?
Whan will you come back again?
Come, promise, tell me true.'

'When the sun an the moon meets in yon glen,
Hey, lady Mother, ho, lady Mother,
Whan the sun an the moon meets in yon glen,
For I'll return again.[19]

Blood – Lady Mother – brother – this is indistinguishable from ballad-English, but 'owre clear' and 'wadnae' perform the same service for 'Son David' that 'nae' did for Betsy Whyte's version of 'Sweet William's Ghost'. In any case, the clear, simple, dignified diction of the great ballads could hardly be more eloquently exemplified. But listen now to a snatch of Jeannie's conversation, recorded – I have to admit it! – without her knowledge; it's a graphic description (recorded in her house in 1954) of an Aberdeen lad who was a kind of local 'King of the Liars':

sittin' tellin' people a lot o' lees. But ye had to show your manners: ye had to bear this lees; ay, ye had to listen tae them. I jist gaes aboot the hoose – I jist looks at him like that, I says, God bless us Johnnie – God forgive ye … I says, I canna help for tellin', I canna. … And still, I kent that he was a guid laddie tae – and he's always made welcome in the hoose when he comes in here. But we ken he's a liar! We ken Johnnie cannae open his mooth withoot tellin' one!

A voice: Ye can aye get a good laugh at a good lee.

Jeannie: But still – wanst upon a time – I dinna ken whit like he is noo, but I still think he could sing. Because – he used to come tae oor hoose doon there, and he sung bloody good at that time!

A voice: Oh, he's a lovely singer.

Jeannie: Doon there he sung tae hiz often. Many's and many's the night he sung to hiz doon there. Because at nights, Hamish, maybe a fiddle played – the pipes played – Johnnie sung – I sung – maybe some of the rest o them sung, and the nicht passed by …[20]

On the double LP 'The Muckle Sangs' (Tangent TNGM/119/D) a couple of the finest examples of auld-style ballad-Scots in the archive of the School of Scottish Studies can be heard in two incomplete but complementary versions of the classic ballad 'Clyde's Water' (Child 216) – one sung by John Strachan of Crichie, near Fyvie, and the other by Willie Edward of Craigellachie. (For an account of the life and exploits of the farmer-singer John Strachan, see Part II: People). The ballad is about a pair of ill-starred lovers, victims of their malignant mothers, who in one way or another wish them ill and bring them to destruction. Willie's mother does not want him to ford the Clyde on horseback, and she curses him when he decides to 'put trust in his ain horseheels'. Here is John Strachan's 'wey' of the central part of the ballad, which describes the hero crossing the river in spate:

> So he rade o'er hills and rade doon dales
> And doon yon dowie den,
> But the rush that rose in Clyde's water
> Wad have feared a hundred men.
>
> Oh, Clyde, ye Clyde, ye rollin Clyde,
> Yer waves are wondrous strong;
> Mak me a wreck as I come back,
> But spare me as I gyang.
>
> Oh Maggie, Maggie, Maggie dear
> Oh rise an lat me in,
> For my boots are fu of Clyde's water,
> An I'm shiverin tae the skin.
>
> My stables are full o horses,
> My sheds are fu o hay;
> My beds are fu of gentlemen
> That winna leave till day.

This is a superb example of the supple and sinewy ballad-language praised and

honoured by Gavin Greig. The reader (and listener) readily apprehend how close it lies
to ballad-English, and yet what a totally different impression it makes.

When Willie reaches Maggie's bower, the other hostile mother impersonates her
daughter, and turns Willie away. Now let us hear Willie Edward, another North-East
singer who had the ballad, carrying the story forward at the point where Maggie
becomes aware of her mother's fraud:

> '… oh mother dear,
> Come rede my drowsy dream.
> I dreamt sweet Willie was at my gate:
> Nae yin wid lat him in.'

> ''S lie still, lie still, my Maggie dear,
> Lie still an tak your rest:
> Since your true love was at your gates,
> 'Tis full three quarters past.'

> But it's Maggie rose, put on her clothes,
> An to the Clyde she went:
> The first step noo that she took in
> It took her tae the knee;

> The next step noo that she took in
> It took her tae the chin.
> In the deepest pot in a' the Clyde
> She found her Willie in.

> 'So you have got a cruel mother
> And I have got another
> But here we lie in Clyde Water,
> Like sister and like brother.'

His final verse, written down, is indistinguishable from ballad-English, but – like Betsy
Whyte's verse from 'Sweet William's Ghost', already quoted – it *must* (because of the
Scots in other stanzas) be pronounced *more Boreali*.

After making this recording I asked Willie where he had got the ballad and his reply
was as follows:

> WE   Oh, gosh man, I'm growin' sae auld … it's nae easy mindin' sae faur back,
> [man.
> HIS WIFE   Your grannie, maybe?
> WE   Ay, my grannie was a great singer.
> HH   Was she?
> WE   Ay, she was good at hummin' awa onywey – and sometimes, when she
> was ill-natur'd, she sang tee![21]

The equilibrium of ballad-Scots and ballad-English was maintained well into the
nineteenth century: the same linguistic and conventional techniques as we have encountered in the classic ballads are to be found in many later songs; indeed, they surface
occasionally even in the so-called 'bothy ballads' or farmyard songs. Not long after

making the above recording. Willie was singing 'The Bonnie Parks o' Kilty', a narrative love song which is as clearly couched in classic ballad-Scots as any of the older songs in his repertoire:

> He's ta'en her by the middle sma' and gently laid her down,
> Where the apples and the cherries were a' hanging down,
> The lilies and the green grass were growing all around
> Where they lay on the bonnie parks o' Kilty, O.[22]

At this point let us call as expert witness the late P. W. Joyce, who wrote in his *Old Irish Folk Music and Songs* (1909):

> The Anglo-Irish peasant poets wrote in pure English, so far as lay in their power, and so far as their knowledge of the language extended. They hardly ever used the broken-English words of the Anglo-Irish folk dialect, such as *ould, darlint, nothin,* I'm *kilt* and speechless, *onaisy, wonst* as I *wint* out, *becaze, sthrame,* come *hether, consarnin,* let go your *hoult,* etc. But such words as these were constantly used in conversation, not only by the general run of the people, but by the writers of the songs.
>
> Moreover the composers of Anglo-Irish songs very seldom used Irish words mixed with English, either in correct Gaelic spelling or anglicised: such as *asthore, gon doutha, oyeh,* Katie *eroo, alanna, inagh, angishore,* etc.[23]

Because of the superior status of Scots as a literary language (as compared to Anglo-Irish dialect), and because of the fame of poets such as Burns and Robert Fergusson and the Ettrick Shepherd, there is quite a large body of nineteenth-century Scots folk-song in passable ballad-Scots. Nevertheless, Gavin Greig was undoubtedly right when he commented (writing on 'Traditional Minstrelsy' in *The Book of Buchan,* Peterhead, 1910):

> Remembering the general tendency of lyricism to raise language to a higher plane, we must not expect to find much of the undiluted vernacular in our folk-songs. Education has made our peasant bilingual in a way, so that in the use of language he readily becomes barometric.[24]

The date by which this process may be said – give a decade, take a decade – to have been consummated can be placed with tolerable certainty at the beginning of the nineteenth century. In spite of the massive influx of English broadside ballads, the creeping anglicisation of the eighteenth century was temporarily halted, thanks to the momentary stabilisation of Scots as a language for poetry: this was directly due to the splendid services of Allan Ramsay and Robert Fergusson, and above all to the enormous popularity – I had almost written pop-vogue – of the work of Burns.

(It is by no means unusual for Buchan farming folk who are dab hands at the bothy ballads to be able to recite long screeds of Burns: e.g. 'The Twa Dogs', 'Holy Willie's Prayer', and above all 'Tam o' Shanter'. Where the Ayrshire form of a word is markedly different in pronunciation from the North-East form (e.g. *buit* and *beet*), it is possible to monitor on tape-recordings made at different times a fascinating seismographical fluctuation of locutions – pitching, juddering, settling and finally coming to rest.)

It is essential to remember that many of the songs in ballad-English (or the next best thing) were of English origin – either carried north by word of mouth or (as was certainly often more frequent) in the printed lingua franca of the broadsides. This applies even to songs which, judging from their titles alone, might have been thought to have originated in Scotland – e.g. 'Caroline of Edinburgh Town'. Dozens of songs must have been transported along the sea routes from Yarmouth and Scarborough. It is maybe not sufficiently realised that during the eighteenth and nineteenth centuries there was just as big an influx of English songs into Scotland as there was into Ireland. (Some of these may have boxed the compass, moving to Ireland from Scotland or England, and then returning seaborne to their original starting place.) Here and there one comes across some amusing oddities and eccentricities: e.g. 'an 'usiband both galliant and gay', pickled in aspic in the middle of an Aberdeenshire singer's rendering of 'Villikens and his Dinah'; southern English nasalisations as in 'Caroline of Edin-burgh Teown [tɛun]'; and -ly pronounced *lie* [lai] as in English sea shanties (ear-ly in the morning) and in Victorian barn-stormers' *Bühnenenglisch*.

Beside these meridional curiosities one can set reminiscences of Scots grammatical forms congealed in song when they have long since died out in colloquial Scots, e.g. -*and* instead of -*an* – or -*in*' – as a present participle. In his version of 'An Auld Man Cam Coortin' Me', Willie MacPhee has the pay-off line:

> Syne I crept back tae my dyand auld man.

And Jessie Murray's present participle in -*an* was very marked when she sang:

> Skippan barfut throw the heather.

Some of the linguistic conventions of tinker ballad-Scots *do* seem to echo earlier Scots language forms, e.g. Jeannie Robertson sang (in 'The Gallowa Hills'):

> Wi heather bells and riveris a'.

Paradoxically, songs in dialect (e.g. the Buchan dialect) become more frequent with the increasing provincialisation of Scotland after the incorporating Union of 1707. Some of these dialect songs are excellent – racy, rich, exuberant – but we may lay down as a general axiom that Scots folk-song employing a fairly thick dialect is either very localised or comparatively recent. In Article XII of *Folk-Song of the North-East*, published in 1908, Gavin Greig had this to say about 'Humorous Songs':

> Humour is not a strong feature of traditional minstrelsy. Our old ballads are nearly all serious, with a distinct tendency towards the tragic. Now and again in ballad and song we encounter humorous touches, and occasionally meet with a ditty which deals avowedly with the fun of something: but for the comic song pure and simple we must come down to quite recent days. 'The Souters' Feast' is about as humorous a folk-song as we have ever come across. The situation and the idea may not be original; but the song as we have it is clearly local, and seems to belong to central Buchan – the Maud district, we should say, judging from one kind of evidence or another. It can be traced back for a couple of generations at least, although it does not appear to be old. In a MS collection of songs made by Peter Buchan between the years 1825 and 1830 there is one called 'The Souters'

Feast'. William Walker of Aberdeen is able to give us the first verse:

> There cam' a Souter out o' Oyne.
>> Tum, cerry, avum;
> Ridin' on a muckle preen,
>> Sing cidi, uptum, avum.

For the rest of the song we should have to go to Harvard University, where the MS is now lodged; but we have reason to know that Peter's version would not make for edification though we had it.[25]

The collection to which Greig refers is *Secret Songs of Silence*, but the version of 'The Souters' Feast', which is the first song in it, is (curiously enough) not bawdy in the least; it is a bizarre gallimaufry of fantastical-farcical Breughelesque humour. As William Walker's transcript of the first verse is not accurate, I subjoin the text of that, as it appears in the manuscript, plus a few select verses:

> There came a Soutter out o' Ein,
>> Tum, tirry, arum
> Riding on a muckle prin,
>> Sing – Adli, umpti, arum,
>>> Adli, umpti, dirimdi,
>>> Didle, dadle, darum.

> There came a Soutter out o' Fife,
>> Tum, tirry, arum;
> Riding on a gully-knife,
>> Sing – adli, umpti, arum &c.

> There came Soutters far an' near,
>> Tum, tirry, arum
> Frae Turriff, Fyvie an' New Deer,
>> Sing – Adli, umpti, arum &c.

> And there came Soutters out o' Hell,
>> Tum, tirry, arum;
> Riding on the deil himsell,
>> Sing – Adli, umpti, arum &c. ...

> The Soutter gaed the sow a kiss,
>> Tum, tirry, arum;
> Grumph! said he, it's for my birse,
>> Sing – Adli, umpti, arum &c.

> O gin ye cou'd wash my sark,
>> Tum, tirry, arum;
> As well as ye can grumph an' hark,
>> Sing – Adli, umpti, arum &c.

> An' Oh gin ye cou'd bake me bannocks,
>> Tum, tirry, arum;
> As well as ye can winch an' wannock,

Sing – Adli, umpti, arum &c.

I declare my dearest life,
Tum, tirry, arum;
There's nane but you shou'd be my wife,
Sing – Adli, umpti, arum &c.[26]

Some of the verses in Greig's version, published in 1908, are in much thicker Buchan dialect than the wavering, composite lingo of the Secret Songs version. Here are two late arrivals at the Feast:

An ill-faured skyple cam' frae Crimon'
Tanteerie orum;
A perfect scunner to the women,
The eedle and the orum;
A muckle hypal haveless loon,
Tanteerie orum;
Frae the Fite Steen cam' hoiterin' doon,
The eedle and the orum,
Thee-a-noodle, thee-a-num,
The eedle and the orum.

And when they thocht they a' were come,
Tanteerie orum;
A cripple breet cam' owre frae Drum,
The eedle and the orum;
Ridin' on a cripple mear,
Tanteerie orum;
His apron for his ridin' gear,
The eedle and the orum.
Thee-a-noodle, thee-a-num,
The eedle and the orum.[27]

This, like Peter's version of the same song – though to a greater degree – is clearly more dialect than ballad-Scots. It is blood brother to the robust colloquial Scots of the humorous songs such as 'The Tinklers' Waddin',[28] written by William Watt (died 1859) – which soon joined the older ballads in the repertoires of folk-singers from Buchan to the Border (and beyond). To bring the difference between these varying idioms into focus, let us look at another of the songs in Peter's collection, 'The Whirley Wha':

There was a bridal in our town,
Upon a holy day,
And there was muckle, muckle mirth,
And there was muckle play.

The bells were rung, the auld wives sung,
We to the kirk gied a',
When the bride came hame wi' her silly bridegroom,
To play wi' his whirleywha.

First she turn'd her back to him,
    And then she turn'd her wame,
And lang she look'd for kindness,
    But kindness there was nane.

She took him in her arms twa'
    And hiest him 'gainst the wa',
Says – Ly ye there, ye silly auld diel,
    Ye've lost your whirleywha.

What's this my father's dane to me?
    He's dane me muckle ill
He's wedded me to a silly auld man,
    Sair, sair against my will.

Had I been married to my young man,
    Though never a sark ava'
He'd lovingly squeeze me in his arms,
    And play'd wi' his whirleywha.

Now a' the lasses o' our town,
    They bear me muckle envy,
But gin their case was bad as mine,
    Their cheeks wou'd never dry.

But I'll dress mysell in ribbons fine,
    Nae body e'er sae braw,
And hire some bonny young lad o' my ain,
    Tae play wi' his whirleywha.[29]

In a note to the above item, Peter states: 'This song was written by Mary Hay, daughter of one of the Earls of Errol after she was married to General Scott, from whom she eloped for want of —'. We may be pretty confident, however – as confident as we can ever reasonably be in these things – that the 'wey' of it enshrined in the *Secret Songs* has as truly come into being through oral transmission and recreation as any currently recoverable version of such innocent anonyms as 'The Highland Tinker' or 'The Crab Fish'. Peter has a version of the latter quite different from the dozens already on record:

There was an auld priest's wife
    And she was big wi' lad,
Falaladidum, Faladeraldiri,
    And all that she longed for
        Was a sea crab,
        Sing Fala, &c ...

Gude morrow to ye fishers,
    That fishes in the fleed,
Falala &c.
    Hae ye ony crab fish

To dee a woman gweed?
Falala &c.[30]

At their best the older bawdy anonyms, products of a long folk process, exhibit, almost better than the tragic ballads, the linguistic *stuff* of ballad-Scots, for they – unlike, for example, some of the texts provided by Mrs Brown of Falkland – practically never give evidence of pen-and-paper work. Another delicious example – 'The Wanton Trooper' – has already been quoted in the previously mentioned 'The Ballad, the Folk and the Oral Tradition'.[31] Also referred to in that chapter is 'Slow Men of London', which North-East singers would no doubt have thought of as a 'Scots' song, but which acknowledges its origin no less by virtue of its particular brand of ballad language as by the obvious giveaway of the place-name. However, it *has* undoubtedly been sung into its *Secret Songs* shape – unlike (for example) 'The Dyer of Roan' which is an excellent example of arch eighteenth-century English bawdry, quite plainly the product of a single pen and intelligence. Two verses will provide an adequate sample:

> The Abbot as you may believe,
> Had but little to say for himself;
> He knew well what he ought to receive,
> For his being so arrant an elf;
> His clothes he got on with all speed,
> And conducted he was by the dyer,
> To be duckit (as you after may read)
> And be cool'd from his amorous fire.
>
> Quoth the dyer, most reverend father,
> Since I find you're so hot upon wenching,
> I have gather'd my servants together,
> To give you a taste of our drenching.
> Here – Tom, Harry, Roger and Dick!
> Take the Abbot, undress him, and douse him.
> They obey'd in that very same nick,
> To the dye-vat they take him and souse him.[32]

A singer from Turriff or Strichen would sing the above with the local accent, and an English listener might therefore even find bits of it hard to understand, but it would take a long time for such a composed ditty to get even quarterways naturalised. And yet, as I have hinted above, personal experience in the field suggests that many, if not most, North-East singers (especially in the period when Peter Buchan was collecting) would think of it as a Scots song. In the same – or similar – way, Hume of Godscroft must have thought – or half-thought – that he was writing in his mother tongue when he asserted in his preface to *The History of the House of Douglas and Angus*, published in 1644:

> For the language it is my mother-tongue, that is, Scottish: and why not, to Scottishmen? Why should I contemne it? I never thought the difference so great, as that by seeking to speak English, I would hazard the imputation of affectation. Every tongue hath [its] own vertue and grace. ... For my own part, I like our

own, and he that writes well in it writes well enough to me. Yet I have yeelded somewhat to the tyrannie of custome and the times, not seeking curiously for words, but taking them as they came to hand. I acknowledge also my fault (if it be a fault) that I ever accounted it a mean study and of no great commendation to learn to write or to speak English and have loved better to bestow my pains on forreigne languages, esteeming it but a dialect of our own, and that (perhaps) more corrupt.[33]

If already in the mid-seventeenth century a perfervidly patriotic Scots historian could make a statement so apparently self-contradictory, who will find it strange that three centuries later Aberdeenshire folk-singers could and did move from undiluted Buchan Scots (in songs such as 'McGinty's Meal and Ale'[34] and 'The Wedding of McGinnis and his cross-Eyed Pet')[35] to the unambiguous English of the broadside ballads without seeming to notice the difference – or else paying it scant attention if they did. Here the role played by broadsides from the South, and by wholesale borrowings from them by printers in Scotland, cannot be overestimated. In the nineteenth century, broadsides and chapbooks flooded Scotland in their hundreds of thousands, and in many of these printed sheets songs in one or another form of Scots lay cheek by jowl with songs in English. Taking a lucky dip into my own sizeable collection of chapbooks printed in Glasgow, Stirling and Airdrie I draw out a couple at random; one, embellished with a handsome woodcut of swan surveying its reflection in the water of a wildwood-fringed loch, is printed in Glasgow 'by and for J. Neil' in 1829. It contains the following songs:

1. 'Betsey Baker' (in English), for which the air is given as *Push about the Jorum*, with the added note: 'As sung by Mr Potts, Theatrical Pavilion, Glasgow'. The text includes one English cant phrase:
   > He gammoned her to run away
   > And I lost Betsey Baker.

   One place-name is mentioned: the hero's mother thinks
   > 'twoud ease my mind
   > If I came up to London.

2. 'Who's Master, or A Fight for the Breeches' (in English), also as sung by the popular Mr Potts. A sempiternal comic theme.

3. 'York, You're Wanted' (in English), to the air 'Alley Croaker'. The adventures of a Yorkshire lad who travels to London to seek his fortune, and marries a rich maiden lady.

4. 'The Emigrant's Farewell' (in English, with light sprinklings of Scots). Tune. 'My Guid Lord John'. Three sample stanzas:
   > Farewell, ye hills of glorious deeds,
   > And streams renown'd in song –
   > Farewell, ye braes and blossom'd meads,
   > Our hearts have lov'd so long.

Farewell, the blythesome broomy knowes,
　Where thyme and harebells grow –
Farewell, the hoary, haunted howes
　O'er hung with birk and sloe. ...

Our native land – our native vale –
　A long and last adieu!
Farewell to bonny Tivotdale,
　And Scotland's mountains blue!

The second specimen was printed in Glasgow 'for the Bookseller'. It is undated but looks as if it is approximately from the same period. The woodcut is of an Oriental warrior wearing a turban, and carrying a scimitar and a dagger. The songs are:

1　'He Comes from the Wars' (in English). A wounded soldier finds refuge in a cottage, and dreams of his mistress.
2, 3 and 4 Sentimental love lyrics in genteel English.

5　'Father Paul' (in English). A bibulous friar who prays 'To rosy Bacchus god of wine'.

6　'King David was a Soldier' (in English with sprinklings of Scots). Sample stanza:
　　　　　A soldier and a bonnie lass
　　　　　　Went out together one day,
　　　　　With kisses and kind compliments,
　　　　　　He unto her did say:
　　　　　Love, dare I kiss thy ruby lips,
　　　　　　'Twoud make me something bolder.
　　　　　Oh no, Oh no, my minnie says,
　　　　　　I may na kiss wi' a soldier.

There were many chapbooks circulating which reprinted songs and poems by Burns, Hogg and Tannahill, and other Scots items – including, very occasionally, folk-songs collected from singing or recitation – but the point is that chapbooks like the ones I have described were also there in abundance. Here it is important to recall the often noted fact that simple country folk loved to think of a ballad as 'a true ballad'. In a famous scene in *The Winter's Tale* (IV: 4) Shakespeare pokes gentle fun at the credulous shepherdesses Dorcas and Mopsa who believe – or want to believe – all the whoppers Autolycus peddles when he is hawking his ballads:

CLOWN　What hast here? Ballads?
MOPSA　Pray now, buy some. I love a ballad in print, a-life, for then we are sure they are true.
AUTOLYCUS　Here's one to a very doleful tune, how a usurer's wife was brought to bed of twenty money-bags at a burden, and how she longed to eat adders' heads and toads carbonadoed.
MOPSA　Is it true, think you?
AUTOLYCUS　Very true, and but a month old.

DORCAS   Bless me from marrying a usurer!
AUTOLYCUS   Here's the midwife's name to't: one Mistress Taleporter, and
five or six honest wives that were present. Why should I carry lies abroad?

His next tale is even taller, but he assures them:

AUTOLYCUS   The Ballad is very pitiful, and as true.
DORCAS   Is it true too, think you?
AUTOLYCUS   Five justices' hands at it, and witnesses more than my pack
will hold.

One does not need to rub in the obvious point that for the Mopsas and Dorcases of
North-East Scotland many of the ballads they saw in print, and might not be able to
read – for the reverence for print was in part at least a legacy if illiteracy – were not only
'true' but true *in English*. Thus on the 'folk' level the message of the King James Bible
was powerfully reinforced by Grub Street printers and their like all over the island; it
must have been a relief to many when the good news sank in that entertainment as well
as salvation was available by courtesy of the English language.

And what, in this same period, were the 'crambo-clink' poets – the local bards who
aspired to appear in print, with their work proudly displayed under such titles as *Rustic
Rhymes, Sangs and Sonnets* – making of the language situation they had inherited?
Gavin Greig was later to take an interest in their work, and two exercise books exist
containing the texts of articles on 'Bards of Buchan'.[36] In the second of these Greig
devotes five pages to Peter Still, whom he dubs 'the typical Buchan bard'. The potted
biography which Greig supplies might indeed serve as a prototype of the life-struggle
of dozens of similar versifiers.

He was born in the parish of Fraserburgh, where his father had a small farm, on
1 January 1814. He himself took to farm service, got married before he was out
of his teens, and by-and-by became a day labourer, taking a turn at such jobs as
came his way – casting peats or breaking stones. He suffered all his life from ill-
health, but ever bore manfully up. Latterly he took the Blackhouse Toll Bar,
where he died in 1848, at the early age of thirty-four.[37]

The first poem of his discussed in the article is a blurred sub-Burnsian lookalike
entitled 'The Cottar's Sunday'. The concluding stanza of this poem (which is about
half as long again as Burns's, according to Greig) may be taken as fairly representative
of a wide tract of similar effusions:

Lang may the sound of heartfelt praise & prayer
From Caledonian cottages arise;
An' lang may Sion's holy heavenly lays
Be sweetly warbled to the listening skies;
In this fair Scotia's richest treasure lies, –
Lang may she guard the gem wi' holy zeal;
An' may she ne'er her toil-worn sons despise;
Her fame an' honour rest upon their weal, –
They of her glory are, an' aye will be, the seal.[38]

One has the impression that Greig was leaning over backwards in this article to be kind to these worthy local bards. He even goes so far as to say, referring to another poem of Peter Still's called 'Jeannie's Lament', that 'it sounds a more intense note than had yet been heard from the Buchan lyre'. Here is one stanza from that poem:

> I never thocht to thole the waes
>   It's been my lot to dree;
> I never thocht to sigh sae sad
>   Whan first I sighed for thee.
> I thocht your heart was like mine ain,
>   As true as true could be;
> I couldna think there was a stain
>   In ane sae dear to me.[39]

Compare with this almost any one of the scores of passionate love songs in the Aberdeenshire folk tradition which Greig himself put on record, and one cannot fail to be struck by the extraordinary contrast between the slack, insipid and nerveless lucubrations of the poetasters who wrote with an eye to print, and the verve, spunk and genuine poetry of the anonyms, whether these are celebrating triumphant sexuality, emitting belly laughs at the spectacle of the comedy of sex, or lamenting the tragedy of lost love. Listen, for example, to a version of 'The False Lover Won Back' which Greig himself printed in his column in the *Buchan Observer:*

> As I went up yon high, high hill,
>   And down in yonder glen,
> And the very spot where my love lies,
>   And the sun goes never down;
> And the sun goes never down, bonnie love,
>   And the sun goes never down;
> The spot where my love lies,
>   And the sun goes never down.
>
> *Chorus*
> Oh, love me once again, bonnie love,
>   Oh, love me once again;
> Isn't sair for me that I like you,
>   And you nae me again;
> And you nae me again, bonnie love,
>   And you nae me again.
>
> Oh, fan will ye be hame, bonnie love,
>   Oh, fan will ye be hame?
> When the heather hills are nine times brunt,
>   And a' grown green again;
> And a' grown green again, bonnie love,
>   And a' grown green again.
>
> Oh, that's owre lang to bide awa',
>   Oh, that's owre lang frae hame,

Owre lang for the babe that's nae yet born
   For to be wantin' a name;
For to be wantin', etc.

The first toon that he came to
   He bought her hose and sheen,
And he bade her rue and turn back noo,
   Nae mair to follow him.

The next toon that he came to
   He bought her a wedding ring,
And he bade her rue and turn back noo,
   Nae mair to follow him.

He's mounted on a milk white steed,
   And he's helped Maggie on;
Says, It's love for love that I like best,
   Bonnie love ye shall be mine.[40]

When one speaks of anonyms, of course, one must bear in mind that at many stages of the folk process individual minds – and sometimes, quite clearly, powerful ingenious individual minds – have set their seal on new variants. Sometimes a craftsman-poet, endowed with 'a nice judicious ear' (to quote Burns) and immersed in the musical and linguistic traditions handed down to him, must have composed song-poems in the time-honoured prescriptive idiom which were already halfway towards becoming folk-songs.

   Is one making too big a jump to postulate the existence, at more than one level of society, and at many if not most periods of our history, of makars who foreswore print, and consciously embraced the aesthetic prejudices and the prosodic and musical techniques of an essentially non-literate song poetry? The version of 'Edward' (= 'Son David', Child 13) which Lord Hailes sent to Bishop Percy for inclusion in his *Reliques* might possibly come into this category. Be that as it may, we must surely, on the evidence, make a distinction between the poet who operated with a hopeful eye to print – and the fame (and money) which might accrue from published works – and those who spontaneously and for preference entrusted their wares to the discerning minds and deft mobile tongues of the traditional singers of Buchan and beyond.

   Quite a number of such poets will have been highly literate people, but – as Alan Lomax has pointed out[41] – one of the principal distinguishing characteristics of the Scottish folk-song tradition is the part played in it by bookish individuals. The paradox is not as great as it might at first appear. 'Of the making of books there is no end.' One of the reasons for the excellence of our ballad tradition is without doubt the literate Scot's wilful and purposive suspension of literacy.

   That this predilection for making direct oral contact with a receptive community has been continued right up to our own day is attested by the popularity of the work of such virtuoso music-makars as Adam McNaughtan, Andy Hunter, Eric Bogle and Ewan MacColl. The work of these accomplished poets – and I am not using the word lightly – is naturally much better known to visitors to folk clubs than to the readers of poetry magazines. And if it is objected that this is a 'forced' development due mainly to the efforts of those connected with the current Folk-song Revival, I would counter by claiming that the tradition as it exists today is in large part the heritage of many similar revivals in the past: for example, those which we associate with the names of Gavin Greig, Robert Burns and Allan Ramsay. It is an honourable list, and one that Scotland can be proud of.

To be sure, this phenomenon is by no means exclusively Scottish. Modern Spanish poetry – and particularly the work of Federico García Lorca – exhibits many striking parallels. J. L. Gili has written of Lorca:

> A word or a phrase heard would one day appear in a poem, without his being aware of it. It was all part of his spontaneous approach to his art. Guillermo de Torre, speaking of Lorca's assimilation and subsequent re-creation of Andalusian folk-songs, says: 'He sings them, he dreams them, he discovers them again – in a word, he turns them into poetry.' In this same connection, his brother Francisco says: 'During an excursion to the Sierra Nevada, the mule driver who was leading sang to himself:
>
> > *Y yo que me la llevé al río*
> > *creyendo que era mozuela,*
> > *pero tenio marido*
>
> (And I took her to the river believing her a maid, but she had a husband.) Sometime later, one day when we were speaking of the ballad "The Faithless Wife", I reminded Federico of the mule-driver's song. To my enormous surprise, he had completely forgotten it. He thought the first three lines of the ballad were as much his as the rest of the poem. More than that, I thought I could tell that he did not like my insistence, for he continued to believe that I was mistaken'[42]

It is fitting, then, to conclude with some pertinent lines from Lorca's poem 'Balada de la Placeta' (Ballad of the Little Square):

LOS NIÑOS
¿Qué sientes en tu boca
roja y sedienta?

YO
El sabor de los huesos
de mi gran calavera.

LOS NIÑOS
Bebe el agua tranquila
de la canción añeja.
¡Arroyo claro,
fuente serena!
¿Por qué te vas tan lejos
de la plazuela?

YO
¡Voy en busca de magos

y de princesas!

LOS NIÑOS
¿Quién te enseñó el camino
de los poetas?

YO
La fuente y el arroyo
de la canción añeja.

The Children: What do you feel in your mouth scarlet and thirsting?
Myself: The taste of the bones of my big skull!
The Children: Drink the tranquil water of the antique song. Clear stream, serene fountain! Why do you go so far from the little square?
Myself: I go in search of magicians and princesses!
The Children: Who showed you the path of the poets?
Myself: The fountain and the stream of the antique song.[43]

Notes

1 John Ord, *The Bothy Songs and Ballads of Aberdeen, Banff and Moray, Angus and the Mearns* (Paisley, 1930)
2 Ord, op. cit., p. 111 ('The Green Woods o' Airlie')
3 Ord, op. cit., p. 315 ('Nairn River Banks')
4 Ord, op. cit., p. 267 ('The Gallant Shearers')
5 Stanley Hyman, 'The Language of Scottish Poetry', *Kenyon Review* (Gambier, Ohio: Winter 1954), p. 35
6 *The Poems of William Dunbar*, ed. W. MacKay MacKenzie (Edinburgh 1932), p. 14
7 Hyman, op. cit., p. 36
8 Hugh MacDiarmid, *The Complete Poems* Vol. I (London 1978), p. 314
9 M. J. C. Hodgart, *The Ballads* (London 1950), p. 57
10 For John Strachan's and Jeannie Robertson's versions, see Bertrand Harris Bronson, *The Traditional Tunes of the Child Ballads* (Princeton, New Jersey 1966), Vol. III, p. 9
11 Bronson, Vol. IV, (1972), Addenda, p. 473. It is curious that a parallel stanza (No. xx) in the version of 'Clerk Saunders' in Scott's *Minstrelsy* has likewise one single Scots locution:
> My mouth it is full cold, Margaret,
> It has the smell, now, of the ground
> And if I kiss thy comely mouth,
> Thy days of life will not be lang.
This might have been thought to be merely the whim of a sophisticated man of letters, were it not for the tape-recorded evidence (SSS Archives, SA1952/42. B29) of a non-literate tinker woman.
  Incidentally, when Jean Ritchie re-recorded Betsy's beautiful fragment a year later in my company (copy tape 1953/2 in my possession) the text was identical.
12 Peter Buchan, *Ancient Scottish Tales* (1829: printed Peterhead 1908), p. 25
13 Peter Buchan, op. cit., pp. 41–2
14 Ed. Alan Bruford, *The Green Man of Knowledge* (Aberdeen 1982), pp. 17–18
15 Peter Buchan, op. cit., p. 21
16 *Lallans*, No. 18 (Edinburgh, Whitsunday 1982). David Purves informs me that

when he was a child he heard the name Caermoulis from an uncle of his who lived in Selkirk. Caermoulis was a sort of bogie-man figure.

According to Dr Katharine M. Briggs (*The Fairies in Tradition and Literature*, (London 1967), p. 37), 'Killmoulis is the mill spirit in the Scottish Lowlands. He is a grotesque creature, with an enormous nose and no mouth, though he is said to be very fond of pork. He bewails any misfortune coming to the mill, but for all that he is fond of mischievous pranks, and can be controlled only by direct invocation from the miller. Occasionally in an emergency he will leave his corner to thrash grain or to fetch a midwife, but as a rule he is more of a nuisance than a help.

17 *Tocher* 23, pp. 266–73 and *Tocher* 24, pp. 320–3. The 'run' quoted will be found in A. Bruford, *The Green Man of Knowledge*, op. cit., p. 44.

18 Quoted in *Chapbook*, Scotland's Folk Song Magazine, ed. Arthur Argo (Aberdeen 1965), Vol. 2, No. 5, p. 3

19 'Son David' (= 'Edward', Child 13). SSS Tape Archive SA1960/3. B2. A recording of Jeannie singing this ballad will be found on the LP *Heather and Glen*, Tradition Records, New York, TLP 1047, Side 1, Band 8. For discussions of 'Son David', see Herschel Gower and James Porter, 'Jeannie Robertson: the Child Ballads', in *Scottish Studies* 14 (1970), pp. 41–2, and James Porter, 'Jeannie Robertson's "My Son David", A Conceptual Performance Model', in *Journal of American Folklore* 89 (1976), pp. 7–26.

For Jeannie's own comments on the ballad, see Herschel Gower, 'Jeannie Robertson: Portrait of a Traditional Singer', in *Scottish Studies* 12 (1968), pp. 113–26, on p. 125.

20 SSS Tape Archive SX1955/4 A4. (Example Tape: 'The Language of Scots Folksong')

21 *The Muckle Sangs*, Double LP on the Tangent Label, London, TNGM 119/D, Side 4, Bank 1

22 Cf. Ord, op. cit., p. 113

23 P. W. Joyce, *Old Irish Folk Music and Songs* (Dublin 1909), p. 242

24 Gavin Greig, article on 'The Traditional Minstrelsy of Buchan' in *The book of Buchan*, ed. J. F. Tocher (Peterhead 1910), p. 233

25 Gavin Greig, *Folk-Song of the North-East* (Hatboro, Pennsylvania 1963), Article xii

26 *Secret Songs of Silence* by Sir Oliver Orpheus, Bart. of Eldridge Hall [Peter Buchan]. MS Volume in Harvard University Child Memorial Library (25241. 9). The verses from 'The Soutter's Feast' are on pp. 1, 2 and 3.

27 Gavin Greig, FSNE, Article xii

28 Robert Ford, *Vagabond Songs and Ballads of Scotland* (Paisley 1904) one-vol. edition), pp. 1–4

29 *Secret Songs of Silence*, p. 80

30 *Secret Songs of Silence*, p. 22

31 Ed. Edward J. Cowan, *The People's Past* (Edinburgh 1980), pp. 79–81

32 *Secret Songs of Silence*, p. 121

33 Quoted in David Reid, *The Party-Coloured Mind* (Edinburgh 1982), p. 1

34 Gavin Greig, *Folk-Song of the North-East*, Article cxxxvi

35 G. Greig, FSNE, Article cxxxiv (under title 'Sheelicks')

36 G. Greig, *The Bards of Buchan*. Two MS notebooks, the second in my possession. (Dr William Donaldson informs me that Gavin's notes on these minor North-East poets were published intermittently in a defunct weekly, the *Peterhead Sentinel*, in 1913–14.)

37 Greig, *Bards of Buchan* II, p. 26

38 Greig, *Bards of Buchan* II, p. 29

39 Greig, *Bards of Buchan* II, p. 30

40 Greig, FSNE, Article xciii (*A* Version)

41   Alan Lomax, Sleeve-note for *World Library of Folk and Primitive Music*, Vol.
     VI (Scotland), Columbia Masterworks LP KL-209
42   *Lorca*, Introduced and edited by J. L. Gili (Penguin Poets), Harmonds-worth
     1960, Introduction, pp. xiv-xv
43   *Lorca*, pp. 2–3

The title of this Chapter ('At the Foot o' yon Excellin' Brae') is a line from 'Courtin' Amang the Kye', as sung by the late Willie Mathieson, Dudwick, Ellon; Willie learned it from his second wife. The text appears in the first of his MS songbooks (p. 102); copies of these are in the archives of the School of Scottish Studies. The School also has tape-recorded versions sung by Charlie Reid, Longside and John Adams, Glenlivet.

Gavin Greig printed a version ('Cauries and Kye') in his column in the *Buchan Observer* (FSNE, Article vi).

Scotland and the Lowland Tongue, ed. J. Derrick McClure, AUP, 1983.

The Ballad and Popular Tradition to 1660

Scotland, like Switzerland, is – and seems always to have been – a 'multi-ethnic' country, and the various strands of its popular tradition necessarily reflect this chequered linguistic past. Never throughout its entire history has the country had one single unitary language, covering its whole area. It is only recently, with the death of the last Gaelic-speaking monoglots in the Western Isles, and the gradual loss of ground of Scots to English in the former's once impregnable seeming redoubt in the North-East, that the great metropolitan world-language seems set to move in for the kill.

To throw these centennial cultural confrontations into sharp relief, we may recall that when in the mid-fourteenth century John Barbour, archdeacon of Aberdeen, was writing his *Bruce* – a poem whose rough-hewn couplets sometimes evoke the rhythm and even the idiom of the Scots ballad stanza – Gaelic was still being spoken, sung and composed on the middle reaches of Deeside less than thirty miles from the 'ryall bruch'. And St Machar's, the cathedral he officiated in, itself recalls by its very name the ubiquitous band of Celtic saints who christianised – or re-christianised – half Western Europe in the Dark Ages.

That Highlanders and the men of the 'plain land' fought together against the English host at Bannockburn is attested by Barbour himself:

> The ferd bataile the noble king   [fourth]
> Tuk till his awne governyng.
> And had in-till his cumpany
> The men of Carrik halely
> And off Arghile & of Kentyr
> And off the ilis quharof wes syr
> Angus of Ile, and but all tha
>
>   (XI, 337–43)

Much of the material used by Barbour in his *Bruce* must have been assembled from orally transmitted accounts in the immediate aftermath of the War of Independence. But that some of these were perpetuated in song is expressly stated by the archdeacon:

> I will no*cht* rehers the maner
> For quha-sa lik*is* thai may her
> Young wemen quhen thai will play
> Syng it amang thaim ilk day.
>
>   (XVI, 527–30)

Indeed, reading the many passages which vividly describe early fourteenth-century warfare, one cannot help surmising that echoes of actual balladry have occasionally found their way into the narrative:

Then w*ith* a will till him thai yed	[went]
And ane him by the bridill hynt,	[seized]
Bot he raucht till him sic a dynt	[fetched] [blow]
That arme and schuldyr flaw h*im* fra.	

(III, 112–15)

If so, echoes of this sort constitute – together with one verse of a song of triumph over the English defeat at Bannockburn, which is preserved in Fabyan's *Chronicle*, and quoted by Marlowe in *Edward II*[1] – the earliest (and tantalisingly fragmentary) indications of the existence of 'ancestor' ballads which anticipate the 'riding ballads' of the sixteenth century by over 200 years.

There is, moreover, a curious ballad-like link with Barbour's *Bruce* at the beginning of a 246-line poem entitled 'ane taill of Sir colling ye knyt'. This poem, under which the date 1583 is scribbled, is an earlier version of the classic ballad 'Sir Cawline' (Child 61), which appears in the mid-seventeenth-century English MS used by Bishop Thomas Percy as the basis for his famous collection *Reliques of Ancient English Poetry*. The first lines of the Scottish poem (which is written in consecutive lines unbroken into stanzas, but which often betrays an underlying stanzaic pattern) are as follows:

Jesus Chryst and tryniti	
That deitt wes on the ruid	[cross]
to send him grace in all digne	
That luiffis the Scottis bluid	
This be ane knyt corporall	
hardie was and guid	
Sir Coling was the knyt's name	
ane kingis sone was hie	
ut Edvaird the bruce he fuir to fecht	[went]
In Irland biyond the sie[2]	

In the Percy version, the opening lines are:

Jesus, lord mickle of might,
   Thay dyed ffor us on the roode,
To maintaine us in all our right
   That loves true English blood.
Ffor by a knight I say my song,
   Was bold and ffull hardye;
Sir Robert Briuse wold fforth to ffight,
   In-to Ireland over the sea.

(1–8)

Child dismissed these stanzas as 'manifestly belonging to a historical ballad', and the version he printed begins at verse 3 of the Percy MS ballad, but this recently recovered Scottish poem effectively restores them to their rightful place. The story-line of 'Sir

Colling' details the heroic combat of the hero with 'ane alreche [eldritch] knyt', a three-headed giant and a lion – all widely diffused folklore motifs – but the opening lines firmly attach the action to time and place, in the way beloved of traditional singers the world over.

On the evidence of the text, therefore, it looks as if the attitude of the 'Sir Colling' poet to his 'folk' source material bears some resemblance to that of the English 'Gawain-poet', who – at the beginning of that astonishing masterpiece 'Sir Gawain and the Green Knight' – frankly acknowledged the oral sources of his tale:

> I schal telle hit as-tit, as I in toun herde,
> with tonge.

In Barbour's *Bruce*[3] 'Schyr Colyne Cambell' appears among the Scots fighting in Ireland with Edward Bruce, and it seems a reasonable inference (in view of the localisation at the beginning of the poem) that the unknown makar of 'Sir Colling' borrowed the name of his hero from this passage. The Scots who fought with the Bruces in their Irish campaign were (according to M.P. McDiarmid) mainly from the Gaelic-speaking west, and the 'Sir Colling' of the poem accomplishes his feats of valour in order to win the hand of the daughter of the lord of Argyll.

When Barbour was writing his heroic documentary, by far the greater part of Scotland was still Gaelic-speaking, and there are quite a number of passages in late medieval and Renaissance Scots poetry which testify to the currency of tales about Gaelic legendary characters among the Lowlanders. The most frequently mentioned heroes are Fyn Makowll (Fionn MacCumhail) and Gow Macmorn (Goll MacMorna). When the Pardoner, in Sir David Lindsay of the Mount's *Ane Satyre of the Thrie Estaits*, is laying out his wares to tempt the gullible (and not so gullible) public, he describes two of his wonder-working relics as follows:

> Heir is ane relict lang and braid
> Of fine Macoull the richt chaft blaid,
>   With teith and al togidder:
> Of Collings cow heir is ane horne;
> For eating of Makconnals corne,
>   Was slaine into Baquhidder.[4]

Here we have an incongruous mixture of fabulous legend and local news item, for – *pace* Campbell of Islay, who suggested that the horn of Colling's cow must surely belong to some beast with mythological significance – it seems more likely that the poet, in characteristic Scots 'doon-takin' style, was contrasting the exalted memory of the legendary hero with the sort of small-clachan gossip which would find ready entry to a country newspaper in this or any other century.[5]

The religious reformers of the sixteenth century were also well aware of the strength of Gaelic popular tradition, and they naturally sought to combat it in the interests of the Protestant faith. This is explicitly acknowledged in the dedicatory epistle to that notable work, the translation into Gaelic of the *Book of Common Order* executed by John Carswell, Bishop of the Isles, and printed in Edinburgh in April 1567. Carswell, writing in the literary Gaelic common to both Ireland and Scotland in his day, has this to say about the secular tales circulating in the bounds of Argyll:

And great is the blindness and darkness of sin and ignorance and of understanding among the composers and writers and supporters of the Gaelic, in that they prefer and practise the framing of vain, hurtful, lying, earthly stories about the Tuath de Dhanond, and about the sons of Milesius, and about the heroes and Fionn Mac Cumhail with his giants, and about many others whom I shall not number or tell of here in   detail, ...[6]

Some of the 'Ossianic' tales here denounced by Bishop Carswell can be collected in the North Highlands to this day, so we can be sure that in the sixteenth century they must have been in common currency from Caithness to the Mull of Kintyre. And it is probably not being too sanguine to assume that already many versions of the international tales to be found (in some cases) throughout Europe and into Asia had already penetrated the Gaelic world, and assumed their localised identity. When, in 1859 and 1860 the great Highland collector John Francis Campbell of Islay (Iain Og Ile) assembled the texts of stories gathered for him by various helpers, he found that many of them closely resembled wonder-tales already being put on record in various parts of Europe. The pioneering work of the Brothers Grimm had sparked off similar collecting efforts in a number of countries, and in the massive index *The Types of the Folktale*, begun by the Finnish scholar Antii Aarne and later vastly enlarged by the American Stith Thompson, the Scottish Gaelic versions which will be found listed beside (for example) versions in Czech, Lithuanian, Turkish, Italian or Greek, are mostly those printed in Campbell's *Popular Tales of the West Highlands*.[7] Since then the number of such stories collected in Scots Gaelic versions has increased twenty-fold following the setting up of the School of Scottish Studies. For this the dedicated and self-sacrificing collecting work of the late Calum MacLean is largely responsible.

The international folktales which have surmounted the barriers of language, geography and culture can usefully be referred to by their numbers in the Aarne/Thompson index: e.g. Campbell's 'Cath nan Eun' (the Battle of the Birds) is AT 313. In many cases the versions of international tale types which have found their way into the Gaelic world must have crossed the broad culture-zone inhabited by speakers of English and Lowland Scots. Until comparatively recently, the number of folk-tale versions in English and Scots which had been put on record was surprisingly small, but the fieldwork of the School of Scottish Studies among the Scots-speaking 'travellers' (or tinkers) has disclosed an enormous folk-tale treasury until now hidden away in their own secret world. Examination of this vast corpus of narrative artistry, and comparative study of the same or similar tales on record as being in the repertoires of storytellers as far away as Turkey, Iran and India, make it clear that we are dealing with an international *Märchengut* going at least as far back as the Middle Ages – and, in the case of maybe a hundred tale types, probably a good deal further.

An example of one of these – which must stand for many – is the type already mentioned, AT 313 ('The Girl as Helper in the hero's Flight', alias 'The Magic Flight'), of which the Jason and Medea legend provides one early example. That the story penetrated the Gaelic world very early is indicated by the vast number of versions – 'several hundred', according to Bealoideas XII (1941) – in the archives of the Irish Folklore Commission: it is referred to as 'one of the most popular of all Irish folktales'. Scottish Gaelic versions have been put on record by J. F. Campbell, and by collectors working for Edinburgh University. However, the version which is in many ways the most illuminating, as far as the most obscure corners of the tradition are concerned, is one couched in the most delectable, racy Aberdeenshire Scots, which was collected from Geordie Stewart, a 'traveller' then in his mid-twenties, in Jeannie Robertson's house in Causewayend, Aberdeen. Although the characters in Geordie's story speak in mid-twentieth-century 'Aiberdeen-awa', internal evidence links his version with the already mentioned anonymous romance 'Sir Gawain and the Green Knight'. There is evidence to suggest that an unrecovered English folk version is one at least of the sources of this remarkable poem.

A much lighter piece of work, the *Schwank* (comic folktale) 'Silly Jack and the Factor' (= AT 1600, 'The Fool as Murderer'), which was one of Jeannie Robertson's favourites, is in her 'wey o't' as firmly and elegantly domiciled in the Scottish North-East as 'The Green Man of Knowledge'; consequently, the listener (or reader) could be forgiven for imagining it to be a local short story belonging to the eighteenth century at the earliest, but a glance at its widespread distribution throughout northern Europe (and particularly along the Baltic coast) leads to the irresistible conclusion that here, too, we are dealing with a piece of popular tradition which must have been imported to Scotland – if not, like the Pardoner's relics:

> 'fra the Cam of Tartarie,
> weill seald with oster-schellis,[8]

quite possibly on a vessel bringing merchandise from one of the Hanseatic ports, after 'the Illuster and Vailyeand Campioun, Schir William Wallace' wrote to re-open the trading connection.

Just as many of these prose narratives were undoubtedly imports, so many of the narrative songs which were to find their way into Child's *English and Scottish Popular Ballads* were just as certainly incomers from across the North Sea, or 'land-loupers' which came up from the South, after crossing the English Channel – in some cases starting their fabulous migration in the Mediterranean world.

A revealing example of this latter peregrination is provided by 'Lord Randal My Son' – as Salinger calls it in *The Catcher in the Rye* – which is No 12 in Child. The version printed by Sir Walter Scott in his *Minstrelsy of the Scottish Border* in 1802 can claim to be one of the two most famous ballad texts in the world (the other is 'Edward'), and generations of Scots poetry lovers have undoubtedly accepted without question the wholly Scottish national identity of this haunting piece. However, the truth is that it is only one version of a very widely diffused international ballad, and that the earliest indication of its presence in a particular culture comes from Italy, where it seems to have been popular 350 years ago. A Veronese broadside of 1629 gives the first three lines of 'L'Avvelenato' (The Poisoned Man), an unmistakable first cousin of 'Lord Randal':

> Dov' andastu iersera
> Figliuol mio ricco, savio e gentile?
> Dov' andastu iersera?

Since then, dozens of versions have been recorded up and down Italy. In Germany 'die Schlangenköchin' (literally, the woman who cooked snakes) is manifestly the same ballad. Although the texts we have are all from the nineteenth century, or later, it is plain that they represent a centuries-old tradition, as do (for example) the Dutch, Swedish, Danish and Hungarian variants.

'Lord Randal' is an 'all-dialogue ballad': that is, the entire action is unfolded through conversation between the protagonists – here a mother, and her son who has been out hunting or courting (or maybe both). The ballad commonly called 'Edward' (whatever the hero's name) is No 13 in Child; it, too, is an all-dialogue ballad involving a son and a mother. The version sent by Sir David Dalrymple (later Lord Hailes) to Thomas Percy for inclusion in his *Reliques of Ancient English Poetry* is generally now accepted to be a re-write by a gifted poet (probably Hailes himself) of a traditional ballad which had probably reached him by oral transmission. Professor Archer Taylor, who made a detailed study of Child 13, regarded it as 'a revision of a folk-song, a re-writing which may justly compare with Goethe's "Heidenröslein"'.[9] Although the name he gave the ballad was 'Edward', Child did not make the Hailes version his A or principal text; the pride of place in this section of his great thesaurus goes to 'Son Davie', which was collected by William Motherwell from a Mrs King of Kilbarchan, and printed by him in his *Minstrelsy, Ancient and Modern* in 1827. This is, quite unmistakably, an unamended version collected from a folk-singer.

It may well be asked, at this point, how legitimately we may enrol ballads like the Scott 'Lord Randal' and the Hailes 'Edward' – or indeed the Motherwell 'Son Davie' – which were all put on record in the eighteenth century or later, among the products of popular tradition 'before 1660'. The answer has to be sought in studies like the one, already mentioned, by Archer Taylor; if a ballad story appears in the tradition of a number of countries – in the case of 'Edward' there are numerous Swedish, Danish and Finnish versions – we can confidently assume a much longer history than the evidence of collection might indicate. Taylor's own conclusion about 'Edward' was that it probably originated in Scotland or England during the Middle Ages, and subsequently travelled to Scandinavia.

Supporting evidence is provided by the 'props' in the older versions; the murderer has a hawk, a hound, a steed, and a bloodied sword; he has landed property ('towirs and ha'), and the whole atmosphere is aristocratic; as Taylor expresses it, 'this courtly background ... implies customs and manners quite foreign to the world in which the modern traditional forms move'.[10] Here he is evidently thinking of the versions collected in this century in the United States.

As the indefatigable Aberdeenshire collectors Gavin Greig and the Revd James Duncan of Lynturk did not recover a version of 'Edward' in the early years of this century – although theirs is one of the largest folk-song collections in the world – Taylor was forced to conclude that Child 13 had died out in the country of its presumptive origin. This conclusion suffered a spectacular disproof in 1953, when the Aberdeen ballad singer Jeannie Robertson sang a version for collectors which she had learnt from her aunt Maggie Stewart. Jeannie was a settled urbanised 'traveller' (or tinker), but her version undoubtedly makes the most 'aristocratic' impression of the lot.[11]

Another of the ballads in the repertoire of Jeannie's aunt Maggie was 'Little Sir Hugh and the Jew's Daughter' (Child 155). Here again, we encounter what is mani-festly a Mediaeval ballad, although the earliest recorded text belongs to the eighteenth century (sent to Percy from an unidentified Scottish source, and printed by him in 1765). Another justly celebrated version is that provided by Mrs Brown of Falkland, who mentions 'merry Lincoln', thus providing proof positive that the story of the ballad derives from the legend of Hugh of Lincoln, which is told in the Annals of Waverley, under the year 1255, by a contemporary writer. This Hugh was a boy supposed to have been crucified by the Jews; outbreaks of irrational panic occasioned by such rumours led to brutal persecutions of the Jews in a number of countries throughout the Middle Ages.

Yet another ballad undoubtedly originating in medieval England is 'Young Beichan' (Child 53), which clearly has some connection with the legend of Gilbert Beket, father of Saint Thomas, the martyred Archbishop. However, the essential features of the storyline – the hero being rescued from prison 'in furrin parts' by his jailor's daughter, and the latter eventually coming by sea to claim him, and prevent his marrying another woman – are widely diffused motifs found in several separate national traditions. Mrs Brown knew two quite distinct versions of this ballad, and gave them both to Robert Jamieson in 1783; one is Child's A text ('Young Bicham') and the other his C text ('Young Bekie'). For this latter Mrs Brown provided a tune.

In his *The Ballad and the Folk*, David Buchan endeavours to show that Mrs Brown was able, although an exceedingly literate woman who wrote verses and read Ossian, to recreate her ballads at every singing, using the techniques employed by non-literate singers:

> The traditional singer does not learn individual songs as fixed texts, but learns instead both a method of composition and a number of stories. By this method he re-composes each individual story every time he performs. While, however, he re-creates the story's narrative essence, he actually creates the individual lines and shapes the individual structure at the moment of performance: he composes the text as he re-composes the story. Each rendering of the story is, then, an 'original text'.[12]

Buchan's central contention is that Mrs Brown was able to perform this feat but his arguments have been strongly challenged by Holger Olof Nygard, by Flemming Andersen and Thomas Pettitt and by the present writer.[13] What is and will remain undisputed is that – however they came into being – the ballad texts put on record by Mrs Brown in 1783 and 1800 are among the very finest ever collected.

Her obvious favourites nearly all belong to the 'magical and marvellous' category, and include such treasures as 'Gil Brenton', 'Willie's Lady', 'The Twa Sisters', 'Allison Gross', and 'Thomas Rhymer'. These can all be assigned to a period long anteceding the mid-seventeenth century, irrespective of the dates when they were first put on record. These ballad texts are unexampled for aesthetic power and grace, and would alone entitle their preserver to the gratitude and love of subsequent generation.

It is when we approach the broad acreage of the Scottish historical ballads that we can feel less defensive about dates and centuries. 'Gud Wallace' (Child 157) is evidently based on a story in the fifth book of Blind Harry's *Wallace* – although, as in the case of Barbour's *Bruce*, it is by no means unlikely that an earlier ballad or ballads on the same subject may have entered the epic poem, and then (so to speak) found an oral outlet from its confines.

A fragment of a Border ballad probably composed not long after the event it describes is preserved by Hume of Godscroft in his *History of the Houses of Douglas and Angus* (1644): this is 'The Knight of Liddesdale':

> The Countesse of Douglas out of her boure
> she came,
> And loudly there that she did call:
> 'It is for the Lord of Liddesdale
> That I let all these teares downe fall'.
>   (Child 160)

Sir William Douglas, the Knight of Liddesdale, was assassinated in 1353, while hunting in Ettrick Forest, by the retainers of his godson William Lord Douglas – the motive being, according to Godscroft, a well-founded suspicion that the dead man had been having an affair with his murderer's wife. The sole piece of evidence for this – but not one to be disregarded – is the above mentioned lost ballad.

A far more resounding event which became famous in Border song and story was the Battle of Otterburn, fought on 19 August 1388; this affray had the honour of being described in vivid French prose by Froissart, and in heroic songs by English and Scottish ballad makers; the best known of these – by name at least – is 'Chevy Chase' (Child 162). There were two distinct ballads about the battle, and the other, 'The Battle of Otterburn' (Child 161), is generally regarded as the older. It is certainly the one which spawned the variants collected in the eighteenth and early nineteenth centuries which put the Scots – as opposed to the English – point of view. It is also the one which modern Revival singers have put back into 'folk' currency in recent years:

> But I have dreamd a dreary dream,
>   Beyond the isle of Sky;
> I saw a dead man win a fight,
>   And I think that man was I.

This is strong poetry, and there is nothing in the other rather laboured ballad to match it.

In the 'Complaynt of Scotland', there is a reference to the 'Hunttis of Chevat' as being among 'the sangis of natural music of the antiquite' sung by shepherds. Another song mentioned there is 'The Battel of the Hayrlau'; this undoubtedly refers to the famous set-to between MacDonald of the isles and a Royal Army under the Earl of Mar which took place in 1411 in the Garioch district of Aberdeenshire. The earliest known text of the 'folk' ballad of Harlaw – 'folk' as opposed to the ornate literary ballad about the battle which Ramsay printed in his *Ever Green* (1724) – appeared in Alexander Laing's *The Thistle of Scotland* (1823); it is a three-verse fragment, and it includes an incongruous reference to 'the red-coat lads'. Since then several lengthy versions of the ballad have turned up, including a splendid one sung by Jeannie Robertson; this is in the archives of the School of Scottish Studies. Like all 'modern' versions it seemingly flies in the face of history by giving the Forbeses a leading part in the battle, and killing off 'the great MacDonald' (who did not die at Harlaw). These anomalies have led several critics – including Child himself – to dismiss the 'folk' ballad as a comparatively modern production, but David Buchan has subjected the historical facts behind the ballad to fresh scrutiny, and powerfully reinforced the idea that the nineteenth- and twentieth-century versions are descendants of a very old traditional song, inevitably altered and occasionally 'distorted' in the course of time.[14]

Although the Robin Hood ballads are distinctively English, and their setting is invariably Nottingham and environs, there is plentiful evidence that they were as popular in Scotland as they were south of the Border. In April 1577 the General Assembly of the Kirk of Scotland requested the King to 'discharge [prohibit] playes of Robin Hood, King of May, and sic others, on the Sabbath day'. A fragment of 'Robin Hood and Little John' (Child 125) was recorded from John Strachan, an Aberdeenshire farmer, by Alan Lomax and the present writer in 1951, and a version of 'The Bold Pedlar and Robin Hood' (Child 132) turned up in Aberdeen in 1954; it was sung by Geordie Robertson, a veteran North-East traveller.

A possible contact in the Middle Ages with the Celtic world of Welsh-speakers is suggested by the nomenclature of one ballad: this is 'Glasgerion' (Child 67), which was preserved in the Percy MS. A Scottish variant, 'Glenkindie', was collected from an old woman in Aberdeenshire at the end of the eighteenth century. Kittredge's head-note to this ballad in the one-volume reduction of *English and Scottish Popular Ballads* (1904) draws attention to the appearance of 'The Bret [Briton] Glascurion' in Chaucer's 'House of Fame', where he is joined with the harpers Orpheus, Orion (Arion) and Chiron. Glascurion is also mentioned by Gavin Douglas (copying Chaucer) in his 'Palice of Honour'. There is a strong possibility that this character can be identified with Y Bardd Glas Keraint (Keraint the Blue Bard), who is said to have been 'an eminent poet of distinguished birth, son of Owain, Prince of Glamorgan'. The version in the Percy MS opens:

> Glasgerion was a King's own sonne,
>   And a harper he was good.
> (Child 67)

The Glenkindie version likewise sets the hero in a courtly setting:

> Glenkindie was ance a harper gude,
>   He harped to the King.
> (Child 67)

In *The Ballad and the Folk*, David Buchan (amplifying a definition of J. E. Housman) describes the most promising area for the creation of the 'muckle sangs':

> Traditional balladry flourished in a nonliterate, homogeneous, agricultural society, dominated by semi-independent chieftains, that is situated in a remote, hilly, or border region where cultures meet and feuds and wars abound; this kind of society provided both subjects for ballad-story and occasions for ballad performance, and lasted till the advent of widespread literacy.[15]

In view of the abundant evidence of ballad composing up and down Scotland and England, this definition may seem uncomfortably narrow; however, there can be no doubt that it fits the two areas in Scotland which *have* manifestly created a great mass of balladry: the Borders, and the North-East. In the latter, several songs reflecting the 'clannit society' which lingered on in some parts as late as the eighteenth century have been put on record. 'Captain Car', alias 'Edom O' Gordon' (Child 178), bears gory witness to the ferocity of the blood feud which raged between the Gordons (Catholic partisans of Mary Queen of Scots) and their bitter rivals the Forbeses (supporters of Protestantism, and the 'King's Party'). In 1571 Adam Gordon sent Captain Thomas Ker to take the house of Towie in Strathdon and, because the mistress of the house refused to surrender it, it was burnt together with the whole household. The infamy of this deed was grist to the ballad composer's mill, and frequent reshaping engendered stark poignant poetry:

> O bonny, bonny was her mouth,
>   And chirry were her cheiks,
> And clear, clear was hir yellow hair,
>   Whereon the reid bluid dreips!
>
> Then wi his spier he turnd hir owr;
>   O gin hir face was wan!
> He said, You are the first that eer
>   I wist alive again.
>
> He turned hir owr and owr again;
>   O gin her skin was whyte!
> He said, I might ha spard thy life
>   To been some mans delyte.

> 'Busk and boon, my merry men all,   [prepare to set out]
>   For ill dooms I do guess;   [fates]
> I cannae luik in that bonny face,
>   As it lyes on the grass.'
>   (Child 178)

'The Baron of Bracklay' (Child 203) conflates two episodes in the feud between the Gordons and the Farquharsons of Inverey; the first of these took place in 1592 and the second in 1666. A verse from Child's A text (Laing's *Scarce Ancient Ballads* 1823) expresses in two lines the ineluctable obligation of 'deidly feid':

> Up spake the son on the nourice's knee,
> 'Gin I live to be a man, revenged I'll be.'
>   (Child 203)

Writing about the terrain in which the so-called Border ballads flourished, A. L. Lloyd stated:

> The bare rolling stretch of country from the North Tyne and Cheviots to the Scottish southern uplands was for a long time the territory of men who spoke English but had the outlook of Afghan tribesmen; they prized a poem almost as much as plunder, and produced such an impressive assembly of local narrative songs that some people used to label all our greater folk poems as 'Border ballads'.[16]

Well, whether the Borderers spoke 'English' is a moot point, but an inspection of the 'riding ballads' of the Border Marches amply demonstrates that the comparison with the folkways of Pathan tribesmen might not be resented by the one side only. G. M. Trevelyan found another parallel which transfigures the wild Border reivers who figure in these ballads into epic heroes of classical antiquity:

> Like the Homeric Greeks, they were cruel, coarse savages, slaying each other as the beasts of the forest; and yet they were also poets …[17]

Personally, thinking of the manifold grotesqueries and bizarre incidents which give occasional ludicrous colour to the 'riding ballads', I have sometimes wondered whether an apter parallel might not be with Harry the Horse, Spanish John and their Brooklyn gangster mates in the Prohibition-era short stories of Damon Runyon. Just as much blood soaked the sordid reality of that particular period, in any case.

In this connection, it is curious that T. F. Henderson in his *Scottish Vernacular Literature* referred to the ballads as 'solemnly serious, and devoid of wit and humour'.[18] Even a cursory reading will show that many are impregnated through and through with what can properly be called sardonic gallows-humour; Christian Morgenstern (of *Galgenlieder* fame) is of the same *galère* as the makers of 'Hughie Graham', 'Dick o' the Cow' and 'Jock o' the Side'.

Nearly all of the best known of the Border ballads belong to the sixteenth century: that is, to the century immediately prior to the Union of the Crowns in 1603, and a majority of them belong to the second half of it. It is almost as if the Borders were determined to make gainful use of the threatened Border while the going was good. An excellent description of the mores then prevailing has been provided by George MacDonald Fraser in his book *The Steel Bonnets*,[19] and a rare imaginative poetic assessment of the songs themselves by James Reed in his *The Border Ballads*.[20]

In many ways the most impressive of these blood-drenched story-songs is 'Johnny Armstrong' (Child 169), which chronicles the arrest and execution of a redoubtable magnate of the 'Debatable Land' by James V. In the 'Complaynt of Scotland' this ballad is styled 'Jhonne Ermistrangis Daunce', and indeed the feelings it evokes are very similar to those Carlyle describes when recollecting his first hearing of 'McPherson's Rant' – also a song about the execution of a freebooter:

> Sae rantinly, sae wantonly,
> Sae dauntinly gaed he.
> He played a tune and danced it roon
> Below the gallows tree.

The dance of the tragic hero is a recurring theme in literature, and nowhere is it executed with more death-defying smeddum than in these two splendid songs. The ballads, still danced in the Faroes, may no longer have called Scots on to the dancing floor in the sixteenth century, but if any ballad in the whole Child canon could reasonably have entered the lists as a candidate for this sort of treatment, it is certainly 'Johnny Armstrong'. In all versions of the ballad King James V is quite explicitly charged with perfidy in the apprehension of Johnny. In this case, as in most others, the sympathies of the ballad maker are strictly with the local hero: he seldom operates on a 'national' scale.

It is a curious fact that in spite of the highly spectacular career of Mary Queen of Scots – ballad material of the most enticing, one would have thought – there are only two ballads which refer to her, and she is not the central figure in either. One is 'Earl Bothwell' (Child 174); this is about the murder of Riccio, and the subsequent assassination of Darnley at Kirk o' Field. It is, however, a highly partisan English production which must have been composed very soon after Mary's flight to England (May 1568); it ends 'now in England shee dothe remain'.

The other is 'Mary Hamilton' (Child 173), which at one point spawned the well-known 'singer's digest' usually called 'The Queen's Maries'. Although at first sight this ballad seems firmly localised at the court of Mary and Darnley, and to have some connection with an incident of 1563 which involved the Queen's apothecary and 'a Frenchwoman that served in the Queen's chamber', there are several puzzling features which have never been adequately explained. First, the name of the protagonist. The Queen's four Maries (who had been with her in France, and returned to Scotland with her in 1561) were surnamed Fleming, Livingstone, Seton and Beaton: yet Hamilton is the name found in most versions of the ballad hitherto recorded.

Furthermore (as Child points out, following Charles Kirkpatrick Sharpe) 'there is a quite extraordinary coincidence between the ballad and the fate of a Mary Hamilton who, in the reign of Peter the Great, was one of the maids of honour to the Russian Empress'. There are also the strange references to the 'jolly sailors, that sail upon the main'; these are charged not to

> 'Let on to my father and mother
> But what I'm coming hame '
> (Child 173)

which suggests that Mary Hamilton is to die in a foreign land.

Whatever the truth of this still unresolved problem – and it really does seem as if we have here a unique confluence of two distinct ballad traditions – the fact remains that the queen herself is a marginal figure; in Child's A version (Sharpe's *Ballad Book*, 1824, p. 18) she is even referred to as the 'auld queen', a truly incongruous epithet if Mary is accepted as the queen concerned.

Her son King James VI fares not better. His appearance in one of the most celebrated of all ballads is hardly to his advantage; he is tacitly accused of conniving at the murder of the bonny Earl of Moray (hero of Child 181), who was 'unmercifully slain' by the Earl of Huntly at Donibristle in Fife in February 1592. Huntly held a commission to apprehend and bring Moray to trial, on suspicion of his being in league with Bothwell against the king. Edward J. Cowan argues that the ballad was 'Kirk inspired':

> Moray was widely regarded as the champion of the Kirk, as were all who had borne his title. What is less familiar is that three days before Moray's death, Sir John Campbell of Cawdor was assassinated in Argyll. It later transpired that Cawdor's slaying was part of a widespread conspiracy, in which Huntly was involved, to assassinate the young Earl of Argyll. The murders of Moray and Cawdor were thus connected in a conspiracy which aimed to destroy the two great champions of Scottish Protestantism.[21]

The ballad cannot have helped but lower still further James's already base public image: it must be regarded as a trenchant piece of propaganda in favour of the Presbyterian party. It is one of the mysteries of this type of orally powered artistry that such a made-to-order polemical song should, with the passing of the years, have engendered the powerful elegiac poetry of what emerged as a magnificent, terse, clear-cut narrative song.

We may take leave of the theme of historical and Border ballads with a mention of one of the finest, and also one of the least known. This is 'Lord Maxwell's Last Goodnight' (Child 195). There existed for many years a feud between the Maxwells and their rival clan the Johnstones. John, ninth Lord Maxwell, and Sir James Johnstone came to an arranged tryst on 6 April 1608, each bringing one follower. After the parley began, there was an affray between the two followers, and in the confusion which followed Lord Maxwell shot Sir James Johnstone in the back. He fled the country, and the ballad maker composed for him a suitable 'Goodnight' or 'Farewell'.

> Adiew, fair Eskdale, up and down,
>   Where my poor friends do dwell!
> The bangisters will ding them down   [bullies]
>   And will them sore compel.
>
> But I'll revenge that feed mysell   [feud]
>   When I come ou'r the sea;
> Adiew, my lady and only joy!
>   For I maunna stay with thee
>   (Child 195)

Four years later Lord Maxwell returned to Scotland, was betrayed into the hands of the Government by the Earl of Caithness (who was a kinsman of his), and beheaded at Edinburgh on 21 May 1613.

'Thus was finally ended', noted Sir Walter Scott, 'by a salutary example of severity, the "foul debate" betwixt the Maxwells and the Johnstones, in the course of which each family lost two chieftains: one dying of a broken heart, one in the field of battle, one by assassination and one by the sword of the executioner'.[22]

Lord Byron, in the preface to *Childe Harold's Pilgrimage,* says: 'The goodnight in the beginning of the first canto was suggested by Lord Maxwell's Goodnight in the Border Minstrelsy'. This is by no means the only debt Byron owed to balladry: 'So, We'll Go no More A-roving' is without doubt a reminiscence of the chorus of one version of 'The Beggar Man' (Child 279) in Jeannie Robertson 'wey o't':

> Nae mair I'll gang a-rovin'
>   Sae late into the nicht;
> Nae mair I'll gang a-rovin'
>   Though the meen shines ne'er sae bricht.   [moon]

This is the ballad which in popular tradition is credited to King James V, in his guise of the 'Gaberlunzie Man'.

Writing about the song 'Mo Nighean Donn a Cornaig' in a paper, 'Realism in Gaelic Poetry', Samuel MacLean (i.e. the poet Sorley MacLean) has this to say:

> The subject is tragedy of crime and circumstances, the murder of a young girl by her brothers to prevent a marriage of which they disapproved. The poem is

characteristic in its simple intensity, its sheer economy of word, the lack of any romantic appurtenances, the horror that makes little comment, letting the story speak for itself. It crystallises an attitude to tragedy strangely common in Lowland Scots poetry as well as in Gaelic poetry. It is life contemplated with intense emotion, an emotion that is all the greater because of its reticence; there is no haze or mysticism of any kind. Hence it is essentially a realistic poem if the realism is on the level of the realism of tragic poetry.[23]

The theme of 'Mo Nighean Donn a Cornaig' is in fact related to that of 'The Cruel Brother' (Child 11), but Sorley's words touch on deeper resemblances. Sir James Fergusson is clearly referring to the same general poetic sensibility when he writes:

In those generations of the sixteenth and early seventeenth centuries that pro-duced the best of the ballads there must have existed remarkably widely the instinct for those strokes which distinguish the ballads and make them one of Scotland's principal contributions to European literature. These characteristics I would distinguish as direct movement of the story to its catastrophe, economical statement, a telling choice of episode and memorably succinct dialogue. The story does not move laboriously on from point to point, as in the medieval romances, but – in the best of the ballads – by a swift succession of scenes, almost in the manner of a film, between which much is left to the imagination of an audience obviously accustomed to exercise that faculty.[24]

These particular characteristics are, of course, shared by all European ballad commu-nities, and can be attributed to the techniques and workings of oral creation and recreation themselves – the reader is referred to Chapters 8–11 in David Buchan's *The Ballad and the Folk* – but the Scots seem to have taken particularly kindly to this type of 'folk art'. Maybe it has something to do with the terse epigrammatic speech of the people, documented in dozens of historical anecdotes. Fergusson himself says that 'reported speech from authentic history is full of phrases which might have come straight out of the ballads – or gone straight into them', and he gives several examples of this. Here is one which he does not. In *The Historie and Cronicles of Scotland*, completed in the 1570s, Lindsay of Pitscottie described the meeting of James V and Johnny Armstrong (June 1530) as follows:

When the King saw him and his men so gorgeous in their apparel, and so many braw men under a tyrant's commandment, throwardly he turned about his face, and bade 'take that tyrant out of his sight, saying, What wants you knave that a King should have?'

In the version of the ballad in Allan Ramsay's *Ever Green* 'copied from a gentleman's mouth of the name of Armstrong, who is the 6th generation from this John', verse 26 reads:

> Ther hang nine targats at Johnys hat,
>   And ilk ane worth three hundred pound:
> 'What wants that knave that a king suld haif,
>   But the sword of honour and the crown!
>   (Child 169)

Later in Pitscottie's account comes the following passage:

> He, seeing no hope of the King's favour towards him, said very proudly, I am
> but a fool to seek grace at a graceless face.

Verse 22 of the same version of the ballad runs as follows:

> To seik het water beneth cauld yce,
>   Surely it is a great folie:
> I haif asked grace at a graceless face,
>   But there is nane for my men and me.

Variants of this last-quoted verse appear in versions of the ballad published in
seventeenth-century English broadsides and miscellanies – see Child's headnote to No
169, Vol. 3, pp. 362–3 – but verse 26 of the *Ever Green* copy is unique.

Pitscottie, therefore, in the sixteenth century is quoting practically verbatim a ballad
version not printed until the eighteenth, but presumably circulating in his own day – or
does Ramsay's ballad owe something to Pitscottie? Or do both the historian's account
and the ballad version echo actual speech borne to each on the wing of oral transmission? It would be a bold man who would support only one of these possibilities, to the
absolute exclusion of others.

This merciless tight-lipped sardonic utterance is echoed in scores of folk-rhymes
which have come down to us from earlier centuries. Here are a few examples:

> Says Tweed to Till
>   Whit gars ye rin sae still?
> Says Till tae Tweed
> Though ye rin wi speed
>   And I rin slaw
> Yet for ae man ye droon
>   I droon twa.

And this, again from the Borders:

> Happy the craw
> That biggs on the Lammerlaw   [builds]
> And drinks o' the Water o' Dye
> For nae mair may I.

And this, from Aberdeenshire:

> Twa men sat doon on Ythan Brae
> And the teen tae the tither did say,
> And fit-like men may the Gordons o' Gight hae been?

The supreme example in our whole ballad-literature of this devastating, epigrammatic
terseness is surely the final stanza of 'The Twa Corbies' (the Scottish analogue of the
English 'The Three Ravens'):

> Mony's the ane for him maks mane,
> But nane sall ken whaur he is gane.

Ower his white banes, when they are bare,
The wind sall blaw for evermair.

(Child 26)

If, as has been argued, this version was 'worked over' by Scott or Charles Kirkpatrick Sharpe, that only underlines how fortunate we have been to have ballad-collectors and editors whose speech-habits and mental attitudes so closely corresponded to the authentic tradition of ballad-Scots.

There seems little doubt that many of the ballads found in Scotland now, and probably current in the sixteenth century – for example, 'The Death of Queen Jane' (Child 170), which is about Jane Seymour's demise shortly after giving birth to the future Edward VI – came to us from England.

However, the multi-ethnic origins of Scottish folk culture must surely be regarded as constituting in the main a strength and not a weakness. The hybrid is often more resourceful and resilient than the pure-bred. Scots folk-song has been able to welcome and assimilate material of the most diverse origins. As Gavin Greig wrote in the first article he contributed to the *Buchan Observer* in December 1907:

> As we pursue the subject we are carried beyond the bounds of Scotland and quite away from the present time; for the field of folk-song admits of no delimitation either in a geographical or a secular way, reaching forth ultimately to the ends of the earth through countless affinities, and back to primeval times through an unbroken chain of derivation.[25]

The ballads, therefore, illustrate and shed further light on a phenomenon already documented in the work of the great makars Dunbar and Henryson – that much Scottish literature is both 'Inglis' and 'Scottis'. There was a two-way process: many ballads migrated 'on the hoof', so to speak. 'Geordie' went South and 'The Bold Pedlar' came North. There was fusion at several levels – but no one listening to a recording of Frank Jordan of Shropshire singing 'The Outlandish Knight', and then (for example) to one of John Strachan of Fyvie singing 'Glenlogie', could doubt that he was listening (in every sense) to two different voices.

The Border, marauders' highway and frail political barrier, was – and remains to this day – a cultural and linguistic watershed. Anonymous Scottish ballad-composers and ballad-singers have given these great songs 'a local habitation and a name'.

Notes

1 'Maydens of Englonde, sore may ye morne/For your lemmans ye have loste at Bannockisbourne!/With heve a lowe./What wenyth the Kynge of Englonde/So sonne to have wonne Scotlande?/With rumbylowe.' According to Fabyan, 'This songe was after many dayes sungyn in daunces, in carolles of the maydens and mynstrellys of Scotlande, to the reproofe and dysdane of Eng-lishmen, *wt dyverse other which I over passe*.' See *Edward II*, Act 2 Sc. ii, 190–5.

2 Marion Stewart, 'A Recently Discovered Manuscript', *Scottish Studies* 16 (1972), p. 23.

3 *Barbour's Bruce*, M. P. McDiarmid and J. A. C. Stevenson (eds), 3 vols, STS (Edinburgh and London, 1980–1), III, p. 126.

4   Sir David Lindsay, *Works,* D. Hamer (ed.), 4 vols, STS (Edinburgh, 1931), II, p. 205.

5   It is this ludicrous contrast, in my view, that makes the passage funny. However, others have drawn attention to the practical usefulness of the horn in pastoral society; to the lasting popularity of the song *Crodh Chailein* (Colin's Cattle); and even to the sacred aura surrounding the bull of Cooley in the Irish heroic saga Táin Bó Cuailnge.

6   John Carswell, *Book of Common Order,* ed. and trans. by Thomas M'Lauchlan (Edinburgh, 1873), p. 19.

7   (Edinburgh, 1860–2).

8   School of Scottish Studies Sound Archive, SA 1954/90/B9.

9   Archer Taylor, *'Edward' and 'Sven i Rosengård': A Study in the Dissemination of Ballads* (Chicago, 1931), p. 26.

10 Archer Taylor, p. 55.

11 *Scotland and the Lowland Tongue,* J. D. McClure (ed.) (Aberdeen, 1983), pp. 109–10.

12 David Buchan, *The Ballad and the Folk* (London and Boston, 1973), p. 52.

13 Holger Olof Nygard, 'Mrs Brown's Recollected Ballads', *Ballad and Ballad Research* (Seattle, 1978); Flemming Andersen and Thomas Pettitt, 'Mrs Brown: A Singer of Tales?', *Journal of American Folklore* 92, 1979; Hamish Henderson, 'The Ballad, the Folk and the Oral Tradition', *The People's Past,* E. J. Cowan (ed.) (Edinburgh, 1980).

14 David Buchan, 'History and Harlaw', *Ballad Studies,* E. B. Lyle (ed.) (Cambridge, 1976), pp. 29–40.

15 Buchan, *The Ballad and the Folk,* p. 47.

16 A. L. Lloyd, *Folksong in England* (London, 1967), p. 159.

17 G. M. Trevelyan, *The Middle Marches* (Newcastle, 1935), p. 25.

18 T. F. Henderson, *Scottish Vernacular Literature* (London, 1898), p. 370.

19 (London, 1971.)

20 (London, 1973.)

21 Edward J. Cowan, 'Calvinism and the Survival of Folk' in *The People's Past,* pp. 32–57.

22 Sir Walter Scott, *Minstrelsy of the Scottish Border,* T. F. Henderson (ed.), 4 vols (Edinburgh and London, 1902), II, p. 175.

23 'Realism in Gaelic Poetry', *TGSL,* XXXVII, p. 89.

24 In *Scottish Poetry: A Critical Survey,* James Kinsley (ed.) (London, 1955), pp. 99–118 (p. 110).

25 Gavin Greig, *Folksong of the North-East* (Hatboro, Pennsylvania, 1963).

History of Scottish Literature, ed. R.D.S. Jack, vol I, AUP, 1986.

The Midnight Ceilidh
in the Sun Lounge of the Angus

Every Festival worthy of the name is bound to develop its own fringe. People get tired of officially delimited boundaries, and want to spill over them and occupy new territory. These new gains may get organised and, so to speak, policed in their turn, but the moment of break-away invariably engenders a marvellous feeling of freedom.

One such moment took place almost palpably on a lovely summer's night in 1968 in the little Perthshire town of Blairgowrie, during one of the first Festivals of Scottish traditional music and song. There had been a series of officially organised concerts and ceilidhs at various halls and hotels, and the folk *aficionados* had turned out loyally and enthusiastically to applaud such justly famous characters as Jeannie Robertson, Jimmy MacBeath and Mary Brooksbank. Everyone knew that when the official programme was over the fun would continue all over the town into the small hours, but I think no one could have foreseen what was going to happen at one of these impromptu sing-songs.

On the first floor of the Angus Hotel was a room called the Sun Lounge, overlooking the Wellmeadow, and it was getting on for midnight when I got a message telling me that an old friend of mine, Willie Mitchell, a butcher from Campbeltown in Argyll, had arrived in town, and was waiting there in the Sun Lounge to have a dram with me. I had been at a ceilidh in the Glen Ericht Hotel, and I brought Willie Scott – the Border shepherd and renowned ballad singer – with me to meet Willie Mitchell, for I could foresee that this particular confrontation was going to be great fun for all concerned. What it turned out to be was a creative explosion which was to affect the folk revival in an incalculable fashion.

Willie Mitchell, whom I had recorded some years previously, was a notable singer in his own right, but he was also an enterprising and imaginative local collector, and his repertoire was drawn from the items he had collected from local singers in various parts of Kintyre – especially songs he had got from the MacShannon family, Jimmy, Jock and Alec – three brothers who were lineal descendants of the shennachie brought across to Scotland from County Antrim by General Alistair MacDonald, the legendary Colkitto of the Montrose wars. With Willie Mitchell was his daughter Catherine, and her husband John Kerr. Together these Kintyre singers made an impressive and attractive trio, and I knew that Willie Scott would take to them.

The old Borderer walked up the stairs in front of me, and on into the Sun Lounge of the Angus. He's a tall, dignified, commanding figure – looking exactly like an old-time laird, as Jeannie Robertson used to say – and he was already a popular character at these

Festivals; Willie Mitchell, on the other hand, was in Blair for the first time. However, it seemed only a matter of minutes before the two Willies had struck up a respectful, friendly relationship, and were beginning to vie with each other in the unostentatious but quite definite manner that singers who know they're singers nearly always exhibit on such occasions – both were clearly on their mettle.

Not that they were left to sing on their own – the room rapidly filled up with other singers and musicians, and eventually the gathering included Archie Fisher, Arthur Argo and Davie MacQueen of the Peebles Folk Club – the last two, alas, are no longer with us. There was plenty of good singing, but eventually the two champions were left to engage in friendly single combat – and in the memory of everyone who was there, the midnight ceilidh in the Sun Lounge of the Angus turned into something quite special.

The song of Willie Mitchell which lingered in Willie Scott's mind afterwards was the emigrants' song, 'Callieburn', or 'Machrihanish bright and bonnie' which he had heard sung by the MacShannons. This was a Kintyre song of the early nineteenth century, and the Mitchells – father, daughter and son-in-law – sang it with such power and eloquence that it electrified the entire company. No wonder the younger singers called for it again later in the session, but the folk process this time was not so much a matter of transmission from older to younger, as of older to still older. Before the night was out, and the dawn was up, I saw the two Willies in a huddle – and it was plain to see that the old alchemy was at work.

Three months later I recorded 'Callieburn' from Willie Scott – a really magnificent performance – but it wasn't the 'Callieburn' Willie Mitchell had sung. The words were more or less the same, for Willie Mitchell had written them down for his new friend the shepherd – but the tune had become totally transformed. And it wasn't long before the younger singers of the Revival had latched on to it – and a new and noble folk-song variant was riding high on the billows.

For me, therefore, that ceilidh in the Sun Lounge marked a real moment of qualitative break-through – tradition and revival, working together, had actually made it. As the late Arthur Argo once put it, if all our efforts in the Folk Revival were now to drain away into the sands, it would have been worth it for that midnight ceilidh.

Scottish Home Service (BBC Scotland).

'Glasclune and Drumlochy'

This poem is a product of the folk revival – it grew and developed as spoken (and sung) poetry at Edinburgh International Festival readings in the mid-sixties. These took place mainly at the original Traverse Theatre building off the Lawnmarket, and in the Crown Bar (now demolished) in Lothian Street, where the Edinburgh University Folk-song Society held its reunions.

Right from the earliest period of the People's Festivals in Edinburgh (1951, 1952, 1953) poetry readings were an integral part of the growing 'folk scene'. The first of these were organised by the late Alan Riddell, founder of *Lines Review*. Excerpts from Hugh MacDiarmid's *A Drunk Man Looks at the Thistle* were given at the 1951 People's Festival ceilidh, between the rumbustious ballad singing of John Strachan and the vivacious piping sprees of John Burgess. Young poets were encouraged to contribute to these sessions. Much of the work of Alan Jackson and Tom Leonard has its ultimate origin in this particular creative blend of oral poetry and traditional Scottish song. Matt McGinn's work was also to a considerable extent inspired by it.

Alan Jackson's version of 'The Minister to his Flock', an ancient, orally transmitted joke which can be found in Richard M. Dorson's *Folk-Tales Told Around the World*, was given by him at one of the Traverse ceilidhs in 1963:

> Aye, ye're enjoyin' yoursels noo wi' your drinkin' and your women and your nights oot at the pictures, and never a thocht given to the Word of God, and his great and terrible laws.
>
> But ye'll change your tune when ye're doon below in the fiery pit, and ye're burnin' and ye're sufferin', and ye'll cry: 'O Lord, Lord, we didna ken, we didna ken.' And the Lord in his infinite mercy will bend doon frae Heaven and say: 'Well, ye ken noo.'

This joke, which epitomises the barbaric black humour of Calvinist Scotland, was energetically applauded by a predominantly English youthful audience which assumed that it was by Alan himself – and indeed it fell naturally into place between such poems as 'Knox' and 'Lord Save Us, it's the Minister'. It appears – attributed to Anon – in Alan's collection *Well, Ye Ken Noo*, produced in Bristol with the aid of the CND duplicator in 1963.

'Glasclune and Drumlochy' is based on a historical tale which I heard in Glenshee, Perthshire, when I was a child. The subject-matter is clearly blood-brother to many tales of Appalachian feuds. As children we naturally believed the story to be true, and indeed it may well be founded on fact.

The ruins of the castle of Glasclune are about three miles north-west of Blairgowrie, home of the Stewarts of Blair. Glasclune is described in the *Ordnance Gazetteer of Scotland* (1884) as 'an ancient baronial fortalice on the border of Kinloch parish, Perthshire, crowning the steep bank of a ravine at the boundary with Blairgowrie parish. The stronghold of the powerful family of Blair, it was once a place of considerable strength, both natural and artificial, and is now represented by somewhat imposing ruins.' The ruins were decidedly less imposing when we played around them – and in them – as children in the 1920s, and since then decay has proceeded apace. Indeed, Glasclune has gradually become for me a symbol like the mill which Hugh MacDiarmid apostrophises in 'Depth and the Chthonian Image' (a long poem which is subtitled 'On looking at a ruined mill and thinking of the greatest'):

> The mills o' God grind sma', but they
> In you maun crumble imperceptibly tae.

However, Glasclune is still there: the keep of Drumlochy, which bore the brunt of cannon fire, has disappeared off the face of the earth. (The Mains of Drumlochy is a farm.)

Glasclune appears once – and dramatically – in medieval Scottish history. It was the scene of a battle in 1392, when one of the sons of Alexander Stewart – son of Robert II, and well known to history as the Wolf of Badenoch – made an incursion into Stormont and the Braes of Angus. This foray was a kind of curtain-raiser to the more famous Highland invasion of 1411, when Donald of the Isles, leading a large army of 'Katherans', was fought to a standstill at Harlaw. In Wynton's *Original Cronykil of Scotland* (Book IX, Chapter XIV) there is a graphic account in verse of the battle of Glasclune, including an episode in which a knight from Dundee called Sir Davy de Lyndesay speared a Highlander, and was himself wounded by the dying cateran who writhed up the spear-shaft and cut Lyndesay's boot and stirrup leather and his leg to the bone:

> Sua, on his hors he sittand than,
> Throw the body he strayk a man
> Wytht his spere down to the erde:
> That man hald fast his awyn swerd
> In tyl his neve, and wp thrawand
> He pressit hym, nocht agayn standand
> That he wes pressit to the erd,
> And wylh a swake thare off his swerd
> The sterap lethire and the bute
> Thre ply or foure, abone the fute
> He straik the Lyndesay to the bane.
> That man na straike gave bot that ane
> For thare he deit: yeit nevirtheles
> That gude Lord thare wondit wes,
> And had deit thare that day,
> Had nocht his men had hym away
> Agane his wil out of that pres.

Wynton locates the battle at 'Gaskclune', but this is certainly the Glasclune of my childhood, for it is referred to as being in the Stermond (Stormont); furthermore Bower, in the *Scotichronicon*, locates the conflict in 'Glenbrereth', probably Glen Brerachan, which is the same general area. Bower informs us that Walter Ogilvy, Sheriff of Angus, was slain *per Cateranos quorum caput fuit Duncanus Stewart filius don-ini Alexandri comitis de Buchan* (by caterans whose leader was Duncan Stewart, son of the lord Alexander, Earl of Buchan).

It is interesting to note that it was a brother of this same Duncan, leader of the caterans, who as Earl of Mar led the Aberdeenshire army *against* Donald of the Isles at Harlaw. So much for the oversimplified view of these conflicts as being simply and solely between 'Highlands' and 'Lowlands'.

My poem is, as it were, an echo of this old warfare, as it still remotely pulsates in the folk memory. The 'clannish confine' lies in jagged outline across Scottish history. I was thinking also of the millennial internecine conflict of humankind, which in our century bids fair to write *finis* to the 'haill clanjamfrie'. The sung part of the poem is the ballad pastiche, and is in italics. The tune is a variant of 'Cam ye by Atholl':

> From the summit of Cnoc-mahar
>   I look on the laigh …
> On fat Strathmore, and its braw
>   largesse of lochs;
> Black Loch and White Loch, Fengus, Marlee, Clunie
>   where the bolstered curlers come …
>
> But back I turn
> northward, and stand at nightfall under Glasclune,
> by the canyon cleft of the shaggy shabby Lornty
> (the shaggy shabby, the dowdy, duddy Lornty)
> that marked the clannish confine.
>
> There were two castles,
> two battled keeps, Drumlochy and Glasclune,
> that kept a bloodfeud bienly on the boil.
> They sat on their airse and they girned fell gyte at ither
> ('I'll paisley your fitt', 'I'll brackley your invereye')
> … and atween, the scrogs of the dowdy duddy Lornty.
> Drumlochy's laird was a slew-eye dye-blue bloodhound
> who fought, as his sires had fought, with steel (cold steel!)
> and said the other mugger couldn't take it.
> But Glasclune knew six of that: he was progressive,
> and to be in tune with the times was all his rage.
> Now, one day he went out and bought a cannon
> (a quare old toy unknown to the lad next door):
> with this he gave Drumlochy a thorough pasting –
> dang doon his wall, gave his stately pile the shakes:
> in fact, blockbust him quite.
>
> 'The moral of this,' said Glasclune, with 'ill-concealed'

hidalgo satisfaction, 'is that Right
– unready starter in the donnybrook stakes –
must still rise early to possess the field.'

Now wae's me Glasclune
Glasclune and Drumlochy
They bashed ither blue
By the back side o' Knockie.

Drumlochy focht fair,
But Glasclune the deceiver
Made free wi' a firewark
Tae blaw up his neebor.

Then shame, black shame, ay, shame on the bluidy Blairs!
Shame on the Blairs, an' sic wuddifu races.
They think nae sin
when they put the boot in
In the eyes of all ceevilised folk tae disgrace us.

Ochone Drumlochy
    Glasclune and Drumlochy –
Twa herts on ae shiv

    An' a shitten larach.

The People's Past, ed. E. J. Cowan, Polygon, 1980.

Folk-songs and Music from the Berryfields of Blair

Lying in the lee of Grampian foothills, and sheltered from snell east winds by the twenty-mile-long range of the Sidlaws, Strathmore is the great soft-fruit-growing district of Scotland. Raspberries are the main crop; at berry-time, which is usually about mid-July, pickers converge from every corner of the land to spend a week or two camped near Blairgowrie, a thriving little burgh which is the centre of the industry.

If the weather's good, Strathmore is a lovely place to be in. There is a string of glittering silver-surfaced lochs to the west of Blair – Black Loch and White Loch, Fengus, Marlee, Clunie – and many of the berry fields lie only a stone's throw away from one or other of these. On hot afternoons, the youth of the picker community spend quite a lot of time in the water. Even when there is work to be done (and quite often the pickers work marathon hours) there's always a relaxed and leisurely atmosphere about the berry fields: the iron grip on the neck of urban humanity is loosened, and folk feel they can take it easy, whether they decide to, or not.

The Scots cities – principally Dundee and Glasgow – send biggish contingents to the berry fields; these are mainly working-class folk who want a holiday in the country which will pay for itself. At the height of the season you can find representatives of every trade and walk of life imaginable strung out along the green foliaged rows, and resolved to pick berries and have a good time. But the pickers who give the berry fields their distinctive atmosphere, who set the tone, and do most to make the whole area a vast pounding maelstrom of folk music and song are the 'travellers' – members of the semi-nomadic Scots tinsmith clans Stewart and MacPhee, or English and Irish gypsies. They, in chief, are the carriers, dispensers, performers and glorifiers of one of the most voluminous oral cultures in Europe, and the all-star cast of the world's most successful unofficial folk festival.

Most of the recordings on this disc were made in the Standing Stones berry field (it gets its name from an ancient druid circle, a familiar landmark on the road to Essendy). Unlike most of the rich berry field owners in the area, the then proprietors of the Standing Stones were of traveller stock – Alex and Belle Stewart, themselves notable folk performers – and they were naturally on intimate friendly terms with the gaberlunzie families, still 'on the road', who camped on their land and helped to harvest their crop of berries. This gave the Standing Stones the feel almost of a little traveller principality of its own, a joyful snook cocked at orthodox law and order, like Garcia Lorca's 'City of the Gypsies'.

Down the verges of the field, when berry-picking was in full swing, you could see

ragged rows of tents, and here and there battered second-hand cars, the veterans of
countless scrap-dealing forays. A wooden hut near the entrance sold lemonade and
miscellaneous groceries. Bold commandos of children ranged all round ... Beyond the
berry field lay matted wildwood of birch, oak, fir and larch, a happy hunting ground
for firewood seekers: in the distance, the outline of the grey-green Sidlaws.

The pickers usually worked in little groups, and all day long you could hear voices
raised in song in one corner of the field or another. Sometimes the songs were on-the-
spot improvisations about the work itself:

> I'm working in the berryfields, I'm working night and day;
> I'm working the roses aff ma cheeks for very little pay

or else an Irish lad from Donegal or Connemara would reminisce about the rammy of
the night before:

> O whisky, you're the divil ... you're leading me astray.

After the day's picking was over, and the evening feed cooked and eaten, there was a bit
of moving to and fro between the camp-fires. Two or three folk from one 'camp' would
join their neighbours, and a ceilidh would get under way. Sitting on the ground, or
squatting on their hunkers, the travellers would gossip and exchange banter – folk-tales
were told as if the protagonists were all still alive: 'and the last time I passed by Jack's
castle, I gied him a tune on my auld pipes, and he gied me a dram and a golden geeny'.

Then the singing would begin, or else a melodeon might be fetched out of the tent,
and one of the gypsies would give a brilliant display of step-dancing on a bit of board
laid down for the purpose, encouraged by hoochs and admiring cries.

By this time, four or five similar ceilidhs might well be going on in the one berry
field, and the excited collector would have to decide whether to stay on at the first
camp-fire of his choice, or move to another ... from which maybe, he could hear
tantalising fragments of a rare 'Child' ballad, or the high flamenco-like cadences of a
Gaelic tinker love lament. Recording in the berry fields, in fact, was – and is – like
holding; a tin-can under the Niagara Falls; in a single session you can hear everything
from ancient Ossianic hero-tales, whose content reflects the life of primitive hunter
tribesmen, to the caustic pop-song parodies thought up by Clydeside teenagers the
same afternoon.

On this disc we have aimed at presenting a cross-section of the kind of material that
berry field singing sessions yield in abundance. It includes selections on the accordion,
harmonica and Highland war-pipes; the classic ballad 'The False Knight upon the
Road', not collected in Scotland since the early nineteenth century; fierce ribald
drinking songs, and the snap and lilt of mouth-music for the dance; songs carried to
Strathmore by the Northern Highlanders, the Irish and the English gypsies who make
the trek to Blair at berry-time; 'MacPherson's Rant', which celebrates the Robin Hood
of the North-East, an outlaw who was a fiddler as well as a fighter; night-visiting songs,
songs in the Lowland travellers' cant, virile bawdry of the 'Merry Muses' variety, and
a love song known from Texas to Tarwathie – all are represented on this unique disc of
field recordings.

The items have the authentic bloom of the open air on them; they are the sort of
material which can never be adequately recaptured in studio recordings. More

important still, they carry the listener to the very centre of a way of life which, although profoundly alien to most industrialised Western society, has a permanent appeal, validity and attractiveness of its own:

> Field of the travellers, who
> That saw you could forget you soon?
> Let them seek you in my forehead,
> The playground of the sands and moon.

Sleeve note (Prestige/International 25016), 1962.

Folk-song from a Tile

In 1955 I got word from the novelist Neil McCallum that he had been shown a most singular 'brick' by its owner, Douglas Mickel, of the Edinburgh firm of building contractors, MacTaggart and Mickel. This object, which had been found on a building site in Corstorphine several years earlier, had what appeared to be a verse of a song or a poem written on it.

I took an early opportunity of calling on Mr Mickel at his office in North Andrew Street, and proceeded to examine the singing brick. It turned out to be a segmental interlocking drain-tile, strawberry-red in colour, and hollow; its dimensions were 9 in. by 6 in. by 22 in. What made it remarkable was the fact that it bore, scratched on its face, eight lines of what appeared to be a folk-song. They were in quite a stylish copybook hand, and read as follows:

> As I was a walking one fine Sumers evening
> one fine summers evening it happened to be
> There I spied a damsel she appeared like an angel
> and she sat neath the shade of a bonny green tree
> I stepped up unto her as I seemed to veiw her
> and said my pretty maid will you no marry me
> Ill make you a lady of high rank and houner
> If you share me the half of your bonny green tree

I asked Mr Mickel what he knew of the brick's history, and he told me that it had been found on a building site at Broomhall Avenue, Corstorphine, not long before the start of the Second World War. It had formed part of the wall of a culvert, conduit or aqueduct carrying a stream across a field on what had once been Broomhouse Farm. He thought it might be over a hundred years old. I asked him if he could hazard an opinion as to where the brick had been made, and he said that, judging by the clay, it might have come from a kiln in the Prestonpans area. The words on the tile had obviously been scratched in the soft clay with the point of a nail or knife before it was fired.

The Director of the Wemyss Development Company kindly provided the information that a tile of this 'extruded' form used to be produced in Fife for lining circular well-shafts. The Corstorphine example could not be older than the nineteenth century.

At my request, the poet Alan Riddell, who was at that time a reporter on the *Edinburgh Evening Dispatch*, came along to Mr Mickel's office with a photographer,

THE BONNY GREEN TREE

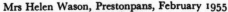

Mrs Helen Wason, Prestonpans, February 1955

and an illustrated article appeared on 3 February 1955. Two days later, a letter from Prestonpans appeared in the correspondence columns of the same newspaper; Mrs Helen Wason, wife of a miner, had written in to say that she knew the whole song, which she had learned more than fifty years before from her mother, who came from Fisherrow. Her version of the text was included in the letter. On receipt of it, I wrote at once, inviting Mrs Wason to come to the School of Scottish Studies and record the song; I also paid her a visit, and prospected for more material. About a week after her letter was published, she recorded her version in the School. It goes as follows:

> As I went a-walking one fine summer evening,
>   A fine summer evening it happened to be,
> I spied a fair damsel, she appeared like an angel,
>   'Twas under the shade o' a bonny green tree.
>
> I steppèd up to her, 'twas only to view her.
>   I said, my kind maiden, you've sair wounded me.
> I'll make you a lady of high rank and honour
>   If you'll shelter me under your bonny green tree.
>
> O I'm not a lady of high rank or honour,
>   I'm but a poor girl of a lowly degree;
> Your friends and relations would all look down on me
>   If you were to marry a poor girl like me.
>
> What do I care for my friends or relations,
>   My friends and relations have nothing to do with me.
> I'll make you a lady of high rank and honour
>   If you'll shelter me under your bonny green tree.
>
> All you young maidens, from me take a warning:
>   Ne'er go into young men's company,
> For all that they want is to spoil your chàracter,
>   And then they will leave you, as my love left me.

There are one or two minor discrepancies between this version, which is transcribed from her singing, and the text which she sent in to the *Dispatch*.

Not long after Mrs Wason's visit, I received the following letter (which accompanied yet another text of 'The Bonny Green Tree'):

> 17th Febr   Mr Henderson
> Dear Sir
> I enclose the full part of the song I noticed in the *Dispatch*, it's 65 years past since I used to sing it at the Dances in Ashkirk. Another played the Fiddle to me, I've given you the words.
>
> I enclose another old one if you think it worth while to accept only from memory have none in Print. But excuse me if you care to call on me sometime I could talk better than writing much at my Age, trust I am not too ready at saying so much, only it is some one like you I would like to have a talk with on years gone bye, my memory is so clear trusting you will excuse me my address added.
>
> Your M. Simpson

The writer was Mrs Mary Simpson, a native of Nemphlar, Lanarkshire; at that time she was eighty-six. Here is her version, just as she wrote it:

> As I went awalking yae fine Summers Evening,
>   Yae fine Summers evening it happened to be,
> I espied a wee lass she appeared like an Angel,
>   She sat under the shade of a bonnie green tree,
>
> I stepped up to her as I seemed to view her
>   And said my wee lassie will ye marry me
> I'll mak ye a Lady o high rich and honour,
>   A Lady you'll be of a high high Degree –
> Your friends and relations would frown upon you
>   If you was to marry a poor girl like me,
>
> My Friends and relations I hae got but few –
>   My friends and relations care nothing for me.
>   Your a poor girl and I a rich boy
>   tomorrow we'll wed My Bride ye shall be
>
> It's doon on the green grass he sat doon beside me
>   He made a vow to marry me but when he arose
> He shook hands and pairted and told me
>   to look for one of my own degree   (He *was fallse*)

>   *last verse*
>   Come all ye pretty fair Maids
> I pray take a warning, ne'er trust
>   a young man of ony Degree
> for all that they want is the spoil on your Character,
>   And then they will leave you
>   As my love left me –

The other song Mrs Simpson enclosed was a folk version of 'Auld Lang Syne'. She appended these words to it:

PS its to be all Scotsh –
as *I am. Scotsh*

I called on Mrs Simpson, who lived in Dunedin Street in Edinburgh, and found her a delightful old lady. She had a number of songs, most of which she had learned when fee'd as a servant girl at Ashkirk; 'The Bonny Green Tree' was one of these. Unfortunately, her memory was failing, and she was never able to recall the tune properly; I attempted to record it several times, but without success. The following year, however, I was lucky enough to stumble on yet another version while camped in the berry fields of Blairgowrie; it was sung by Mrs Margaret Stewart, a Banff tinker then in her late sixties, and seemed closely related to Mrs Simpson's version. Here are the two final verses:

Mrs Margaret Stewart, Banff, August 1956

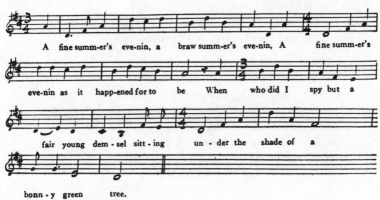

A fine summ-er's eve-nin, a braw summ-er's eve-nin, A fine summ-er's eve-nin as it happ-ened for to be When who did I spy but a fair young dem-sel sitt-ing un-der the shade of a bonn-y green tree.

She sat now down, and he sat down beside her;
    That's the very place that he vowed tae marry me.
But when he approached me, he found me a virgin –
    Sayin', tomorrow we'll get married – but your bride I'll
                                         never be.

Come all you fair maids, O come and take a warning;
    Don't pay any heed whit any young man they do say,
For when they get the wills o' you, it's then they will
                                         leave you –
    O it's then they will leave you, as my love left me.

Mrs Stewart learned this version from her grandmother, who came from Wick. However, she was very emphatic that the 'bonny green tree' of the song was located in Macduff.

    I am indebted to Mr W. Turner Berry, ex-Librarian of the Printing Library of St Bride, Bride Lane, Fleet St, London, for information concerning a song sheet 'The Shady Green Tree: A New Song', which was lent to the Arts Council exhibition of street literature in 1954 by John Cheney of Banbury. The text, as it appears on this song sheet, is as follows:

    As I was walking one midsummer morning

Down by a shady green tree
There did I behold a beautiful virgin
     Sitting all under the shady green tree.
I stepped up to her and said, my dear jewel
     You are the first girl that ever wounded me.
You will not want for gold or silver
     If you will set your mind on me.

She said, kind sir, you are better deserving
     I am a poor girl of low degree.
Besides your parents will always be scolding
     So in my station contented I'll be.
Talk not of friends or any relations
     As have no portion at all to give me;
As I am a young man, and you are a virgin
     Married tomorrow to you I shall be.

She sat herself down, I sat myself by her,
     There did I rifle her beautiful charms.
With sweet melting kisses and fond embraces
     We slept together in each other's arms.
The space of three hours all in the green grove
     All under the shady green tree.
And when I awaked, I found her no virgin:
     Married to you I never shall be.

She said, kind sir, you are my undoing.
     Can you, O can you so cruel be?
How can I pass any more for a virgin
     Since you have had your will of me.
Come all pretty maidens now take warning
     Never trust a man in any degree,
For when they've enjoyed the fruits of your garden,
     Then they will leave you, as he has done me.

In a letter, Mr Turner Berry states: 'I'm afraid there is no way of tracing the printer or place, but after comparing paper and type with many other songs in our possession, some of which are dated, I would guess that the date of printing was circa 1790 ... The item in question is called a "new song", but so are many others, and I would guess that this statement means very little.' Examination of the song-sheet text and of the text inscribed on the tile suggests that both are variants of a song that has had time to develop along more than one line.

   In conclusion I should add that the song has also been recorded in Ireland. It was collected by Sam Henry from James Carmichael of Ballymena, under the title 'Under the Shade of the Bonny Green Tree', and is No 794 in the Henry collection. The tune and the last three verses of that version are here added as envoi (I am indebted for the information to Ivor A. Crawley, City Librarian of Belfast):

UNDER THE SHADE OF A BONNY GREEN TREE

The laddie sat down, and she sat down beside him;
He swore and he promised that married they'd be;
But when he arose his mind it was altered:
And he said, 'If I marry, my bride you won't be.'

'Now I may go; I may go broken-hearted;
Ill bodes the day that I sat on his knee:
My first and my last was a false-hearted lover,
Under the shade of a bonny green tree.

'Come all ye young lassies, pray now take a warning,
And ne'er court a young man above your degree;
For love is a blossom that quickly will wither,
And you will be left as my lover left me.'

Scottish Studies, vol. 5, 1961.

An Aberdeen 'White Paternoster'

In 1957, during an Aberdeenshire field trip, I asked Jeannie Robertson to list as many children's rhymes – especially skipping and stotting songs – as she could remember. Here is one of these rhymes as recorded from Jeannie and her daughter Lizzie a few months later:

Ding dong the Catholic bells –
Fare you well, my mother.
Bury me in the old churchyard
Beside my oldest brother.

> My coffin shall be black,
>   Six little angels at my back:
> Two to preach and two to pray,
>   And two to carry my soul away.
>
> Ding dong the Catholic bells –
>   Fare you well, my mother.
> Bury me in the old churchyard
>   Beside my oldest brother.

Versions of this song, bearing close textual resemblance to the above, have been reported from other parts of Britain. Here is one from Cornwall, as preserved by the Revd Sabine Baring-Gould:

> Ding, dong, the parson's bell,
>   Very well my mother.
> I shall be buried in the old churchyard
>   By the side of my dear brother.
> My coffin shall be black,
>   Two little angels at my back,
> Two to watch, and two to pray,
>   And two to carry my soul away.
> When I am dead and in my grave,
>   And all my bones are rotten,
> Jesus Christ will come again
>   When I am quite forgotten.

According to Baring-Gould, this form of the rhyme was used on the Cornish moors, and was repeated by a boy at Alterton who had learned it from his aunt (Baring-Gould 1928: 32 Notes).

Jeannie and Lizzie chant their version with impressive solemnity, but in Edinburgh and London what is virtually the same rhyme does duty as a skipping song. Norman Douglas, in his *London Street Games*, supplies the following text:

> I am a little beggar-girl,
>   My mother she is dead,
> My father is a drunkard
>   And won't give me no bread.
> I look out of the window
>   To hear the organ play –
> God bless my dear mother,
>   She's gone far away.
> Ding-dong the castle bells
>   Bless my poor mother –
> Her coffin shall be black,
>   Six white angels at her back –
> Two to watch and two to pray,
>   And two to carry her soul away.

Douglas adds: 'Not a very cheerful rope-song, you'll say; but our girls love it; you can't think how it makes them laugh' (Douglas 1916: 71).

An almost identical version, 'I am a little orphan girl', which is also used as a skipping song and is rattled through at high speed, was recorded in 1950 by James Ritchie from children in the Norton Park School, Edinburgh. Alan Lomax included it on the *Scotland* LP (Vol. VI) of the Columbia World Library of Folk and Primitive Music. The only textual difference worth noting is that in place of lines 11 and 12 in Douglas's version, the Edinburgh children sing:

> My coffin shall be white,
> Six little angels by my side.

In the *Journal of the Folk-Song Society*, No 22, Annie Gilchrist has a note on 'The Lady Drest in Green', and other fragments of tragic ballads and folk-tales preserved among children. She prints a 'White Paternoster' offshoot, recorded from a little girl at Saunders Street Orphanage, Southport, in 1915, prefacing it with the statement that the verse was associated with a prose form of the ballad of 'Little Sir Hugh and the Jew's Daughter', Child 155). The final quatrain blends in curious fashion the funeral motif shared by all the foregoing, and a carefree bairnsang formula –

> Blue bells, cockle-shells,
> Bury me against my mother,
> Bury me in the old churchyard
> Against my dear mother.
>   (Gilchrist 1919: 86)

All these rhymes are descendants of the medieval 'White Paternoster' referred to by Chaucer in 'The Miller's Tale':

> Jhesu Crist, and seinte Benedight
> Blesse this hous from every wikked wight
> For nyghtes verye, the White Paternoster ...

One of the most familiar English variants is printed by Halliwell in his *Nursery Rhymes*:

> Matthew, Mark, Luke and John
> Guard the bed that I lay on.
>   Four corners to my bed,
>   Four angels round my head,
> One to watch, one to pray
> And two to bear my soul away.
>   (Halliwell 1843: CCXXIII)

Countess Martinengo-Cesaresco, who included a chapter on the 'White Paternoster' in her *Essays in the Study of Folksongs* (1886), states that the charm 'in the form of "Matthew, Mark, Luke and John" was, till lately, a not uncommon evening prayer in the agricultural parts of Kent ... Prayers that partake of the nature of charms have always been popular, and people have ever indulged in odd, little roundabout devices to increase the efficacy of even the most sacred words'.

Jeannie's mother Maria, who kept a little shop in the Gallowgate of Aberdeen, was the person from whom Jeannie first heard 'Ding dong the Catholic bells'. Maria also had a version of the 'parent' charm, and she often used to repeat it when putting the children to bed, or when going to bed herself. Here it is:

> As I lie down this night to sleep
>   I give my soul to Christ to keep.
> If I should die before I wake
>   I pray the Lord my soul to take.
> They are four corners in my bed
>   Holy angels laid and spread
> There's Matthew, Mark, Luke and John.
>   God bless the bed that I lie on.

According to Jeannie, her mother always added: 'Good night, sound sleep, and a surprise waukenin.'

The 'White Paternoster' is a widely diffused international charm. Versions in French, Provençal, German, Spanish and in various Italian dialects are on record. According to Seán Ó Súilleabháin, it is common throughout the Irish Gaeltacht (1952: 193, and note 296). The formula is referred to in the magical treatise *Enchiridion Papæ Leonis*, published in Latin at Rome in 1502. If recited three times in the evening and three times in the morning, it was supposed to ensure Paradise for the reciter. The Church of the Counter-Reformation, on the other hand, regarded the 'White Paternoster' as superstitious, and proscribed it.

From the frequency with which it has been reported, it would seem that the charm was once universally known in Christendom; by virtue of the fact that it invokes the protection of angels and evangelist-saints for the sleeper, it is 'white' – as opposed to 'black' – magic. Evidence is not lacking, however, that its Christian dress is not the first that it has worn. There is on record a Lincolnshire ague-charm, which was supposed to be repeated after three old horse-shoes had been nailed to the foot of the patient's bed, and a hammer placed cross-ways upon them; a local woman described it thus:

> 'I teks the mell (hammer) in my left 'and, and I taps them
> shoes, and I ses –
>> Feyther – Son – And Holy Ghost,
>> Nail the davil to the post;
>> Throice I stroikes with holy crook,
>> One for God, and one for Wod, and
>> one for Lok.'
>>   (Gilchrist 1919: 88)

Annie Gilchrist subjoins the following note to the above:

This curious blend of Christian superstition and Northern Mythology – Wod and Lok being (apparently) Wodin and Loki, and the hammer symbolic of Thor – suggests that the invocation of the four evangelists to guard each corner of the bed (their heads were sometimes carved as terminals to the posts) was only the successor of an older pre-Christian charm against the perils of the night, by the performance of which the bed-posts became the warder of the occupant.

It is not hard to see why a comforting little charm which promises a direct 'safe-conduct' to heaven if the reciter dies when asleep has become a sort of dance-dirge on the lips of skipping children. The association of sleep with death is made fearless and explicit in the 'White Paternoster', and the angels clustering around the bed-posts become in folk-imagination the 'white watch' convoying the sleeper beyond the grave to St Peter's gate. For children, who in their own way are coming to terms with the knowledge that death is a reality –

> Water, water wall-flower
> Growing up so high,
> We are all ladies,
> And we must all die –

this elemental folk-poetry is more than a 'cry in the street' – it is a joyful assertion of youth and life which names the bogey and (with vigorous thwack of the rope on the pavement) jumps over him, and lays him. The laughter of Norman Douglas's school children is like the Mexican *fiesta* of the dead; it is the exultation of a momentary triumph over the 'auld enemy'.

References

Baring-Gould, Revd Sabine (1928) *Songs of the West.* 7th edn in one vol. London.
Douglas, Norman (1916) *London Street Games.* London.
Gilchrist, Annie G. (1919) Note on 'The Lady Drest in Green', *Journal of the Folk-Song Society*, No 22: 86–90. London.
Halliwell, J. O. (1843) *The Nursery Rhymes of England.* 2nd edn. London.
Martinengo-Cesaresco, Countess (1886) *Essays in the Study of Folksongs*, London
Ó Súilleabháin, Seán (1952) 'Scéalta Cráibhtheacha', *Béaloideas* 21. Dublin.

Scottish Studies, vol. 6, 1962.

How a Bothy Song Came into Being

In the spring of 1952, while on a collecting tour in the Turriff area of Aberdeenshire, I was given the name of John MacDonald of Pitgaveny, Elgin, my informant assuring me that he knew many old songs. Not long after, I met Mr MacDonald for the first time. He is a mole-catcher and rat-catcher; in addition, he runs a flourishing local concert party, and is well known as a performer on the melodeon.

Among the first of his songs to be tape-recorded for the School's sound archive was 'The Rovin' Ploughboy', which he had listed among his favourites – he declared that it had 'a lovely air', which indeed it has. The following is a transcription of this recording (RL 935 A9).

Stanza 1. Briskly. ♩= 132   R.L. 935·9

Come sadd-le tae me my auld grey mare, Come sadd-le tae me my po-ny O, And I will tak' the road and we'll go far a-way Aft-er the rov-in' plough-boy O — Plough-boy O,

accompaniment (melodeon)

ploughboy O, I'll foll ow the rov-in' plough-boy O.

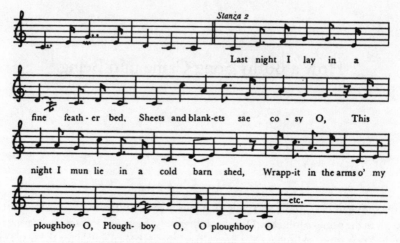

Come saddle tae me my auld grey mare
   Come saddle tae me my pony O
And I will take the road and we'll go far away.
   After the rovin' ploughboy O

    Chorus   Ploughboy O Ploughboy O
                 I'll follow the rovin' ploughboy O.

Last night I lay in a fine feather bed
   Sheets an' blankets sae cosy O.
This nicht I maun lie in a cold barn shed
   Wrappit in the arms o' my ploughboy O.

A champion ploughman my Geordie O –
   Cups an' medals an' prizes O.
In bonny Deveronside there are none can compare
   Wi' my jolly rovin' ploughboy O.

Sae fare ye weel tae auld Huntly toon
   Fare ye weel Drumdelgie O
For noo I'm on the road, and I'm goin' far away
   After the rovin' ploughboy O.

A month before the above recording was made, John had sent me a written text: this latter includes a verse which he did not sing. It goes as follows:

   Whit care I for a fine hoose an' land.
      Whit care have I for a fortune O?
   I'd far raither lie in a cold barn shed
      Wrapped in the arms o' my ploughboy O.

In the MS text, this verse is No 3, coming before 'A champion plough- man ...'.

   When I asked him about the origin of this song, John told me: 'I learned it off a ploughman my father had when I was a laddie – it was his father composed it, he said. His name was Donald MacLeod.'

Now it was immediately apparent to me that the first part of the song is nothing more nor less than a displaced fragment of a version of 'The Gypsy Laddie' (Child 200). Here are a few specimens of the 'parent' verses, as they appear in versions of the ballad printed by Child:

> 'Come saddle for me the brown,' he said,
>   'For the black was neer so speedy,
> And I will travel night and day
>   Till I find out my ladie.'
>   (Child 200 I 4)

> 'Yestreen I lay in a fine feather-bed,
>   And my gude lord beyond me;
> But this nicht I maun lye in some cauld tenant's-barn
>   A wheen blackguards waiting on me.'
>   (Child 200 C 6)

> 'O what care I for houses and land?
>   Or what care I for money?
> So as I have brewed, so will I return;
>   So fare you well, my honey!'
>   (Child 200 G 10)

The remaining two verses of 'The Rovin' Ploughboy' had obviously been added at a later stage. Was this where Donald MacLeod's father came in? My instinctive feeling was that the Aberdeenshire place-names were quite recent importations into the song – Drumdelgie, the famous 'fairm-toun up in Cairnie', is now known far beyond the North-East because of the bothy song which bears its name – and I had an idea that the singer could enlighten me on this point. A tentative question brought a perfectly plain and straightforward answer: the song as he had heard it, was 'a bittie short', and needed a better ending, so he had provided it himself.

So much for the words – but what of the tune? Was it related to any previously recorded tune for 'The Gypsy Laddie'? Looking into Gavin Greig's *Last Leaves*, I found that he had collected two tunes for the ballad, the first of which seemed clearly related to 'The Rovin' Ploughboy' tune. I am indebted to my colleague Gillian Johnstone for the following note: '[Tune] 1b [the second of the three variants of Tune 1 printed in *Last Leaves*] is very reminiscent of "The Rovin' Ploughboy"; its shape is broadly speaking the same, and it has the distinctive rising octave in the second line of the quatrain.'

Alexander Keith, editor of *Last Leaves*, appends the following note to the airs he prints for 'The Gypsy Laddie': 'Tune 1, which does not appear to have been printed before, is the usual, almost the only, air used in the north with this ballad' (Greig/Keith 1925: 128).

We have therefore a fascinating example before our eyes of the evolution of a bothy song. A fragment of Child 200 goes its own way and becomes a lyric song, some ploughman chiel or other following a time-honoured practice by substituting 'plough-man' for 'gipsy'. (It seems a fair guess that this was Donald MacLeod's father's principal contribution.) And when it reaches John MacDonald (himself a folk poet, with a number of songs to his credit), it acquires the local touches which give it its characteristic stamp – in effect, make it a North-East bothy song.

Interestingly enough, the process did not stop there, for when Jeannie Robertson heard 'The Rovin' Ploughboy' on tape, she at once spotted the connection between it and 'The Gypsy Laddie', and when I paid her a visit in Aberdeen only a very short time after she had first heard the tape, I found that she had already set a long version of the 'Child' ballad, got orally with a different air from her own folk, to the 'Ploughboy' tune. It only remains for somebody to use her re-created 'Gypsy Laddie' as the starting point for a new lyric song, and the wheel will have come full circle.

Reference

Greig, Gavin and Keith, Alexander (1925) *Last Leaves of Traditional Ballads and Ballad Airs*. Aberdeen.

Scottish Studies, vol. 5, 1961.

A Colliery Disaster Ballad

The Scottish miners have a rich folk-song, much of which understandably reflects the arduous nature of their work, and its ever-present perils. Disasters such as the Blantyre Explosion of 22 October 1877 and the Donibristle Moss Moran Disaster of 26 August 1901 have been movingly commemorated in rough-hewn ballad stanzas. The following song, never previously recorded, was obtained from Rab Morrison, a miner in his fifties, who is at present working in the Woolmet Colliery, Midlothian.

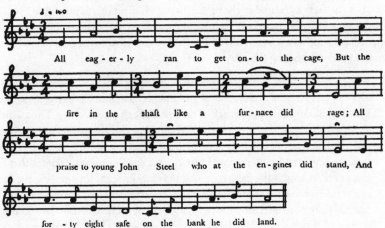

It was 18 and 70, Aprile the ninth day;
Ninety-six men and boys for their work took their way.
In health and in strength down the shaft they did go,
Never dreaming of how many would lie low.

For about twelve o'clock on that same fatal day,
'The pit-shaft's on fire!', the roadsman did say.
And quick through the workins the alarum he gave,
All praying to their maker their sweet lives to save.

All eagerly ran to get on to the cage,
But the fire in the shaft like a furnace did rage.
All praise to young John Steel who at the engine did stand,
And forty-eight safe on the bank he did land.

William Ralston, William Rushford and young David Muir,
By that terrible disaster you will see them no more.
Patrick and Peter M'Comiskie, aye, and Swanson likewise,
By that terrible disaster in their cold grave now lies.

Now widows and orphans who are now left to murn,
By that awful disaster they will never return.
But God is so merciful, as all mankind knows,
He will share in their sorrow, and soften their woes.

Rab Morrison, the singer, was born at Northrigg, two miles from Armadale, West
Lothian. His father was a miner. He started working in the pits when he was thirteen,
getting 1s 11d a day in the Woodend Colliery. Since then he has been all round the
Lothian pits, and has learned songs wherever he has gone.

He first heard the 'Starlaw Disaster' ballad sung when he was eighteen, but he had
seen the text of it before then; it was on a ½d broadsheet which his father had 'lying
about the house'. A young miner, Jimmy McGovern, knew the tune of the ballad, but
did not have much of the text; consequently, a fair exchange was promptly effected.

Rab thought the song was about the 'Blantyre Disaster' – this was, indeed, his title
for it – but the facts as related in the ballad do not confirm this supposition. The date,
and the names of the deceased, identify the event as the Starlaw Disaster, which
happened on Saturday 9 April 1870. The following account of it appeared in *The
Scotsman* on the following Monday:

> A colliery accident, by which seven men lost their lives, and several others were
> more or less seriously injured, took place at Starlaw, near Bathgate, on Saturday.
> It was caused by the wood work of the upcast shaft catching fire. The alarm was
> given a few minutes before noon, and at this time there were 56 men and boys in
> the pit. The work of extricating them was carried on under prodigious difficul-
> ties, the unfortunate men being literally dragged through the flames that filled
> the shaft. At length the cage rope was burned through, thus sealing the fate of
> seven men who remained in the pit, and whose bodies were not recovered till the
> fire had been got under, and the ventilation of the pit restored at a late hour in the
> evening. Of those who have been injured, one lies in a hopeless and another in a
> precarious condition.

On another page of the same issue of *The Scotsman*, a more detailed account of the
disaster shows that the words 'all praise to young John Steel' were amply deserved.
They refer to the engineman, James Steel, who saved the lives of most of his mates by
raising and lowering the cage with the utmost expedition.

> The attempt to quench the fire proved utterly futile. In spite of all the water that
> could be poured down, the flames kept gathering strength with frightful rapid-
> ity, till they blazed out with such violence as to render it almost impossible to
> approach the pit-mouth. Meanwhile, the brave Steel, though exposed to scorch-
> ing heat, stuck manfully to his engine, lowering and raising with the utmost
> precision the cage which formed the only hope of the poor miners below. Of
> course, only the cage in the downcast was available. The other being attached to

the same drum, had made two or three descents into the roaring furnace of the upcast, when the rope yielded to the fire, and it dropped to the bottom. Fortunately, the rope in the downcast held on for a few minutes longer, though it, too, caught fire shortly after the other. Thanks to Steel's nerve and presence of mind, no time was lost, the cage, we are told, being lowered and raised in little more than a minute. For five or six trips it came up loaded with miners, eight or nine men having in each case packed themselves into a space intended for four. So deftly was the operation managed, that as fast as the poor fellows, running from various distances in the workings, arrived at the pit bottom, the cage was there to receive them and whirl them aloft to safety. It may readily be supposed, however, that the passage to the open air, swift as it was, seemed all too long to the occupants of the cage. The wood-work of the apparatus caught fire; the iron-work was nearly red-hot; in the upcast shaft, separated from them only by a thin partition, a raging furnace threatened destruction; while the burning rope by which they were suspended seemed likely every instant to give way and leave them to their fate. So far, the actual progress of the fire had been confined to the upcast, but the down-draft carried the smoke and flame over the top of the partition into the downcast, and so into the pit, rendering the air quite stifling ... At length, after several batches of eight or nine each had been safely brought to bank, the cage on its next descent came up empty. By this time, the fire had burst through the top of the partition and was blazing in full volume from both sections of the shafts, cutting off all possibility of ventilation, and giving rise to the most serious apprehensions as to the safety of those still in the pit.

Four more men – one of whom, William Rankine, subsequently died – were brought to the surface by the heroic James Steel; then the rope broke, and all hope for the seven miners still below had to be abandoned. Here are the names of the doomed seven, as printed in the newspaper:

> James McNeill (45) leaves widow and four children.
> William Rushford (35), widow and five children.
> John McNeil (35), widow and five children.
> William Wands (22), three months married.
> Peter Comiskie (27), widow and one child.
> Patrick Comiskie (24), widow and one child.
> William Muir (17), unmarried.

Exactly a week after the disaster, a meeting of Lothian miners (convened at the instance of Alexander MacDonald, President of the National Association of Mineworkers) was held in the Masonic Hall, Dalkeith. MacDonald spoke ('to a crowded hall') about the Mines Regulation Bill, then before Parliament. He declared that the then prevailing system of mine inspection was a farce, and that the government inspections were mere 'accident enquiries'. The new Bill should, he said, provide for heavy penalties in cases where mine owners failed to provide adequate safeguards, and where culpable negligence led to loss of life.

By late April, the campaign to secure amendments to the Mines Regulation Bill, a shilling advance in wages and shorter hours had gathered such momentum that MacDonald decided to issue an appeal for a one-day strike:

> I would take the liberty of suggesting that you would suspend labour in every colliery, in every district, in every mining county in Scotland on the 13th or 14th of May. (Page Arnot 1955: 51)

Meanwhile, the balladmaker was probably already at work. The *Scotsman* report, quoted above, is proof that the song provides an excellent factual précis of the event; it is both chronicle and elegy. We may safely infer that the author was a miner-balladeer who composed the song almost immediately after the disaster. 'It goes to the heart, the thought of the pitman stirred by the drama of some strike or disaster, who sits by candle-light with a blunt pen in his fist, staring at a piece of paper on which he has written the opening phrase: "Come all ye bold miners ...", and who wrestles by scratch and score with his rough, stubborn muse, till day dawns and the pit buzzer blows, and another ballad has come bawling or timorous into the world' (Lloyd 1952: 17).

One of the dead miners, as we have seen, was a boy of seventeen. No wonder, therefore, that the unknown balladmaker chose for his tune a variant of a familiar Scottish tune for 'The Bonny Boy is Young But he's Growing' – the exquisite elegiac ballad, not in Child, which Cecil Sharp called 'Still Growing'. Although it has been collected all over the British Isles, and in America, 'Still Growing' is very likely of Scottish origin. Robert Burns collected a fragment of it, and 'embellished' it with other stanzas of his own composition (Johnson 1792: No 377). James Maidment prefaced the version ('The Young Laird of Craigston') which he printed in *A North Countrie Garland* (1824) with a circumstantial historical note identifying the 'bonnie lad' with John Urquhart, Lord Craigston, who was married to a girl several years his senior, and died in 1634 while still a youth. Maidment's version retains some prosaic details ('He's likewise possessed of many bills and bonds') which suggest that it is an 'ancestor' variant of 'Still Growing' as it now circulates, and not merely an early Scottish localisation.

In 1960, I recorded from Lizzie Higgins (daughter of Jeannie Robertson) a version of 'Still Growing' which she had learned in the tattie-fields of Angus. The text of this version is as follows:

> O father, dear father, pray, what is this you've done?
> You have wed me to a college boy, a boy that's far too young.
> For he is only seventeen and I am twenty-one.
> He's my bonny, bonny boy, and he's growing.
>
> For we were going through college, and some boys were
> playing ball
> When there I saw my own true love, the fairest of them all.
> When there I saw my own true love, the fairest of them all –
> He's my bonny, bonny boy, and he's growing.
>
> For at the age of sixteen years he was a married man,
> And at the age of seventeen the father of a son.
> And at the age of twenty-one he had become a man,
> But the green grass o'er his grave it was growin'.
>
> I will buy my love some flannel, I will make my love's shroud;
> With every stitch I put in it, the tears will flow down.
> With every stitch I put in it, the tears will flow down,
> And that put an end to his growin'.

I am indebted to my colleague Gillian Johnstone for the following note on the resemblance between Rab's tune for the 'Starlaw Disaster', and the haunting melody for 'The Bonny Boy' sung by Lizzie Higgins.

The resemblance between these two tunes is indeed striking, and may be seen very obviously in the norms. It must be realised that these 'norms' never actually occur in performance, and may never have occurred; but on the evidence of all the renderings for the several verses, and taking into consideration the normal pattern of spoken word-stresses, it is possible to find a version which may form a kind of ideal, purely conceptual, of which all actual renderings are variations. In the norm here I have transposed Lizzie Higgins's tune from E^b to A^b to facilitate comparison.

Both melodies have a simple four-line structure, the first AB, CD, C^{1}D, and AB, and the second a little more complicated, ab, cd, cd^1, b^1 b-shortened. There are two main differences between them, in phrase endings and in degree of ornamentation, and I would like to suggest that these are modifications of a single tune under the influence of two very different traditions of singing style and applied to two different types of song.

Rab Morrison has the classical ballad style, where the melody is the vehicle for the words but does not enhance them except in a very general way. It is a narrative style, with a steady, fairly fast movement, carrying the listener through a series of events in different moods, moods which are rarely commented on by the singer in his rendering. The structure of the song is foursquare, each line considered basically a unit, as in spoken ballads, and each mid-line phrase ending carrying the melody directly on to the next phrase. Lizzie Higgins, in contrast, has a much slower, more declamatory, expressive way of singing, and this demands ornamentation. Not only are all possible gaps in the basic melody filled with repeated and adjacent notes, but grace-notes are found in addition to these. 'The Bonny Boy' is a one-mood song, and the melody has a dramatic shape of its own. It opens prosaically, not even a modulation disturbing or quickening the even flow of the first line. This turns out to be an effective introduction to the bold emotional heights and depths of the second and third lines. The song finishes with a quiet tailpiece of a fourth line, in a delicate contrasting rhythm, its finality and plathos emphasised by the shortened last phrase. The second and third lines have a four-part structure of their own, with a sustained climax in the middle of each which is perfectly

Norm 1 (Rab Morrison, "The Starlaw Disaster")

Norm 2 (Lizzie Higgins, "The Bonny Boy")

borne by the repeated notes at the end of the first phrase and beginning of the second. The modulation at the end of the third line provides a breakwater for the emotion and prepares the listener for the relief and balancing effect of the fourth.

Thus the modifications of the norms evolved in the different singing styles are seen to be functional, and the two songs, basically so alike, perhaps indeed the same, turn out to be in detail and effect so very different.

References

Johnson, James (1792) *The Scots Musical Museum*. Vol. IV. Edinburgh.
Lloyd, A. L. (1952) *Come All Ye Bold Miners*. London.
Maidment, James (1824) *A North Countrie Garland*. Edinburgh.
Page Arnot, R. (1955) *A History of the Scottish Miners*. London.
Sharp, Cecil (1904) *Folksongs from Somerset*, Vol. I. London.

Transcriptions and Musical Notes by Gillian Johnstone

Scottish Studies, vol. 6, 1962.

The Buckie Wife

The present folk-song revival has already thrown up some excellent folk poets. In Glasgow there is Matt McGinn, a native of the Gallowgate, whose songs have all the smeddum and sardonic verve of a great proletarian city. Edinburgh has (among others) Bob Bertram, who has written over fifty songs in the last five months. Some of these are mere ephemeral squibs about current affairs such as the Profumo imbroglio, but others look as if they might prove more durable.

These song-writers are nearly all products of the folk-song clubs which have sprung up all over Britain in the last two years. The clubs often invite famous traditional singers such as Jeannie Robertson to sing to their predominantly youthful audiences, and the results are nearly always beneficial; the introduction to the world of traditional song thus afforded stimulates the more gifted of the club members not only to sing but also to create in the 'auld style'. In one or two cases, the results have been extraordinary.

Before he began visiting the evening sessions in the Waverley Bar, St Mary's Street, Bob Bertram had never had any knowledge of, or interest in, Scottish folk-music. Although born in Melbourne, Australia, he has lived nearly all his life in Edinburgh. He went to Niddrie Marischal school, left it at fourteen, and after six months in a biscuit factory and two years in the army he got a job with Scott's, the wholesale ironmongers in the Grassmarket. At present he is working in the costing department.

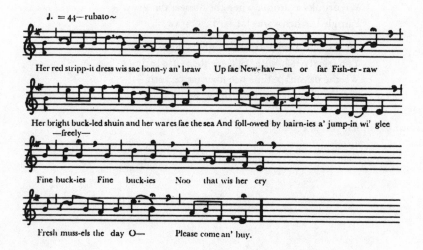

For most of his songs Bob takes over and adapts already existing tunes in the time-honoured fashion, but he has also composed some striking original tunes of his own. The air of 'The Buckie Wife' is somewhat reminiscent of a gangrel family of Irish ballad tunes, but it has its own very marked identity. Bob says that the song 'is about life in Edinburgh, when the Newhaven fisherwives used to come around selling buckies and mussels, and actually it echoes a lot of the thoughts … and the scenes I witnessed when I was a boy.' It was given its first public performance during my seminar on 'Scots Folk-Song Today' in the school of Scottish Studies in November 1963.

When I was a laddie in Auld Reekie toon,
I looked for the buckie wife comin' aroon –
Wi' a creel on her back, and a strap tae her broo;
In each hand a tin pitcher o' mussels quite fu'.

Chorus
Fine buckies
Fine buckies
Noo that wis her cry.
Fresh mussels the day O
Please come an' buy.

Her red-strippit dress was sae bonny an' braw,
Up frae Newhaven, or far Fisherraw.
Her bright buckled shuin, and her wares fae the sea,
And followed by bairnies a' jumpin' wi' glee.

A' shoutin' for buckies, as roon her were seen;
Each wi' a poke and a wee tiny peen.
If we wanted mussels, wi' spoons there we ate,
And supped them a' up fae oot o' a plate.

And late at night, when the pubs a' shut doon,
It's there she'd be seen at the tap o' the toon;
Wi' drunks a' aroon, when the hunger did gnaw –
Fair gled o' her wares fae far Fisherraw.

Bit alas and alack, noo, this sight is quite rare.
Yon frienly fish-wife we'll see there nae mair;
Wi' the passin' o' time nae mair tae be seen –
The buckies, the mussels, the wee tiny peen.

Scottish Studies, vol. 8, 1964.

'The Lassies in the Coogate'

Among the many rhymes inherited by Jeannie Robertson from her mother is the following bairn sang:

> The lassies in the Coogate
> Kaim doon their yallow hair;
> The lassies in the Coogate,
> They sing for evermair.
> But woe be to the rovin' boys
> That sings the rantum voo,
> And woe be to the sailor lads
> That fills the lassies fu'.

The lass-ies in the Coo-gate kaim doon their yall-ow hair The

lass-ies in the Coo-gate they sing for ev-er — mair But

woe be to the rov-in' boys that sings the rant-um voo And

woe be to the sail-or lads that fills the lass-ies fu'.

Jeannie thought that this was just a fragment, and when I first recorded it (Sept. 1954) she stated that her mother had had more of it, but that this was all that she (Jeannie) could remember.

In *A Ballad Book*, edited by Charles Kirkpatrick Sharpe (1823), there is a short song (No 2) which goes as follows:

> The lasses o' the Canongate,
> O, they are wond'rous nice, –

They winna gie a single kiss,
　　But for a double price.

Gar hang them, gar hang them,
　　Heich upon a tree,
For we'll get better up the gate,
　　For a bawbee.

Sharpe adds a note saying that this song and No 3 'I'll gar our gudeman trow' were 'remembered thirty years ago, by an Old Gentlewoman'. No 2 'seems to be a satire on the Court Ladies of Edinburgh'.

The 'lasses o' the Canongate' in Jeannie's version have become the 'lassies in the Coogate', but the length of the caustic little squib preserved by Sharpe is the same as that of the Aberdeen street song. It seems possible, therefore, that Jeannie's sprightly eight-line song, which has never been recorded from anyone else, contains a thin echo of the days when Edinburgh was a capital with a court, and court ladies, and a stylish Holyrood *demi-monde*.

A' doun alang the Canongate were beaux o' ilk degree,
And mony ane turned roun' to look at bonnie Mally Leigh.
　　　　　　　　　　　　　　　　　　　　(Ford 1904: 177).

If the two items are related, the song has clearly suffered a drop in social status, and the high-born ladies have turned into somewhat blowzier street-walkers; on the other hand, what was little more than a coarse gibe has become a vivid lyric of Auld Reekie low-life, reminiscent of some of Fergusson's and Burns's essays in the same genre.

References

Ford, Robert (1904) *Vagabond Songs and Ballads of Scotland* (one-vol edn). Paisley.
Sharpe, Charles Kirkpatrick (1823) *A Ballad Book*. Edinburgh.

Scottish Songs at Work

Donald MacCormick. *Hebridean Folksongs: A Collection of Waulking Songs*. Partly translated by Allan McDonald. Completed and edited by J. L. Campbell. Tunes transcribed by Francis Collinson. 375pp. Clarendon Press: Oxford University Press.

Sixty years ago, Mrs Kennedy-Fraser, who had been collecting folk-songs in the Western Isles with the help of primitive recording apparatus, published the first volume of *Songs of the Hebrides*. This consisted not of the actual material she had found but of exceedingly skilful musical arrangements, and Gaelic texts accompanied by rather ornate translations by the Revd Kenneth MacLeod. This attractive 'tartan box' enjoyed almost immediately an enormous popular success.

The merits and demerits of Mrs Kennedy-Fraser's work have often been discussed. On the credit side, it must be said that she and her collaborator drew the attention of the world to the extraordinary richness of folk-song and folk-music in the Highlands and Islands, and particularly in the Outer Hebrides. The snag was that so many liberties, both musical and textual, had been taken that a very misleading idea of Scottish Gaelic folk-song was implanted in the public mind.

The denaturing of much of the material – in the most blatant cases caricaturing is hardly too strong a word – is nowhere more evident than in the case of the waulking songs included in her collection. These were the work songs which accompanied the hand-fulling or waulking of new-woven cloth; intimately linked to the hard manual labour at the waulking-board, whose motive power (so to speak) they provided, these superb songs were naturally recalcitrant to the process of transmogrification into concert-hall pieces. It is true that one or two folklorists – Annie Gilchrist, for example – did point this out at the time, while drawing attention to the happily undoctored versions in Frances Tolmie's collection (published in the *Journal of the Folksong Society*, No IV, 1911). But the effective unravelling of this tangle has been the work of present-day folklorists working first with wire-recorders, and then with the new and improved tape-recorders which have revolutionised folklore collecting in the past twenty-two years. Pre-eminent among these are Dr John Lorne Campbell and his wife, Margaret Fay Shaw; their indefatigable labours have illuminated much of the 'Celtic twilight' obfuscations of the Gaelic folk-scene. The late Dr Calum I. MacLean, of the School of Scottish Studies, also played a major part in this work before his tragically early death in 1960.

The present volume, to which Francis Collinson has contributed meticulously accurate transcriptions and valuable ethnomusicological notes, is a milestone in Celtic folk-music research. It is the culmination not only of Dr Campbell's own collecting but also of his devoted editorial work on the Nachlass of Fr Allan McDonald of Eriskay, a remarkable priest who pioneered the linguistic survey of Hebridean Gaelic dialects, and did intensive folklore collecting around the turn of the century – at a time, therefore, when the popular traditions of the Outer Isles were still in full flower.

References in Fr Allan's folklore notebooks to a collection of waulking songs made in 1893 by Donald MacCormick, of Kilphedar, South Uist, started a search which ended (by happy accident, it seems) when a document sent more or less out of the blue turned out to be the long-lost notebook.

The texts brought together by MacCormick are printed here as well as three songs collected by Fr Allan. Tunes – in several cases, with two or more variants – are provided for all but one of the forty items. The tunes are transcriptions of Dr Campbell's own recordings, made from 1938 onwards. Textual and musical examination shows that this at first sight risky rapprochement of words and airs from different sources is eminently justified.

Here, then, for the first time, are the Gaelic waulking songs, presented as well as the printed page can do it. What is displayed is a surging, pounding, maelstrom of song, into which has been drawn material from the most disparate sources: love songs, hunting songs, flytings, eulogies, laments, and even swatches of versified folk narrative. Very few – No XXVI here is an exception – make a unitary impression of connected meaning. Elements have become locked together, and have disengaged, some changes probably occurring in the free flow of improvisation – the result perhaps of the momentary whim of some long-dead soloist – and others (one senses) corresponding to a deep underlying aesthetic pattern. As in rowing songs documented in various cultures – for example (to remain in Scotland) the 'dreg songs' of the oyster fishers of the Firth of Forth, also investigated by Francis Collinson – hard physical labour imposes its own overmastering will on diverse material, often producing (when the song is heard) a surprising impression of coherence and unity. Publication of MacCormick's texts clears the causeway for a detailed structural analysis of the morphological relationships which might well be shown to exist between the various 'mobile props' and lyrical commonplaces which sustain these truly fabulous song-poems. It is the study of this sort of material, like the study of the Yugoslav folk-epics which have lived on into this century, which can help to illuminate the nature of 'Homer's music'.

The poetry of the waulking songs – which the modern Gaelic poet Sorley MacLean has referred to as one of the finest achievements of Scottish culture – resides in its nature as the intimate song-poetry of the women. Here, at the waulking-board, where the surge and beat of the song often reaches a pitch which one can only call ecstatic, the whole inner life of the women comes to the surface in uninhibited self-expression; desire scorn, reproach, desolation – all the sexual joys and agonies of the women come pouring out like a burn in spate. One feels, at times, that all this emotion is only bearable because it is confined between the banks of traditional formulaic utterance. One understands, too, the good sense of the Hebridean doctor who (according to Alexander Carmichael) advised a woman suffering from some mental or emotional disturbance to attend the waulkings.

On the editorial side, Dr Campbell supplies introductory notes on the metres of the songs; on what is known of the waulking process itself from travellers' accounts, and other sources; on the waulking song as a 'literary' art form in the work of eighteenth-century Gaelic poets such as Alasdair MacMhaighstir Alasdair; and on the attempts of Mrs Kennedy-Fraser and others to use waulking songs as the basis for their own musical compositions. Mr Collinson is lucid and enlightening on the 'waulking pulse', on the scales of the tunes, on the variations to be found in these, and on their musical form. (Here, MacCormick's precise descriptions in his notebook of the manner of singing the songs – e.g., 'a third of the refrain is always to be sung after every line, besides which the refrain is to be sung twice when the rhyme is changed' – usefully supplement the evidence of actual recordings.)

Mr Collinson is alive to features which link traditional Celtic music and modern urban 'pop-folk' culture, as when he observes, referring to the dotted rhythm characteristic of much Gaelic song, that it 'approximates to the dance-band interpretation of dotted rhythm, particularly by the saxophone team in popular dance numbers'. Dr Campbell and Mr Collinson join forces to provide a fascinating chapter on the meaningless refrain syllables which 'may possess a very remarkable antiquity'.

One major criticism of the book must be made; this relates to the English versions which face MacCormick's Gaelic texts. These are either the translations by Fr McDonald which supplied the first pointer to the existence of MacCormick's notebook, or else (where English versions by Fr Allan could not be found) translations 'completed in Fr Allan McDonald's style'. In view of Dr Campbell's faithful and painstaking stewardship, one can well understand the reasons which impelled him to use Fr Allan's translations rather than others. However, remembering the sad history of tinselly glamorisation which has so often made translations of Gaelic song poetry ridiculous – Dr Campbell himself quotes with approval Agnes Mure MacKenzie's remark about 'the dreadful soulfulness' of the English versions in *Songs of the Hebrides* – it is disconcerting to find that one can still be faced with the sort of translation capable of throwing up a line as ugly and impenetrable as –

None did I nor aught so wrong am

– and even of thinking up a weird nonsense like 'Weema' (for *muime*, 'foster-mother'). 'Clownish fledgling' for *balach*, which here simply means 'boy', is an exceedingly unpalatable mouthful, and 'while I gently did caress you' is not an adequate equivalent for a Gaelic line which means 'and my hand on your white breasts'. Phrases like 'I am a-phrenzied' are all too frequent. The English text is not even free of ordinary errors, such as 'grandson' for *an t-seannduin'*. Furthermore, the jog-trot metre employed conjures up on almost every page incongruous echoes of Hiawatha:

Thou my darling art my heart's one,
Son of him from gabled castle.
Well I know the style you're heir to. ...

At their best, these translations are watery dilutions of the strong poetry of the Gaelic texts; at their worst, they are travesties. This is really a shame, for it leaves a bad blemish on a good book. What is needed now is for a poet such as Iain Crichton Smith, equally at home in Gaelic and English, to make worthy English translations which would give some idea of the rare eloquence of the originals.

The Times Literary Supplement, 29 May 1970.

Folk-song Heritage of the North-East

The Greig/Duncan Folk Song Collection Vol. 1. Editors: Patrick Shuldham-Shaw and Emily B. Lyle. Published by Aberdeen University Press for Aberdeen University in association with the School of Scottish Studies, Edinburgh University.

Why are some communities richer in folk-song than others? For the last two centuries at least, the contribution of the North-East of Scotland to the sum total of our traditional song has been exceptionally high.

The eighteenth century saw the publication of David Herd's magnificent collection, the roots of which are undoubtedly in the North-East, and the most famous single figure in Scots ballad-history – Mrs Brown of Falkland, née Anna Gordon – provided the cognoscenti with ballad-texts of extraordinary literary quality which have continued to be argued over to the present day.

Aberdeenshire has continued to supply collectors with fine folk-song of every description, as the archives of the School of Scottish Studies amply testify.

It must always be remembered that it takes two (at least) to record a folk-song or folk-tale: the informant and the collector. The North-East has been lucky in that it has thrown up in practically every generation a thoughtful, knowledgeable and painstaking collector who has acted as a 'remembrancer' of North-East traditional song.

Indeed, at the beginning of this century it threw up two – Gavin Greig, a country dominie who from 1876 until his death in 1914 was headmaster of Whitehill School, near New Deer, in the heart of Buchan – and the Revd James Bruce Duncan, United Free Kirk minister of Lynturk, near Alford, who joined with his 'yoke fellow' in a grandiose project to put on record the entire traditional song-literature of the North-East, as it existed in their day.

Both men were assiduous – one might even say fanatical – workers, and by the outbreak of the First World War, they had gathered in a harvest that one can truthfully call 'a burstin' kirn'.

It consisted of 3,050 folk-song texts and 3,100 folk-song tunes, one of the largest collections of traditional song material in the world. Greig and Duncan did not live to put their work in proper order, and since their day it has remained a permanent challenge to Scottish folklorists and ballad scholars.

This does not mean, of course, that it remained totally unutilised. In 1925 the late Alexander Keith produced for the Buchan Club a volume which brought together a large number of the texts and tunes of the 'Child' or classic ballads in the Greig/Duncan Collection, and this book (*Last Leaves of Traditional Ballads and Ballad Airs collected in Aberdeenshire*) rapidly attained an international celebrity: it showed the world of folk-song scholarship that excellent versions of the classic ballads were still being sung in the North-East of Scotland in the early years of this century.

More significantly, however, the Gavin Greig Collection (housed behind a rather forbidding looking iron grille in King's College Library, Aberdeen) served as a mine of information and stimulation for a corps of young folk-song *aficionados*, and it was appropriately enough a great-grandson of Gavin Greig – the late Arthur Argo – who acted as energiser and catalyst in the good cause of restoring North-East folk-song to the folk – and particularly to the young.

In so doing he was in a sense repeating a service which Greig himself had provided for the singers of the North-East when he published a series of articles in the *Buchan Observer* between December 1907 and June 1911.

These articles served a double purpose. First and foremost, they were a valuable and efficient collecting tool, for the readers of the *'Buchanie'* sent in versions of songs Greig was prospecting for, and sometimes supplied new leads to entirely fresh material. However, these articles had in reality a vastly more important role: they were the means by which a general interest in the folk-song of the North-East was re-invigorated throughout the area.

It is quite likely that a good number of songs – or versions of songs – that might otherwise have died were kept going by Greig's *'Buchanie'* articles, and consequently it is not inappropriate to think of the years immediately preceding the First World War as the 'Gavin Greig Revival'.

In the early 1970s a determined effort got underway to 'do the right thing' by the great collection, and make it accessible both to the world of international folk-song scholarship and to the general reader. This was clearly going to be a colossal task, but the late Patrick Shuldham-Shaw faced it undaunted, and before his untimely death in 1976 he had laid a firm foundation for the work which Dr Emily B. Lyle is now committed to bring to completion.

Her edition is to appear in eight volumes and the first – containing nautical, military, and historical songs – has just appeared. The later volumes will contain narrative songs; songs of the countryside and of home and social life; songs of courtship, night-visiting songs, and songs about particular people; and (last but not least) love songs (the Greig/Duncan Collection is extremely rich in exquisite lyric love songs). The final volume will contain – in addition to songs of parting, children's songs, and nonsense songs – general notes and commentaries on the entire collection, together with complete indexes.

Vol. 1 (beautifully produced by Aberdeen University Press) is in itself a monumental achievement of devoted folk-song scholarship on the part of both editors. As most of the tunes were written out in staff notation by Greig and Duncan, it has been possible to reproduce these photographically.

The texts, which were transcribed by the collectors into 70 notebooks (64 of these Greig's), are given in full with a minimum of editorial emendation – the latter being occasionally necessary for the sake of clarity and coherence.

The traditional division of folk-song into classic (or 'Child') ballads and 'the rest' (second-class citizens) has been sensibly rejected by the editors, and consequently songs such as 'Sir Patrick Spens' and 'The Mermaid' appear alongside more recent sailors' songs such as 'Andrew Ross' (a harrowing account of the sufferings of a young Orkney sailor at the hands of a brutal ship's captain), 'The Loss of The Nightingale', and 'The Bold Princess Royal' (a stirring ballad of attempted piracy on the high seas).

Following the soldiers' songs, which illuminate and enrich social history by providing us with the poor folk's reaction to recruiting sergeants, brutal military discipline, and the rigours of hard-fought campaigns, there is a section of songs 'in which characters adopt the dress of the opposite sex'.

These songs are quite numerous enough to warrant a section of their own. They represent the wish-fulfilment of a masculine society which, denied female companionship, compensates by inventing for itself a flighty insubstantial corps of handsome cabin boys, bold female halberdiers, and intrepid drummer girls.

Ironically, there is substantial eighteenth-century evidence that quite a number of women did in fact manage to join up and fight alongside their menfolk. Maybe this is one of the cases where folk-song can help to flesh out the bare bones of an over-etiolated historical record.

Glasgow Herald, 12 December 1981.

This Scorching, Sunburnt Land of Hell

The 'new' countries have always, understandably, been interested in their folk-song – in the popular culture which expresses their exploit and dream. This leads, among their scholars, to an interest in the nature of popular culture itself. It was no accident that the greatest ballad editor of the English-speaking (and Scots-speaking) world was an American – Francis James Child.

The *Penguin Book of Australian Ballads* is a lyric history of the big boy of the Antipodes. Quite rightly, it interprets the word 'ballad' in a strictly non-purist sense. The convicts who were transported to Botany Bay did not care whether the songs they sang were from London broadsides or were the rough-hewn productions of the involuntary colonists. Anything which lifted the horror of their lives to a level above brutal experience was poetry. Looking at it from this distance in space and time, we realise (maybe not without astonishment) that it often *is* poetry.

Take these lines of 'Frank the Poet' (Francis MacNamara, a Dubliner transported for uttering forged notes in 1819) in Russel Ward's book:

> Early in the morning when day is dawning,
>   To trace from heaven the morning dew,
> Up we are started at a moment's warning,
>   Our daily labour to renew.
> Our overseers and superintendents –
>   These tyrants' orders we must obey,
> Or else at the triangles our flesh is mangled –
>   Such are our wages at Moreton Bay!
>
> For three long years I've been beastly treated;
>   Heavy irons each day I wore;
> My back from flogging has been lacerated,
>   And oftimes painted with crimson gore.
> Like the Egyptians and ancient Hebrews,
>   We were oppressed under Logan's yoke,
> Till kind Providence came to our assistance,
>   And gave this tyrant his mortal stroke.

Reading these lines, one realises why they speak with such poignant lyric eloquence. The reason is that they sing. They are in the direct line of descent from the anonymous Leinster bards who hymned Father Murphy's exploits in the rising of 1798 – and indeed, they can be sung to the same tune:

O come all ye heroes, and renowned nobles,
    Give ear unto my warlike theme,
And I will tell you of Father Murphy,
    How he lately roused from his sleeping dream.
Sure Julius Caesar, nor Alexander,
    Nor the brave King Arthur never equalled him,
For armies formidable he has conquered,
    Though with two gunmen he did begin.

In his excellent *Penguin Australian Song Book* (which 'accompanies' the *Australian Ballads*) my old friend John Manifold prints two tunes for this song. One is related, as we might expect, to the tune which Colm O Lochlainn prints, in his *Irish Street Ballads*, for one of the Father Murphy songs; it is also, more or less, the tune that McCall used for his 'Boolavogue'. No wonder, then, that a sizeable contingent of the items in both books derives from the Irish ballad tradition.

Not all, however. Manifold prints a song, 'My Last Farewell to Stirling', which is at least as good as any of the Van Diemen's Land songs. It was first recorded in Aberdeen-shire by Gavin Greig, and since then has been recorded, here and there, off and on, by the School of Scottish Studies. It has an exceedingly beautiful elegiac tune. A collated version, based on two of the variants in the school's archives, was supplied by me to Ewan MacColl for his *Scotland Sings*, and it seems likely that this is the ultimate source of the version printed by John Manifold. However, it makes no odds. If it was not an Australian ballad before, it will certainly become one, thanks to this book.

The sections 'Pastoral Australia' and 'The Nomads' in Manifold's book, and 'Traditional Bush Ballads' in Russel Ward's, bring a whole epoch of Australian history before our eyes, with a violent immediacy which no factual historical account could possibly equal. Take these lines from 'The Great Australian Adjective':

He came up to a bloody creek;
The bloody horse was bloody weak;
    The creek was full, and bloody floody.
He said, 'This moke must sink or swim,
The same for me as bloody him:
    Bloody! Bloody! Bloody!'

This is a folk-variant of a 'literary' bush ballad – as opposed to an 'anon' bush ballad – but, as Russel Ward points out: 'The popular 'folk' character of much balladry of this period is indicated by the fact that practically nothing, beyond their names, is known of many balladists, even of prolific ones.' A close study of a period such as this can throw light on the processes of creation of our own classic ballads.

On 23 October 1942 the 9th Australian Division went into action at El Alamein, and knocked hell out of the enemy. The 51st Highland Division was doing the same thing, at the same time. I like to think that the *élan* and fury of these Scots and Australians, which broke the 'German iron', sprang – to a certain extent, at least – from this old rebel strain, that speaks out so clear in their balladry, and ours. Good-o, my lucky lads, and down with the wowsers!

Scots Magazine, September 1965.

Edinburgh University Folk-song Society

On 18 April 1958 the first meeting of a newly founded Edinburgh University Folk-song Society was held in the SRC Hall, Old College. The aim of the Society was described by its President, Stuart MacGregor, as the provision of a forum for discussion, and of a 'folk-song workshop' in which student balladmakers and singers could learn their craft, swop songs and extend their knowledge of the traditional music of Scotland and other countries.

In order to encourage its members to learn direct from authentic traditional singers, the Society had invited Jeannie Robertson of Aberdeen to be guest artist at this inaugural meeting. Jeannie contributed three of her already famous classical ballad versions, 'Son David' (= the 'Edward' ballad, Child 13), 'Harlaw' (Child 163) and 'The Twa Brithers' (Child 49), together with several other North-East folk-songs. Among the other singers were two young Americans, Christopher Wren of Marlow, New Hampshire, and Danny Botkin of New York, both of whom have done a considerable amount of field collecting on their own account in the United States. Danny Botkin, a physicist, is the son of the distinguished American folklorist Professor B. A. Botkin, author of *The American Play-Party Song*, and of a classic work on the Southern slave states, *Lay My Burden Down*.

Also present at the first meeting was Norman Buchan, then a Glasgow schoolmaster, who gave an account of his work in popularising Scots folk-song among Rutherglen schoolchildren.

The second meeting of the Society was devoted to examples of the 'Love Song'; these were provided by singers from Japan, Hungary, Canada, the USA and the Isle of Lewis. The third ('North American Folk-song') was the proper occasion for a little friendly rivalry between the two Americans already mentioned, and Pat Fulford, a Canadian girl then studying at the College of Art.

The fourth, held on 23 May, was a public ceilidh, at which Calum MacLean, School of Scottish Studies, acted as *fear an tighe*.

Scottish Studies, vol. 2, 1958.

Scots Folk-song: A Select Discography

Part 1

Western man, being attuned to books as the repositories of learned culture, has taken quite a long time to adjust to the idea of recorded sound as a legitimate adjunct to the printed library. Phonograph recordings of oral material were consequently for a lengthy period very definitely 'second-class citizens' in the academic world, even when they were accompanied by extensive documentation, and edited with careful scholarship. In protesting against this state of affairs in the late 1940s the voice of Compton Mackenzie was so lone as to appear positively eccentric. Pioneers in this still disputed field were Americans; they were the officials of the Library of Congress who supported the work of John A. Lomax and his friends and allies. The School of Scottish Studies was comparatively late in the race – only beginning to bring out its Scottish Tradition series in the 1970s – although in fairness to individual collectors it should be recorded that the first proposal (over the names of Calum I. MacLean and other staff members) for a School of Scottish Studies record series goes back over twenty years.

Between the wars Beltona records brought out quite a number of 78s of Gaelic and Scots folk-song; these included rumbustious renderings of Aberdeenshire bothy songs by Willie Kemp and George Morris of Old Meldrum. It was not, however, until the LP appeared on the scene, and the American record companies began to display a very laudable interest in Scottish folk music, that something like justice began to be done to the enormous 'underground' of our native folk scene.

First in the field by a long chalk was Columbia, which in 1950 commissioned Alan Lomax (son of John, and previously head of the Archive of American Song in the Library of Congress) to compile and edit a series of LPs entitled 'World Library of Folk and Primitive Music', and liaise with the various folklore institutes that were willing to co-operate. In Scotland, there being as yet no School of Scottish Studies, he found himself obliged to operate through individual collectors. Calum MacLean gave him invaluable guidance in the Highlands and the Hebrides, and the present writer assisted him in the North-East. The result was Vol. VI (Scotland) of the Columbia World Library of Folk and Primitive Music (SL209); this had Gaelic song on the one side and Lallan song on the other. First published in 1953, it remains to this day a stimulating and by no means unrepresentative 'sampler' of one of the richest and most variegated folk music traditions in Western Europe.

It is Side 1 (the Lowlands) which concerns us here. It includes John Strachan's splendid version of the classic ballad 'Glenlogie' (Child 238); the same singer's 'Tinkler's Waddin' and 'The Bonnie Lass of Fyvie'; Jimmy MacBeath's gallus 'MacPherson's Rant' (shortly to become one of the most popular songs of the Revival), and his far-travelled version of 'Come a' ye Tramps and Hawkers'; the bothy song 'Sleepytoon' sung by John Mearns; a lyric love song 'Portknockie Road' sung by Blanche Wood, and two virtuoso performances by Ewan MacColl, 'The Dowie Dens o' Yarrow' (Child 214) and 'The Chevalier's Muster Roll'. In addition, the Lowland side includes a Common Riding Day performance of 'The Soutars o' Selkirk'; children's singing games from Edinburgh; dance music played on the accordion by Jimmy Shand, and on the fiddle and guitar by Tom Anderson and Willie Johnston; and the haunting 'Bressay Lullaby', sung by Elizabeth Barclay.

Between 1950 and 1957 Alan Lomax collaborated with Peter Kennedy in England, and with Seamus Ennis in Ireland, in a number of collecting projects. Using material gathered on these expeditions, and also songs recorded for the BBC Sound Archive and other bodies by Patrick Shuldham-Shaw, Bob Copper, Sean O'Boyle, Marie Slocombe, Cyril Tawney and other collectors, Lomax and Kennedy put together in the late 50s a series of ten albums entitled 'The Folk Songs of Britain'. These were first published in the USA by Caedmon Records Inc. of New York, and eventually brought out in Britain in 1963 by Topic. The list of titles is as follows: Songs of Courtship; Songs of Seduction; Jack of all Trades; Child Ballads 1 and 2; Sailormen and Servingmaids; Fair Game and Foul; A Soldier's Life For Me; Songs of Christmas; Animal Songs.

Together these form an impressive and exceedingly useful collection. Jeannie Robertson had not been discovered when the Columbia album was put together; nor had many others of the traveller singers of the North-East. The contribution of these singers to the albums (and particularly to the two Child Ballad LPs, 12T160 and 12T161) would alone serve to make the series memorable.

Tocher, 25, Spring 1977.

Part 2

The best-known label in the entire folk-song recording sphere is undoubtedly the New York company, Folkways, which has performed a service of truly incalculable value to comparative ethnomusicology. Folkways is the creation and the life work of Moses (Moe) Asch, the son of the renowned Jewish writer Sholem Asch. Moe was born in 1905, and brought up partly in France, partly in the USA. Introducing a two-part interview with him in the American folk magazine *Sing Out* – the first part appeared in Vol. 26, No 1, 1977 – Josh Dunson wrote:

> The more than 3000 records Moe Asch has issued since 1939 on Asch, Disc and Folkways stand as the greatest single documentation of the world's folklore and the folk cultures of the United States. Moe's way of doing things reflects a world view shaped by a childhood with revolutionary relatives and exposure to the world's greatest artists, actors and writers through his novelist-father Sholem Asch.

Moses Asch senses the universal while relishing the specific differences that make life and its folk music sparkle with contrasts. He could challenge, fool, stimulate and encourage the musicians he recorded.

The man who interviewed Moe for *Sing Out* was Israel G. Young, who for many years led the team which edited the magazine – itself one of the most important fertilising agents of the entire modern folk revival. The ten cassettes of conversations he recorded with Moe certainly constitute a vital historical document, and it is to be hoped that the transcript will eventually be published in its entirety. Among the many points of interest which emerge from the interview is the fact that Moe has been for years in the forefront of technical innovations in the recording field, and is in fact a pioneer in the development and use of the microphone for folk documentary purposes. 'I understand very well my mode, my way, my machinery, the guts of what I work with. I understand my instruments.'

The enormous range covered by Folkways releases can best be indicated by listing a few of the section headings in its catalogues, with examples of the contents:

* *Ethnic Folkways Library* (ranging from 'Eskimos, Alaska, Hudson Bay', FE 4444 to 'Songs and Pipes, Hebrides', FE 4430).
* *International Literature Series* ('Poems and letters of Robert Burns and Poems of Dunbar', FL 9877).
* *Folktales for Children* ('Uncle Bouqui, Haiti', FC 7107).
* *International Series* ('New British Gazette', Ewan MacColl and Peggy Seeger, FW 8732; and 'Singing Street', Ewan MacColl and Dominic Behan singing Scots and Irish children's songs, FW 8501).

Four titles merit special mention here. First, *The Borders: Songs and Dances of the English-Scottish Border*, recorded and documented in 1960 by Samuel B. Charters and A. R. Dansberg with the help of the School of Scottish Studies, FW 8776. This splendid LP includes songs by the veteran Dumfriesshire shepherd Willie Scott (subject of the feature in *Tocher*, 25), by his elder brother Tom, by Willie's son Jimmy and Jimmy's wife Nan; a recitation ('MacAlister dances before the King') by Willie's younger son Sandy; Border fiddle music by Rob Hobkirk, a shepherd from Teviothead; and piping on the Northumbrian small pipes by Tom Breckons, a farmer from the 'other side'. Outstanding among the songs is Tom Scott's 'Jimmy Raeburn'; Willie's 'Shepherd's Song' (the text of which appears in *Tocher*, 25); and Jimmy Scott's rumbustious 'Tinker's Weddin'. The booklet accompanying the album contains much useful background material, and complete transcriptions of the song texts.

From October 1959 to July 1960 Kenneth S. Goldstein, who had been awarded a Fulbright research grant, did intensive field-work in Aberdeenshire under the aegis of the School of Scottish Studies. He was introduced to the Stewart family of Fetterangus, and made them his principal subject of study. The singer he worked with most was Lucy Stewart, a spinster henwife, the family's most important tradition-bearer. Lucy recorded over 175 ballads and songs for him, and nine of the classic ballads in her repertoire appear on Folkways FG 3519 (Lucy Stewart, Traditional Singer from Aberdeenshire, Vol. I, Child Ballads). The songs on this outstanding album are: 'The Battle of Harlaw' (Child 163); 'Two Pretty Boys' (= 'The Twa Brothers', Child 49); 'Tifty's Annie' (= 'Andrew Lammie', Child 233); 'The Laird o Drum' (Child 236); 'Doon by the Greenwood Sidie O' (= 'The Cruel Mother', Child 20); 'The Beggar

King' (= 'The Jolly Beggar', Child 279); 'The Bonnie Hoose o Airlie' (Child 199); 'Barbara Allen' (Child 84) and 'The Swan Swims So Bonnie O' (= 'The Twa Sisters', Child 10). The accompanying booklet is interesting and informative, particularly as regards Lucy's biography, and the notes on the ballads are competent and workman-like – but unfortunately not without the occasional error here and there. (For example, in the note on 'The Bonnie Hoose o Airlie', King Charles I is confused with Prince Charles Edward). It is to be regretted that the other volumes promised in the Lucy Stewart series – Vol. II, Broadsides and Other Ballads, and Vol. III, Folk-songs and Lyric Songs – have never appeared.

Ewan MacColl has recorded several albums for Folkways – e.g. *Jacobite Songs*, FW 8756 (with Peggy Seeger) and *Songs of Robert Burns*, FW 8758 – but the one to which we would wish to draw special attention displays to excellent advantage this gifted singer's powers of assimilation and recreation. *Bothy Ballads of Scotland* (FW 8759) draws partly on printed sources (e.g. *The Miscellanea of The Rymour Club* and Ord's *Bothy Songs and Ballads*), and partly on oral sources, either live or recorded (e.g. the singing of Jimmy MacBeath and Jeannie Robertson). On the album Alf Edwards provides accompaniments on concertina, ocarina and five-string banjo. The linguistic purist may cavil about Ewan's highly idiosyncratic synthetic Scots accent, which often seems far enough removed from the characteristic 'Aberdeen-awa' of Buchan farm servants, but at any rate as far as the present disc is concerned this deficiency seems to me more than compensated for by the vivid – indeed dynamic – artistry of the singer. 'The Band of Shearers', 'The Skranky Black Farmer', 'The Monymusk Lads' and 'The Lothian Hairst' are all impressive performances, but the track which really stands out is 'Lamachree and Megrum' (reputedly one of Gavin Greig's own favourite bothy ballads, as also of the late Pat Shaw). With its off-hand, allusive, dead-pan text, its strange incantatory refrain and its dragging hypnotic tune, this song is capable of exerting a disquieting effect on the listener, and Ewan contrives to project in a masterly fashion its latent sinister quality, its capacity for giving the unsuspecting listener a 'cauld grue'. (Incidentally the farm Auchtydore, mentioned in the text, was the home of the late Jean Matthew, a fine singer who was one of the School's earliest informants in Buchan.)

The last of the Folkways albums singled out for special mention is *Ding Dong Dollar* (FD 5444). This LP brings together fifteen of the anti-Polaris and Scottish republican songs which became popular among left-wing youth around 1960 and 1961, and which were carried far and wide by CND visitors from all the airts who had come to join the native 'sitters-down' at the Holy Loch. It was of this politico-cultural movement that Hugh MacDiarmid was later to write: 'These young poets have created a new Scots folk-poetry in their ballads against the siting of the Polaris base in Scotland.' A witty and erudite booklet comes with the record, but the poets who earned MacDiarmid's accolade remain anonymous, as do the singers. (Several of the items on the disc were in fact workshopped by a kind of folk-song collective.) Among the songs are 'Ding Dong Dollar', a favourite of Pete Seeger's, which is styled 'rebel-direct'; 'The Misguided Missile and the Misguided Miss' ('rebel-vaudeville'); 'The Freedom Come-All-Ye' ('rebel-bardic') and 'Ye'll no sit here' ('rebel-burlesque').

Tocher, 27, Winter 1977.

Part 3

The Aberdeen ballad-singer Jeannie Robertson was 'discovered' in the summer of 1953, and the work of recording her vast repertoire of songs and stories for the School's archive began immediately. Recordings were also made the same year for the BBC by Peter Kennedy, and a series of 78s was produced by the Corporation for its own use. These can be consulted in the BBC sound archive.

The first record company to offer Jeannie a contract was the New York firm Riverside, and Bill Leader made recordings of her on their behalf in April 1956. At the express wish of the record company, some of the items were accompanied on guitar by the late Josh Macrae. After this record (*Songs of a Scots Tinker Lady*) had appeared in the States, Topic brought out an abbreviated 'British' version of it which dispensed with guitar accompaniments and changed the title (which the singer had found embarrassing) to *Jeannie Robertson*. Originally numbered 12T52, the British LP was reissued in 1965 with the number 12T96.

It remains probably the best single 'sampler' of Jeannie's extraordinary power, virtuosity and glamourie. It includes two classic ballads ('The Gypsy Laddie', Child 200, and 'Lord Lovat', Child 75); a folk variant of Mrs Grant of Carron's remake of 'Roy's Wife of Aldivalloch'; John Stuart Blackie's translation of 'MacCrimmon's Lament' as transmitted orally over two or three generations of traveller singers; a ribald fragment 'My Plaidie's Awa'; 'The Bonnie Wee Lassie who never said No', a bothy ballad on the familiar theme of a country lad out on the tiles; and two exquisite love laments, 'When I was new but sweet Sixteen' and 'What a Voice' (this latter a version of 'O Waly Waly, alias 'I wish, I wish').

In 1959 a small record company, Collector, brought out the first of three EPs featuring the singing of Jeannie Robertson. In addition to the title song, *The Gallowa Hills*, (Collector JES 1) included 'Cuttie's Waddin', 'Yowie wi' the Crookit Horn', a fragment of Skinner of Lonmay's 'Reel of Tullochgorm' and two Lallan *puirt-a-beul*.

The second of these EPs (Collector JES 4) has three songs. A superb performance of the classic ballad 'The Twa Brothers' (Child 49) occupies the whole of one side, and on the other side are 'Davy Faa' (archetypal vaunting song of the gangrel traveller clans) and 'My Rovin' Eye' (a Fife version of the song usually known as 'The Overgate'). Unobtrusive guitar accompaniments for the first and third of these items are provided by Robin Hall.

I Ken Where I'm Going (JES 8) is less successful. These are two items accompanied on guitar ('The Cuckoo's Nest' on side 1 is accompanied by Jimmy MacGregor and 'The Handsome Cabin Boy' on side 2 by Robin Hall) but these accompaniments are ill-conceived. However, the record is worth listening to for Jeannie's family version of 'MacPherson's Farewell' and also for 'Oh Nellie My Darling', which is a song of her own composition.

There followed – also from Collector – a 10-inch LP, *Lord Donald* (JFS 4001). This is the first known to me to devote one whole side to a single song. Jeannie's fabulous version of the classic ballad 'Lord Randal' (Child 12) has its own little niche in ballad history, for this recording was Willa Muir's first introduction to the singing of Jeannie Robertson. On the other side of the record are 'The Twa Recruitin' Sergeants' (already, in Jeannie's version, one of the most popular songs of the folk-song revival); 'Rollin' in the Dew'; 'O Haud your Tongue, dear Sally'; and a folk variant of Robert Tannahill's 'The Braes o' Balquhidder'.

Next in the field was His Master's Voice, which produced an EP of Jeannie's singing entitled *Jeannie's Merry Muse* (HMV 7EG 8534). In spite of its title, this record is not so much bawdry, more playful ribaldry and tender love lyricism. The line-up on side 1 is as follows: 'Eenst Upon a Time'; 'Bonnie Wee Grainne'; 'Killiekrankie' (not so much military glory, more 'life-giving wars of Venus'); 'I'll lay ye doon, Love' (Irish music-hall song into bewitching erotic fantasy); and 'Busk, busk, Bonnie Lassie' (Jeannie's version of a love song which was to become a firm favourite of youthful folk enthusiasts all over Scotland). The whole of side 2 is devoted to 'The Laird o' Windywa's', the burlesque night-visiting song first noted down by David Herd.

In 1960 the American company Prestige International brought out an LP to which they gave, with unabashed transatlantic brio, a most magniloquent title – *Jeannie Robertson: the World's Greatest Folksinger*. A formidable array of quotations from eminent folklorists and other authorities was mustered on the sleeve in an attempt to justify this arm-chancing display of sales-happy hyperbole. In point of fact, however, the record (Prestige International 13006) *did* offer what was by far the most representative and evocative selection of songs from Jeannie's repertoire so far published, and probably persuaded many purchasers that the title was telling nothing more nor less than the literal truth. It included two of Jeannie's finest classic ballad versions, 'Johnny the Brime' (Child 114) and her world-famous version of 'Edward', 'Son David' (Child 13); 'The Deadly Wars', a folk variant of Burns's 'The Soldier's Return'; 'The Laird o' the Dainty Doon-by' (which supplied a tune for a song first printed in Herd's *Ancient Scottish Songs and Heroic Ballads*); 'Twa Bonny Black Een', another of Jeannie's own compositions; 'Tak the Buckles frae your Sheen' (a version of the old 'improper' song – 'O the Shearin's no for You' – whose tune Thomas Lyle borrowed for his mim-mou'd 'Kelvin Grove'); 'Soo Sewin' Silk', a fragment of a 'lying song' collected by Kinloch; and a large gallimaufry of Aberdeen bairn sangs, in some of which Jeannie is joined by her daughter Lizzie.

The success of this record encouraged Prestige to bring out another Jeannie LP; this was *The Cuckoo's Nest* (Prestige International 13075; British release by Transatlantic, Xtra 5041). Among the items included are 'The Laird o' Drum' (Child 236) which was Edwin Muir's favourite among Jeannie's ballad recordings; 'Roy's Wife of Aldivalloch' (an old version taught her by the distinguished ballad scholar Dr William Montgomerie); and the Aberdeenshire ('Ricky Doo Dum Day') version of 'The Overgate'.

When Alan Lomax was assembling material for Vol. VI (Scotland) of the Columbia World Albums of Folk and Primitive Music (SL209) (discussed in the first instalment of this discography in *Tocher* 25), Jeannie Robertson had not yet been 'discovered', and very little of the vast traveller repertoire of songs, tales and other folklore had been recorded. Lomax invited Jeannie to London to take part in a television folk-song series a month or two after he was first given news of her, and he made numerous recordings of her at that time. Three of these appear on side 1 ('Songs from the North-East of Scotland') of the LP *Heather and Glen* (Tradition TLP 1047). All three are outstanding performances – 'Maids when Ye're Young, never wed an Auld Man' has pride of place, and it is followed by 'Wi' My Rovin Eye' and 'Son David' (this last referred to in

Lomax's notes as 'probably the finest performance of 'Edward' recorded from oral tradition'). Also on side 1 are songs by John Strachan, Jimmy MacBeath, Davie Stewart and Blanche Wood.

Side 2 ('The Hebrides') has an unbroken series of marvellous performances. These include Flora MacNeil's 'Mo Rùn Geal Og' (the lament for William Chisholm); Dr Allan MacDonald's 'Oran an t-Saighdeir' (Song of the Soldier); a group of waulking songs sung by Kate Nicholson, Penny Morrison, Mrs Archie MacDonald and others; and the fantastic virtuoso pipe imitations of the late Mary Morrison, of Earsary, Barra.

Tocher, 28, Spring/Summer 1978.

Part 4

One of Jeannie Robertson's most eulogised ballad versions was her splendid 'Battle of Harlaw' (Child 163). When I played the original recording to the Tennessee ballad scholar Herschel Gower, his comment was: 'If only Francis James Child could have heard this!' An even more eloquent tribute was paid to it by Calum Maclean when, three years later, he took a copy of the same recording into hospital when he was first stricken by the illness which was to kill him.

It was therefore with good reason that we reserved 'Harlaw' for the School's first folk-song disc (A.003/4), one of a unique series of long-playing records published in 1960. (The others presented some of our folk-tale finds, Gaelic and Scots, and a heterogeneous but exciting swatch of instrumental music which included *ceol mór* and *ceol beag* on the pipes, as well as items played on jew's harp and accordion, and a selection of fiddle music, from mainland Scotland as well as from Shetland). This folk-song disc – now, like the others, a collector's piece – also included Jock Cameron's 'King Fareweel' (a Jacobite song still enjoying underground currency among Fife and Lanarkshire miners); John Strachan's 'Harrowin' Time', which demonstrated that a seemingly innocuous cornkister could also be a carrier of overt social protest; Edith Whyte's 'The Beggin' Trade', a descendant of an eighteenth- century piece by Alexander Ross of Lochlee which is itself based on older mumper songs; Jessie Murray's 'Jamie Raeburn', a North-East version of a Glasgow street song which can still be collected in every part of the Lowlands; Jeannie Robertson's 'Braes of Balquhidder', a by-ordinar 'singer's digest' incorporating one verse of Robert Tannahill's much anthologised lyric; and two items – 'The Shepherd's Song' and 'The Kielder Hunt' – by the indomitable old Borderer Willie Scott (subject of the feature in *Tocher* 25)

The founding of the Edinburgh University Folk-song Society directed the attention of many Edinburgh students to the work already well under way at the School of Scottish Studies. Among the earliest of the *aficionados* to use our recordings to effect was Jean Redpath, now one of the most sought-after singers of the Revival. The best of Jean's LPs are now difficult to obtain; they were produced by Elektra in the United States, and are listed here for the benefit of collectors:

- *Jean Redpath's Scottish Ballad Book* (EKL 214), a truly fabulous disc which includes recordings of 'Barbara Allen', 'Tam Lin' and 'Clerk Saunders'.
- *Love, lilt and laughter* (EKL 224)
- *Laddie lie near me* (EKL 274B).

Later discs of Jean include:

- *Frae My Ain Countrie* (Folk Legacy FSS 49), which includes breathtaking performances of 'The Gairdner and the Plooman', 'I'll lay ye doon, love', 'Kilbogie' (a version of 'Glasgow Peggie', Child 228) and 'Johnnie O'Breadisley', Child 114).
- *There were Minstrels* (Trailer LER 2106) – includes an exceptionally fine performance of the version of 'Dumbarton's Drums' which she learned from the singing of the Beers family of Montana. (This family – father, mother and daughter – has preserved much fascinating Scottish and Irish folk-song taught to Robert Beers by his pioneer grandfather. Jean's version is therefore the touchdown in Scotland of a song which has described a vast trajectory since it was first launched in the late seventeenth century during the reign of James VII.)
- *Jean Redpath* (Philo 2015), the record notable for her performance of 'Lady Dysie', Child 269 – a superb blend of art and scholarship. (She used a printed melody found in Bronson, and fused it with a powerful text collated by herself.)

Two other women singers deserve honourable mention as heirs of the tradition-bearers on the School's first LP. The first is Isla St Clair, now a well-known television personality, who (like Jessie Murray) is a native of Buckie. Isla's mother Zetta is an important tradition-bearer, as well as a talented singer and song-writer. Isla comes of a long singer ancestry. Her Tangent record (*Isla St Clair sings traditional Scottish songs*, TGS 112) includes versions of 'Annie of Lochroyan' (Child 76) which she sang as the opening song of the Sir Walter Scott Bicentenary Ceilidh in 1971; 'The Plooman Laddies', which has spread far and wide since Lucy Stewart first sang it into her sister's tape-recorder in 1959; and, last but not least, a delicious gallimaufry of ballgame and skipping songs learned in her Buckie playground.

Alison McMorland was born in Clarkston, Lanarkshire; her father was a sheet-metal worker. The family originally came from Ayrshire, where Alison feels that her deepest roots lie. Alison's art is a marvellous blend of inherited tradition and devoted research. She is an authority on children's games, and spends several months every year travelling around the north of England – she now lives in York – singing a variety of songs at local schools. Her film *Pass it on*, the star of which is her youngest daughter Katy, is a most impressive documentary on the theme of children's games and other lore, and their follow-up in adult life. Like Isla, Alison has a record (*Belt wi' Colours Three*, TGS 125) on the Tangent label. The tracks on this record include 'Skippin' Barfit through the Heather' (learnt from Jessie Murray's recording in the archives of the School of Scottish Studies); 'The Swan Swims Sae Bonny O' (a version of 'The Twa Sisters', Child 10) and the title song, a sombre elegiac love lament.

Also well worth listening to is Alison's attractive and ingenious LP of songs for children, *The Funny Family*, which is on Tangent's companion label Big Ben (BBX 504).

Tocher, 30, Winter 1978.

Part 5

In 1978 the 'Sandy Bell's Cup' (which is awarded annually for services to folk music) went for the first time not to an individual but to a company – Topic Records, to be precise, an outfit which has established itself, since it was launched in 1958, as Britain's premier specialist label in the field of folk-song recordings.

In its early days Topic shared an address with the Workers' Music Association in Bishop's Bridge Road, London W2, and its origins are inextricably bound up with that organisation. The late Will Sahnow, secretary of the WMA, and Bill Leader (who later started his own Trailer label) were the prime movers in getting it off the ground. It also received – and has continued to receive – valuable assistance from Ewan MacColl and A. L. Lloyd, pioneers of the Revival, and singers who have over the years recorded many times for the company. It goes without saying, therefore, that throughout its history Topic has displayed a keen interest in industrial song, and material with a strong social content, but it has gradually widened its interests to embrace the entire traditional musical field. In this and the following instalments of the discography we shall be surveying topic's impressive catalogue – which has now over 250 records listed – with special emphasis on the Scottish material it makes available.

At the start of its career Topic performed a useful service by releasing in Britain records which had previously appeared in the USA, chiefly on the Folkways and Riverside labels. These included Jeannie Robertson's first LP (described in *Tocher* 28, p. 263), and records made by such American folk heroes of the Revival as Woody Guthrie, Sonny Terry and Pete Seeger. In the early 60s after Gerry Sharp had been appointed full-time Director, it issued in Britain the ten–LP series *the Folksongs of Britain* (12T157–161, 194–198), which we mentioned in *Tocher* 25, p. 55; this had previously been available only on the American Caedmon label. The ten records have been referred to – and after listening again to a large number of tracks we are inclined to agree – as the most stimulating and thought-provoking 'aural' contribution to British folk-song studies ever made. Amid all these riches I have space to draw attention to just one item – Lucy Stewart's 'Yowie wi' the Crookit Horn', which is on 12T198 (*Songs of Animals and Other Marvels*), the last album in the series. Unlike the two Child ballads sung by her on vols 4 and 5, this is not available elsewhere.

The traveller family Stewart of Blairgowrie (now of Rattray), who were discovered by Maurice Fleming in 1955, do not appear on the FSB albums, but their absence is more than compensated for by their appearance on five other Topic LPs. The first of these (*The Stewarts of Blair*, 12T138) is a really outstanding folk record, with a whole cluster of marvellous performances. Belle, the matriarch of the family, sings the classic ballad 'The Dowie Dens of Yarrow' (Child 214); 'Queen among the Heather', which is related to a song 'Owre the Muir amang the Heather' noted by Robert Burns from a talented vagrant strumpet called Jean Glover; 'Caroline of Edinburgh Town', a widely diffused broadside ballad; 'In London's Fair City', a version of the song better known as 'The Oxford Tragedy' or 'Cruel Jealousy', and 'Huntingtower' the well-known love song (often sung as a duet) which descends from the Child ballad 'Richie Story'. Her daughters Sheila and Cathie share side 2; Sheila's 'Young Jamie Foyers' and Cathie's 'Busk, Busk, Bonnie Lassie' are the items which remain in the memory. In the second of these Cathie is accompanied by her father Alec on the 'goose' (a small set of

Highland pipes – bag and chanter, but minus the drones).

On *the Travelling Stewarts* (12T179) the Blair family are joined by Jeannie Robertson, her daughter Lizzie Higgins, Donald and Isaac Higgins (Jeannie's husband and brother-in-law), Davie Stewart and other singers. Belle's 'Loch Dhui' (a song composed by herself to one of Alec's favourite pipe tunes); Sheila's 'Return to Glencoe'; Jeannie's 'Willie's Fatal Visit' (Child 255) and Lizzie's 'Johnny My Man' ('The Ale-Hoose', see *Tocher* 1, 16–17) are all noteworthy performances.

Back o' Bennachie (Songs and Ballads of the Lowland East of Scotland 12T180) is really a kind of supplement to *The Travelling Stewarts*, although the net is thrown rather wider. Again, the Stewarts of Blair may be said to 'bear the gree' (with Belle's 'Bonnie Hoose o' Airlie' (see *Tocher* 21, 174–5) and Sheila's 'Mill o' Tifty's Annie'), but Jane Turriff's 'Laird o' Drum', her husband Cameron's 'Willie Graham' and Davie Stewart's 'Tarves Rant' are also well worth listening to.

In 1967 the TMSA organised the first Blairgowrie Festival of traditional music and song. (This was the ancestor of the annual sprees which are at present held at Kinross). *Festival at Blairgowrie* (12T181) is solidly based on the 'host' family – Belle's 'Festival of Blair' and her now internationally famous 'Berryfields of Blair' are the opening and closing items on the disc – but Davie Stewart is there to back her up with 'I am a Miller tae my Trade', and Jeannie Robertson is in rare form with 'An Old Man cam coortin me'. John ('Hoddan') MacDonald contributes three Gaelic songs – including *Bàs an Eich* ('The Poor Horse buried at Sea') – and Willie Scott sings 'Irthing Water Hounds', a Border song 'from the other side'. The Marsden Rattlers (old friends, likewise from 'the other side') provide spirited dance music on fiddle, melodeon, wistle and banjo. However, the singer who really steals the show is the late Mary Brooksbank of Dundee, with her 'My Johnny' and 'The Jute Mill Song'.

Lastly, *Queen among the Heather* (12TS307), which comes with excellent sleeve-notes by Geordie MacIntyre, and consists exclusively of unaccompanied singing by Belle Stewart, is by way of being a tribute to a figure who has exerted an incalculable influence on the folk revival. Among the titles included are her version of the night-visiting song 'Here's a Health to all True Lovers', 'The Twa Brothers' (Child 49), 'Leezie Lindsay' (Child 226), and 'Busk, Busk, Bonnie Lassie' ('Bonnie Glenshee') which is now universally popular among the young singers of the Revival, and indeed is sometimes used as a parting song.

Part 6

Referring to the pantagruelian bawdry which is such a characteristic, entertaining and copious component of the Scots folk-song heritage, Gavin Greig once wrote: 'It must be admitted that there is a considerable body of traditional minstrelsy still in circula-tion which is so frankly pagan in its dealing with sexual relations that it must be relegated to the *Index Expurgatorius*'. Since Greig's approach to this controversial subject is certainly representative of the viewpoint of a majority of Scottish folklorists and antiquarians – at any rate until quite recent years – it is agreeable to be able to record that the first totally uninhibited LP devoted to Scots bawdry was made from the singing of a great-grandson of Greig himself, the late Arthur Argo.

Arthur, whose untimely death in April 1981 at the early age of forty-five was deeply mourned by a wide circle of friends, and not least by the staff of the School of Scottish

Studies, did a great deal of valuable field collecting in his native Buchan; he also contributed with inspirational energy and enthusiasm to the development of the Scottish Folk Revival, not only as an organiser and as editor of the magazine *Chapbook* but also as a folk-singer in his own right. He excelled in the lighter and more skittish items in what became quite an extensive repertoire, and his Prestige-International LP *A Wee Thread o' Blue* (INT 13048), which is vol. 2 of Lyrica Erotica, contains a number of delightful performances; these include 'The Lobster' (a version of the song often called 'The Sea Crab'); 'Hame Drunk Came I' (= 'Our Goodman', Child 274); 'Torn a' Rippit a''(Arthur's own gallimaufry, to the tune of Brochan Lom, which is based on a fragment recorded for the School by Jimmy MacBeath); and 'Ye Ken Pretty Well What I Mean' ('Green leaves sae Green O'), which Arthur got (text only) from an elderly relative, and himself put a tune to.

John Greenway's elegant, erudite notes complement and enhance the entertainment value of the material; for example, when commenting on Jim MacLean's amusing squib 'Poor Wee Lady Chat', he quotes a review of Lady Chatterley's Lover which appeared in *Field and Stream*, a publication concerned with outdoor sports: 'Although written many years ago, this fictional account of the day-to-day life of an English gamekeeper is still of considerable interest to the outdoor-minded reader, as it contains many passages on pheasant-rearing, the apprehending of poachers, ways to control vermin, and other duties of the professional gamekeeper. Unfortunately, one is obliged to wade through many pages of extraneous material in order to discover and savour these sidelights on the management of a Midlands shooting estate, and in this reviewer's opinion, this book cannot take the place of J. R. Miller's *Practical Gamekeeper.*'

Although most of the texts used by Ewan MacColl on *The Merry Muses of Caledonia* (Folk Lyric DLP 2) are every bit as 'blue' as those on Arthur's LP, this notable record makes a somewhat different, and in general a rather less carefree impression. It is, of course, based on Robert Burns's famous collection of bawdry, put together for the delectation of his drinking companions of the Crochallan Fencibles, and constitutes a kind of musical follow-up to the Auk Society edition of 1959, edited by J. DeLancey Ferguson, James Barke and Sydney Goodsir Smith. Ewan brings the full weight of his magnificent vocal apparatus and highly idiosyncratic 'synthetic Scots' singing-style to bear on the material, but in most cases the songs appear too airy, flighty and skittish to stand up to the treatment. This said, it must be added immediately that where he *does* bring it off, the result is a truly splendid performance; I do not think Ewan can ever have sung better on disc than in the versions of 'The Modiewark', 'Todlen Hame' and 'Andrew and his Cuttie Gun', recorded for this LP. The accompanying booklet, with commentary by Kenneth S. Goldstein, is a first-rate production in itself, and several of Goldstein's notes – e.g. on 'Dainty Davie' and 'Logan Water' – are useful and thought-provoking additions to Burns-song scholarship.

The most outstanding modern landmark in this much-fought-over borderline zone, where poetry and music intertwine, is without doubt Serge Hovey's grandiose project of recording the entire corpus of Burns's songs on a series of LPs, with Jean Redpath as vocalist. The first two of these (*The Songs of Robert Burns*, Philo PH 1037 and PH 1048) are now before the public. Not the least of the many breakthroughs which this project celebrates is the decisive jettisoning of the artificial division (implicit in the two records just discussed) between overtly erotic material and songs which deal with other human emotions, experiences and ideals. On the second LP, for example, 'Nine Inch will Please a Lady' falls naturally and satisfyingly into place among songs like 'Hey, How, Johnnie Lad', 'Steer Her Up' and 'Mary Morrison'.

One or two of the items on these albums are sung unaccompanied – for example 'Auld Lang Syne', to the original tune Burns intended for it – but the majority are pleasing and (in my view) successful settings by Hovey himself, using a variety of instruments, e.g. flute, violin, harpsichord, cello, viola, piano and French horn. Among so many delights it is hard to single out individual items for commendation, but I cannot forbear mentioning (on the first record) 'To the Weavers Gin Ye Go', 'Lady Mary Ann' and 'Wantonness for Evermair', and (on the second) 'Had I the Wyte', 'It was a' for our Rightfu' King' and 'Such a Parcel of Rogues in a Nation'.

Tocher, 35, Summer 1981.

Part 7

'A quick-footed, sporty little character, with the gravel voice and urbane assurance that would make him right at home on skid-row anywhere in the world. ... Jimmy is as sharp as a tack, dapper, tweed suit, quick blue eyes, fast on his feet as a boxer. He's been everywhere and nowhere for fifty years running. And he has a song about it.'

This vivid thumb-nail sketch of Jimmy MacBeath, the celebrated tramp singer from Portsoy, who died in 1972, is by Alan Lomax, the first collector to tape-record part of his vast repertoire. Alan had hired me as a 'native guide' when he arrived in Scotland in 1951 to make recordings for Vol. VI of the Columbia 'World Library of Folk and Primitive Music' (SL 209), and Jimmy was one of our earliest discoveries. At that time he was living in the model lodging-house in Elgin which served as his base, and we brought him by car to Turriff (where we were staying) to record him in the company of the veteran bothy ballad singer, George ('Lordie') Hay. It was an appropriate venue, for Jimmy had for many years been a kenspeckle figure at Porter Fair, the Turra feeing-market. (On his last visit to the town before we escorted him back in triumph, the police had ejected him, with a warning never to set foot in Turra again; luckily they turned a blind eye when they learned he was back: see *Tocher* 12, 145.)

Among the songs we put on tape in a series of very enjoyable sessions was a splendid gallus version of the archetypal ballad of outlaw defiance, 'MacPherson's Rant', which was later used on the Columbia LP.

The first record devoted entirely to Jimmy's singing was an EP *Come a' ye Tramps and Hawkers* (Collector JES 10) published in 1960. Collector was the label of a small London company, Selection Records Ltd, which specialised in folk music. The title song had become by that time Jimmy's own personal trade-mark; first recorded during the joint tour with Lomax mentioned above, and given to the world at the Edinburgh People's Festivals in the early 1950s, it soon became one of the most popular items in the repertoires of young 'Revival' singers. It epitomises the joys, hazards and vicissitudes of Jimmy's own chosen life-style; in the opinion of Dominic Behan – a good judge in these matters – his rendering of it on this record is 'a masterpiece'.

The other songs on the EP are 'Nickie Tams' (the comic bothy ballad composed by G. S. Morris of Old Meldrum); 'The Gallant Forty-Twa' (one of the many songs about The Royal Highland Regiment, better known as The Black Watch); and 'The Moss o'

Burreldales' (another well-constructed composition of G. S. Morris based on an anonymous tinker song of the same name).

Seven volumes of the ten-volume *Folksongs of Britain* series already mentioned in Part 1 of this Discography (Tocher 25) feature songs sung by Jimmy MacBeath, although some of these are unfortunately truncated. They are distributed as follows: on Vol. 1 (12T157: Songs of Courtship), 'My Darling Ploughman Boy', which Jimmy learned from Frank Steele at the ceilidh of the second Edinburgh People's Festival in 1952; on Vol. 2 (12T158: Songs of Seduction) 'The Wind blew the bonnie Lassie's Plaidie awa' (in a comparative section which includes Jeannie Robertson's version of the same song) and a skittish little Lallan *port-a-beul* 'Torn a', rippit a' my goon'; on Vol. 3 (12T159: Jack of all Trades) 'He widna wint his Gruel', a delicious comic song also very popular in the Revival; on Vol. 5 (12T161: the second of two LPs devoted to the classic or 'Child' ballads), 'The Trooper and the Maid' (Child 299), which Jimmy had learned from 'Lordie' Hay during our sessions in the Commercial Hotel at Turriff in 1951; on Vol. 7 (12T195: Fair Game and Foul) 'Van Diemen's Land', a Scottish version of a transportation ballad well known throughout the British Isles; on Vol. 8 (12T196: A Soldier's Life for Me) 'The Forfar Sodger', a spirited ditty of the Napoleonic Wars; and on Vol. 10 (12T198: Songs of Animals and Other Marvels) the 'gargantuan' bothy extravaganza 'The Muckin' o' Geordie's Byre'.

Mr Peter A. Hall of Aberdeen – himself a well-known Revival folk-singer, and founder-member of the group 'The Gaugers' – became a close friend of Jimmy's in his latter years, and did his best to look after the old man's professional and financial interests. Peter produced for Topic Records two excellent LPs of Jimmy's singing, *Wild Rover No More* (12T173) and *Bound to be a Row* (12T303). Both these records have some outstanding performances. My own favourites on the first are 'The Merchant's Son and the Beggar Maid' (learned from his old singing partner on the road, Davie Stewart); 'The Barnyards o' Delgaty', now probably the most widely disseminated of all bothy ballads; 'Drumdelgie', the song about the famous 'fairm toon up in Cairnie' which invariably took a trick at public ceilidhs, and the title song (usually known as 'The Wild Rover'). The second of these LPs brings together a whole battery of his best-loved numbers, including 'The Bonnie Lass o' Fyvie', 'Airlin's Fine Braes', 'Bogie's Bonny Belle', 'The Magdalen Green', 'The Banks of Inverurie' and 'Bold Erin go Bragh'. One item deserves special mention. 'Pittenweem Jo' was written by the Dunfermline singer and master song-writer John Watt, whose 'Kelty Clippie' and 'Fife's Got Everying' have achieved widespread folk currency. John was thrilled on one occasion to be told by Jimmy that he would sing him a song he was sure to like, and then to hear his own 'Pittenweem Jo'. Jimmy had no idea he was singing it to the author.

Heather and Glen (Tradition Records, New York, TLP1047) contains a wealth of items collected by Alan Lomax, Calum Maclean and the present writer. On Side 1 (Songs from the North-East of Scotland) there is a marvellous recording of 'He widna wint his Gruel', which has been described as the most delicate humorous satirical song to be collected in an area in which there is no lack of such.

Last – but by no means least – songs of Jimmy's are featured on two of the albums produced by the School of Scottish Studies in collaboration with Tangent Records. On *Bothy Ballads: Music of The North-East* (TNGM 109) he gives a glorious rollicking rendition of 'The Muckin o' Geordie's Byre' (recorded at the high point of a People's Festival ceilidh, so there is plenty of delighted audience reaction), and he can also be heard singing 'Whistle ower the Lave o't', the old (mildly bawdy) words to a tune now best known as 'Katie Bairdie'. On *The Muckle Sangs*, a double album of classic ballads (TNGM 119/D) he sings a shortened version of 'The Broom of the Cowdenknowes' (Child 217), a Border ballad which is a hardy well-travelled oral migrant, and also 'The Keach in the Creel' (Child 281), the widely diffused comic ballad about a night-visiting rover which has much the same storyline as a late fourteenth-century French *fabliau*.

Tocher, 38, Spring 1983.

PEOPLE

Jimmy Robertson

Oh wasna he a piper?

James ('Pipie') Robertson, composer of 'Farewell to the Creek' and many other splendid pipe-tunes, was born at Scotsmill of Boyne, Banff, in 1886. His father was a blacksmith.

The district known as the Boyne, where he spent the first years of his life, is still among the richest in the North-East for bothy songs.

> When I was young and in my prime,
>   Guid faith, like me there wisna mony.
> I was the best man in the Boyne,
>   And foreman lang at Mullnabeeny.
>
>   Rare, O rare, O dear, O dear
>   Rora, rora, Mulnabeeny.
>   I was the best man in the Boyne,
>   Ay, an' foreman lang at Mullnabeeny.
>
> Oh for back at twenty-one!
>   Hip hurra for Mullnabeeny!
> To ca' blin' Joe the game's but low
>   Besides the hash o' Mullnabeeny.

His first school was Portsoy – Jimmy MacBeath was to follow him there ten years later – but when he was seven the family moved to Coatbridge, and he started the pipes with Willie Sutherland of Clarkston ('The Duke'). Owing to his piping prowess, which was immediately recognised, Jimmy met while still a boy a number of the most famous pipers of the day, including John MacColl of Oban.

In 1905 he joined the 1st Gordon Highlanders. He was a carpenter to trade, and was originally supposed to go to the carpenter's shop at the regimental depot at Bridge of Don, Aberdeen, but George Maclennan, the famous composer who had recently been appointed Pipe-Major of the Battalion, got him into the pipe band.

The battalion was at that time stationed at Cork, and Jimmy frequently referred to the fine times he had when in Ireland. George Maclennan was a great inspiration to young pipers. Jimmy told me, 'We used to listen in to him, anything new, we used to listen for, when he was up in his bunk, playing.' In 1912 Jimmy studied under the great John MacDonald of Inverness, and got the Pibroch Society certificate.

When war broke out in 1914, Jimmy Robertson went to France almost immediately with the battalion, and fought at the Battle of Mons, where he was taken prisoner. After the war he served with his regiment in Turkey and Malta, before retiring from the Army with the rank of Pipe-Major in 1926.

In the same year he became janitor of Banff Academy, and continued there for twenty-six years until his retirement in 1953. Piping was the eternal love of his life, and he judged contests at such places as Aboyne, Braemar, Aberlour, Dufftown, Kennethmount and Turriff.

The Turriff pipe-band was his especial protégé, and when I was recording songs for the School of Scottish Studies in 1952 in the Turra area, I often had the pleasure of hearing him give instruction to the band, which played twenty of his tunes. I also recorded him playing a number of his compositions (he had composed about seventy-five excellent tunes).

'Farewell to the Creeks', his most celebrated tune, was composed in 1915 when he was a prisoner-of-war in Germany. The creeks are the Creeks of Port Knockie, on the Banff coast – an uncle of Jimmy's had a house there, and he spent a holiday at this uncle's when he was a child.

I heard the tune played in the piazza of Linguaglossa in Sicily by the massed pipe band of 153 Brigade of the 51st Highland Division, shortly after the end of the Sicilian campaign in 1943, and wrote the song 'Farewell to Sicily' to this noble tune of Jimmy's almost immediately. Twice, I had the opportunity of sending him greetings by singing the song on the radio.

Jimmy Robertson died at Chalmers Hospital, Banff, after a brief illness in April 1961. His funeral was one of the largest seen in Banff for many years. Two members of Turriff and District Pipe-Band, Pipe-Major George Hepburn and Sgt William Hepburn headed the procession to Banff cemetery; the tunes they played in memory of their former instructor were 'Bruce's Address' and the Gordon's slow march.

At the graveside, Sgt Willie Hepburn – son of Pipe-Major Geordie Hepburn, and one of Jimmy's star pupils – played the lament 'The Flowers o' the Forest' in honour of a fine man and a great piper.

Sing, May 1962.

The Revd Angus Duncan

The death has occurred in Edinburgh of the Revd Angus Duncan, an active champion of the Gaelic cause for over half a century, and a scholar well known in the field of Celtic folklore and folk life. Born at Obbe, Harris, in 1888, he served with the Seaforth Highlanders in the First World War, and after demobilisation attended University where he graduated BD in 1925. His first charge after being ordained was at Sorbie, Wigtownshire, where he made the acquaintance of Andrew McCormick, author of *The Tinkler Gypsies*; this friendship encouraged him to pursue his own folklore researches, which eventually embraced all the Celtic countries.

After seven years in Islay, where he is remembered as an outstandingly eloquent preacher in Gaelic, he accepted a call to Kerr Memorial Church, Ladybank, and remained there until 1948. His last charge was at Duns, Berwickshire.

Mr Hamish Henderson, School of Scottish Studies, writes:

> The foundation of the school in 1951 enabled Angus Duncan to devote several years of his retirement to the cause dearest to his heart – namely, the recording and placing on permanent record of the folk-song and folklore of his native country. As his father's family came originally from Aberdeenshire, he was as interested in Lallan lore as in Gaelic.
>
> Nobody who knew him during the years he worked with us could fail to be impressed by the wide range of his knowledge of comparative ethnology, but even more impressive was the devotion (and the word is not used lightly) which he brought to his pioneer task in Scotland's first university folklore institute.
>
> Modest and diffident to a degree, he nevertheless had a keen and ironic eye for the comedy of the academic scene and when he needed to he could employ an infinitely gentle deflationary humour. He was happiest in the company of tradition-bearers, both Highland and Lowland, and indeed one can say of him without incongruity what Sorley MacLean wrote in memory of his brother Calum:
>
> > Tha iomadh duine bochd an Albainn
> > Dh'an tug thu togail agus cliu:
> > 'S ann a thog thu 'n t-iriosal
> > A chuir ar linn air chùl.
> >
> > (There is many a poor man in Scotland
> > Whose spirit and name you raised:

You lifted the humble
Whom our age put aside.)

Latterly he devoted his attention to the Celtic Congress, drawing attention wherever possible to the civil and cultural disabilities of such ethnic minorities as the Breton.

His wife (a daughter of the Lewis bard, Murdo MacLeod) died in the summer of this year. He is survived by two sons and two daughters.

Scotsman, 2 October 1971.

Jeannie Robertson
as a storyteller

Apart from Jimmy MacBeath's grotesque and tuppence-coloured anecdote-sketches relating to various unfortunate characters in Scottish history, practically no Lowland Scots folk-tales were recorded in the first year or two of the School's existence. (Remarkably few tales in Scots had, indeed, ever been recorded prior to the foundation of the School; the stories in Robert Chamber's *Popular Rhymes of Scotland* comprised practically the only specimens on record up to that date, for Peter Buchan's *Ancient Scottish Tales* are somewhat wooden Anglicised recensions.)

It was the breakthrough into the world of the travelling people in 1952 and 1953 which provided incontrovertible evidence that Lallans *Märchen* were as thick on the ground on the East Coast littoral as in many parts of the Highlands, and that a few virtuoso storytellers existed who were comparable, for repertoire and narrative style, with some of the best Gaelic champions in this thinning field.

The first, and in many ways the best, of these Lowland storytellers to be recorded was the celebrated ballad-singer, Jeannie Robertson. At that time, her hospitable little house served as a veritable ceilidh house for the neighbours – some still semi-nomadic – in the Gallowgate district of Aberdeen, and it soon became clear that storytelling was still a favourite entertainment among these gifted, uninhibited, music-loving travelling folk. The earliest recordings of now famous versions of 'Child' ballads took place in a cheery atmosphere of visit and counter-visit, of conversation and still more conversation, in which the necessary pursuit of the 'lowy' (money) never seemed to take precedence over the paramount claims of leisure. Indeed, the arts of song and story, in which the Aberdeen tinkers took what seemed an insatiable delight, were rooted in an exuberant, colourful O'Casey-like folk-speech, long tracts of which can still be heard rimbombing in the recordings of the early 1950s.

Although they were living in houses for most or all of the year, the travelling people of the Aberdeen Gallowgate almost all had first-hand experience of storytelling around the camp fire. After recording a version of the Schwank 'Silly Jack and the Factor' (AT 1600), Jeannie went on to make a distinction between short humorous stories like that and the long wonder tales of supernatural adventure which the old folk could keep going for hours on end, and maybe (for the bairns' benefit) resume at a subsequent sitting. 'Those that aren't alive now could tell ye a lot o' good stories … they could tell stories, and maybe tell it to ye afore ye went to bed at night, and then it was continued like a continued picture at the desperate bit, the bit ye were aye waitin' to hear. So ye were fair anxious for the first 'oor or twa after … and the story started again.'

160 HAMISH HENDERSON

A year later, at campfires in the berry fields of Blairgowrie, I saw children (and adults) sitting enthralled while accomplished storytellers such as Andra Stewart and Bella Higgins rang the changes on international folk tales with names such as 'The Silver Bridle', 'The Blue Belt', 'Johnnie-One-Tune' and 'The Speaking Bird o' Paradise'. Jeannie travelled down to Blair herself, and she took part in what turned into a kind of impromptu folk festival – the open air ancestor of the events later put on by the Traditional Music and Song Association of Scotland. What stood out a mile (even allowing for the added stimulus of the tape-recorder and the work of the collection) was the creative *joie de vivre* of the Scots travellers: rare classic ballads were recorded cheek by jowl with songs in the folk idiom composed the same day, and stories I had heard in Aberdeen in one guise reappeared in Blair in braw new gear. The lively traveller storytelling style, the exact opposite of deadpan delivery, was there in strength, just as Jeannie had described it: 'He'd gae through a' the acts, like. He would show to you what they were like, and if it was eerie or oniething like that, his voice soundit eerie – his voice would change as he was telling the story. If it was comin' to the right desperate bit, he wad get desperate too. And he's a' the bairns roon' the camp-fire jist a' listenin', and maybe feart.'

Jeannie's own storytelling style exemplifies the traditional artistry she has inherited from her mother and her grandfather. Just as in ordinary conversation she 'talks for victory', so with the first words of a narrative she conveys a sense of authority and (so to speak) of professionalism; the self-confidence and ease with which she launches into a tale both beguile the listener and compel his attention. Her physical presence is formidable; she turns her great black eyes on a member of the audience, and draws him willy-nilly into a sort of mute participation. In the comic tale, at which she excels, she displays strong natural robust humour, whereas tales of enchantment can bring out in her the same capacity for sustained incantatory – sometimes almost hypnotic – intensity which one senses in her delivery of the great ballads – for example, 'The Twa Brithers' and 'Son David'. And when she tells 'true' stories of ghosts and fairies, and of burkers (the bogey-men of tinker folklore: see *Tocher*, 5, pp. 136–9), it is obvious that she belongs to a culture in which belief in the supernatural is still very much a fact of life, and for which the alien phantasmagoric world of scalpel-toting predators has a more than symbolic reality.

Tocher, 6, Summer 1972.

Jimmy MacBeath

Jimmy MacBeath, last 'King of the Cornkisters', was born in Portsoy in 1894 and died in Tor-na-Dee Hospital, Milltimber, Aberdeenshire on 7 January 1972.

Like his friend and travelling companion, Davie Stewart, Jimmy spent the greater part of his life as a wandering singer, and his travels took him into every corner of the North-East, and (in his heyday) as far as Stornoway, Belfast, the Channel Islands and Canada. Like Davie again, he became one of the few 'professionals' of an earlier period to find a rather wobbly but welcome place in the ranks of the entertainers who have been doing the rounds of folk club and festival since the present Revival got under way in the late 1950s and he was a familiar kenspeckle figure at Blairgowrie, Keele, Loughborough, and Cecil Sharp House. Although his last years were spent in relative poverty – he was for a decade an inmate of the model lodging-house at 33 East North Street, Aberdeen – this new lease of fame and the occasional paid gig did do something to ease an existence that in the end must often have been hard to thole.

We have a description of Jimmy as a schoolboy from an informant who was in the same class at Portsoy School. Jimmy, whose nickname was Scout, sat at the bottom of the class with another lad by-named Piggy and 'made fun of his lessons'. However, he had already begun to store songs and rhymes in his retentive memory, as I discovered when I began to record the fragments of nursery rhymes, playground songs and harvest field gallimaufries which are related to the 'dreg song' of the Lothian and Fife oyster-fishers, and which can still be found here and there, sometimes far from their region of origin. Jimmy listened with interest to the recordings of dreg-song fragments and contributed a version of his own which he had learnt in the playground of Portsoy School:

> Mary Annie, sugar cannie
> Bumbee bedlar
> Saxteen saidler.
> A mannie in a hairy caipie
> Rowin' at the fairy [?ferry] boatie.
> Fairy boatie ow'r dear,
> Ten pounds in the year.
> Jock Fife had a coo
> Black and white aboot the moo.
> Hit can jump the Brig o' Dee
> Singin' Cock-a-linkie.

Jimmy heard this version when he was eight from 'a laddie cried Mair' who also became a farm servant. The 'mannie in the hairy caipie' recalls the lines in Herd's eighteenth-century version:

> Hey hou Harry Harry
> Mony a boat skail'd the ferry

and maybe provides a hint that the horsemen were not the only workers in Scotland to invoke the occasional aid of Hairy, alias Clootie.

Jimmy learned the 'bothy style' – the way of life of the farm servants of the pre-First World War North-East – the hard way. He left school at thirteen and was fee'd at Brandane's Fair to a farm in the parish of Deskford, south of Cullen in Banffshire. His fee for the first six-month term was £4; this was raised to five guineas for a second term. His most vivid memory of that first year was a savage beating with the back chain of a cart for not being in proper control of his horses: 'Ye ca'd oot muck wi' your pair at that time, ye used your pair at that time. The foreman went oot first, and of course I was oot ahin', man; I happened til miss my hin'–sling, o' my cairt, like – and the horse gaed agley, dae ye see. He [the foreman] pulled me oot-ow'r the cairt and thrashed me wi' a back chain – richt ow'r the back wi' a back chain. An' the fairmer was passin' at the time, and never lookit near hand.'

This punishment, meted out to a greenhorn 'halflin', does not seem to have been exceptional. Other informants such as Jimmy Stewart (a Turriff worthy known as 'the Laird o' Delgaty') have recorded similar stories for our archive. No wonder Jimmy MacBeath later described the North-East farm servants of that period as 'a very sad-crushed people, very sair crushed doon'. Conditions of work, living accommodation and the food (generally brose) provided for the lads were all the subject of outspoken complaint in bothy ballads, and when Jimmy sang 'Drumdelgie' to audiences far outside the North-East, he was able to communicate more of the immediate reality of a farm labourer's life in the old days than a hundred Government papers or bureau-cratic reports could possibly have done.

The outbreak of World War I did at any rate provide a chance of a break from this 'hard slavery work'. Jimmy enlisted in the Gordons, and saw service in the trenches of France and Flanders. He also spent some time in Ireland with the RAMC and helped to plant several bothy ballads in the rich fertile soil of Kildare.

When he was demobilised, he was faced with the depressing prospect of re-entering farm service, but fate – in the shape of Geordie Stewart of Huntly, a wealthy travelling scrap dealer, and a brother of Lucy Stewart of Fetterangus – willed otherwise. Geordie was a connoisseur of ballad singing, and it was he who put the idea into Jimmy's head that he might be better employed using his by-ordinar voice, with its unique gravelly tone, as a street singer than meekly submitting to the necessity of a return to the bothy life. Geordie not only assured Jimmy that fame, money and a great lyric future lay before him on the road; he also taught him two or three dozen of the songs which he was afterwards to make famous, including the best version collected to date of 'Come a' ye Tramps and Hawkers'.

At first Jimmy seems to have been rather self-conscious about singing on the streets, especially in places where he was known. The same school-friend of Jimmy, whom I quoted earlier, happened by accident to come on him at the very outset of his career, when he was singing in the streets in Banff. As soon as his compatriots appeared Jimmy took one look at them, stopped in mid-song and moved off. But it was not long before he had that awkward hurdle behind him and was fully prepared to sing anywhere, and on any occasion, at the drop of a hat – or the crack of a nicky tam. His became a welcome 'weel-kent face' at all sorts of events, public and private, in Aberdeenshire – from Aikey Fair to a local football team celebration. Mr MacKenzie, of MacKenzie's tearooms in Elgin (where Jimmy was later to work as a kitchen porter in the mid-1950s) informed me that it was not uncommon for Jimmy to earn as much as £25 in a single day, when he was at the top of his form, and this was naturally quite a lot of money in the 1920s and '30s. But money always flowed through Jimmy's hands like water: he spent quite a lot of it on booze, and was always ready to 'stand his hand' in company, but he was also an impulsively – one might almost say compulsively – generous person and had a real sympathy with those who happened to be less fortunate than himself – as anyone can testify who ever saw him together with blind people.

The time of the year when Jimmy really came into his own was Aikey Fair, the famous 'Continental Sunday' Fair which is held in July on a brae not far from Old Deer, and in sight of Drostan's Abbey. (Aikey Brae was the locality of the final defeat of the Comyns by Robert Bruce in 1308.) This used to be a celebrated horse market (held on a Wednesday) but with the gradual disappearance of the horse as a working beast on North-East farms, this side of the Fair faded out. However, the Sunday Fair is still a great occasion, and attracts singers, pipers, fiddlers, melodeon players and other wandering folk artists – the majority of them 'travelling people' – from all over the North-East, and even further afield. There are also revivalist preachers who occasionally have a tough time of it if the musicians feel like drowning their fire and brimstone by the direct method. When Jimmy MacBeath turned up, he at once became the centre of a lively group of farm servants, who urged him on to sing 'The Banks o' Ross-shire', 'Torn a', rippit a', 'The Ball o' Kirriemeer' and other colourful items from his repertoire. (In this he seems to have been in the direct line of descent from blind Jamie Rankin, the singer Peter Buchan employed to collect songs and stories for him – cf. Gavin Greig and Alexander Keith, *Last Leaves*, pp. 279–80.)

Afterwards Jimmy would repair to a hotel bar in Old Deer, and the fun would continue. I remember well seeing him in his glory in that same bar in the evening of the Fair Day in 1953; one of the young farm servants, who had obviously formed a strong attachment to him, was sitting and listening attentively, while Jimmy taught him 'Airlin's Fine Braes' verse by verse. I felt it was a real privilege to witness the actual act of oral transmission, especially when the transmitter was none other than the reigning 'King o' the Cornkisters'.

Jimmy also used to sing at 'Turra Market' (Porter Fair), and it was in Turriff that Alan Lomax and I made our first recordings of him in 1951. The lead that carried us to Jimmy came from 'Lordie' Hay, a veteran bothy singer whom I had met on an earlier tour. This was the same humorous blue-blooded 'Lordie', brother of 'Princie', who is mentioned in the bothy ballad 'Wester Badenteer':

Syne Lordie wi the auld Scotch sangs nae heard in music halls.

We recorded a number of songs from him in the Commercial Hotel in Turriff; in addition, he provided a graphic account of the career and personality of Jimmy

MacBeath, and obligingly told us where we would probably find him; this turned out to be the North Lodge, a model lodging-house in Elgin.

The following day we drove west from Turriff, via Banff and Buckie. Alan dropped me off at Jessie Murray's house in Buckie, and drove on alone to Elgin to pick up Jimmy. Jessie, a great ballad singer, was in rare fettle and I hardly noticed the two hours go by, when suddenly I heard Alan's car draw up in front of the house. A moment or two later, Jessie and I had a simultaneous first vision of Jimmy's beaming, rubicund, booze-blotched face as he walked into the kitchen, followed by Alan. There was a moment of silence. Then Alan said: 'Hamish … Jessie … I want you to meet Jimmy MacBeath.'

Half an hour later we were *en route* for Turriff, and Jimmy was singing in the back of the car. To start the ball rolling, I had sung him a short four-verse variant of 'Come a' ye Tramps and Hawkers' which I had learned from a Dundee-born farm servant Tam MacGregor when I was a student. (Tam and I had been 'chaulmered' together on an Appin farm, and I learned several songs from him in the authentic bothy style, when we were lying on adjacent bone-shaker beds). Jimmy at once sang his own version, now world-famous, and we were away.

When he learned that we were heading for 'Turra toon', Jimmy was none too confident of his reception. The last time he had been there, he had been slung out of the town by the local police, who had told him never to set foot in Turriff again. However, Alan assured him that this was a 'special case' – as indeed it was – and Jimmy rode back into Turra in triumph. He was shortly taking his ease, and a royal dram, in the best hotel in the town.

Indeed, Jimmy, who was never slow to claim descent from the Macbeth who 'stabbed King Duncan through the mattress' – and, given any encouragement, from the best-looking of the three Weird Sisters too – was quick to realise that here, in the shape of two wandering folklorists, was fate in a Ford Anglia, and that his reappearance (against all the odds) in Turra Toon signified a qualitative change in more than his own personal picaresque career. Those early recording sessions in the Commercial marked the intersection in space and time of the old world of Aikey Fair and the new world of the as yet undreamed-of Keele Festival of the future, with its hundreds of youthful enthusiasts from all over Britain gathered to hear Flora MacNeil, Ewan MacColl, Margaret Barry, Felix Doran, Belle and Alex Stewart – and Jimmy MacBeath himself, the symbolic unifying factor in the whole clanjamfrie.

So in the Turriff hotel bedroom which I was shortly to re-occupy when Edinburgh University finally 'bought' the idea of subsidising a collecting tour, Jimmy really went to town. He gave an uproarious performance of 'The Moss o' Burreldales', the song which epitomises the Scots tinker way of life; he delighted us with a lovely rendering of the 'Forfar Sodger' complete with gesticulations; he put on gallus red-hackled swagger for 'The Gallant Forty-Twa'; and, after telling us the story of James MacPherson, the tinkler-gypsy outlaw hanged at Banff in November 1700, he went on to sing the folk version of 'MacPherson's Rant' which was shortly to supplant Robert Burns's cloak-and-dagger re-write on the lips of folk-singers all over Scotland.

Later that summer Jimmy came to Edinburgh to sing at the first People's Festival ceilidh organised by me for the Edinburgh Labour Festival Committee. This was held in the Oddfellows' Hall, just across the road from Sandy Bell's bar, and in both places

Jimmy created a sensation. His first song in the hall was 'Come a' ye Tramps and Hawkers', and Alan Lomax's tape-recordings of the ceilidh communicate the elated atmosphere of that memorable occasion. Jimmy was much affected by the reception he got, and at the end of the show he informed the audience that this was his 'swan-song', the culmination and the conclusion of his singing career: for reasons of ill-health and age he would never be able to sing at a similar function again. (He was to visit Edinburgh and sing at my ceilidhs for close on another twenty years.)

After the 'official' ceilidh had finished, we carried on in St Columba's Church Hall in Johnstone Terrace, and there Jimmy excelled himself. Ewan MacColl and Isla Cameron joined us, the Theatre Workshop show having finished, and the sight of Ewan's face, when he first received the full impact of Jimmy's personality and performance, remains vividly in my memory. Other singers and musicians present were Flora MacNeil, Calum Johnstone, John Burgess, Jessie Murray, Blanche Wood and John Strachan. Hugh MacDiarmid honoured us with his presence; parts of *A Drunk Man Looks at the Thistle* were spoken during the evening, and at the end of a second or 'unofficial' part of the show he was so moved that he publicly embraced old John Strachan after the singing of 'Goodnight and joy be wi' ye a'.

A month or two later, in Alan Lomax's programme 'I Heard Scotland Singing', Jimmy's voice was heard for the first time on the radio, together with the voices of several of the other singers mentioned above. This was the beginning of a protracted and often frustrating attempt on my part to get authentic traditional song on the BBC programmes, the 'polished' lyric gem being what the public was supposed to want and – whether it wanted it or not – what it certainly got, in full measure.

We had two valuable allies in London, however; these were Peter Kennedy and Seamus Ennis, who at that time made up a small folk-song section in the BBC, under the aegis of Marie Slocombe. After the second People's Festival in 1952, I brought Seamus Ennis to the North-East, and in the Royal Oak Hotel, Banff, we recorded some wonderful sessions with Jimmy, 'Lordie', Frank Steele and other singers. The BBC discs made from these tape-recordings gradually began to get heard on the radio even in programmes put out by BBC Scotland – although the latter showed a curious reluctance, literally for years, to use Jimmy and the other authentic bothy ballad singers to anything like the extent to which they could – and should – have been used.

It was in 1953 that Alan Lomax invited Jimmy to London, to take part in his first television series presenting folk-singers from Scotland, Ireland and England, and it is from his appearance in this series – which was much commented on – that one can really date Jimmy as an international celebrity on the folk scene. This was further enhanced by the appearance in 1954 of Volume VI (Scotland) of the Columbia Albums of Folk and Primitive Song, which I helped Alan to edit. Later records which featured his singing include the Caedmon Series of 'Folksongs of Britain' (issued in Britain by Topic), and our own Bothy Ballads LP on the Tangent label. In 1960 Collector brought out an EP of his singing (JES 10); recordings had been made at the Linburn Ceilidhs for War Blinded, organised by the School of Scottish Studies, and in 1968 Topic produced an LP (*Wild Rover No More*, 12T173) edited by Peter A. Hall.

The festivals organised by the Traditional Music and Song Association of Scotland at Blairgowrie and Kinross made Jimmy's name and fame known to an up-and-coming generation of folk-song *aficionados* in the 1960s, and in 1966 *Chapbook* devoted a special number to him (The Rt Hon. Jimmy MacBeath Vol. 3 No 2). At roughly the same time *Sing* (Britain's earliest folk-song magazine) produced a marvellous, illustrated bumper number devoted to the first (1965) Keele Folk Festival; the text was by Eric Winter, *Sing*'s founder. In this number 'bright-eyed' Jimmy appears as already very much an 'Establishment' figure on the folk scene. 'Jimmy MacBeath, King of the tramps and hawkers, and a surprise only to those who had never heard him before, endeared himself to his listeners with gesture, twinkling toes and throaty singing.'

Jimmy's last public appearance in Edinburgh was at the bi-centenary ceilidh in honour of 'The Shirra and his Gang' (Sir Walter Scott and his confederates) which was held in the Portobello Town Hall on 17 August 1971. In spite of worsening chest ailments he put on a gallant performance, and was much acclaimed by an audience which included scholars from many parts of the world.

Jimmy MacBeath died a few days after Hogmanay in 1972. Some months later the BBC made amends for years of neglect by broadcasting a splendid programme in his honour, put together and presented by Arthur Argo, and produced by James Hunter.

Tocher 12, Winter 1973.

Ah got that sang aff Geordie Ross, the Beauly tramp ... he had many sangs ... Oh, he wis a little wee man tae look at ... a wee stoot ... cheery kin ... and he paiddled aboot with a box an he wis very crabbit at times tae. If onythin gaed against him he wis very contermashus ... he would pretend that he wis a great knocker-oot, as it were, when he got this twa-three drams in o him an that, an when he startit tae pit up his fists he aye drew them doon again. Och! it wis the dram that was speakin. He'd face up [in a fight] but he'd aye fail. When the drink's in the wit's oot. Oh, he wis a great dancer. He hed a dance whit he caa'd the Pin Reel ... he could dance on ae leg ... he jist diddled himsel, and he had me play the mouth organ tae him ... dancin the Pin Reel ... on his one leg, an of course it took a bit o daen tae dae that.

SA 1952/30/A2 Recorded from Jimmy MacBeath by Hamish Henderson.

Davie Stewart

One of the most frequently encountered names among the Scots travelling folk is the old Royal name itself: Stewarts are to be found up and down the high roads and low roads of Scotland, and there are flourishing colonies of them in the Isles. As might be expected, the traveller genealogists can identify several different branches of this formidable tinker clan – for example, the Hebridean Stewarts, who are by-named the Tearlachs or 'Siamaidhs' (Jamies), and the Huntly Stewarts, who seem to have more than a dash of Romany in them – but the great central stem is undoubtedly the 'brochan' (or 'breacan') Stewart clan, which has its heartland in the Perthshire Highlands, and which has sent its gangrel offshoots as far north as Sutherland. The 'brochan Stewart' patriarch who sired (and grand-grand-sired) the most notable contemporary families bearing the name was 'auld Jimmy Stewart of Struan', and it was from him that the late Davie Stewart, folk musician and singer extraordinary, claimed descent.

About the middle of the last century 'auld Jimmy of Struan' crossed from Perthshire into Aberdeenshire, via the Devil's Elbow, and his descendants are now to be found all over the Central Highlands and the North-East. Pipers, fiddlers, melodeon players, tin whistlers can be counted among them in hundreds, and you practically never encounter an indifferent performer. Belle and Alex Stewart of Blairgowrie belong to the 'brochan Stewart' clan, and so did the redoubtable Davie Stewart.

I first heard about Davie from the late Donald Higgins, husband of Jeannie Robertson. It was during one of the marathon recording sessions of 1954, during which the entire travelling community of Aberdeen seemed to be passing in never-ending relays through Jeannie's house in Causewayend. Those visitors who could not contribute songs or music did their best to think up new names as possible contacts, and at one point I overheard a reference to a character called the 'Galoot'. The by-name was jotted down in a note-book, and later in the evening I asked Donald who the 'Galoot' was. 'Oh,' said Donald, 'that's Davie Stewart the box-player, he's a frien (relation) o' ours; he was in Ireland for years, but he's back in Scotland now. I'll get his address for ye.' Which he did, so that my first summer tour the following year was directed to Dundee, to find and to record this celebrated stravaiging Davie.

Although Davie was known to travellers throughout the length and breadth of Scotland as the 'Galoot', this by-name was never given to his face, and it is questionable whether he ever got to know that this was his 'steady' nickname. One year I made a collection of traveller nicknames, culled from the memories of about a score of informants, and the 'Galoot' cropped up almost as frequently as 'Burnt Bonnet',

'Wooden-sleeves' and the 'Half-hangit Minister'. A month or two later I collected some more from Davie himself, and at the finish I asked him - as innocently as possible - what his own by-name was. Without a moment's hesitation he informed me that, because of the long time he had spent in Ireland, travellers called him the 'Wild Colonial Boy'.

When I proceeded to Dundee on Davie's track in the early summer of 1955, I was accompanied by Frank Vallee, a Canadian anthropologist who had recently concluded a study of the island of Barra. After reviewing the results of field-work among traveller communities in 1953–4, Frank and I had decided to combine forces on what we called the 'tinker project'; this latter was a research programme which we hoped would eventually be able to call on the majority of the School's field-workers, and which was designed to survey the entire traveller set-up in Scotland from a historical, anthropo-logical and folk-cultural point of view. Although he did not know it, Davie was the first target of this ambitious 'tinker project'.

Davie and his family were at that time living in Peddie Street – a street which we found was occupied to a large extent by urbanised travelling folk. A caustic Dundee street song communicated the majority feeling about the area among the working-class of the city:

> Just like the lads o' Peddie Street:
> Talk o' work, and they tak their feet.
> Bye-bye, blackbird.

When we found the right house, Davie's Irish wife Molly told us that her husband was out busking for a cinema queue. Our first sight of him, therefore, was well and truly 'on the job': bunnet cockily – almost aggressively – tilted way back on his head, eyes focused in the middle distance, and the fine 'Roman-Scotch' head itself cocked jauntily at a rakish angle. His whole stance seemed to convey a spirit of rodomontade, a swaggering devil-may-care attitude to the world at large, and it was fitting therefore that among the first songs we heard him sing to the cinema queue on that May evening was the archetypal ballad of outlaw defiance, 'MacPherson's Rant'.

Trying to choose the right moment, we introduced ourselves to Davie, and told him we wanted to record him for the School of Scottish Studies. He decided on the spot to stop work for the evening, and soon we were back home in Peddie Street, enjoying a cup of tea, and listening to Davie's reminiscences of a life-time on the roads. His mind seemed to be full just then of his Irish experiences, and as he told anecdotes of horse fairs and hurling matches, a juicy brogue made itself audible over and above the demotic North-East 'travelling' accent.

We were eager to record 'MacPherson's Rant', not only because Davie's was certainly the finest folk version we had heard since Jimmy MacBeath's, but also because it was clear that his attitude to his text and his tune was highly fluid and improvisatory; the text of verses, and the order of verses sung were noticeably variable, and we felt something could be learned from these variations. Davie also had the tendency to fill in partly remembered lines with meaningless syllables - a tendency I had noted among non-literate singers in Aberdeen such as 'Shepherd' Robertson. (This last, a very old man when I recorded him, was related by marriage to Davie; one of the latter's sisters was married to one of 'Shepherdie's' sons. Davie got quite a number of songs from the old man, including his ever-popular version of 'The Tarves Rant'.)

Later the same summer I took advantage of Peter Kennedy's visit to Scotland to organise a filming session with Davie; again he sang 'MacPherson's Rant', and again it was plain that his text was much less 'settled' than, for example, Jimmy MacBeath's version of the same song.

Gradually, over many recording sessions, Davie told us his life story. His father, Robert Stewart, was a hawker and a tinsmith, like his father before him, and from earliest childhood Davie became familiar with the ancestral gaberlunzie routines of the rag and scrap-iron trade, and of buying and selling horses. He first went to school in Aberdeen when he was four years old, and like most traveller children spent the autumn and winter months at school, and the spring and summer months on the nomadic beat 'up and doon the Don', and into the heart of Buchan. His last school was at Fraserburgh, and he left it at the age of nine 'wi' nae regrets'.

He seems to have developed a strong sense of independence very early on, and by the age of six or seven had begun to go off on his own for a week or even longer during the summer months, attaching himself to other traveller groups, and trying his luck at the hawking and begging trade. By the age of ten he was a travelling singer, spending a lot of time in the ploughmen's bothies and learning songs wherever he went. The Aberdeenshire country folk are very kind to travelling people – North-East tinkers are called 'milk and breid eaters' by their less fortunate mates in the South – and Davie seldom lacked a good 'tichtener' when he went the rounds of Buchan farms. He seems to have become quite a favourite with the 'bothy chiels' in a number of districts, and was 'aye welcome back' when he showed up again in the parts where he was known. In this way he got to know the highways and byways not only of the North-East but also of the North Highlands – Easter Ross and Easter Sutherland – long before he was into his teens.

When the First World War broke out, he was thirteen and a half; all his cousins enlisted, and Davie – dismayed at the thought of being left alone – attempted twice to join the Gordons. He was twice reclaimed by his father, who was able to prove to the company office that he was under age; however, the third time proved lucky (as he saw it) and he was shipped off to France when he was barely sixteen years of age. He spent the rest of the war there, in the Gordons, and was wounded three times. Eventually he joined the pipe-band, having been an 'instinctive' piper from childhood, and for a time had the benefit of tuition from the great John MacLennan himself.

When he was demobilised, at the age of twenty, he resumed his old life of singing, hawking and playing music. In addition to the pipes he now took up the accordion. For a year or two he found it an agreeable way of life to combine occasional farm service – hoeing neeps, lifting tatties – with the role of wandering musician around the Aberdeenshire farm bothies. Then, when he was twenty-two, he fell in with another strolling singer, who was likewise to achieve fame in later years on the revivalist folk scene – Jimmy MacBeath. The following graphic account of how Davie first met Jimmy was recorded by Carl MacDougall, and was published in *Chapbook*, Vol. 2, No 6 (a special number devoted to Davie Stewart). We reprint it here, by permission of the collector and the Editor:

> The first time I met Jimmy MacBeath was in Turra [Turriff] market. He was singing at the market and I was about twenty-one or twenty-two at that time,

but I could hardly play the accordion, I didna ken a lot o' tunes on the accordion. I was a piper but the tunes I kenned I used to try on the accordion. Och, it was only a ten-key accordion that I got in Aberdeen for 4s 6d. I got it off a man that kept a lot o' junk in the Castlegate at Aberdeen, they call him 'Cocky' Hunter.

So I gaed awa oot tae the market that day. Of course I used to sing before I had the accordion, but man I tried tae fiddle awa wi' the thing, and I played a tunie or twa tae the ploomen, but they started laughing at me. Then they got me to start to sing the cornkister songs, then they were a' roon me.

Anyway, we a' gaed intae a pub in Turra. My God, we got a good drink wi' that being the night o' the Turra show. There's a sort of show and Highland trottin' there, trottin' wi' horses. Turra is oot o' Aberdeen, and they have a Highland games and show, farm stuff and horses, football teams, dancing and piping, lots o' things.

And, of course, I made a few bob a' richt, and that was the first time I met MacBeath was when he came in the pub. So I heard Jimmy MacBeath singing and I says tae mysel' like: 'God, he isnae a bad singer at a'.' He sang a lot o' songies, well, one or twa, like, and the baith o' us were in the pub and we had a drink thegither. Och, that's years and years ago, and ever since that I've kenned Jimmy MacBeath. In fact we took a turn thegither, and we did this market and the next market, but I had a different voice tae him someway.

When we were thegither Jimmy would go away one road in the mornin', and played a different toon. And he maybe did his day's work at singing all round the different villages, and I gaed awa my own way, and we used to meet at night and muck in thegither, like. If I was at a market wi' Jimmy he would just stand beside me and collect the money for me, and I would collect it for Jimmy. But still we never sung thegither, no, I kept my own money and Jimmy kept his money. When the summer was over Jimmy went back to Elgin. That was his depot. He comes from up that way, Portsoy. I went back to Aberdeen. I always went home in the winter-time. Jimmy too. Jimmy travelled, aye, all over the summertime but in the wintertime he didn't travel so much.

Towards the end of the last century an Angus hawker by-named 'Brechin Jimmy' and 'Besom Jimmy' – his real name was Jimmy Henderson – composed a song called 'Come a' ye Tramps and Hawkers'. It rapidly became popular among the fraternity, and in recent years it has been carried (in Jimmy MacBeath's version) to every corner of the English – and Scots-speaking world. The last verse goes as follows:

> I think I'll go to Paddy's land, I'm making up my mind
> For Scotland's gettin' gammy noo,　　　　[difficult, hard to operate]
> I can hardly raise the wind.
> But I will trust in Providence, if Providence will prove true,
> And I will sing of Erin's Isle when I come back to you.

In the early 1930s Davie responded to the message contained in this stanza, and left for Ireland – leaving behind him in the North-East divers personal problems and obligations which had become too much for him. Davie always used to say afterwards that his original intention was only to stay a few months; however, in the event he stayed in Ireland for the best part of two decades, and made a reasonably good living doing the rounds of fairs and sporting fixtures. 'I'd sing and take my accordion or whatever I had, bagpipes even. On a Sunday there's always hurling matches in the Free State ... I've seen me going to the matches there on a Sunday and making a good few pounds.' Davie also acquired an Irish wife, Molly, when he was across the water, and the hundreds of Scottish fans who made the family's acquaintance after Davie decided to return to his native soil in 1950 will agree that he picked a winner.

In the same year that Davie returned from Ireland, Alan Lomax arrived in Britain to make recordings for the Columbia Albums of Folk and Primitive Music; the following year, the School of Scottish Studies was founded, and the enormous wealth of song and story to be found among the travelling people began to get recorded on tape. Davie was quite lucky in his life-rhythms, therefore, and after the filming session with Peter Kennedy (mentioned above) things moved quite fast for him. Alan Lomax paid him a visit, and used recordings of him in a radio series on British folk-song which attracted great attention; soon Davie was getting invitations from as far afield as London, and – like his old friend Jimmy MacBeath – found himself at a late stage in his career a respected – indeed almost revered – figure among the youthful *aficionados* of a new folk revival.

In March 1962 he moved from Dundee to Glasgow, and shortly after became a 'regular' at the Glasgow Folk Centre which had been started up in Montrose Street by Andrew Moyes. An article in the *Glasgow Herald* (11 January 1963) fixes Davie in time and space as the king-pin of a new and expanding folk-cultural principality. It hits off the situation so well that it is reproduced here in full:

> 'They don't sing the same nowadays,' said Davie Stewart, street musician and wandering minstrel from Aberdeenshire, as he sat in the back room of the Glasgow Folk Centre (recently converted from a rainwear factory in a Montrose Street tenement). It was his turn to sing. He took off his cloth bonnet and stood up, a grey-haired man with a firm weather-beaten face and spectacles. The sound of a genuinely sung cornkister filled the tenement.
>
> Around him his audience drank coffee from cardboard cups and joined in the choruses – students, apprentices, a banjo-playing British Railways lorry driver who collects folk-songs on his journeys, a young Belfastman, a geography teacher who strums Irish songs on his guitar, a former electrical engineer who now runs the club.
>
> He sat down, after loud clapping, and replaced his cap. A man started to sing 'The Barnyards o' Delgaty'. 'Nothing beats the old songs,' said Davie Stewart approvingly. 'This rock n' roll business – I don't understand it. The music is all right, but the words are wrong.'
>
> The walls of the room were papered with news-sheets, with a few hand-prints in turquoise paint. 'I've been singing since I was eight years old,' said Davie Stewart. 'My people were travellers, and I travelled from market to market, from fair to fair ... I've sung through the whole of Scotland, I've played the accordion, I've played the violin, flute, the tin whistle. I played the bagpipes with the Gordons in the '14 war.'
>
> He played in the London streets, in clubs and restaurants, in bothies, at the

Braemar Games, has had the School of Scottish Studies come with tape-recorders to his home in Maryhill, has sung 'The Barnyards o' Delgaty' on LP. He went
to Ireland – 'I thought I would take a wee trip' – and stayed eighteen years: 'I
sang in the North and the South, Limerick, Cork, Kerry to Clare.' He married a
girl from Cork – 'she's a crack singer' – and now all their children sing; even his
nine-year-old daughter is mastering 'The Bonnie Lass o' Fyvie'.

The folk-singers were dispersing. 'I've done everything. I've even sold boot-
laces, and I used to be a pearl fisherman.' He gave a vivid description of
freshwater pearl fishing on the Don and the Spey, on how you use bags over
your feet if you haven't got waders. 'My people were all pearl fishers, all pipers.'
His father piped in the Gordons before him, his uncle was piper to the Duke of
Atholl; he knows Stewart history inside out, and dips into Highland history
generally.

Ten months ago he came to Glasgow and started coming to the folk-singing
club after one of its members spoke to him at his stance in Sauchiehall Street.
Another summer, perhaps, and he'll be back in London – 'people take to you
more there, people are more generous to buskers.' He lit a cigarette, spoke to
someone in the cant, discussed a new recording. 'I'm no song-writer,' he said,
'but I make up a few songs.' In response to general demand he started to sing.

The 'uncle who was piper to the Duke of Atholl' was old John Stewart, father of Alex
and Belle, the 'Stewarts of Blair'. Jock was a renowned pibroch player, earning the
respect of John MacDonald of Inverness, Angus MacPherson of Invershin and many
others in the top flight of the piping world.

Old Jock and his nephew Davie definitely shared some very marked idiosyncrasies
of character. Both took it as a matter of course that homage should be paid to their
talents by all cognoscenti. Jock used to talk in terms of easy familiarity of such men as
John MacDonald of Inverness, preceptor to hundreds of pipers: 'If he played a good
march, he played a bad pibroch; and if he played a good pibroch, he played a bad
march.' Asked who he thought was the finest piper he had ever heard, he replied in the
true tradition of Alan Breck Stewart – with due pride, but without the slightest trace of
arrogance – that he had never heard a better than himself.

Not long after this article was written, Davie did indeed get a chance of revisiting
London – and the unexpected dénouement of that visit could serve as an epitome of his
whole off-beat lifestyle. The BBC producer René Cutforth wrote to me, telling me that
he was preparing a radio series to be called 'Tinker Tailor Soldier Sailor', and he wanted
me to supply a genuine Scots tinker. Figuring that this would be a good way of assisting
Davie to make some extra 'lowy' (cash), I suggested him for the job, and he was duly
contracted and provided with the appropriate travelling instructions. I got the BBC to
send him up a sizeable advance of expenses, and on the day appointed he took the train
to London. As arranged, a BBC emissary met him at King's Cross, and in a short time
he was installed in what he later described as a 'real posh hotel'.

The only snag was that no arrangements had been made to entertain him on a purely
human convivial level, and after he had had a meal and explored his new abode, Davie
naturally began to feel a bit bored. He finally decided to take a stroll through the streets
of London, and – as was usual with him – he took his melodeon along, slung over his

shoulder. It wasn't long before he found what seemed a likely place to make a little extra 'lowy', and he proceeded to entertain the passers-by with marches, jigs, strathspeys and reels, and a selection of bothy ballads.

As Davie often explained, one of the secrets of the busker's art is to know when to stop. On this occasion he was unlucky, because a London copper suddenly appeared out of the blue, and before Davie knew what was happening, he was being 'lifted' for unauthorised music-making in a public place.

At the police-station he attempted to explain the reason for his visit to London, and also to describe where he was staying, but his accent – and the fact that he had come down from Glasgow without his teeth – totally defeated the local constabulary. Davie protested and expostulated, but it was all no good – he shortly found himself in the lock-up. And so it came about that on the first night in his life that he was booked into a posh hotel in the West End of London, Davie spent the night in a London police-cell.

By the early 1960s, quite a number of Davie's songs had begun to appear on Folk LPs. His splendid 'Merchant's Son' was included on Vol. 2 (*Songs of Seduction*) in the Caedmon Folksongs of Britain Series (subsequently issued in Britain by Topic: Vol. 2 is 12T158). The notes, by Alan Lomax and Peter Kennedy, refer to this item as follows: 'As rendered in the wild, ranting street singer style of Davie Stewart, it seems one of the great ballad performances on record.' (Another recording of the same song was later used on the Prestige/International LP *Folksongs and Music from the Berryfields of Blair: INT 25016*). On Vol. 3 of the Caedmon/Topic Series (*Jack of all Trades*: 12T159) can be heard Davie's vicarious reportage of the hardships undergone by the farm-servants of Drumdelgie, the famous 'fairm-toon up in Cyarnie', the commentary makes it plain that the singer is not so much a ploughboy, more a 'strolling accordion-playing troubadour'. For the second of the two 'Child' ballad LPs in the same series (12T161), Davie's 'Dowie Dens o' Yarrow' was chosen against what must have been very heavy competition. The editors' comment is worth quoting: 'He plays his modern piano accordion like some ancient non-tempered instrument, teasing strange chords out of it that suit his outlandish tunes.'

The Prestige-International record mentioned above also includes Davie's overweening hidalgo-like 'MacPherson's Rant', in some ways the most extraordinary performance of the lot.

Later in the 1960s, the popularity of the Blairgowrie festivals organised by the Traditional Music and Song Association of Scotland was reflected in the production of a Topic LP (12T181) which drew on material recorded at various ceilidhs formal and informal. The *Festival at Blairgowrie* which the record celebrated was that of 1967 – a bumper year, as many will remember. Davie was much to the fore, an honoured – one might almost say a loved – veteran among the crowds of youthful folk fans. It cannot have been an easy job to select a song to represent him from among the richesse of his repertoire recorded by Bill Leader; the choice fell on an ever-popular old favourite 'I am a Miller tae ma Trade', a bawdy ballad in which the singer imitates the clatter of the mill wheel by dint of quite complicated fist and elbow work on the table. The notes on the sleeve of this excellent record are by Pete Shepheard, founder and leading spirit of the TMSA.

At about the same time that this LP appeared, Topic issued another with closely related material: *The Travelling Stewart* (12T179). On it Carl MacDougall – a close friend and benefactor of Davie's throughout his final Glasgow years – assembled material from a number of 'brochan Stewarts' and their friends. Davie's contribution was the well-known comic song 'McGinty's Meal and Ale', a real *chef d'oeuvre* of sappy and savoury Aberdeenshire Lallans. Carl's notes relate that this was apparently one of the first songs that Davie ever learned – 'and he has sung it from Aberdeen's Castlegate to Glasgow Stow Street Market – and everywhere else he has been'.

Carl also prints, in his introductory note on the sleeve of this record, a thought-provoking remark of Davie's about another race of travellers who have arrived in Scotland in more recent years: 'You'll never see me laughing or shouting at a Pakistani or anybody like that; no, never ... Long, long years ago when I was a wee boy, my auld mother told me that all travellers came from the same place as these people, and so I never do anything that might offend them. Anyway, they're having a hard time of it, just like the travellers.'

Davie here seems to be identifying all travelling folk with the true gypsies, whose land of origin is generally agreed to have been somewhere in North-West India; however, although this remark is in itself of the highest interest (coming, as it does, from a Scots travelling man with a strong sense of clan tradition) it is probably better evidence of Davie's innate kindness and powers of empathy than of a deep-seated self-identification with the gypsies. It is impossible to speak with any certainty of the origins of the tinkers, but the likelihood is that they are descendants of an ancient caste of itinerant metal-workers who were part – and an important part – of tribal society; if that is the case, the native tinker clans must have been travelling their own territories centuries before the arrival of the Romany gypsies in North-West Europe.

When the latter did arrive in Scotland in the sixteenth century, they encountered native itinerant groups sharing a similar way of life, and there was undoubtedly a certain degree of socio-biological fusion – and it is consequently safe to say that there cannot be many Scots travelling folk today who have not got a dash of gypsy blood in them – but as of now gypsies and tinkers regard each other as quite distinct groupings, and there is not much love lost between them.

The beauty of Davie's forthright statement is that it breaks through all such social and historical barriers, and reminds that, whether we are travellers or not, we are 'a' Jock Tamson's bairns'.

Davie Stewart died suddenly in October 1972, while on a visit to the St Andrews Folk Club. Although at Kinross, a month or two earlier, he had clearly been far from his usual self, his death came as a profound shock to all his friends, in Scotland and outwith our borders. The very large attendance at his funeral in Dundee bore witness to the real love and affection in which Davie had been held, not only by hundreds of his own folk, but also by the entire Scottish folk-song revival.

Tocher 15, Autumn 1974.

Patrick Shuldham-Shaw

'Gang doon wi' a sang, gang doon'

Patrick Noel Shuldham-Shaw – outstanding collector and maker, and 'Admirable Crichton' of the post-Second World War English Folk Dance and Song society – died suddenly on 16 November 1977, not yet sixty. His loss was a major blow not only to international folk-song and folk-dance scholarship but also to the still developing and expanding folk revival scene, of which he was a generous and sympathetic if at times shrewdly critical friend.

Pat was born, in a manner of speaking, into the EFDSS. His mother, Winifred Shuldham-Shaw, was a tower of strength in the Society in its early days, particularly on the dance side, and Pat carried her work forward with quite spectacular virtuosity. After studying music at Cambridge – his preferred instrument while he was an undergraduate was the oboe – he made pioneer collecting trips to Shetland in the mid-1940s and noted down a considerable quantity of previously unrecorded fiddle music.

He also 'collected' the Papa Stour sword dance, and eventually became so much part of the North Isles scene that he was several times invited to play an official role in the flamboyant Viking ceremonial of Up-Helly-Aa, the Shetland New Year.

His greatest coup in the Northern Isles was, however, his recovery of a version of 'King Orfeo' (Child 19) from John Stickle of Baltasound, Unst, in April 1947 (*Scottish Studies* 20: 124). Bronson expressed the importance of the discovery very well when he wrote (in *Traditional Tunes of the Child Ballads*, Vol. 1, p. 275): 'That a tune should in the midst of the twentieth century be recovered for this whisper from the Middle Ages was as little to be expected as that we should hear "The horns of Elfland faintly blowing".' Pat's recording of this rarest of ballads can be heard on the Topic LP 12T160 (Child Ballads, No. 1).

In England itself he went on collecting tours into the Forest of Dean with Maud Karpeles, the principal trophy of their forays being a beautiful version of 'The Cherry Tree Carol'.

Pat's foremost preoccupation at all times, however, was the dissemination – the 'ploughing back' – of what he and others had collected. An accomplished dancer himself – morris, sword, 'country' – he carried the standard of English folk dance not only through the length and breadth of the other country but also as far afield as the USA, where he was a much-loved figure at such institutions as Berea College in Kentucky. He composed dances in the American idiom for the mountain kids in this college, including one 'Levi Jackson' – which won a prize in a special dance competition.

Pat was also a frequent visitor to the Netherlands, where he taught English folk-dance to an enthusiastic Dutch society for a quarter of a century. (He was due to spend Christmas with these Dutch friends, and to celebrate his sixtieth birthday among them. It would have been his twenty-seventh annual visit to the Netherlands.)

It should be mentioned, in this connection, that Pat was a marvellous linguist, and that he was capable of picking up not only new languages but also dialects and patois with seemingly effortless ease. (When the cast of *Umabatha*, the Zulu 'Macbeth', visited the School of Scottish Studies, he was heard speaking to them in their native tongue.)

Among the English dances he composed were: 'Silver for the Matthews' (in honour of the Silver Wedding of old EFDSS friends in 1955); 'Margaret's Waltz' and 'Walpole Cottage' (in the 1960s); and 'Ganiford's Meggot' (1974). He had an amazing facility for composing tunes in a variety of idioms; they were mostly catchy tunes, and lay as close in to their dances as the skin to the apple.

A year or two ago Pat was invited by Aly Bain to a party in honour of a newly married couple, and there was a good deal of exuberant music-making. At one point Aly told Pat he would play him a tune he had picked up in Canada, and he was surprised when Pat immediately joined in on his piano accordion. Aly's find was Pat's own tune 'Margaret's Waltz'! (I can personally vouch for the truth of this anecdote which already circulates in folk variants, for I was present at the party.)

In 1971 Pat was awarded the Gold badge of the EFDSS in recognition of his services to folk-song and dance, and of his contribution to the overall work of the Society. Nan Fleming-Williams received the award in the same year.

For the past five years Pat had been working on the great Greig/Duncan collection of Aberdeenshire folk-song, and it is nothing short of a tragedy that he has not lived to carry this work through to its conclusion – work for which he was uniquely fitted – or even to see the first fruits of his labours in print. His friends at the School of Scottish Studies – and there has never been a more popular adopted member of the School staff – have good reason therefore for an additionally deep and poignant sense of loss.

Willie Scott

In October 1961 the Howff Folk Song Club in Dunfermline held its first meeting. John Watt, the founder and organiser, had a promising corps of locals lined up, and he had invited several performers from the 'parent' Howff in the High Street of Edinburgh, but the man who stole the show at that memorable opening night was neither from Fife nor from Edinburgh. He was a tall, slow-spoken, silver-haired shepherd from the Borders, sixty-four years old at that time, who was employed at Kingseat of Outh, above Kelty, and had come along after hearing that the Club was starting and that there was a seat reserved for him.

When Willie Scott rose to sing that evening he was well aware that the audience of youthful folk fans gathered in the smoky room was probably not too familiar with the sound of traditional Scots folk-song. Furthermore, there was always a possibility – seeing that the Howff was a completely new venture – that one or two of the younger ones might be tempted to 'take the mickey'. Any fears of this sort were instantly dispelled when Willie started singing. He struck up 'There's Bound to be a Row' with easy confidence and confiding drollery, and it was clear before he had come to the end of the song that he had completely won over this new audience.

In previous years Willie had performed hundreds of times at herds' suppers and at the Border kirns, to audiences sharing his own background, predilections and speech idioms. His father – also a shepherd – had been a singer, and Willie remembers well the jollifications at fairs and sales all over the Border country when he was a child. 'There was aye singin at the clippins, and at night the fiddle would come oot and they'd start dancin.' The same pattern of life continued, with very little change, throughout his working career, and the Scottish revival folk-scene was therefore lucky to become the beneficiary of a tradition so vital, and yet so solid and homogeneous. At Dunfermline the world of John Leyden and James Hogg seemed to communicate directly with the new cosmopolitan folk audience of industrial Scotland through the lips and personality of this masterly veteran tradition-bearer.

William James Scott, scion of a long line of Border shepherds, was born at Andrews Knowes in the Dumfriesshire parish of Canonbie in 1897; his father was working there at the time as a gamekeeper. Canonbie is just about as near the Border as you can get in that area, so Willie was born a Scotsman by an even narrower margin than Hugh MacDiarmid (a native of Langholm three or four miles to the north). He was one of a family of seven children, nearly all of whom turned out to be gifted singers and musicians – particularly his elder brother Tom whose voice can be heard on the

Folkways LP *The Borders* (FW 8776). Tom (who died in 1970) was also a versatile performer on fiddle, accordion, 'moothie' and Jew's harp. John, in 1977 by then in his early eighties and living in Hawick, was source singer of one or two of Willie's most popular songs. When he was a wee loon, Willie taught himself to play the fiddle, and a love for traditional Lallan folk-music – particularly the dance tunes – has remained with him throughout his life.

As Willie's father took a job across the Border in Cumberland just after the turn of the century, Willie got his first schooling near Brampton, so he early became acquainted with the lore of the 'land of the beck' as well as with that of the 'land of the burn'. (It is noteworthy that two of his most popular items, 'Irthingwater Hounds' and 'The Kielder Hunt' are songs from the English side.) After three years, however, his father was back in Scotland, and Willie got the rest of his schooling at Ewes, near Langholm, and later at Allanwater, in the parish of Teviothead.

Willie left school at eleven to start work on a farm at Stobs near Hawick. He worked a twelve-hour day – 6 a.m. to 6 p.m. ('or later, if you could still see'). For these long hours of farm service he received 7s (35p) a week – which was all that was left of his wage after the cost of his keep had been deducted. Willie stayed at Stobs until he was sixteen; he then accompanied his father to Northhouse, Allerybar, Teviotdale, where he did the same work (general farm service) until he was eighteen.

Willie Scott married when he was nearing twenty; his bride was Frances Isabel Thomson, the daughter of a Canonbie ploughman. The wedding took place in 1917 at Almondside, Canonbie. Frances was a champion whistler, who won every whistling competition on the west marches of the Border; she was also a good singer – Willie learnt his version of 'The Bonnie Wee Tramping Lass' from her – and no mean accordionist. In addition, she was fond – like Willie himself – of taking part in amateur dramatics; Frances and he appeared together in one of Joe Corrie's plays. They had six children, all of whom to a greater or lesser extent inherited their parents' musical talents. Willie and his wife were together for forty-three years; she died in 1960.

Willie Scott's life from 1917 until his retirement in 1968 was very much the life described in 'The Shepherd's Song' (which latter, incidentally, he learnt from his elder brother Tom, who got it from John Irvine of Langholm). Not long after his marriage he went to Dryhope in what he himself calls the 'Jimmie Hogg' country; he herded at the Hirsel, two miles up St Mary's Loch. After a year at Dryhope he moved to Braidlee, near Hermitage Castle, and remained there for nine years. His longest stay in one place was during his next engagement, at the Nine Stane rig (where the famous warlock Lord Soulis was boiled); here he remained for sixteen years. Following this he shepherded at Hartwoodmyres, staying there for nine years (during which period Francis Collinson discovered and recorded Willie and his elder brother Tom for the School of Scottish Studies: this was in 1953.)

His next job took him away from the Borders for the first time; he went to Kingseat of Outh, which is in the Cleish Hills above Kelty, and was there for nearly eleven years. It was during this period that he 'crashed' the modern folk scene. In 1963 he moved to Upper Monynut, on the borders of East Lothian and Berwickshire, and remained there for the next five years. His subsequent career brought him many further moves, including trips as far afield as the USA and Australia.

About the shepherd's life there is no space to write here: readers are referred to R.

B. Robertson's *Of Sheep and Man* (1957) and Richard Perry's *I went a-Shepherding* (1944). However, it may not be out of place to remind readers that there can be few jobs which call for such self-abnegating devotion to one's charges as that of a shepherd. One single story – not from Willie, although he has his own memories of shepherds who perished in the snow – must serve to remind us of this easily forgotten fact. On 6 May 1956 the *Sunday Mail* carried a story about a seventeen-year-old shepherd, Ralph Forlow, who loved his sheep and died for them in 1954, in a blizzard high up in the Galloway hills. A search party found him days later lying dead in the shelter of a wall; the howls of his faithful collie had guided them to where it stood over the body. A memorial cairn was erected at the foot of Millfire, where the boy died: on a tablet set in the cairn are the following lines:

> On Scotland's page o' gilded fame
> Inscribe the shepherd hero's name.
> Gie him a place amang the great
> The men o' war, or kirk or state,
> An' add this message, chiselled deep:
> The guid herd died tae save his sheep.

There is another old saying, which Willie would no doubt endorse: 'Ony fule can write a book, but it taks a man tae herd the Merrick'.

After Willie's entrée to the folk scene via John Watt's howff in Dunfermline, he became almost a resident singer at this establishment. Then things moved very fast indeed. Bruce Dunnet (who was working for Arnold Wesker's Centre 42) invited him to appear at the Singers' Club in London in 1961; thereafter he was continually receiving invitations form all over Britain. He appeared at the traditional folk music get-togethers at Keele and Loughborough; got invitations to Edinburgh and Glasgow, and to Whitby, Redcar, Girvan and many other festivals, rapidly becoming one of the best-known figures in the entire revival. When the Blairgowrie festivals, organised by the Traditional Music and Song Association of Scotland, began in the mid-1960s, he presented a cup for the Men's Traditional Singing and promptly carried it off himself. When 'Blairgowrie' became Kinross, Willie stayed with it and helped to build up its nationwide popularity. New ventures such as the Keith Festival (first held in 1976) received his enthusiastic support, and on his own home ground he helped to make the Newcastleton Festival one of the most enjoyable events of the summer folk season.

As many who have followed his career in the Revival can confirm, his involvement with the 'new wave' of singers and musicians has been by no means solely a one-way process. If hundreds of young folk benefited greatly from making his acquaintance and hearing him sing, he too drew a great deal of sustenance and inspiration from this ever-widening folk-scene. It also gave him an opportunity which he might otherwise not have had of meeting a number of traditional singers from widely differing parts of Scotland. What could happen in this maelstrom of creativity and community experi-ence is vividly illustrated by the development, on Willie's lips, of the Kintyre song 'Callieburn' ('Machrihanish Bright and Bonnie'). This song, which refers to an emigra-tion from Kintyre in the early nineteenth century, was preserved in the repertoire of the MacShannon family in and around Machrihanish: I first heard it from the late James MacShannon (also a shepherd) in 1940. Eighteen years later Willie Mitchell, a butcher from Campbeltown, recorded it for the School of Scottish Studies; he sang a longer version which he had collected from Mr Reid, the farmer at Callieburn. At this same session in 1958 Alec MacShannon recorded the short version preserved in his family.

For several years I had tried to get Willie Mitchell to come with members of his family to one or other of the folk music events of the period; eventually he turned up at the Blairgowrie Festival of 1968, and the scene was set for a creative fusion of considerable interest.

Willie Scott takes up the tale: 'It was ae night in the Sun Lounge of the Angus Hotel. It was one of the best parties I've ever been at. I'd never met Willie Mitchell – I never kent there was such a man. He stole the show earlier on at the Men's Singing. I asked him for songs I'd heard from shepherds at the ram sales ... right back ... and I ca'd him Mr Mitchell. He said, 'Dinna put handles to my name – nae misters. I'm just Willie Mitchell.' 'Weel', I said, 'I enjoyed you. Hearin you in the hall – "Nancy's Whisky" – made my festival.' On that occasion, Archie Fisher gave of his best, and several other people sang, but Willie Scott demanded more songs from Willie Mitchell, and eventually he sang 'Callieburn' using the tune already recorded from the MacShannons; his daughter and son-in-law joined in. Willie Scott was tremendously struck by the song, asked later for it to be sung again, and got Willie Mitchell to write out the words. A few months later I recorded him singing it. The words were as he had received them from Willie Mitchell, but the tune had been totally transformed. For interest's sake, we append both tunes, with the short MacShannon text as recorded in 1958, and the longer text obtained by Willie Mitchell from Reid of Callieburn which Willie Scott sings in its entirety.

Willie has often taken shepherds' crooks carved by himself to the various festivals he has attended, and those who have seen them will acknowledge that in this sphere too he is both craftsman and artist. He has received many prizes for his outstandingly beautiful crooks, and while at Kingseat of Outh he received a commission from the Duke of Edinburgh to make a crook. For years he has been a familiar figure at the Highland Show at Ingliston, exhibiting his produce.

In October 1969 Willie was admitted to Peel Hospital, Galashiels, and underwent a major operation. He was kept in hospital for six months, but thereafter made a very successful recovery.

It remains to add that Willie's children and grandchildren are carrying on the tradition of the singing Scotts. Sandy (now in Australia) and Jim are excellent singers, and Douggie sings and plays the accordion. Willie's grandson Lindsay – the son of Robert, who died three years ago – is one of the 'wild rovers of the Revival'. The son whom Willie regarded as the best singer of the lot – Thomas – was killed over the Netherlands on New Year's Day 1945 while serving with the RAF. He is buried at Cleves.

In March 1977 the Edinburgh Folk Club, based at 23 George Square, paid a friendly visit to the Hawick Folk Club, where they were received by Willie Scott. Willie liked the look of the Sandy Bell's Broadsheet T-shirt and expressed a wish to acquire one. But there was one snag. 'The trouble wi thae T-sarks,' he said, 'is they're ower sma'.'

A crook and a T-sark! This seems a fitting escutcheon for Hawick's Will Scott, whom we greet with affection, admiration and gratitude on the occasion of his eightieth birthday.

Tocher, 25, Spring 1977.

Willie Mitchell

From Runabay Head, on the north-eastern coast of County Antrim, the Mull of Kintyre (if visible) looks like a small green hump on the horizon. From the Mull, on a clear day, you get a grandiose vision of a great wide stretch of the coast of Ireland; the closest distance between the two countries is less than twelve miles. A familiar phrase in classical Irish literature – and in Joyce's *Ulysses* – tells of the 'sea-divided Gael', but a visit to the peninsula of Kintyre provides ubiquitous evidence that the North Channel has been, for millennia, a crowded causeway rather than a barrier. This easy, inviting sea-route has been in constant use since prehistoric times, and with itinerant soldiers, traders, missionaries and colonists have travelled songs and stories, artefacts and minerals, languages and learning.

It is important to remember that the traffic has always been in both directions; if the most important single event in early Scottish history can be said to have been the foundation of the kingdom of Dalriada by *Scoti* (Irish Gaels) who had crossed that same strip of water, it is also true that Ulster history has often been influenced by visitors from across the Moyle. It was not for mere literary effect that Camden (in his *Britannia*) described the peninsula of Kintyre as thrusting itself 'greedily towards Ireland'. Another historical fact which has to be borne in mind, when one scrutinises the cultural mix, is that both Ulster and Kintyre were successfully colonised, in the seventeenth century, by Lowlanders from Renfrewshire and Ayrshire, and that in both areas the Gaelic language has co-existed with Lowland Scots right up to the present century.

My first prospecting foray into Kintyre was in the summer of 1940, just before I joined the Army. I had the good fortune to meet a shepherd, Jimmy McShannon, who not only gave me open-handed hospitality at his cottage at Kylepole, above Machrihanish, but also spent a good deal of the night singing Kintyre folksongs – including one or two that were instantly recognisable as 'bothy songs', blood brothers of the racy Aberdeenshire cornkisters. I asked Jimmy to tell me about his surname, which I had never come across before, and he explained that the original form of the name had been MacShennack; he believed his family was descended from the *seanchaidh* (historian/storyteller) who had come over from Ireland with General Alexander MacDonald – this being the famous Alasdair Mac Colla Chiotaich, alias Young Colkitto, who played such a dramatic part in Montrose's campaign of 1644. (McKerral, in his *Kintyre in the 17th Century*, published in 1948, gives four forms of the name, viz. Macoshenag, Makcochenell, McCochennan and Shannon, and states that the family were harpers to the Clan Donald in Kintyre. The first mention of them is in a rental of 1505; in that year Murdoch or Muriach Macoshenog held a 4 merkland rent-free for his service as harper. Descendants of this Murdoch who became proprietors of Lephenstrath changed the name to Shannon in the eighteenth century.)

From this one fortunate encounter I could see that there must be a great deal to be collected in Kintyre, but circumstances prevented my return there till 1956. It was while I was working in Aberdeenshire in 1954 that I was given information (by J. S. Woolley, of the Linguistic Survey of Scotland) about a 'very interesting man' in Campbeltown; this was a character called Willie Mitchell, a butcher to trade, who was also an ardent collector of songs, and a prolific local poet. Woolley had made recordings of this Kintyre bard singing and reading some of his own productions; he let me hear these, and they at once caught my fancy; but the piece of information which decided me to make Kintyre a priority was the news that Willie Mitchell had written a large number of songs in a book. My own field-collecting in 1951 and 1952 had been greatly helped by the discovery of the scholar-ploughman Willie Mathieson, who had written upwards of 400 songs in three large ledger books, and I had a hunch that Willie Mitchell's work would provide a similar springboard. This expectation turned out to be well and truly justified.

In December 1956, at his home in Smith Drive, Campbeltown, I found Willie Mitchell – a relaxed, friendly, obviously very fit wee man; a face full of humour and sympathetic intelligence, and with that familiar ruddy sheen which seems the cachetic birthright of all butchers. His charming family (wife Agnes, and daughters Agnes, Mary and Catherine) all seemed to share his enthusiasms in full measure, and these included – in addition to poetry, singing, music-making and collecting – a passion for cycling; he told me that he had covered thousands of miles on holidays in Ireland and England, as well as in the Highlands. One of his songs, which was written in 1950 for a Cycling Club concert in Machrihanish, neatly brings it all together. (The tune is 'Courtin' in the Kitchen').

> We are the Mitchells three,
>   We're members of the wheelers,
> And you can plainly see
>   With the doctors we're not dealers.
> We cycle every day;
>   It keeps us bright and merry.
> We could cycle all the way
>   From the Pans to Inveraray.
>
> Ri tooral ooral ay…

He showed me his manuscript song-book, which he had started in 1945, and it proved to be an exemplary – and quite fascinating – specimen of its kind. The book contained (in 1956) forty-nine items, of which twenty-three were songs obtained from oral tradition in Kintyre; the remainder consisted of twelve songs copied from print (e.g. old numbers of the *Campbeltown Courier*); nine poems and song-texts obtained from Campbeltown residents and people living in the area; four songs composed by Willie himself, and one sentimental nostalgic 'homeland song' ('Oor Ain Glen'), with the composer and the writer of the lyric both duly credited. The last mentioned item happened to be the first song written in the book, and its presence provided another reminder of Willie Mathieson's manuscript collection made in Aberdeenshire and Banff, for the first item in the latter is Kenneth Macleod's well-known and much anthologised 'hiking song', 'The Road to the Isles'.

The songs from local oral tradition in Willie Mitchell's book are all painstakingly documented; the source-singer is given in every case, and detailed notes relating to the song are usually appended. For example, 'Killeonan Braxy Skin' has the following note:

> Supplied by James McShannon, he has no particulars, but the McQueen mentioned was policeman at Stewarton and grandfather of the present councillor McQueen (1949). Time about the year 1870. See sheet version supplied by Archd McEachran, Kilblaan.

On 'Campbeltown Once More' Willie comments:

> The chorus of this one is familiar to fishermen. It was written in Salonika, during the '14–'18 war, by a Campbeltonian Peter Gilchrist. It is based on a Welsh song 'In Swansea Town Once More'. Also 'The Holy Ground'.

Examining the collection, I observed that, of the songs from local oral tradition, five had been obtained from Alec McShannon and two from James McShannon. These, Willie informed me, were brothers, and it soon emerged that James was the same Jimmy McShannon, shepherd at Kylepole, who had sung to me sixteen years previously. A recording session with all three McShannons – for there was another brother, Jock – was soon arranged, and I enjoyed a reunion with my host of 1940. It seemed appropriate that members of a family which had for many generations supplied harpers to the Clan Donald in Kintyre should be the principal tradition-bearers discovered by Willie Mitchell. All three brothers were excellent singers. Their father, John McShannon, had been a shepherd in Glen Breakerie, near the Mull of Kintyre, and Jimmy had followed in his footsteps. Jock had worked for a time as a miner in the small coal-mine at Drumlemble, near Machrihanish; later he got a job at the pier and worked in Campbeltown itself, so Willie Mitchell got to know him before the other two. Alec had spent most of his life since childhood in farm-service; at the age of nine he was driving a reaper on the farm of Hillside. He had also worked for a spell at the aerodrome ('keeping the Wrens warm'). These three brothers – the 'Shennacks', as they were nicknamed – together made a formidable impression of robust humour, camsteerie drollery and devil-may-care spunk.

Another name which caught my eye when looking through Willie's song-book was that of Archibald McEachran. I have already mentioned the reference to him in the note to 'Killeonan Braxy Skin'; he reappeared in a note to Alec McShannon's Kintyre-localised version of the Irish song 'The Blazing Star o' Drum'. Here is Willie's note:

> Alec McShannon supplied this one, about a blacksmith, an Irish lad possibly, who courted the lass in the Drum farm. Alec thought he went overseas, but the song [in Alec's version, H. H.] suggests that the girl travelled too. See also McEachran's version, p. 64.

Turning to that page, I found 'The Blazing Star o' Drum', described as 'Irish Version', with the note:

> This is the original song as supplied to me by Archd McEachran, Kilblaan, who obtained it from Sam Henry, the well-known collector of Irish folk-songs. Mr McEachran thinks the tune we use is a genuine Kintyre melody.

Here was concrete evidence of friendly Scots-Irish scholarly collaboration, and a few pages away I came on another. This was in the note to 'The Thatchers of Glenrea', one of two items supplied with a tune (in sol-fa notation). The note reads as follows:

> This song was composed by Hector McIlfatrick, a thatcher of Ballycastle, who died there about 1900. It was supplied to the collector of Irish songs, Sam Henry, by Mr A. McEachran of Kilblaan, who collected it from Hugh McMillan of Kilbride, who in turn heard it from the author. This is a real country tune, it's a pity that all the words are not worthy of being sung.

With 'The Thatchers', therefore, we traverse the Moyle in both directions; it was written by an Irish labourer while working in 'the shire of Argyle'; was learned by a Kintyre man direct from the author; was passed on by the Kintyre man to a local collector, and later transmitted by this collector to Sam Henry in Coleraine. It seems possible that the McMillan who erupts in the last verse of the song might be a relative of the McMillan who learned it from the author:

> Then down comes McMillan, he gave a wild roar:
> 'The big Irish thatchers have arrived on our shore.
> My master he wants you without any delay
> For to go an' theek rashes, but not to Glenrea.'

There is even a mixture of Scots and Irish dialect in an earlier verse:

> 'I can theek wi' ould rashes, wi' heather or ling,
> Bent, bracken, or dockens or any wan thing.'
> 'Oh, you're just the man 'il get plenty tae dae,
> And I'll get you a ladder,' says McNeill o' Glenrea.

The next item in the book is a poem 'Lines on Beagwal of Ancient Carskey', a lively piece of crambo-clink about a 'wee mystic creature' who haunted the mansion of Col. McMillan McNeill of Carskey. The author of the poem is given as John McInnes, 208 Cumberland Street, Glasgow, and again the ascription follows: supplied by Archd McEachran.

Mr McEachran, a diligent local collector, was a farmer at Kilblaan (McEachrans had been in Kilblaan at least since 1830). According to Willie, he probably collected songs at markets and fairs. The link between the two men was one Captain Taylor, of the Keil Hotel, Southend, who took an interest in local folklore and in antiquarian pursuits of various kinds; it was Taylor who – knowing of Willie's interest in Kintyre songs - recommended him (sometime in the late 1940s) to contact Archie McEachran. Willie corresponded with Archie, and finally the latter paid him a visit in the butcher's shop, thus inaugurating a fertile co-operative friendship. Archie McEachran died suddenly in 1956; by a strange coincidence, this was the very day Willie Mitchell brought the

McShannons together for the first ceilidh recorded for the School in his house in Smith Drive.

McEachran is one of the oldest names in Kintyre. According to McKerral 'The Maceachrans of Kilellan were the Mairs of Fee of South Kintyre, and were represented in 1505 by Colin of Kilellan, who, in 1499, had received a charter of his lands of Kilellan and of his office of Mair of Fee, from King James IV. He is almost certainly the Colin who, with his spouse Katherine, is commemorated in the fine but injured Celtic Cross which lies in Kilkerran cemetery, and most probably was either a brother or nephew of Ivar Maceachran, Rector of Kylreacan (probably Kilneachtan in Islay), who is commemorated on the Town Cross of Campbeltown. They lost their estate temporarily during the Montrose wars, but recovered it from the Marquis of Argyll in 1659.' McEachran is derived from Gaelic *each*, horse, and *tighearna*, lord, therefore 'Lord of the horses'. It is curious to note, in this connection, that the first name for Kintyre on record is that given by Ptolemy, *Epidion Akron*, which must mean 'the promontory of the *Epidii*' – 'the horse-people'. The name suggests that the form of Celtic spoken by the inhabitants of Kintyre in the first centuries of the Christian era was P-Celtic (i.e. a type of primitive Welsh or possibly Pictish) rather than Q-Celtic (Gaelic). Ironically, the South-West Lowlanders of the seventeenth-century plantation, who gradually subverted the Gaelic language brought to Kintyre from Ireland in those same early centuries of the Christian era, must themselves have been, in large part, descendants of the P-Celtic speakers of the ancient British Kingdom of Strathclyde.

The name Mitchell first appears in Kintyre in the mid-seventeenth century; it seems certain, therefore, that Willie is of planter stock. He was born in Campbeltown in 1904. His father was a riveter in the 'Trench' shipyard (the name commemorates the entrenched camp or fort on the north side of Campbeltown Loch which was erected in 1639 by the Marquis of Argyll as a precaution against possible invasion by the Earl of Antrim). In the early years of this century the Trench was a flourishing business, with usually three or four ships on the stocks; the work force consisted of about 300 men. 'An army of men marched out and back every day along to the yard.' There were over a hundred fishing skiffs in Campbeltown at that time. Willie used to bring his father his dinner at the middle of the day – he came out of school for his own dinner, and after collecting his dad's he ran across to the Trench with it. The men nicknamed him 'Filly' because he 'skipped and scampered along'. 'There were wee sheltered corners in the shipyard where each man went with his lunch. They boiled their tea on the smithy fire, and drifted away to each wee corner and took their meal there. And then the bell went.'

Willie stayed at school till he was fifteen. As he was a promising scholar, interested in history, geography, English and poetry – he specially remembers the period devoted to poetry on Fridays – the Rector wanted to move him into a higher class, but Willie (much against his parents' wishes) decided to 'pack it in'. 'Financially it would have been out of the question – there weren't the same chances in those days.' In 1919 he got his first job with Dougal Smith, 'a butcher over on the Dalintober side', and stayed there for five years. Then after another seven years working in the Cooperative butcher's shop, he left the town temporarily and got jobs in Carradale and Tarbert. In 1934 he married Agnes Morrison, the daughter of a Campbeltown mason, and moved back to the town where he got a job with yet another butcher. In 1954 he was at last his own boss, and he ran a butcher's shop in Long Row with great efficiency and vigour until 1977, when he retired, and his son-in-law Alastair Stewart took it over.

A poem he wrote in 1940 which is in the form of a monologue delivered by 'an auld Glesca wife' paints a witty self-portrait of 'Willie the butcher'. It is entitled 'Evacuees at Mile End'. The lady concerned quite likes Campbeltown, but ...

> There's just ae wee flaw,
>   for there's ane I can't stan' –
> the pompous wee butcher
>   wha comes wi' the van.
> He says he's a bard,
>   but I've heard that his verses
> are used by his cronies
>   for dichtan their erses.
> Still, we aye get a laugh
>   when he comes in tae vend
> his mutton an' beef
>   tae the folk at Mile End.

A book of his own poems and songs, started eight years before the book containing the folk-songs he collected, includes a number of pieces in the folk idiom. The following was written in 1939:

> As Hitler was a-walking in his garden one day,
> Along came wee Goebbels and to him did say
> 'Oh Fuehrer dear Fuehrer, it's worryin' me
> Just why you are scuttling all the German navee.'

> 'I will sink all the ships in the German navee
> And send them to the depths with the Admiral Graf Spee.
> Then I will drink poison and bid you farewell,
> And be met by Auld Nick when I get down to Hell.'

Other pieces in the poetry book are directed to be sung to tunes such as 'The Tinkler's Waddin', 'The White Cockade', 'Robin Adair', 'Father O'Flynn', and 'We're no awa tae bide awa'.

It was in the late 1930s that Willie began to take an increased interest in the folk-songs of Kintyre. He had learnt songs in his younger days, particularly from 'Maxie' Thomson, miner in the Drumlemble colliery. ('A Tidy Smilin' Wife', printed on p. 16, came from Maxie.) However, it was after making the acquaintance of the three Shennacks (McShannons) that his interest was really awakened. In 1937 Jimmy McShannon married his second wife Polly, and the wedding festivities lasted all night with much singing, 'dancing and deray'. In the same year Willie went to Drumlemble every week to sing in the Gaelic choir, and got to know Alec McShannon who lived there. (According to Alec, 'they aye cam in for their tea efter the choir'). Alec's wife Lizzie, who came from Drumlemble, had a 'lovely singing voice', and husband and wife often sang duets such as 'The Crookit Bawbee'. Jock McShannon, the 'brother in the middle', lived in Campbeltown, and because he used to compete at the Fair Day concerts was the best known of the three.

The songs learned from Alec, in addition to those already mentioned, were 'The Shepherd's Daughter', 'Machrihanish Bay' (a version of an Irish song, 'The Wreck of the *Enterprise*'), 'Jock the Ploughboy', 'Jorum Bog', and a version of 'Callieburn', the strikingly beautiful emigrants' song already printed in *Tocher*, No 25.

In 1957 Alan Lomax devised and presented a series of radio programmes entitled 'A Ballad-Hunter Looks at Britain', and I collaborated with him on the two Scottish ones. We used Willie's 'Nancy's Whisky' (sung to the second of the two tunes printed below) in one of these, and it attracted a great deal of attention and comment from all over the country. Dominic Behan (Brendan's brother) was particularly impressed by it.

Willie's cycling tours, which started in 1928 with a trip to Glencoe, brought him into contact with other singers. In 1948 he cycled all over Ireland, taking in Belfast, Dublin, Cork and Galway. In 1952 he was again in Ireland, spending a week in Dundalk. On the roads of Argyll he was a kenspeckle figure. Right through the 1960s he and his family enjoyed a marvellous series of weekly ceilidhs at the inn in Bellochantuy, and one of his own songs (to the tune of 'Villikins and his Dinah', alias 'The Ould Orange Flute') communicates vividly the pleasure that he got from these halcyon nights on the spree:

> It's always a pleasure when the day's work is done
> To mount on the bike and go out on a run.
> By Westport and Tangy the road's by the sea,
> An' it's ten miles frae Campbeltoon tae Bellochantuy.
>
> By the side of the road there's a cosy wee inn
> Where you are made welcome when you tirl at the pin.
> It's there you may sample the sweet barley bree
> For they aye keep the best o't at Bellochantuy ...
>
> There's big Jimmie Sterie, the boss o' the bar,
> He's fond o' the mandolin and the guitar.
> If ye ask for a drink while the music is playin',
> He has filled oot a gill ere he kens what he's daein'...

They always finished these sessions at Bellochantuy with the 'The Parting Glass' (an Irish version of 'Good Night and Joy be wi' ye a'"). 'When we made for home,' says Willie, 'there was moonlight on the water ... we were home at midnight ... life was a good thing.'

Willie has three daughters, Agnes, Mary and Catherine, all of whom are fine singers and guitarists. (Mary's first instrument was the mandolin – which has been Willie's own favourite instrument since 1921, when he sent 30s to a shop in Hastings for one he had seen advertised. Later Agnes, Willie's wife, learned to play the mandolin too.) When the girls were young, they heard plenty of singing: Burns songs such as 'Ye Banks and Braes' and 'Afton Water', and ditties out of a book *The Globe Song Folio* that Willie had bought in 1925 (it included 'My Old Kentucky Home', 'I dreamt that I dwelt in Marble Halls' and Byron's 'Dark Lochnagar').

For about twelve years, from the mid-1960s to the late 1970s, Willie's family operated as a folk group called The Mitchells, performing at various functions in and beyond Kintyre, at old folk's homes, for the Salvation Army etc. It started when Willie was asked to do a programme for the Kintyre Music Club, and he called in the rest of the family to assist him. In the early days, according to Willie, it was more a 'sing-song' than a group, but when he and his wife stopped coming out with the rest of the family, it developed along 'popular lines' into a disciplined domestic musical unit. Traditional songs still featured in their repertoire, but the group also used a lot of the Corries' material, making their own arrangements of it. (According to Agnes, Willie's eldest daughter, they 'got fed up with "O Flower of Scotland" before audiences did'). Until 1970 they sang quite a number of Irish songs, but with the coming of the present Troubles some of these disappeared from the menu. The needs and wishes of their local audiences dictated the nature of the programmes ... 'they wanted something lively ... drinking songs ... something they could get a laugh from.' Numbers which always retained their popularity included 'Ye Jacobites by Name', 'Nancy's Whisky' and Willie's own song – which we print here – 'The Road to Drumlemble'. (Willie himself did not quite approve of the Mitchells' arrangement of the last named item. 'There are some songs, you feel they shouldn't have an arrangement, they shouldn't have a harmony. They had to alter the time ...'). Another song of Willie's – 'Western Ferries', which celebrated a spirited challenge to the MacBrayne monopoly, and which was partly written by Agnes, Willie's wife – enjoyed a temporary popularity. When there was a campaign to save the postal name of Argyll – the Post Office wanted to change it to West Strathclyde – Agnes, Willie's daughter, wrote a song 'We'll fight to save Argyll' to the tune of 'Campbeltown Once More', and this undoubtedly contributed to the success of the campaign.

The final line-up of the group consisted of Agnes; Mary, and Mary's second husband Frank Macnaughton; Catherine, and Catherine's husband John Kerr. At the sessions in May 1979 when the group temporarily reformed for the benefit of the School's tape-recorder, Agnes's husband Alastair Stewart joined them for one or two items.

Revisiting the family this year, I found that Willie's book contained several new items – one of these being 'Sally's Garden', a version of the folk-song which Yeats used as a basis for 'Down by the Sally Gardens'. The wheel had now turned full circle, for the note following the song read:

> Copied from *Tocher* 11, Oct. 1973. In 1956 it was recorded by Hamish Henderson (for the School of Scottish Studies, Edinburgh University) from Jock and Jimmy McShannon. The brothers McShannon sang slightly different tunes.

The next new item in the book was a song 'Ceilidh at Trodigal'; this had been written by Willie himself to the tune of 'Sally's Garden', and it retained the original chorus intact. The most recent addition was an Irish version of 'The Wreck of the *Enterprise* – which Alec McShannon had sung many years before, calling it 'Machrihanish Bay' – and the note following this contains a quotation from the *Belfast News Letter* (6 March 1827) identifying the time and place of the wreck.

Willie has continued to write poetry, just as he has continued to ride his push-bike along the coast roads of what George Campbell Hay called 'lovely long Kintyre'.

Let me close with a poem he wrote in 1970:
I am grown old
Next birthday I'll be sixty-six.
I should be sitting at the Dam corner
With the old men, smoking a pipe,
'Going a stretch', an adventure,
Grouped together for protection
Like sheep, lest the marauding fox
Snaffle the straggler lamb
… so Brother Death would
Follow us, weeding us one by one.

I am grown old, I challenge the hill
And the brae, the wind and the rain.
I cycle and walk in defiance of age.
Perhaps some day, when travelling alone
The wheels will stop, Time will stop.
If I have my way, it will be on a day
When the beauty of Spring makes the earth live anew.
This I have loved with the vigour of youth.
I am grown old; thus would I go,
My wheel on the road, my face to the brae.

Tocher, 31, Summer 1979.

Jock Cameron

In the early 1950s the Scottish Miners' Gala Day, always held in the first week of May, was a much bigger affair than it is now, but the principal attractions were the same; and of these, the Pipe Band competitions, held on the greensward under the shadow of Arthur's Seat, invariably drew large and appreciative crowds. I usually joined old friends from Fife or Lanarkshire for the march from Hillpark Terrace to Holyrood Park, and as often as not found myself following one of the champion pipe bands. One year I had the privilege of conveying the greetings of Sean O'Casey to the gathering; Sean was in Edinburgh for the première of his play *Purple Dust*, but was too infirm to join the march, or even to visit the park. However, he sent a message of solidarity to the miners, recalling that he too had played in a pipe band when he was a young man, and had marched out quite often to Sandymount Strand.

Every year, without fail, I ran into pipers I had met during the Second World War, in Africa or Italy, and in 1954 a member of the Shotts and Dykehead pipe band gave me a rendezvous for an evening sing-song in a bar in Johnston Terrace, near the top of the Lawnmarket. When I turned up, the sing-song was in progress in the back room; it was a very well-conducted affair, with a master of ceremonies keeping punctilious order, and a series of remarkably good tenor and baritone voices regaled us with juicy Edwardian ditties. (Many Scottish miners – particularly the Fifers – are by no means inferior to their Welsh confrères, as far as vocal quality is concerned, and, oratorios excepted, their musical tastes are not dissimilar.) One of the miners present, a man with strong, humorous, aquiline features, seemed rather older than the average of the company, and sat slightly apart from his mates; although the order of the day was very definitely 'sang-aboot', I had the impression for a moment, when it came to his turn, that the MC was going to pass him over. However, he *was* called on to sing; and after a moment's thought he slowly got to his feet, and sang a previously unrecorded Jacobite song, the now famous 'King Fareweel'.

As soon as was decently possible, I got him away from the company, and asked his name and where he had got the song. He told me he was called Jock Cameron and was originally from Fife, but was now living in Granton, Edinburgh; he had learnt the song from his grandfather, a native of Culcabock, just outside Inverness. His grandfather had come to the Fife coalfields as a young man, and there been initiated into the Orange Order by fellow-miners; his son, Jock's father, had also been a fervent Orangeman, and had inherited the family repertoire of folk-songs. Thus it came about that a song which reflected the ideals and achievements of Prince Charlie's followers in 1745 was preserved on the lips of a dynasty of militant Orangemen.

Jock Cameron was born in Cowdenbeath in 1906, and died at his home in Wardieburn Terrace, Granton, in 1971. He was the eldest of thirteen children. His father had worked in the Fife pits for most of his life, and Jock himself first went down the mine at the age of thirteen. In 1925 he joined the Army, and served for three years with the Royal Horse Artillery, mainly in England, but also for a spell with the British Army of the Rhine. At the time he was getting demobbed, at The Black Watch depot in Perth, he met Ruby Ferguson, a cook in the Nurses' Home, and married her in 1928. Jock used to point out, with satisfaction, that after she married him, Ruby's initials were RFC – the same as those of Rangers Football Club! Ruby knitted him a big orange scarf, with blue ends and tassels; Jock used it occasionally 'to cairry the bairn aboot in'. Ruby also knitted him a pair of orange and blue socks which he wore down the pit; according to her 'he got many a beltin' doon there because of them'.

Not long after they were married, the couple moved to Hamilton; Jock worked in a number of pits in the west, sometimes cycling twenty-four miles a day to his work and back again. His children Joan and John were born in 1929 and 1933 respectively. In 1936 the family moved to Edinburgh, and for three years Jock worked at Newtongrange; he got 8s a day, and had his own bus fares to pay.

On the outbreak of war in 1939 he joined the Royal Air Force and stayed in it till 1951, reaching the rank of sergeant. The last four or five years of his service were spent in Northern Ireland – a highly congenial posting for a man with his convictions. After he was demobilised, he returned to the Lothian coalfields and worked at the Lady Victoria mine, Newtongrange. Severe chest trouble at last forced him to leave the pit in 1961, and he spent nine months in the Royal Infirmary. His widow thinks his illness was probably silicosis, although this was never specifically stated. Jock's son had followed him into the pits, but Jock insisted that he should give up coalmining when he himself was admitted to the Infirmary.

The Orange Order meant a great deal in Jock's life. His father had been taken across to Ulster by *his* father to be 'made' an Orangeman at Aughalee; Jock himself was 'made' at a place near Magherafelt, and whenever possible, in later years, he crossed to Ireland for the 'Twelfth'. The closure of many of the Lanarkshire mines after the Second World War led to a migration eastward of West of Scotland Orangemen, and this led to the formation of new lodges in the Edinburgh area and Kirkcaldy. In 1954 Jock described this process as follows: 'They are bringing the Orange seeds with them … the old tree is sort of withering, we'll say, in Lanarkshire … well, it's shooting branches out in the Lothians and Fife.'

Before Jock retired he reached the rank of District Master, and although, by his widow's wish, he did not have a full-scale 'Orange' funeral, he was buried wearing his sash, as his father had been before him.

Jock's whole-hearted commitment to the Orange cause did not prevent him from giving due honour to the memory of another breed of 'Loyalists' who had fought for a different cause in the eighteenth century. Although he always maintained that the mainstream of Scottish patriotism was that represented by Knox, Melville and the Covenanters, he recognised the Jacobites as having been in their own way Scottish patriots. At a ceilidh in 1955 he surprised a predominantly nationalist student audience, who were aware of his Orange affiliations, by introducing 'King Fareweel' as 'an answer to the Battle of Harlaw, and where Hey Johnnie Cope originated'. He explained that his grandfather, from whom he got the song, had been an old Black Watch man, and that 'King Fareweel' was 'one of the Scotland's own'.

At a party later the same night Jock provided a delicious example of the quirkish quizzical sense of humour that always came to the surface when he had had a few drams. Some of the students present must have seemed very well-heeled to Jock, who was still a miner at the coalface, and at least one of them was patently of the same type that half a century earlier had regularly taken the mickey out of the 'great McGonagall' at specially rigged social functions. When this particular individual asked – in a 'gin and macaroon' Edinburgh accent – for a repeat of 'your nice Jacobite song', Jock fixed him with a stern eye and sang (in place of the first verse as printed on the next page):

> O ye've feather beds and carpet rooms –
> Could ye no put up a wee German lairdie?

Jock loved children. When his own two had grown up, he adopted Marie, a really beautiful child, whose father was a West Indian. Marie's welfare became one of his chief preoccupations. He also gave frequent 'wee pairties' for the other children in Wardieburn Terrace. The lamentation of one of the twins who lived up the stair on hearing of his death provides one fitting epitaph for him: 'Why had it to be Mr. Cameron? Could it no have been somebody else?' Another epitaph – and the one he would have most appreciated – is his widow Ruby's gallus and well-deserved tribute: 'He was a hardy tyke!'

Tocher, 34, Winter 1980.

John Strachan

The ceilidh of the 1951 Edinburgh People's Festival was a notable occasion – not least because of the first public appearance in the capital of two magnificent traditional ballad singers from the North-East. One of these was Jessie Murray, a fishwife from Buckie; when she sang her version of 'Lord Thomas and Fair Ellen' (Child 73), there was instant recognition throughout the audience that this was in the most literal sense an extraordinary event, and the same response went out to a bluff seventy-six-year-old Aberdeenshire farmer who rose to sing 'Johnnie o' Braidisley' – his version of the song Child had called 'this precious specimen of the unspoiled traditional ballad' (it is No 114 in *English and Scottish Popular Ballads*). The enthusiasm was justified; it was undoubtedly the first time in history that native folk-singers from the North-East (the great heartland of traditional balladry in Scotland) had ever been heard singing splendid unaccompanied versions of classic ballads at a public gathering in Auld Reekie.

The farmer was John Strachan, of Crichie, St Katherine's, near Fyvie; he had come down from Aberdeen by train the previous day and put up at the Harp Hotel in Corstorphine, because he had been promised an introduction to Helen Cruickshank, a poet for whose work he had a lively regard. Helen lived in Hillview Terrace, just up the hill from the Harp, and poet and singer spent a memorable evening together. When John walked up the hill again the following morning, Helen expressed the hope that he had slept well. 'Never a wink, quine,' said John, 'I was rummelin' and tummelin' in my bed the haill nicht lang, thinkin' aboot ye.'

At the ceilidh that evening John sang on the same platform as the wandering street-singer Jimmy MacBeath – also a conspicuous repository of North-East folklore of all descriptions – but their social backgrounds could not have been more different. Jimmy had come straight from the model lodging-house in Elgin where he was then living; his world was that of the feckless *bas-fonds* described by Jessie Kesson in *The White Bird Passes*. John, on the other hand, was one of the wealthiest farmers in Aberdeenshire; the handsome substantial farmhouse he would return to in a few days was solid evidence of the shrewdness, capacity for hard work and financial acumen that he shared with the formidable class from which he sprang. Yet, in spite of his well-deserved reputation as a skeely and highly efficient farmer, John's chief fame in the North-East was – paradoxically – as a champion of the bothy ballads: of the farm servant's folk-song, that is, a popular song-literature which was often explicitly anti-farmer. From the earliest '2–BD' days of Aberdeen broadcasting from Belmont Street, his rich Buchan voice had

become familiar to listeners all over the North-East, reminiscing about the vicissitudes
of farming life, and singing bothy songs such as 'Harrowin' Time', with its forthright
final verse:

> So now I mean to end my song,
> And I will end wi' this –
> May the plooman get mair wages,
> It is my earnest wish.
> It is my heartfelt wish, I say,
> It is the ploughman's due;
> For he sustains baith rich and peer   [poor]
> By the handling' o' the ploo.

However, John tended to play down the harsher aspects of the old-style bothy chiels'
life: 'Och, they werena oppressed, ye know, like what ye would hear aboot – plenty o'
fun and frolic!'

In 1930 John had been visited by the American collector James Madison Carpenter
and had made several recordings for him – and also helped him to collect from others,
as we shall see later – but the full range of his extraordinary song-repertoire, which ran
the full gamut from fine versions of classic ballads to bawdy Lallan *puirt-a-beul*, did
not become fully apparent until an intensive series of recording sessions in the spring
of 1952 put it on record. Sitting in the conservatory attached to the farmhouse, with a
glass of whisky and ginger wine in front of him, and able to talk or sing *ad lib* about
things that pleased him most, John was properly in his element. A visitor to Crichie
that same year made the observation that even in his late seventies there was something
Byronic about this Buchan farmer – and not only because of the stylish fancy
waistcoats he continued to wear: one of them, in dark blue embroidery bound with
grey, was all of sixty years old, and still seemed well in the fashion.

His animation when singing his favourite ballads has been vividly described by
Alan Lomax, who made a number of recordings from him during our joint tour of the
North-East in the summer of 1951.

> He sang the song ['Johnnie o' Braidisley'] ... with the rant of the old-time singer
> of tales. His eyes sparkled, his face flushed with pleasure, his burry Scots voice
> romped through the verse as he swung his powerful arms in time to the beat of
> the ballad.

Another visitor had remarked, a year or two before, that in spite of his solid hearty
exterior, he had a temperament like quicksilver, and was 'as alert as a monkey'.

John Strachan was born at Crichie – a farm where he lived most of his life (and
where he died) – in 1875. Crichie is about three miles south of Fyvie, and twenty-three
miles north-west of Aberdeen; it lies in the midst of a great tract of rich farming
country. In 1868 John's father, who had made a large amount of money through horse-
dealing, rented Crichie from Lord Aberdeen. The family which had previously farmed
Crichie for many years were the Williamsons (by-named the 'stately Williamsons');
these were – according to John 'a' big men' and great cattle-dealers who in the old days
had walked their herds down from the Muir of Ord to the Falkirk Tryst. However, this
formidable tribe of Williamsons 'ran to daughters', and Strachans moved into their

territory. The vehicle of social mobility, which had earlier been cattle-trading, had thus become – for the Strachans, at any rate – the horse-trade.

It should be added that John himself became a well-known authority on the Clydesdale horse – his love for the breed amounted almost to a passion – and as a breeder and judge he enjoyed a great reputation. He was also renowned in his day as a producer of commercial cattle.

John attributed his father's financial success to the Franco-Prussian war, fought five years before he was born.

'I think,' he wrote in a notebook, 'I am about the only one left that would know about the horse trade. I think the French and the Germans were both here buying horses before the war commenced, and little bits of mares were making £100 freely.' Yet the day of the 'twal ousen plough' was not long past in the North-East, when John was born. In the same notebook he wrote: 'At a Literary Society meeting at Tarves I heard this Mr Mackie give a lecture; I don't remember what it was about, but he told us he was once goadsman at Collynie, that is the man or boy who carried a long stick with a sharp point, and gave any of the twelve oxen a prod when not doing their share of the work. There were very few horses at that time he said.'

About 1888 John's father rented another farm from Lord Aberdeen – this was Craigies, in the parish of Tarves.

> The family went to Craigies, leaving my brother, who was fifteen to sixteen years old, to carry on the work, and a sister to keep house for him. The old man visited every other day, a drive of over seven miles … Crichie certainly had to help stock the new farm. The best of everything went to Craigies. Crichie was not thought much about … I was sent to Gordon College in Aberdeen when I was ten years old and was boarded with one of the masters for two years. I never liked to stay in Aberdeen, and when the Craigies Farm was taken I said I would like to go by bus from Tarves to Udny Station, and then by train to Aberdeen, so as to get home every night. I left a little before seven in the morning and got back about six at night, and during that year a boy from Craigdam, a small cluster of thatched houses near Tarves, came and conveyed me home from the bus every evening, just over a mile, for a whole year. I engaged this lad the first year I was farming when he was sixteen for foreman and I remember the wages paid. This lad, William Diggins, got £12 for the half-year and was supposed to have a very big fee for his age. Samuel Dunn, second horseman £9 and William Wilson £8. The cattleman was a married man and he got £30 per year, a house, meal and milk, a few drills of potatoes and turf in a moss not far away which he had to cut and drive home in his own time. I saw Wilson in Aberdeen not long ago and had a bottle of beer with him and he spoke about the fun we had yoking horses, etc., but not a word about the small wage.
>
> I came home from school in Aberdeen the second year we had the Craigies farm, and got my food with two single men in the kitchen. I was thirteen. The second year I was home we got a binder (Bisset, Blairgowrie, was the make of it) and the people came from far and near to see it.

John often recalled the time when Canadian cattle were being brought to Scotland in shiploads, and landed at Pocra Quay, Aberdeen. The cost for conveying a truckload by rail to the nearest station from Craigies was 7s 6d, but rather than pay that sum his father made John get up early, walk six miles to Udny Station with the dog, take the train to Aberdeen, collect the cattle off the pier and walk them back the sixteen miles to Tarves on foot. Sometimes he collected other folk's cattle too, which further lowered the expense.

In 1895 another farm, Balquhain Mains, was taken for John's brother, and he himself was sent back to Crichie.

It was a real neglected kind of a place when I went back – far too much thrift, and saving expenses. Farm implements of all kinds were needing repairs.'

One thinks of a trenchant verse in a version of 'The Barnyards o' Delgaty', which Jimmy MacBeath got from his father:

> When I got hame tae the Barnyards,
>   Tae wark the wark I took in han',
> I saw the horse they were poorly fed,
>   His harness wisna worth a damn.

When John was twenty-four, his father turned Crichie over to him to run 'on his own hook'. In 1918 Lord Aberdeen sold a large part of his estate, and John bought Crichie and the farm of Greenmyre. By 1939 John owned no less than five farms, but he sold three of them during the Second World War and kept Craigies for his son Billy. Crichie remained a solid base for John himself until his death on 2 November 1958.

It will be seen that when John Strachan was writing notes for lectures (e.g. for the Turriff Agricultural Association, of which he was at one time President) he wrote a careful Gordon's College scholar's English, but when he spoke it was in the raciest of North-East Doric. Here, brought together to form a continuous narrative, are various recordings made over the years: they add a new dimension of colour, life and zest to the bare autobiographical details set down above:

'Fan first I hae mind o' my farm the dwelling hoose was wind and water ticht but had few of the comforts ye find in maist farm hooses the day. There was mebbe a carpet in the best room but sheepskins were the usual covering for the weel scrubbed fleers in the ither rooms. The kitchie fleer was made of stampt earth and it was regularly washed, though hoo that was possible withoot turning the fleer into dubs I cannae imagine. Het, or even caul' water laid on in a house was quite unknown, and usually the well or pump was a good bittie away: candles and lanterns were our source of licht in these days, and were considered a great improvement on the aul' oil cruisies. I mind my mither telling me that she made wicks for them oot o' rashes in her young day. Speaking o' my mither minds me o' the wark she used to dae, and hoo ony of the farmers' wives in these days fitted all their duties into ae day beats me. Mind you the *men* werenae idle. I can mind on the men workin' eleven hours a day at hairst; they used to tak their meals in the field to save time: they got hame brewed ale, aye, hairst ale we ca'ed it, and cheese and oatcakes at ten o'clock, an' their denner at twa o'clock was maistly stoved tatties or broth, and oatcakes and milk.

'The byres and steading were naething like fat [what] we have the day: the maist o' them were gey laich i' the reef, and dark and badly ventilated, and sae ill arranged that they caused a lot of extra wark. Still, the wark was aye deen, an' deen wi' pride, which speaks weel for the men. Fat a *pride* the farm servants in these days took in onything they did, and fat interest and competition and even jealousy there was amon' them ower the heids o' their wark: I've kent a man stay on anither term because he was promised a new piece of harness. Country tradesmen took a pride in their wark tae: I can mind on a tradesman fa was sae prood of a piece of work, that he refused payment when the least fault was found in it. Mind you, labour was more localised in those days, and in the case of farmhands, a gweed man micht shift to a neighbourin' farm just because he wanted a change, and like as not he'd come back to his original farm the next time he shifted. Lord, *foo weel* we *kent* ane anither, an' fat stories an' fat fun an' fat contentment we had in our little self-contained communities! We had some ootside fun tae: dancing was the great amusement, but nae the kind ye see noo. A class was held annually in my district, and master an' servant attended it with the greatest delight. We were taught by Dancie Morrison, an' no sergeant-major ever kept stricter discipline than he did. There was nae patent slippers in these days, but the way these folk in their Sunday beets [boots] went through the steps of a highland fling, a reel, a schottische or a sword dance wad *humble* the tired slitherin' dancers I see the day, an' *shame* the fag-smoking croods round the doors at our dances nooadays.

'Though we worked harder, an' though wages were smaller, an' we had bad houses, little sanitation and nae panel doctors, yet it seems to me that farmers an' their men were bigger and healthier fifty years syne than they are noo. I can mind on five farmers fa bade within three miles of my faither's farm, an' fa weighed twenty to thirty stone each, in fact the heaviest of them weighed thirty-twa stane, an' he was a first cousin of my father's. I'll tell ye a story aboot some o' these lads, an' I can promise you that it's the truth I'm telling ye. John Donald, fa weighed twenty-nine stane was telt by a frien o' his that Kelly, the tailor in George Street, was advertising in the papers that he would mak' a suit for £3, sae John, the first time he was in to market, went to see the tailor an' said he had come for ane of his suits. The tailor couldnae even *measure* the man: he was sae big that he had to get an assistant to haud ae end of the tape on the man's stomach while *he* ran roon aboot him wi the other end, an' when he had done measurin' he told John that if he made him a suit for £3 he wad hae a *deid loss* o' £2 on't. Sae John said to the tailor that the next Friday he would bring in his *twa loons*, an' the tailor could mak the suits for the hale three o' them at £3 each, an' that wad gie him a chance tae square things up. The tailor was fine pleased to get oot of the awkward situation this way, an' agreed. Next Friday John walks into the shop an' says to the tailor, 'Here's ma twa loons', an' fan the tailor looked he saw twa of John's neighbours, Stoney and the Lethen, an they weighed twenty and twenty-two stane respectively. *I* ken fit the tailor said fan he saw them, but I cannae repeat it here. It was real good.

'Newsin' of these days mak's me think of the changes in transport that I've seen in the last fifty year. Fan I was a young man horses an' gigs were the only means of conveyance we had, an' in winter we used sleighs. Even the winters seem to be milder noo than they used to be, but I can mind when the snaw was sae deep that ye couldnae see the taps of the dykes an' jist had to guess which was road and which was field when ye were drivin a sleigh. Ye can well imagine we had plenty of spills in these circumstances, an' I mind a nicht fan I set oot with two neighbours to gang to a dance at Daviot. We had a drive of twal miles each way, an' the roads were completely blocked wi' snaw, sae to save my good trousers frae gettin' soaked fan the sleigh overturned, I hauled a pair of aul' navy blue breeks ower them.*

'Fan we got to the hall I took aff the extra pair of breeks an' hung them on a nail in the porch, an' I clean forgot to take them wi' me fan we set oot for hame. Twa days later an advertisement appeared in the *Free Press*: "Gentleman who left his trousers at the Daviot dance will get same by applying to the secretary." The next issue of *Punch* quoted the *Free Press* advertisement, and headed it "How to dress in the ballroom" or "Oh wert thou in the cauld blast!" Well, this went all round the country, and when I went into a cattle sale in Aberdeen a day or two later there was a kind of a titter went round the place, and a farmer, an awful well-behaved kind o' a man, comes up to me and says "It was never you that left yer breeks at the Daviot ball, wis't?" and I says, "Mercy aye', and then to give this awful well-behaved kind o' a lad a bit o' a shock I says: "And I'll tell ye a lot better than that. I took a young lady the whole way home sitting on my knee and she never noticed." Aye, but in those days a dance was a real good affair, an' there was none o' this tired slitherin' kin' o' shufflin' that passes for dancin' nooadays. When we danced we took a pride in it, and we did proper dances like "The Flowers o' Edinburgh".

'Mercy, what lads the farm servants were to dance. They had nae slippers mind you – they just danced in their Sunday boots. But they werena a *bit* heavy – they put in every beat and patter. Doing square dances they just went through them to perfection, like well-trained soldiers. And they had tremendous good manners – they never bumped you. Though mind you, if they were roused they were a kind o' rough deevils. I mind on one dance where a farm servant asked one o' the maids from Fyvie castle to dance, and she thought she was too good for a farm servant and said no thanks. The lad was a kind o' insulted by this and made up his mind that if she wouldna dance with him she'd not dance with any other body. So he just stood near her. It wisnae lang before another man came up and asked her to dance, but before she could get to her feet the farm servant steps up to the man and says "Ye surely wouldn't dance with that creature would ye? She has a wooden leg", and the man fairly took to his heels.

'But the farm servants cannae dance nooadays – nae the way they used to. They've been contaminated by this jazz music and stuff o' that kind. But I must admit that when I was a young lad we fairly enjoyed nigger minstrel songs, and I suppose they were the kind o' forerunners of jazz. I hiv a good Scots tongue in my head, but I used to make some kind o' a shape at singing songs like "The Water Melon".'

---

* John Mearns, who heard John telling the same story on several occasions, has put on record an amplified version of this part of it:

'However, when changin' intae my dance suit I thocht it wid be a good idea tae pull my thick workin' breeks on abeen my thin anes.

'It wis a real coorse nicht when I set oot, but I'd a good shalt [pony], an' wi' my feet among strae, twa pair o' breeks, a good thick coat, a luggit bonnet, an' a pair o' hummle doddies [thick gloves with no separate compartments for the fingers], the journey wis mair comfortable than I expected.

'The dance wis startit by the time I arrived, an' I found difficulty in gettin' a place tae hang up my coat. I didna ken the twa-three lads that were standin' in the porch, so jist for fun I said: "Is there ony wye here that I could take aff my breeks?" I got some gey queer looks until they sae I wis wearin' twa pair, an' then they enjoyed the joke.'

John often used to reminisce about the old meal-and-ales held at Crichie for the lads and their lasses at the end of the harvest.

'It was one dance after another … if you had a minute's halt between the dances they were agitatin' for the next one. Ye never saw the marra o't.

'There were aye mair men than lasses, and everybody danced the last dance wi' their bonnets on, because if ye went for your bonnet when the dance was ower, somebody else stole your quine.'

Trying to steal a lad's quine could naturally cause ructions. 'There were aye fights,' according to John although he would add, 'Och, I'd rather hae a fight than nae fun at a'.'

Several of John's favourite songs – such as 'The Laird o' Drum (Child 236), and 'The Forfar Sodger' – were heard in early childhood from the servants on his father's farm, but quite a few he got from his mother, a native of Pitglassie, Auchterless, who was musical, and taught her sons to sing. The boys also got dancing lessons from one of the foremost local instructors, Forbes Morrison ('Dancie' Morrison). John used to recall with mock-rueful amusement how, when visitors were paying social calls, he and his brother would be summoned to the parlour to dance the Highland fling for them, while their mother played the piano.

John's interest in the old songs extended to all the background information he could accumulate about them, and he would impart this to listeners with a relish and gusto which often made these communications an integral part of his performance. Here, for example, is his description of the colourful career and fate of James MacPherson, hero of 'MacPherson's Rant':

'Weel, he was jist a robber – but he wasnae supposed to be bad to the poor – he didna rob the poor, he may have robbit the rich, and stolen their cattle, an' a' that bloomin' kin' o' caper. And then they were gyaun to hang him in Banff … an' he wis gyaun to be hanged … He was fightin', ye see, and his back against the wa', and some auld wife, she drappit a blanket on him, and that fairly tethered him … He was back to the wa', an' neen o' them could win, neen o' them …

'I believed it when I was young, I'm nae sure, I wad need to ask aboot it yet – it was said to be that the Banff folk had aye to keep their time a quarter fast for aboot a hunner year efter they put up their clocks and hanged him when the reprieve was comin ower the Deveron – that was said to be a kind of ban on Banff.

'That was the story aboot this MacPherson – they hanged him ower quick, ye see … he was gyaun to get a reprieve, but the folk were … some o' them, the gentry would ha' been a' daith on him; the poor folk liked him because he was supposed to be kin' o' good to them … And he was a fiddler as weel's a fighter.'

It will be obvious from much of the foregoing that John took a kindly paternalistic interest in the welfare of his fee'd men, but being from the other side of the social divide he had never been admitted to membership of the Horseman's Word, the farm servants' freemasonry; not unnaturally, therefore, he took a decidedly dim view of the antics which went on at its clandestine meetings:

'They were supposed to shak hands wi' the Deil, and a lot o' *dirt* o' that kind.'

He liked referring to the case of 'a loon ca'ed Peter Grant' who had laboured under the delusion that after he was a 'made Horseman' he could do anything with horses. 'It [the Horseman's Word] made a mess o' him. This horse – a little grey horsie – turned on him, and Lord, he got a proper fleg! Peter was bad-usin' him – trying to get him to follow him roon' the place. The horse turned on him, and he was just gaun tae guzzle him – he wid either 'a'hit him wi' his forefeet, or eaten him, or bitten him. I never saw a horse dee't but that one time.'

Dealing with historical events such as the Battle of Harlaw (fought in 1411) John would 'news awa' as if they had happened yesterday. His account of the events leading up to this great confrontation and its aftermath was nothing if not laconic: 'The Provost, he gathered up a lot o' men. God, it's an amazing thing what wey this lads cam' fae the Isles, and got that length ... He [the Provost] heard o' them comin', and gathered up an army, and stopped the whole affair.'

John's frequent visits to markets, ploughing matches and feeing fairs gave him plenty of opportunity to make and maintain contact with singers: consequently, when James Madison Carpenter arrived in Aberdeenshire in 1930 to record its folk-song on wax cylinders, John was able to give him valuable assistance. Here (transcribed from a tape recorded in 1952) is his description of Carpenter's arrival at Crichie, and the quest for a version of the song variously entitled 'The Loch of Sheelin', 'The Lake of Coolfin' and 'Willie Leonard':

'Well, this Dr Carpenter came to my house one night, late, aboot twelve o'clock, an' I knew, whenever I went to the door, that he was somebody! So he introduced himself an' said he was Dr Carpenter from the Harvard College in America. An' I said – well, it's too long a story to tell ye, but he came collectin' a lot o' this stuff. An' I gave him a bumm o' this thing – I never liked it, this "Dark and Shallow Water" – the tune's awful good but the words were dreich to me, an' I never had it. And, "Man," he says, "that's a beautiful old toon: where did ye get that?" An' I said that it was a man Jimmy Smith an' I said, "That man's alive, we might get it tee ye." And he had the terriblest day's work to go to that – get that man: we went here an' there an' everywhere, an' after we'd gone aboot fifty mile we finished be gettin' him away up at Coull, an' it's aboot – och, it's maybe seeven or eight mile fae Tarland, up i' that country. An' when I went to the door this man was at his supper, an' he knew me when I spoke to him. An' I began aboot this song, but oh, he didnae mind a thing aboot it, not a word. But I began to sing some old words and verses, and the tune, an' he began to look a kin o' ... and then he began to sing the last line o' the verse wi me. An', "Now look here, Jimmy," I said, "if you'll sing a' that the whole day tomorra, jist the one verse if ye've only one – keep singin', ye'll get anither, ye'll get anither' – an' in a week that man sent me about seven or eight verses which I gave tae Carpenter. An' if I'd known 'at any body would ever want it again I would ha' kept a copy o' them ...'

HH: 'I'm sure Dr Carpenter was mighty pleased wi' the stuff ye gave him anyway, John.'

JS: 'Well he wis: I don't know hardly why, but he offered tae take me oot tae the Harvard College tae do a lot o' this things in America. But I wis pretty busy, I'd a lot o' farmin to do, an I'm disappointed to this day 'at I didn't go! ... But that man collected a great lot o' stuff.'

John was very emphatic about Carpenter being 'an independent cratur', who seemed to be sleeping and even eating in his car. However, a day or two after the trip in search of Jimmy Smith, he caught a severe chill, and John insisted on bringing him into the farmhouse and putting him to bed. In a few days Mary, John's wife, had nursed him back to health.

In December 1935, when John was sixty, two events took place which remained red-letter days in his memory. The first was a radio programme, 'The Farm Year', which was broadcast live from Crichie; the script was by J. R. Allan, and the producer was Moultrie R. Kelsall, the Aberdeen station director. According to all accounts, this programme must have been a rare spree for the participants. It embraced all seasons of the farm year, from ploughing and spring sowing to the reaping, stacking and binding at 'hairstin' time', and genuine sound effects were provided by implements and animals. A journalist who covered the show paid particular tribute to the horses: 'like old troupers they showed no sign of nervousness when, yoked to the plough, the reaper and binder in turn, they paraded with harness jingling, and responded to the farm hand's "Wheesh, min!"'

Several local characters – well-known to listeners to Aberdeen radio – were naturally invited to take part, including Willie Kemp, the 'cornkister', who featured in the bothy scene, dunting his 'tackety beets' on the cornkist and joining in, while John Mearns sang 'The Bonny Lass o' Fyvie'.

The team in the stackyard even recreated a 'sound picture' of Muckle Friday Fair in the Castlegate of Aberdeen. 'In one part a bagpipe player skirled away, cars were driven up and down, with horns sounding to give the street effect, folks were chattering, a cornet player was blaring forth, and Capt. Donald Campbell, the well-known Deeside playwright, was banging away at an instrument which admirably reproduced those "ring the bell" strength machines associated with Muckle Friday'(*People's Journal*, 20 December 1935.)

John Mearns takes up the tale, in a letter written on 28 November 1981:

'When the broadcast was over all connected with it were invited to a meal in the farmhouse. The large company settled round a long extended table in the spacious dining room, and when grace was said the meal began. Some meal, I tell you!

'A servant lass, in white apron, brought in a huge roast of Aberdeenshire beef, and placed it, for serving, in front of John's wife Mary, while another placed an ashet with two hens in front of John.

'All went well until, when John had completed the serving of both fowls, he looked round the table and remarked: "Noo then folk, hiv ye a' got something tae eat?" Then looking over his specs and seeing someone still to be served, he called to his wife, "Mary, there's a man here hasna got onything tae eat yet. Tell them tae bring ben anither hen."

'Another hen was brought forthwith, and after the meal, that memorable evening ended in a happy atmosphere of music, song and story.'

John's second 'experience of a lifetime' came a week later, when he was invited to contribute to the Christmas Day radio programme which included King George V's speech. John came on the air in a worldwide link-up just after a family in Ottawa had spoken, and he sent greetings to a farmer in South Africa:

'Ay, ay, London, I hear ye. A happy Christmas to you an' a'. Noo, fat was I tell't tae speak tae ye aboot? Oh, ay, I was tae tell ye faur I bade. Weel, I bide in a fairm in the North-East o' Scotland – an' I'm sittin' i' the kitchie o' that fairm i' noo, an' lookin' oot o' the window. Mebbe you wadna ca' the view awfu' bonnie; I ken 'at it looks bare kin', an' I ken it has nae trees worth speakin' aboot, bit I wadna leave't, nae though ye gied me a thoosan' acres o' the promised laan'.

'I wish I could dae something tae mak ye feel it was Christmas Day in Buchan, bit ye see Christmas was never a thing we took muckle notice o' – nae until we were colonised by the English, like. I could lat ye hear the grieve, or even the first horseman, singin' "Christians Awake", bit, oh! Lord, I dinna think it wad jist gie ye the richt impression, for the grieve's nae fat ye'd ca' musical, an' the first horseman has a burr.'

Mrs Strachan – Ay, but John, dinna be sae dowie aboot it all.

Mr Strachan – Ay, wife, sae ye've come in aboot, hiv ye? Lord, ye've pitten on ane o' yer braw goons for the occasion!

Mrs Strachan – Well, you never know with this broadcasting, there might be television agoing, and us not knowing.

Mr Strachan – Weel, weel, 'an; fat are 'e wantin' onywye?

Mrs Strachan – I'm just wanting to keep you in mind of the fact that you're supposed to be sending a message of goodwill instead of girning about the men.

Mr Strachan – Michty, I'm daein' ma best. I'm sure I'm jist foo o' gweedwill tae a'body, and especially the Dominions. I couldna very weel be onything else, seein' 'at Canada's near aboot populated wi' cousins o' oors, and ane o' the best grieves 't ever I had's in Australia i' noo.

Mrs Strachan – Well, well; never mind about that now, John. Just get on with whatever you've got to say.

Mr Strachan – Weel, I some think I've near aboot said a' 'at I can, except that the wife an' me, ay, an' the haill o' Scotland, wish ye a Gweed Christmas and a Gweed New Year – ay, fan it comes – like. We send special greetings tae a' fairmers and countryfolk, mair especially tae the fairmer, far ayont the sea, that's tae speak next in this programme. His name's Mr Smithers, and his fairm, I'm tellt, is about ten mile fae Cape Toon in South Africa. Ay, ay, Mr Smithers, can ye hear me? The wife and me send oor best respects tae you and your family in South Africa.'

John's wife Mary (née Finlayson), who kept him right in this memorable broadcast, came from Tain; she survived him, and lived on to the age of ninety-five. They had four children – three sons and a daughter. The eldest son Derek returned to Aberdeenshire after war service with the Lothian & Border Yeomanry, and he farmed Bruckleseat, Methlick, from 1948 till John's death in November 1958, when he took over at Crichie. Derek, who had a reputation as a spunky devil-may-care chiel, was killed in a motor-cycle crash in 1967; since then his widow Isabel – whom John used to call 'a bloody topper' (the highest compliment in his vocabulary) – has farmed Crichie herself.

I am greatly indebted to Isabel for generous help in the preparation of this piece.

Tocher, 36/37, Winter 1981.

Calum Iain MacLean

In her fascinating book *Essays in the Study of Folk-Songs*, first published in 1886, the Countess Martinengo-Cesaresco refers to a story which circulated about the distinguished pioneer folklorist Wilhelm Mannhardt (the first man to use printed questionnaires as a collecting tool, and the first to do systematic research into traditions relating to agriculture):

> It is on record that Wilhelm Mannhardt, the eminent writer on mythology and folklore, was once taken for a gnome by a peasant he had been questioning. His personal appearance may have helped the illusion: he was small and irregularly made, and was then only just emerging from a sickly childhood spent beside the Baltic in dreaming over the creations of popular fancy. Then, too, he wore a little red cap, which was doubtless fraught with supernatural suggestions. But above all, the story proves that Mannhardt had solved the difficulty of dealing with primitive folk: that instead of being looked upon as a profane and prying layman, he was regarded as one who was more than initiated into the mysteries – as one who was a mystery himself. And for this reason I recall it here. It exactly indicates the way to set about seeking after old lore.

Although the reference to 'primitive folk' would have made Calum MacLean's hackles rise, for he always poured scorn on the patronising attitudes of researchers who surveyed their informants *de haut en bas*, he would certainly have endorsed the Countess's general sentiments, as expressed in this passage, if he had happened to come across them. (And the anecdote itself would undoubtedly have tickled his sense of humour.) But this is by no means the only reason for quoting the passage. Calum was himself the ideal exemplar of the kind of folklorist that the Countess envisaged: any trace of condescension towards the 'folk' was anathema to him, and he took pride in sharing the beliefs and mental attitudes – and even maybe, at times, some of the wilful prejudices – of the ordinary folk among whom he worked. His often forcibly stated opinion of the purely 'academic' folklore pundit was in heartfelt agreement with the wise words of A. N. Whitehead: 'The self-confidence of learned people is the comic tragedy of civilisation.'

But there is yet another and very down-to-earth reason for quoting the Countess's story. Calum MacLean, by-named Calum Beag, was himself a small man – 'a very small man with a very big heart', as an Irish friend put it – and it is not unlikely that this simple physical fact did play a certain part in calling forth the unstinting solicitous response that his own generous approach elicited everywhere he went. One of the people for whom he formed a close regard in his latter years – and who reciprocated his affection in full measure – was the great Aberdeenshire ballad singer Jeannie Robertson, and I well remember the characteristic expression on Jeannie's face when she was together with Calum: it was a compound of love and concerned protectiveness, not unmixed with a sort of reverential awe.

Calum himself had no inhibitions about referring to his size. He once told John MacInnes that on one occasion, when he was conducting Åke Campbell and other Swedish scholars (whom he had met in 1952 during a year of intensive training in Sweden) on a leisurely tour of Ireland, the party stopped for a drink in a bar. The Swedes were all huge men, said Calum, but – 'Ged is e sgoilearan matha a tha anns na Suainich, chan eil iad math air òl idir. Bha mise a' cur eagal an diabhail orra – na bha mi ag òl, is mi cho beag.' ('Although the Swedes are good scholars, they are not good at drinking at all. I was putting the fear of the devil in them with the amount I was drinking, and me so small.')

Calum Iain MacLean, by general consent the finest single collector of Gaelic folklore our country has yet seen, was born on 6 September 1915 on the island of Raasay. He was the third son of Malcolm MacLean, the tailor of Raasay, and Christina Nicolson, who was a native of Braes in Skye. His uncle Angus Nicolson was a fine singer with a wide repertoire, and both his father and his aunt Peggy MacLean were singers too, so Calum's interest in Gaelic traditional song was no doubt kindled in his earliest childhood. It was an exceptionally gifted family. Calum's parents were keen, in the old Scottish style, that their children should have the best opportunities possible for education and advancement, and of Calum's four brothers and two sisters two became doctors and four teachers. One of the latter (now happily retired from teaching) is the great Gaelic poet Somhairle MacGill-eain (Sorley MacLean), who has written some of the best poetry Scotland has seen in this century, and the best Scottish Gaelic poetry for over two hundred years.

From Portree High School Calum went up to Edinburgh University, where he studied Celtic under W. J. Watson; he graduated in 1939 with First Class Honours, and continued his studies in Ireland under Osborn Bergin and J. Lloyd-Jones. Much of his time was spent in the library of the Irish Folklore Commission's headquarters in St Stephen's Green, and it was Seán Ó Súilleabháin who spotted him as a potential collector for that body. Seán gave him his initial training for operations in the field, and he did splendid collecting work in the Connaught Gaeltacht. (Séamus Delargy used to say that he was the best collector the Commission had ever had.) When Delargy decided, towards the end of the Second World War, to 'colonise' the Gaelic-speaking areas of Scotland, Calum was the obvious man for the job, and he proceeded – with Irish funds – to the West Highlands. In Benbecula he spent the best part of three years, working notably with the redoubtable storyteller Aonghas Barrach (Angus MacMillan), and by the time the School of Scottish Studies was founded he had taken down in his meticulously tidy handwriting what may well be the largest collection of folk-tales recorded by one man in Scotland up to that time, and had distinguished himself already as a worthy successor to Campbell of Islay.

I had the privilege of meeting him at the very start of his period in Scotland under the aegis of the Irish Folklore Commission. This was in early 1946, on the Isle of

Canna, to which I had been invited by *Fear Chanaidh* – John Lorne Campbell. Another guest was the late Séamus Ennis, the renowned Irish uilleann piper – he was engaged on transcribing material on some of the cylinders recorded on Barra and South Uist by Campbell and his wife Margaret Fay Shaw – so Calum had every excuse for reverting to unabashed Irishism. My first impression of him, curled up in a window seat and surveying the new arrival with quizzical interrogatory eyes, was of a friendly but ever watchful brownie – or better, maybe, leprechaun – and I have to admit that the story about Mannhardt did momentarily flash across my mind.

Later that evening he regaled us with some of the Irish songs (in English) which he had picked up in Dublin. The ones I remember best are 'The Bould Thady Quill', 'Mrs McGrath' and 'Moriarity' ('The Pride of the DMP') – and I can hear as if it were yesterday the inimitable triumphal lift that he gave to the punch line:

'Flap your wings, Moriarity!'

Not to be outdone, Séamus Ennis pulled the window curtains round him, so that he looked like a pawky Biddy Mulligan, and lilted: 'There was an old woman tossed up in a blanket.'

On New Year's Day 1951 Calum joined the newly founded School of Scottish Studies as its first Research Fellow, and so began the decade of unremitting dedicated labour which transformed the state of folklore studies in Scotland, and gave the School's sound archive a treasure of recordings – songs, stories, legends, proverbs, memorates, historical anecdotes – that on any account may truly be called fabulous. Remembering that a great deal of his work was done while he was fighting against pain and the first onset of the illness that was to kill him, one can hardly withhold the term 'heroic' if one seeks to pay adequate tribute to his amazing achievement. Calum was above all else a Scottish patriot (and a convinced political nationalist), so it is not maybe out of place to recall the words of Robert Burns (often quoted by the great Aberdeenshire collector Gavin Greig):

> E'en then a wish – I mind its power,
> A wish that to my latest hour
>   Shall strongly heave this breast –
> That I for puir auld Scotland's sake
> Some usefu' plan or book might make,
>   Or sing a sang at least.

Calum did not make a song of his own, but he put on record thousands that had been created and had taken shape on the anonymous tongue of the people.

Although his Irish and Swedish training had made him extremely competent in the conventional disciplines of folk-tale scholarship – the identification of tale types, motifs etc. according to the Aarne and Thompson classifications – Calum's interest in 'oral literature' was more artistic than academic. He felt passionately that what had been transmitted orally in Gaelic *was* literature of a high quality, and a most important part of the national heritage of Scotland. Dr John MacInnes writes: 'He took a definite stance on "oral versus MS" so far as folk-tales were concerned. He gave primacy in all cases to the oral tradition, e.g. when stories like Conall Gulban were discussed. Calum's opinion was that although there were MS versions of these in existence, they had originally been composed orally, had been transmitted orally, and the MS tradition was a kind of side-line. He believed the version of the *Táin* he got in South Uist was to be regarded as oral – in continuity – from the materials from which the literary versions had been made. Had he lived, he would probably have written something about this.'

Although Calum was certainly (as David Greene remarked) a 'master of the spoken word', he also developed a most agreeable prose style when writing in English, as many passages in his book *The Highlands* bear witness – particularly those in which he describes his safari in search of the Sutherland travelling folk in 1955. (*The Highlands*, incidentally, is very much the Gaelic insider's view of his homeland.) I have it on Dr MacInnes's authority, furthermore, that he was also a master of Gaelic prose. He did not write much in his native tongue, but what he did write shows that in expository prose he displayed a limpid clarity and a trenchant economy in the use of idiomatic Gaelic that has not been surpassed. It is one of the many regrets attaching to his tragically premature death that he was never able to bring to fulfilment the promise he had shown as a Gaelic prose stylist.

I have referred to Calum's zest and wonderful comic verve when giving renditions of Anglo-Irish songs such as 'Mrs McGrath', but it was when he was singing Gaelic love songs – and especially songs of tragic love – that he was at his most moving as a singer. To quote John MacInnes again: 'The pathos with which he sang elegies and the like was arresting ... I remember him singing *Is daor a cheannaich mi an t-iasgach* in Norman MacCaig's house one night. He brought out the rhythmical beauty of it with great sensitivity.' At Edinburgh University Highland Society ceilidhs in the late 1940s and early 1950s his favourite seemed to be *Ho luaidh 's truagh nach deachaidh sinn* (which became a sort of 'pop number' in the Society), and there was no questioning the feeling and the deep poignant seriousness which he conveyed when singing that haunting song. It seemed more than sad to one close friend (the Canadian anthropologist Frank Vallee) and probably to many other people too that a man who had inherited the magical incantatory eloquence of these superb Gaelic love songs never himself married.

The most lasting memory of Calum as a man, however, remains the warmth, humanity and sense of fun which came over in his conversation. When on form he had a marvellous gift for striking (and often very witty) turns of phrase which sometimes recalled the innocent-seeming deadpan cracks of Damon Runyon. Indeed, I think he could easily have been – if he had ever wanted to try his hand at the game – a masterly comic-satiric novelist after the Flann O'Brien model. Creative writing of some sort would in any case have suited his temperament much better than the somewhat mechanistic structuralist analysis of folk literature now so much to the fore.

In the autumn of 1950, Alan Lomax arrived from the United States to gather material for the World Albums of Folk and Primitive Music which Columbia Records were sponsoring, and he approached me for help with the Scottish LP. I agreed to assist him in the North-East, and asked Sorley and Calum to do likewise in the Gaelic-speaking West, pointing out that the tape-recorder he had brought with him was streets ahead of any other portable recording machine I had so far encountered, and that this seemed a golden opportunity to put on record a good number of the virtuoso tradition-bearers known to them. Both readily and generously agreed to help him, and the result was the first twenty-five copy-tapes in our sound archive. Lomax never

forgot the co-operation he had received from Calum on that occasion, and he recently
sent me the following appreciation of their fruitful association:

> It was my great privilege to be initiated into the Gaelic culture of the West of
> Scotland by that wise and generous scholar Calum MacLean. He took me under
> his wing when I got to Edinburgh with my tape machine in 1951, made me hear
> Flora MacNeil and the pibroch, made me read Carmichael and, in many cosy
> talks over whisky, acquainted me with the deathless spirit of Gaelic culture. He
> insisted that I go to the Western Isles, telling a somewhat sceptical American that
> I had a priceless experience in store. And then he gave me a few addresses and
> made a few judicious telephone calls that opened the way. There followed
> meetings and music making and wonders that are still as vivid in my heart today
> as they were thirty years ago. For me the culture of the Hebrides that MacLean
> devoted his life to is the finest flower of Western Europe. And Calum in my
> mind's eye is the man who understood it and represented it as well as any one
> man could. I grieved on that day in 1960 when I heard that he had gone away
> over the hill, but rejoice to know that he left behind so many good friends and so
> much fine work.

These are the words of one of the most knowledgeable of modern American
folklorists, and might well serve as a summation of what I have tried to write in
Calum's honour. But the tribute which comes nearest to telling the whole truth is his
brother Sorley's superb elegy. I close with three short passages from it:

Tha an saoghal fhathast àlainn	*The world is still beautiful*
Ged nach eil thu ann.	*though you are not in it.*
Is labhar an Uibhist a' Ghàidhlig	*Gaelic is eloquent in Uist*
Ged tha thusa an Cnoc Hàllainn	*though you are in Hallin Hill*
Is do bhial gun chainnt.	*and your mouth without speech.*
Tha iomadh duine bochd an Albainn	*There is many a poor man in Scotland*
Dh'an tug thu togail agus cliù;	*whose spirit and name you raised;*
'S ann a thog thu 'n t-iriosal	*you lifted the humble*
A chuir ar linn air chùl.	*whom our age put aside.*
Thug iad dhutsa barrachd	*They gave you more*
Na bheireadh iad do chàch	*than they would give to others*
On thug thu dhaibh an dùrachd	*since you gave them the zeal*
Bu ghrìosach fo do bhàigh.	*that was a fire beneath your kindness.*
Mhothaich iadsan an dealas	*They sensed the vehemence*
A bha socair 'na do dhòigh,	*that was gentle in your ways,*
Thuig iad doimhne throm do dhaondachd	*they understood the heavy*
	depths of your humanity
Nuair a b'aotroime do spòrs.	*when your fun was at its lightest.*
Ghabh thu an ràtreuta,	*You took the retreat,*
Fhir bhig a' chridhe mhóir,	*little one of the big heart,*
Ghabh thu do dhìon air cùl a' ghàrraidh	*you took your refuge behind the*
	wall

Far 's mìlse muran na Gàidhlig,	*where the bent grass of Gaelic is sweetest,*
Fhir bhig an treuntais mhóir.	*little one of the great heroism.*

Ghabh thu an ràtreuta	*You took the retreat*
Gus an iomall shiair,	*to the western edge,*
Thusa nach do ghabh am bristeadh,	*you who did not take the breaking,*
Nach do bhristeadh riamh,	*who were never broken,*
A ràinig bial na h-uaghach	*who reached the mouth of the grave*
Is do spiorad sìòr bhuadhach.	*with your spirit always the victor.*

Tocher, 39, Spring 1985.

Roy Williamson

Roy Williamson, the Scots folk-singer who was one half of the popular duo known as The Corries, died at his home in Forres on 12 August 1990 after a long battle with cancer. He was fifty-four.

Roy was born in Edinburgh on 25 June 1936, and educated at Gordonstoun. Although he had been a delicate child, suffering from asthma, the school's spartan regime encouraged him to become an enthusiastic all-round sportsman. Asthma baffled his ambition to join the Royal Navy, and so after leaving school he spent some time as a coastguard and with mountain rescue teams.

It was at Edinburgh College of Art, where he was a student from 1955 to 1959, that he began to experiment with various music groups, progressing from trad jazz through skiffle to the newly burgeoning folk revival. Visits to the School of Scottish Studies introduced him to the singing of traditional champions such as the Aberdeen traveller, Jeannie Robertson, and in 1962 he teamed up with Bill Smith and Ronnie Browne to form the Corrie Folk Trio. By a stroke of luck a talented young woman-singer from Belfast arrived in Edinburgh at the same time, and Paddie Bell's sweet voice greatly enhanced the group's attractions.

A television series called *Hootenanny* brought them to the notice of a wider public, and they were able to give up their jobs – Roy and Ronnie were art teachers – and turn professional. Roy was soon displaying amazing versatility with a variety of string instruments, and Ronnie Browne's talents developed simultaneously. Paddie had to leave the group for personal reasons in the mid-1960s, followed shortly after by Bill Smith, but The Corries were by this time the most popular folk group in Scotland, and Roy and Ronnie continued for the next two decades as a duo.

The two were indeed perfect foils for each other. On stage Roy projected a diffident, even aloof persona, seeming at times 'away with the fairies'; Ronnie treated the audience to boisterous fun, coaxing douce members from Edinburgh to join in choruses by dint of Rabelaisian mockery and insults. All this developed into a vastly sophisticated double act, and if a few purists could occasionally be heard at the bar complaining that this was more music hall than folk-song, they were invariably countered by *aficionados* who pointed to the honourable folk tradition represented by Scots music hall itself.

The song for which Roy will be long remembered, 'Flower of Scotland', caught the imagination almost immediately and was soon to be heard at football matches across the country; it has become, in effect, an unofficial national anthem. When Scotland's rugby team beat England at Murrayfield in March 1990 to clinch the 'Grand Slam', it was sung by 50,000 spectators. Roy and Ronnie were to have led the singing before the match, but Roy was too ill to attend.

Roy's own attitude to the tremendous success of the song was one of almost comical puzzlement, but he was obviously moved by the fact that 'Flower of Scotland' had been drawn by seemingly irresistible force into the mainstream of Scottish folk tradition. His premature death will be deeply mourned by friends not only in Scotland but also far beyond its borders.

Guardian, 16 August 1990.

Ewan MacColl

Of Jimmy Miller, who became world-famous as the folk-singer and playwright Ewan MacColl, one can say without exaggeration that he was a man of many parts. The son of a Stirling ironmoulder, often blacklisted for left-wing activism, he was born in Salford and brought up there; its street-songs constituted – together with his Auchterarder-born mother's Scots ballads – his earliest musical experience. Although his speech always retained its native Lancashire intonation, he became an acknowledged master of sung ballad-Scots; some of the recordings in our archive are without doubt among the very finest examples of Lowland Scots ballad artistry ever put on tape. Outstanding among these is the version of 'Lord Randal', sung as a duet with his mother – old Betsey singing the mother's part of the dialogue, and Ewan the doomed son's.

It was not as a singer, however, but as an actor and playwright that Ewan first achieved celebrity. He had worked in theatre – street theatre, experimental groups – between 1929 and 1940, and after the Second World War he collaborated with Joan Littlewood in setting up Theatre Workshop; plays like *Uranium 235*, *The Other Animals* and *Operation Olive-Branch* (his free adaptation of the *Lysistrata* of Aristophanes) won enthusiastic plaudits from Hugh MacDiarmid, Bernard Shaw and Seán O'Casey. All of these plays were brought to Scotland by the Edinburgh People's Festival, the vigorous 'alternative' festival organised in 1951 by the political parties of the Left, and by the organs of the Scottish working-class movement. It seemed possible at one time that Theatre Workshop itself might settle in Glasgow, but eventually it found a permanent home in Stratford East, and became for a fruitful decade the standard-bearer of left-wing avant-garde theatre.

By that time Ewan's own career had diverged from Joan's; with Peggy Seeger, who had come into his life thanks to Alan Lomax, he devoted himself more and more to the folk-song revival, becoming its most redoubtable militant champion. He teamed up with the late A. L. Lloyd to produce a series of valuable folk-song LPs, and with his mettlesome Critics group – a sort of New Model Army of traditional songsters – he may be said to have left a lasting imprint on the singing styles and folk-cultural predilections of a whole generation of revival singers. His most lasting achievement, however, was probably the invention, with the Birmingham BBC producer Charles Parker, of the novel art-form 'radio ballad', an ingenious mélange of song and taped oral history. 'The Ballad of John Axon' (about an heroic train-driver), 'Singing the Fishing' and 'The Big Hewer' were among the finest of these. It is safe to say that it is these marvellous radio-ballads, and the songs Ewan composed for them like 'Shoals of Herring', that will forever keep his memory green.

Two years before his death, while on holiday in the North Highlands, Ewan composed what is arguably his finest song, 'The Joy of Living'. Even without the magic of his splendid voice, and the 'guitar, mandolin and concertina' of Peggy Seeger, it makes a striking and noble impression on the printed page. This is the last verse:

> Take me to some high place
> Of heather, rock and ling;
> Scatter my dust and ashes,
> Feed me to the wind.
> So that I will be
> Part of all you see,
> The air you are breathing –
> I'll be part of the curlew's cry
> And the soaring hawk,
> The blue milkwort
> And the sundew hung with diamonds.
> I'll be riding the gentle wind
> That blows through your hair,
> Reminding you how we shared
> In the joy of living.

Tocher, 43, 1991.

Norman Buchan

Norman Buchan, who died on 23 October 1990, just a few days short of his sixty-eighth birthday, was a firm friend of the School of Scottish Studies, and a doughty champion of the Scottish Folk Revival.

He was born in Helmsdale, of Aberdeenshire parents; most of his childhood was spent in Orkney, where his father was Fishery Officer. His career at Glasgow University was bisected by the war; he fought in Africa and Italy, first in a Light Ack-Ack unit, and later in the Second Battalion of the Royal Tank Regiment. His final day in action in 1945, when he was a loader/wireless operator in a 'Honey' tank on the Po Front, is described in the last article he wrote before his death (published posthumously in the *Glasgow Herald*, 10 November 1990).

Although he had a noteworthy if somewhat chequered political career during his twenty-six years at Westminster – he was a Parliamentary Under-Secretary at the Scottish Office, 1967–70; Opposition spokesman on Agriculture, Fisheries and Food, 1970–74; and Minister of State at the Ministry of Agriculture for seven battlesome months of 1974 – he will undoubtedly be best remembered as an inspirational schoolteacher, and as a valorous standard-bearer of the Folk Revival.

His interest in Scottish traditional song was mightily kindled in 1951 when he attended the now famous ceilidh organised for the Edinburgh People's Festival. At that event he represented the Cultural Committee of the Communist Party, one of the founder bodies, and he was visibly moved by the singing of virtuoso tradition-bearers like John Strachan, Jessie Murray, Flora MacNeil and Calum Johnston. The 'idea' of a folk revival was already in the air, and Norman, following the example of Morris Blythman (the poet 'Thurso Berwick'), was keen to bring traditional singers from country districts to perform for schoolchildren in the Glasgow area. His club at Rutherglen Academy was a veritable seed-bed of talented revival 'folkies' like Anne Neilson and Gordeanna McCulloch, and future champions such as Archie Fisher and Matt McGinn owed much of their early inspiration to the encouragement given them by this dedicated and knowledgeable mentor.

At the end of the 1950s Norman founded the Glasgow Folk Club, which carried on the same work of evangelisation, and he continued to help to run it until his election in 1964 as Labour MP for West Renfrewshire obliged him to hand over the reins to others. If he had achieved his ambition of becoming Minister for the Arts in a Labour government – as Roy Jenkins put it, he was 'the best Minister for the Arts Britain never had' – there is no doubt he would have befriended the Traditional Music and Song

Association of Scotland, and would have done his best for the School of Scottish Studies, of whose Appeal he was one of the original sponsors in 1982.

Norman will be greatly missed by his friends, not least in the School. He always radiated a glowing atmosphere of enthusiasm and encouragement, and his kindly help, given without stint, will keep his memory green wherever the traditional arts of Scotland are honoured.

Tocher, 43, 1991.

FOLK-TALES

Introduction
to Duncan and Linda Williamson's
A Thorn in the King's Foot:
Stories of the Scottish Travelling People

In the mid-nineteenth century, the great Highland collector John Francis Campbell of Islay uncovered an enormous treasure of folk narrative in Gaelic-speaking Scotland, and fruitful collecting has continued there right up to our own day, particularly in the Outer Hebrides. In sharp contrast, the number of versions of folk-tales in Lowland Scots which had been put on record by the half-way mark of this century was surprisingly small, considering the bounding exuberance of the Scots ballad tradition. Campbell himself thought that story-telling among the Lowland country folk had largely died out by his day, and he stated, in his introduction to *Popular Tales of the West Highlands* (Vol. I, 1860), that he had searched for tales among 'the peasantry of the low country', but with no success to speak of.

Campbell knew of the existence of a manuscript collection of *Ancient Scottish Tales* written down in 1829 by the maverick Peterhead printer-antiquary Peter Buchan, but after examining these he gave it as his opinion that this was probably a collection of Gaelic folk-tales which had somehow found their way into the 'borderland' milieu of the North-East Lowlands.

Campbell's opinion is by no means to be set aside without careful consideration, but in the light of subsequent collecting it can be shown that he was definitely on the wrong track.

One reason for this misapprehension is probably to be located in the language in which Buchan's tales are couched. Although he claimed that the stories were 'from the recitation of the Aged Sybils in the North Countrie', one glance at the text shows that the originals have been lifted as with a crane out of the folk speech in which they must originally have been told, and revamped in a florid stilted English which is all too clearly Buchan's own. Furthermore, in the matter of nomenclature he has allowed his fertile imagination to run riot. Here is an example:

> About the year 800, there lived a rich nobleman in a sequestered place of Scotland, where he wished to conceal his name, birth, and parentage, as he had fled from the hands of justice to save his life for an action he had been guilty of committing in his early years. It was supposed, and not without good show of reason, that his name was Malcolm, brother to Fingal, King of Morven. Be this as it may, it so happened that he had chosen a pious and godly woman for his consort; who, on giving birth to a daughter, soon after departed this life.

This quotation is the opening of a story called 'The Cruel Stepmother', and will be found on page 25 of the first and only published edition of Buchan's *Ancient Scottish Tales*, which was brought out by the Buchan Field Club in 1908, edited by J. A. Fairley. The story is a version of an international tale, 'The Maiden without Hands', which is listed and given a number in a volumin-ous compendium called *The Types of the Folktale*. This latter is an exceedingly useful work begun by the Finnish scholar Antti Aarne and subsequently greatly enlarged by Stith Thompson of Indiana University. Just as the numbers given to classical ballads by Professor F. J. Child in the last century, in his great thesaurus *English and Scottish Popular Ballads*, are a handy ready-reckoner when discussing versions of these (e.g. 'Lord Randal' is No 12), so the international folk-tales which have surmounted the barriers of language, geography and culture can usefully be referred to by their numbers in the Aarne/Thompson index: Buchan's tale 'The Cruel Stepmother' is AT 706.

This does not mean that the motifs in the long, involved 'fairy tales' (often known by their German name of *Märchen*) will necessarily be found together in all versions of a particular story. Sometimes they are so different in sequence and coloration that it is exceedingly hard to pin down the story concerned and give it an AT number. Thus the penultimate sentence of Buchan's 'The Cruel Stepmother' ('Beatrix then relieved her father from the pain which he suffered in his foot by a thorn which stuck in it, and baffled all the medical skill of that part of the country' (*Ancient Scottish Tales*, p. 28)) provides a clue to the possibility that we are dealing here with a far-out relative of the title story of this chapter. However, the rejected child in Duncan Williamson's story is a hunchback boy, and not a girl, and the motif of mutilation – the daughter's hands being cut off – which usually identifies this particular story-type is completely absent.

We can state with assurance, therefore, that Buchan's fourteen tales – although lamentably wooden Anglicised 'recensions' or re-tellings, which reproduce neither the language nor the flavour of the originals – were indeed collected from Aberdeenshire country folk; and, with equal assurance, that at least ten of them had travelled to the North-East of Scotland from much further afield, and had already crossed several language barriers before being transmogrified – or crucified – linguistically by the egregious Peter Buchan. They are easily identifiable international tales, viz. AT 300 ('The Dragon Slayer'); 303 ('The Twins or Blood Brothers'); 313 ('The Girl as Helper in the Hero's Flight'); 325 ('The Magician and his Pupil')' 326 ('The Youth who Wanted to Learn What Fear is'); 425 ('The Search for the Lost Husband'); 510 ('Cinderella'/'Cap o' Rushes'); 851 ('The Princess who Cannot Solve the Riddle'); 955 ('The Robber Bridegroom'); and 706, which we have already mentioned. One of these (303) we shall encounter again in the present volume in the guise of 'Friday and Saturday'.

It is only fair to stress, therefore, for the reasons set out above, that Peter Buchan, most denigrated and slighted of all Scots folk-collectors, deserves all due credit and gratitude for putting on record the first collection we have – and the only one till this century – of tales circulating in the Scots-speaking areas of the North-East.

When Robert Chambers brought out a second revised edition of his *Popular Rhymes of Scotland* in 1841 he introduced a new section of Fireside Nursery Stories; one of these was '"The Red Etin", a Scotticisation' of the first tale in Buchan's collection. Chambers had been lent the manuscript of the *Tales* – almost certainly by Charles Kirkpatrick Sharpe, to whom Buchan had entrusted it – and he had understandably wished to restore something of what he presumed must have been the original language. (The same sort of service, with the same intention, has recently been performed for Buchan's *Tales* by David Purves in the pages of the Scots language magazine *Lallans*.) It is a genuine pleasure, therefore, to turn to Duncan Williamson's 'Friday and Saturday', a really splendid version of the same tale type told in the most delectable racy Scots, which leaves both Peter Buchan and Robert Chambers far behind. Compare the concluding paragraphs of Duncan's 'wey o't' with the following passage from Peter Buchan's 'Red Etin':

> The Etin's power now being gone, an axe was taken up by the young man, with which he cut off the three heads of the monstrous Etin. His next work was to discover the king of Scotland's daughter, and to set her at liberty. The old woman showed him the place where she lay concealed. There were imprisoned along with her a great many beautiful ladies; all of whom he restored to their weeping parents, by whom he was well rewarded, and married by the king to one of the ladies who had been released from a long and dreary confinement. He also restored his brother and the former young man to life and their former shape, and married them to two of the liberated ladies; when they all lived happy, in peace and plenty. This happened through the instrumentality of a persevering and fortunate young man.

It may well be asked at this point: what happened then in the fairly recent past to change the Lowland folk-tale picture so dramatically? Why, in other words, have we now got such a cornucopia of marvellously told tales to offer the public? The catalyst was undoubtedly the discovery by the School of Scottish Studies of the colossal wealth of folk tradition of every conceivable kind which had remained hidden in the tents – and city ghettos – of the travelling people. (or tinkers: a term they very understandably don't like because it has been used by stupid people so often as a cuss-word).*

I hope I will be forgiven if I introduce a personal note at this point. It was when I was on a ballad-hunt in the North-East as a collector for the School of Scottish Studies that I gained entrée to the world of traveller folk-tales. The fact that Aberdeenshire is the uncontested heartland of the Scots ballad tradition led me, in the early 1950s, to concentrate my researches there, and good luck brought me – after a useful hint from a traveller salesman in Fyvie – to the city of Aberdeen and to the late Jeannie Robertson. At first I concentrated on her rich store of song, but in the summer of 1954 – remembering Peter Buchan's *Ancient Scottish Tales*, which I had come across and annotated in the library of the Irish Folklore Commission in Dublin – it occurred to me to ask her for stories. In reply, she started to tell me her version of 'The Dragon Slayer' (AT 300), and I realised that I was standing at the edge of a newly opened subterranean treasure house.

Within a few days I had recorded a number of stories from Jeannie – including a highly entertaining version of the *Schwank* (humorous tale) 'Silly Jack and the Factor' (AT 1600, 'The Fool as Murderer'), which features on one of the School's first LPs of

---

*'Traveller' is the term members of the group use to identify themselves as distinct from outsiders. For literary reasons I prefer 'tinker-gypsy', but this is not to say that the Scottish travellers and Romany gypsies should be understood as one and the same ethnic group – quite the contrary.

folk-tales, folk-songs and instrumental music, issued in 1960, and now sadly unavailable. Furthermore, as a bonus, I began to record stories from traveller visitors to Jeannie's house which included 'The King of England', another fine version of AT 303 told by Andrew Stewart,and later included in Richard M. Dorson's *Folktales Told around the World* (1975) and the now famous version of AT 313, 'The Green Man of Knowledge', which later was to supply the title for Alan Bruford's excellent short selection of tales from Scots oral tradition.

In 1955 the Stewarts of Blair were discovered by Maurice Fleming, and recordings in the berryfields, and in their Rattray home Berrybank, added a rich haul to the already copious store of tinkler-gypsy folktales. Bella Higgins turned out to be a champion story-teller, her 'star turn' being 'The Humph at the Fuit o' the Glen and the Humph at the Heid o' the Glen' (AT 503, 'The Gifts of the Little People'); her younger brother Andrew – nicknamed Andra Hoochten, because of his predilection for diddling songs – supplied another story for the School's first LP, mentioned above. This was the comic changeling story 'Johnnie in the Cradle'.

By the summer of 1956, the sheer bulk of outstanding new material which was flowing into the School's archives had begun to outstrip all attempts to list and classify, let alone transcribe it; so much so that Calum MacLean asserted that same year that there was a good case for the School's research workers dropping everything else, and devoting themselves exclusively to the travellers. (By that time the Gaelic-speaking Sutherland Stewarts – a group of families whose members were still telling many of the stories (including Ossian hero tales) collected by Campbell a hundred years earlier, plus many which he did not collect – had also been discovered, and it was plain that work among them could continue for years.) And yet the man who was in many ways to turn out possibly the most extraordinary tradition-bearer of the whole traveller tribe had not at that time emerged above the horizon: this was the present story-teller Duncan Williamson, who in 1956 was only twenty-eight and therefore a youngster compared to many of the other informants.

When I say emerged above the horizon, I do not mean that he was not already regarded by his own people as a champion folk artist in the making, just as Jeannie Robertson had been by the Aberdeenshire travellers many years earlier. It was only that vast areas of the traveller sub-culture still lay under the waves, and that although significant catches had been netted there were broad stretches still unexplored at the end of the 1950s. One of these was another 'borderland' – Argyll, heartland of the great Clan Campbell, and of their hereditary enemies the MacLeans. This Highland county, lying close on the east to the culture and language of the Central Lowlands, was an area where the travelling people had in the main lost their ancestral Gaelic. (In this they resembled the tinkler-gypsies in the Gaeltachts of the west of Ireland.) In consequence, therefore, the heritage of tales which contemporary Argyll travellers share is drawn largely from the other side of the language divide; in bulk it makes a very different impression from the *Märchengut* of the Sutherland Stewarts mentioned above, and of the other Highland travelling clans north of the Great Glen. (It must be added, though, that the experience of Campbell of Islay in Argyll indicate a very different state of affairs in the mid-nineteenth century, for he refers to travelling tinkers called MacDonald who told stories in Gaelic.)

The language in which Duncan Williamson tells the stories collected in this book is

Gavin Greig, co-compiler of the Greig Duncan Folk Song Collection.

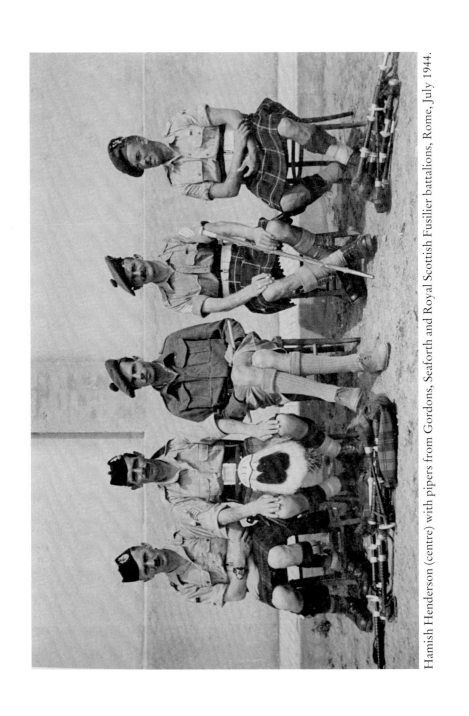

Hamish Henderson (centre) with pipers from Gordons, Seaforth and Royal Scottish Fusilier battalions, Rome, July 1944.

Hugh MacDiarmid and a group of friends after a St Andrew's Night ceilidh, at Bo'ness, 25 November, 1949. L to R: Calum Campbell, Hamish Henderson, Marion and Morris Blythman, Hugh MacDiarmid and Archie Meikle.

Photo: School of Scottish Studies

Hamish Henderson with the Stewart family of Blairgowrie in 1955.

Hamish Henderson with Ali Dall (Blind Alec Stewart), renowned Gaelic tinker storyteller from Sutherland, in 1958.

Photo: School of Scottish Studies

Angus MacNeill and Calum Maclean at Smearisay, Moidart, Inverness-shire in 1959.

Photo: Ian Whitaker

John Strachan, at St Katherine's near Fyvie, Aberdeenshire, about 1925.

Photo: Ian Hardy

Jimmy MacBeath, informant, from a photo taken in Blairgowrie in 1968.

Photo: School of Scottish Studies

Matt McGinn, Glasgow singer, song-writer and socialist.

Photo: School of Scottish Studies

Competitors in the Scottish Folk Music Festival at a ceilidh in the Clifton Rooms, Edinburgh, 30 August 1959. Two folk-singers from Aberdeen, James MacBeath and Jeannie Robertson, (far left and right) lead the singing.   Photo: *Dispatch*

Jeannie Robertson, *c.* 1960.   Photo: Fred Kent

At the Inverness Folk Festival in 1969.
Back Row, L to R: Billy Connelly, Gerry Rafferty, Hamish Henderson, Hamish Bain, Jean Redpath, Archie Fisher, Finbar Furey, Aly Bain, Tam Harvey, Derek Moffat.
Front Row: Cyril Tawney, Eddie Furey, Tich Frier, Andy Ramage, Ian MacCalman.

Photo: School of Scottish Studies

Duncan and Linda Williamson, at their campsite in Cupar in April 1977.

Photo: Peter Cooke

The Stewart family round the campfire at the Lundin Links, Fife in 1982. Photo: R. W. Leitch
L to R: Margaret (Peggie) Stewart, 'Auld Sandy' (Alexander Stewart), 'Young Sandy' (son) and David Stewart.

Hamish Henderson with his wife and daughters in the 1960s.

The end of an auld sang.

an idiosyncratic dialect of 'traveller Scots'; which retains quite a number of archaisms – e.g. 'hit' for 'it', and 'haet' for 'anything' – now obsolete in modern Scots English. It is an exceedingly powerful, colourful and flexible vehicle for narrative, and Duncan manages it with glorious magniloquent skill and flair. Some turns of phrase, and other pieces of internal evidence, confirm that several of the stories have come over from Gaelic into Scots – in all likelihood, comparatively recently – on the lips of bilingual story-tellers. Indeed, Duncan learned quite a number of his stories from a Gaelic-speaking stonemason and drystone-dyker, Neil MacCallum, to whom he was apprenticed at Auchindrain in Argyll in his adolescence. Neil told them in English, with occasional bits of Gaelic interspersed.

A good example is 'The Tailor and the Skeleton' which has been collected several times from Gaelic-speaking tradition-bearers: a version was printed in MacDougall and Calder's *Folk Tales and Fairy Lore* (1910), where the tailor's cool reiterated rebuff to the skeleton which is taking shape before him goes as follows in Gaelic: '*Chi mi sin, agus fuaighidh mi seo*' ('I see that, and I sew this').

In 1935 another version in Scots – 'The Wee Tailor' – was collected in the Blairgowrie house of Bella Higgins, sister of Alec Stewart (the husband in the folk partnership known as the Stewarts of Blair): this was printed in 1959 in the annual *Von Prinzen, Trollen und Herrn Fro: Märchen der europäischen Völker*. In that particular version the Gaelic source of the story is explicitly acknowledged:

> So he's watchin', an' out comes this hand, an' it says in Gaelic: 'Dae ye see that hand without flesh and blood on it?' 'Ah,' says the tailor, 'I see ye, but I'll sew this at the meantime.'

To clinch the matter, Duncan has testified that he always heard his Argyll informants tell the story with this version of the Gaelic sentence quoted above: '*Chi mi sin, fuaighidh mi seo,' thuirt an tàilleir* ('I see that and I sew this,' said the tailor).

The central motif of the story – the gradual coming together of a complete skeleton (or animated corpse) – is a quite widely diffused one. It appears with tremendous dramatic force in 'The Strange Visitor', one of Robert Chambers's *Popular Rhymes of Scotland* (1841):

> A wife was sitting at her reel ae night:
> And aye she sat, and aye she reeled, and aye she wished for company.
> In came a pair o' braid braid soles, and sat down at the fireside;
> And aye she sat and aye she reeled,and aye she wished for company ...

'The Tailor and the Skeleton' is a 'short story', compared to the long convoluted *Märchen* or wonder-tales, of which there are some splendid examples in the present collection. Encountering them, we approach the central redoubt of the Scots travellers' narrative art. Reading 'The Giant with the Golden Hair of Knowledge' – a version of AT 461, which is No 29, 'The Devil with the Three Golden Hairs', in the *Kinder und Hausmärchen* of the Brothers Grimm – or 'Friday and Saturday' (AT 303, 'The Twins or Blood-Brothers', Grimm, nos 60 and 85) – it is easy to visualise the blazing bonfire of the Argyll travellers' camp with enthralled listeners, adults as well as children, hanging on every word and fresh invention of the story-teller, who naturally has a whole battery of different motifs and themes which he can mould into the structure of the stories if and when he might want to diversify it, or spin it out. When an innovative story-teller has his way with one of these wondrous *Märchen*, he may combine two or three tale types in the one narrative, so that attaching an AT number to some of the stories is like trying to spell out a complex chemical formula, when fresh ingredients are being added much of the time.

One can readily imagine a tale of this sort being gradually and artfully elongated, so that it might spill over into two or even three nights' sessions. A sense of almost limitless leisure pervades such stories, and indeed is one of the characteristic features of the travelling people's way of life: working clock-dominated prescribed hours is anathema to them, and their culture tends to shrivel if they find themselves, through force of circumstances, benighted in the urban ant-heap.

Duncan does not consider himself in the category of 'creative' storytellers, I have just defined, and accordingly it is possible, with fair confidence, to attach AT numbers to most of his tales in this collection. 'Mary Rashiecoats an the Wee Black Bull' is AT 511A ('The Little Red Ox': Grimm 130, 'One-Eye, Two-Eyes, and Three-Eyes'), which is related to the Cinderella cycle, and has been found widely distributed throughout Europe, and into Asia. 'The Happy Man's Shirt' – best known, perhaps, in the guise Hans Andersen gave it, although there the joy is in the footwear – readily reveals itself as AT 844, 'The Luck-Bringing Shirt'. It might be instructive, for once, to list the folk traditions in which this tale type has been found: Estonian, Livonian, Lithuanian, Swedish, Irish, Spanish, Catalan, German, Italian, Slovenian, Serbo-Croatian, Romanian, Turkish and 'English–American'. Luck and happiness are every-where, it seems, *sans chemise*, if not *sans culotte*.

'Jack and the Horse's Skin' is a very pleasing and sardonic variant of AT 1535 ('The Rich and the Poor Peasant'). It belongs to a worldwide concatenation of trickster stories which represent the *alter ego* of 'poor Jack' or 'Silly Jack', the boy of intrinsic kindness, generosity and goodness, who shares his wee collop with an unknown stranger (likely to be helpful to him because of that), and of course *has* only a wee collop – with his mother's blessings – because he is leaving her more for herself. As Campbell of Islay wrote to his kinsman, the Marquess of Lorne, son of the Duke of Argyll, dedicating *Popular Tales of the West Highlands* to him in 1860:

> You will find the creed of the people, as shewn in their stories, to be, that wisdom and courage, though weak, may overcome strength, and ignorance, and pride: that the most despised is often the most worthy; that small beginnings lead to great results.
>
> You will find perseverance, frugality, and filial piety rewarded; pride, greed, and laziness punished. You will find much which tells of barbarous times; I hope you will meet nothing that can hurt, or should offend.
>
> If you follow any study, even that of a popular tale, far enough, it will lead you to a closed door, beyond which you cannot pass till you have searched and found the key, and every study will lead the wisest to a fast locked door at last; but knowledge lies beyond these doors, and one key may open the way to many a store which can be reached, and may be turned to evil or to good.

It has to be remarked, however, that the character of the omnipresent 'Jack' of the Jack tales tends to change subtly according to the culture in which he is temporarily operating; in American-English tradition, although a 'good guy', he tends more to the trickster side!

My own personal favourite among all the stories is 'Death in a Nut' (AT 330B, 'The Devil in the Knapsack, Bottle, Cask'), a story whose geographical spread resembles that of 'The Happy Man's Shirt'. Here the story has deeper moral and philosophical implications than is general in folk-tales; the story spells out poignantly the universal tragic truth, human and animal, that there *is* veritably no life without death. It might be as well to remember, at this point, that the mental background of the 'laity' in the countryside through which the Argyll travellers moved was deeply and sombrely Calvinistic; hence, doubtless, the several references to religion in stories such as 'The Sheep of Thorns' and 'The Tailor and the Skeleton'.

With 'The Twelve White Swans' we are once again in the world of marvel, where such grey-as-dust considerations do not apply. This story – and I am giving these AT numbers in every case for the benefit of readers whose interest may be sparked off by one particular story, and who may wish to follow it up – is AT 451 'The Maiden who Seeks her Brothers', which has been found in every corner of Europe from Finland to Turkey, and has relatives as far away as India and China. 'The Ugly Queen' (AT 302, 'The Ogre's [Devil's] Heart in an Egg') can boast a similarly vast worldwide diffusion, and has turned up in the New World in numerous French, Spanish and English versions, as well as in the Creole of the West Indies. In South Africa the white farmer and his wife told – and may be sometimes still tell – their children the same basic folk-tales of the human race as their black neighbours; one can claim, therefore, that the science of folklore can, properly employed, serve as a powerful, humane, liberating discipline.

The remaining international tale to which we can attach an AT number is also the most easily identifiable: 'Jack and the Moneylender' is AT 592 'The Dance among Thorns', which is perhaps best known as No 110 in Grimm ('The Jew in the Brambles'). Because of the tremendous popularity of the Grimms' tales, and the many translations and retellings they have spawned, this is one case where (just possibly) print has contributed to the sustaining of the oral tradition among members of a group which was non-literate until quite recent generations. (The travellers told stories to people who had access to books, and sometimes heard stories from them.)

It is sad to have to relate that this is one case where folklore has been unscrupulously manipulated for political purposes; the Nazis encouraged schoolteachers to use it as a text for anti-Semitic propaganda.

The travellers themselves have all too often been the target of hostile propaganda and discrimination, and a fear of persecution (or even genocide) is reflected in the amazing burker mythology which has grown up among them in the aftermath of the Burke and Hare period of murderous body-snatching in the early nineteenth century. (William Burke was hanged in Edinburgh in 1829 for selling murdered victims to Dr Knox's anatomy school.) The travellers, being defenceless nomads whose disappearance organised society would not worry about, felt themselves natural targets for the burkers, and gradually a whole phantasmagoric scenario took shape in their minds. Until quite recently travellers would steer clear of college buildings in Aberdeen and other Scottish cities. One Aberdeenshire tinkler-gypsy, well known at one time as an accordionist, said in 1954: 'I mind when ye couldna pass the Marischal College or the

King's College for the students would fairly tak a haud o' ye wi' a cleik [a hooked piece of iron] by the leg. They took ye right inside. They wanted fresh bodies.'

According to the travellers the burkers were doctors; but long before Burke and Hare the travellers called medical students 'noddies' or 'shan dodders'. In the belief of some, the burkers' coach draped in black left the college at night, manned by burkers dressed in top hats and swallow-tail coats. The coach was thought to resemble a hearse, with a zinc floor to let the blood run out. The horses' hooves were believed to be muffled with rubber pads, and the chains similarly wound round with cloth to stop them from chinking. To complete this horrific picture, bloodhounds were supposed to lope silently along beside it.

There are literally hundreds of burker stories circulating among the travellers; these invariably make the victims quite close relatives or friends. Duncan's 'The Noddies' is one example of an enormous, distinctive, communal folklore. The fear of genocide has very comprehensible historical roots, for in the sixteenth and seventeenth centuries, under Scots law, it was a capital crime to *be* a tinkler-gypsy. The famous outlaw James MacPherson (hero of the well-known folk-song 'MacPherson's Rant') was hanged in 1700 under this statute.

The travellers, being very family-minded, do not empathise readily in the real world with tramps and other 'gangrels', who are natural loners. The stories about Bartimeus, a blind beggar who solves the problems of the individuals or families he falls in with, constitute an exception to this general rule. Since it can be shown that the culture of the Scottish travellers often reflects aboriginal Celtic folkways, the possibility exists that the travellers' Bartimeus is a far-out relative of the hereditary 'breeves' or law-givers among the Celts who travelled around dispensing justice, or resolving disputes. (These were high-caste members of the *aos dana*, or learned élite – like bards, harpers, doctors, and seannachies, these last being the hereditary genealogists and story-tellers.)

The original Bartimeus, incidentally was the blind beggar healed by Jesus at Jericho: see St Mark 10:46–52.

Another Biblical motif, embedded among the Bartimeus anecdotes, will be spotted immediately by readers who are at all familiar with the Old Testament. This is 'The Judgement of Solomon' (I Kings 3:16–28); it too, like several other stories from the Bible, has an AT number (926).

Stories about 'wise fools' abound in every culture, but the Scots have the distinction of choosing for the name of their archetypal 'king's fool', that of George Buchanan (1506–82), one of the most distinguished scholars in their whole history, and (according to Dr Johnson) one of the best Latin poets of his age. Buchanan taught in Scotland, France and Portugal (where he fell foul of the Inquisition), and eventually became tutor to the boy king James VI at Stirling (1570–8). Far from being this king's 'fool', he was reputed to be a stern disciplinarian. On one occasion a lady of the court came on him while he was giving the young king a vigorous flogging, and tried to intervene. Buchanan finished the job, and then said to her: 'Madam, I have whipped his arse. You may kiss it now.'

It is a curious example of the 'doon-takin' (or deflating) tendency among the Scots that this formidable poet-pedant should have had his name borrowed and given to a fool in folk-tales.

The extraordinary merman story 'La Mer la Moocht' is unique in the archive of the

School of Scottish Studies. Although the language in which it is told shows that it has been thoroughly assimilated into Scots traveller tradition, the possibility cannot be excluded that its ultimate origin is somewhere in a printed text. The shifting nomenclature, and the fact that one of the story-tellers from whom Duncan heard it thought that it came from Greece, might point in that direction. In any event it is quite out of the ordinary on a number of counts – not least in that the physical beauty of a king from the Other World is made attractive to mortals of both sexes.

The only fairy-tale known to me which remotely resembles this one is Hans Andersen's 'The Little Mermaid', but the story-line of that is quite different.

The two ballads – narratives in song – fall into place among the prose narratives with perfect naturalness. Both are magical fairy ballads, the first ('Thomas the Rhymer') made famous internationally by Sir Walter Scott in his *Minstrelsy of the Scottish Border* (Vol. II, 1802), and the second ('Tam Lin') by Robert Burns, who contributed the longest (and, by general consent, the best) version – text, plus tune – to James Johnson's *The Scots Musical Museum* (Vol. V, 1796), no 411).

Both these ballads are now very rare, and both (in Duncan's narrations) are wonderful examples of an 'internal' collaboration of re-collection and re-forming in the mind and on the lips of the singer; together with an 'external' searching for the missing parts of the narrative he did not hear until later in life, in his mid-fifties, from older traveller relations. Duncan's balladry is re-creative folk art in a quite astonishing individual manifestation. We are privileged to be in on the same process that in earlier centuries must have produced many now standard versions of the great classical ballads. Anyone wanting to look up an earlier state in the development of Duncan's 'Tam Lin' will find it in the Addenda section in Vol. IV of Professor Bronson's *The Traditional Tunes of the Child Ballads*.

'Thomas the Rhymer' (No 37 in Professor Child's *English and Scottish Popular Ballads)* is generally believed to have some connection with the famous thirteenth-century prophet and seer Thomas of Ercildoun – this place-name is an older form of the modern Earlston, in Berwickshire – whose prophecies (according to Robert Chambers writing in 1870) were still, in the early nineteenth century, preserved throughout Scotland on the lips of the common people. He was known as True Thomas, because the queen of Elfland was supposed to have given him a tongue that could never lie. It should be added that Thomas is by no means the only character in Scottish history who (according to tradition) disappeared into Elfland, either for seven years or forever; as late as 1692 the Revd Robert Kirk, author of *The Secret Commonwealth of Elves, Fauns and Fairies*, was believed to have been claimed by the subjects of his research, and immured for all time in the fairy mound.

The 'Huntly bank' of earlier versions is on the Borders, but Duncan's version places it in the town of Huntly in Aberdeenshire; and he set Thomas's high legendary status as prophet and seer against a truly lowly beginning – as the grandson of the local clockmaker, and little better than a village idiot. So George Buchanan is not the only one!

Duncan's version of 'Tam Lin' (Child 39) exemplifies the reality of much ballad transmission. In a really thriving ballad community, such as that of the Scottish travellers, a singer will often hear different versions of the same ballad from quite a number of other singers, with sometimes striking variations in both text and tune; if he begins to sing one, his growing version will as likely as not be 'hit' by one or more invading versions (not necessarily the ones he will eventually prefer), and this process can continue virtually for his or her lifetime. However, in most cases (probably) the singer's version will gradually gel, until it becomes pretty fixed and stable, if not immutable; finally, he will be prepared to defend it, and claim hotly that it is the 'right' traditional version. So it is, of course, for him.

The ultimate source of this particular prodigy of recreation was Duncan's grand-mother Bet McColl, 'a real warrior o' a woman', but his sister-in-law Betsy was the immediate provider; the latter had learned it in childhood from Old Bet. As versions of the ballad have been recorded from traveller Johnstones, also west-coast tinkler-gypsies – one of these can be heard on the Scottish Tradition LP *The Muckle Sangs* (Tangent TNGM 119/D) – one can safely assume that Duncan, in the course of his wanderings through Highland and Lowland Scotland, will have heard other versions. What is clear is that, knowing the story-line, and hearing different versions at various times, Duncan has effectively chosen the right lines and events for him out of what were merely fragmented narrations; and has now given us a quite distinctive west-coast 'wey o't'.

Those familiar with Burns's version of 'Tam Lin' from *The Musical Museum* or anthologies may be puzzled to find that the hero (who has been saved from the toils of the Fairy Queen by the intrepid courage of the heroine) is called Lord William in Duncan's version. This is because the final verse is an importation from another ballad, 'The Douglas Tragedy' (Child 7), in which the names of hero and heroine are William and Margaret. Names in any case change in ballads with the protean ease of Tam Lin's transformations in the midst of the fairy throng.

Duncan Williamson was born in a tent on the shores of Loch Fyne, near the village of Furnace in Argyll, in 1928. He was one of a family of sixteen. His mother was Betsy Townsley; his father Jock Williamson, born in 1892, was a travelling basketmaker and tinsmith. Both Duncan's parents were illiterate, but his forebears on both sides were famed singers, pipers and story-tellers, and had an enormous wealth of orally transmit-ted lore.

From the age of five until he was fourteen Duncan went to school in Furnace; then he started work as an apprentice to the stonemason and drystone-dyker Neil MacCallum (mentioned earlier), the source of many of his stories.

When he was fifteen Duncan decided – like Jack in the folk-tales – to 'push his fortune' out in the wide world; he left home with an older brother and travelled through Argyll, Perthshire, Angus and the Mearns; in subsequent years, with a cousin of his mother's, he roamed as far north as Inverness-shire, and as far south and east as Dumfriesshire and Fife. He worked here and there as a farm labourer and harvester; he also learned the trade of horse-dealing, and became an expert at it. However, in the summer months he would always return to his folk on Loch Fyneside.

Throughout his life he has been interested in stories and story-telling, and his peripatetic way of life ensured that he would pick up tales all over Scotland. He gradually came to realise that this meant more to him than anything else, and he became a conscious collector and champion of his people's oral culture. Although stories came first, he was soon adding ballads and songs galore to his capacious memory-holdall.

The first collector to tape-record Duncan was the left-wing poet Helen Fullerton, who in the 1950s became interested in the campaign to secure a fairer deal for travellers as regards camp sites, and the other problems attendant on bourgeois society's often blinkered and bigoted attitudes towards the nomadic families. She got to know Duncan's mother and several of his brothers and sisters in 1958, when she was working in the cookhouse of a hydro-electric scheme in Argyll. At that time Betsy was living in a forester's hut in 'a beautiful piece of woodland at the back of Inveraray which was covered with bluebells in springtime'. The first Williamsons Helen recorded were Duncan's sisters Mary and Rachel; she also recorded Betsy 'cantering', i.e. singing pipes-imitation mouth music. Duncan himself she did not meet till the spring of 1967, when he came over from Fife on a visit to his mother. (Helen herself was by this time a university lecturer at Glasgow.) She recorded him speaking some of his own poems, which greatly impressed her,and various songs and ballads; furthermore, she got in touch with Geordie MacIntyre, the most active collector in the Glasgow area, and told him about Duncan. Geordie visited him in Inveraray in May 1967, and later went across to Fife to do further recordings (near Star) in November of that year. Among other things he recorded five and a half verses of 'Lady Margaret', the ballad which was later to grow into the version of 'Tam Lin' in this volume. He also collected from Duncan a fragment of the classic ballad 'Hind Horn' (Child 17).

In 1966 the Traditional Music and Song Association of Scotland (TMSA), founded by Pete Shepheard, had organised the first Blairgowrie Folk Festival, a pioneering event which gave premier place to genuine traditional performers: revival singers came there as apprentices. These festivals gained strength rapidly, and each year the organisers invited ever more traditional artists such as Alec, Belle, Sheila and Cathie Stewart, Jeannie Robertson, Lizzie Higgins, Jane Turriff and Stanley Robertson to perform for an international public of folk *aficionados*. All of these particular invited guests were travellers, and because of this – and because Blairgowrie is the centre of the soft-fruit growing industry which attracts many travellers in the summer months – members of the 'fraternity' started to attend the traditional festivals in increasing numbers. Among those turning up in 1968 was Duncan, and that is how he first became known to a wider folk public. Pete and the TMSA deserve great credit therefore, for drawing in to the Revival one of the most important of contemporary tradition-bearers.

Furthermore, thanks to him – and the TMSA – there are now dozens of young (and not so young) 'folk addicts' who earlier were unaware that there *were* any such things as Scots folk-tales (let alone story-tellers to do them justice), but who can now tell the long wonder tales in a convincing imitation of the authentic traveller style (and, in some cases, go on to make their own stories, and develop their own personal story-telling style).

Duncan's first wife died in 1971; she had borne him seven children. In 1976 he married the American scholar Linda Headlee, the compiler and editor of the present collection. They have two children, Betsy and Thomas. For the first four years of their married life Duncan and Linda lived in a tent and shared the traditional traveller way of life. Later, as the children grew bigger, they moved into a cottage in Fife. Of recent years Duncan has carried his enthusiasm and his story-telling artistry into schools up and down the country, and most recently has been devoting himself with Linda to the preparation for publication of his staggeringly voluminous wealth of traditional lore.

There can be no question but that Duncan Williamson is one of the most enormously gifted folk artists now living. In a moving tribute to him (printed in *Tocher* 33) his friend Barbara McDermitt has this to say:

> Duncan is a masterly teller of tales and ballad singer. I have heard him perform in public, captivating large audiences, and I have also heard him in the intimate setting of his candle-lit tent. It is the latter that is most memorable to me. With Betsy dozing on his lap and Linda lovingly looking after Thomas, both my ten-year-old daughter, Heather, and I have sat hours on end spellbound as Duncan has taken us into his special world of wonder and magic. Each tale is told dramatically and vividly with an intenseness and directness that draws you in and holds you riveted until the tale's end. Duncan's verbal facility is edged with a razor-sharp timing, and his large powerful hands punctuate his stories with strength and subtlety. He knows how to build suspense, bring out humour and release emotions both tragic and joyful. One cannot listen placidly to Duncan's stories. This is also true of his ballads and songs. He treats them as dramatic stories set to music and sings them with true feeling.
>
> Whether Duncan is telling a tale or sharing a ballad, he does so with such personal impact, you feel he is offering part of himself, an unforgettable gift, and as listener, you cannot help but be touched deeply by the experience.

I cannot better that description, which springs from a deep, intimate knowledge of Duncan, his personality and his art. It is cheerful news that a cassette, to be issued by Peter Shepheard's Springthyme Records, will give readers of this book an opportunity to listen at their leisure to recorded examples of Duncan's magical, incantatory, storytelling genius. In this traditional art, it *is* the spoken – and sung – word which ultimately 'bears the gree'.

Penguin Folklore Library, Penguin Books, 1987.

The Tinkers

In Scotland and Ireland, as well as in parts of Scandinavia, there are still to be found nomadic or quasi-nomadic groups whose way of life resembles that of the gypsies, although they have little or no gypsy blood in them. It is impossible to speak with certainty of their origin, but it seems likely that they are the descendants of a very ancient caste of itinerant metal-workers whose status in tribal society was probably high. One of the trades associated with them from early times was that of tinsmith, and it is clear that to primitive man the ability to use metals seemed very close to magic; consequently, both 'black' and 'white' smiths for long enjoyed immense prestige, not only as craftsmen but also as wielders of secret powers.

When the gypsies arrived in Western and Northern Europe in the fifteenth and sixteenth centuries, there was no doubt a certain amount of biological and sociocultural mixing between them and the aboriginal itinerants whom they encountered (and in some areas appear to have displaced). In certain regions a measure of fusion took place between the two groups, and a mixed 'tinkler-gypsy' race came into being, but at the present day the gypsies and tinkers view each other as quite distinct groupings, and there is not much love lost between them.

The ranks of the Scots tinkers have been augmented at various periods as a result of events in the country's troubled history. Some of the tinker groupings make up a kind of 'underground' clan system of their own, and individuals are intensely conscious of kinship and family ties. They want nothing to do with tramps and other solitaries, feeling themselves as distinct from this type of itinerant as they are from the Romany gypsies. A very intelligent tinker youth once put the distinction in a nutshell when, referring to an Irish tramp who used to wander around Scotland, he declared: 'That sort of lad just lives from day to day, but we (tinkers) live entirely in the past.' (It should be stressed that the term 'tinker' itself is disliked by the fraternity because of its frequent use in a derogatory context; tinkers call themselves 'travellers'.)

Unlike the true gypsies, whose language is (or used to be) Romany, the tinkers use a cover-language known as 'cant'. The cant of the tinkler-gypsies of Galloway and south-east Scotland has quite a strong admixture of Romany in it, but north of the Forth/Clyde line the amount of recognisable Romany in the cover-tongue is hardly more than fifteen per cent. The tinkers of the north and west, whose native language is Gaelic (or was, until very recently), have a cover-tongue of their own which resembles one of the secret languages of Ireland. Their name for it is Beurla-reagad (= 'Beurlacheard', or 'lingo of the cairds' – the tinkers). That this is a very ancient cover-tongue is shown by the fact that some of the vocabulary which it reflects and deforms is archaic Gaelic.

Like the gypsies, tinkers sometimes make money by telling fortunes. Quite a number are believed (by themselves and others) to possess the gift of 'second sight'. Belief in the existence of fairies is still very widespread among them. There are in the archives of the School of Scottish Studies a large number of supernatural tales recorded from tinker informants; these include stories about brownies, elves, changelings, water-kelpies, fairy funerals, fairy music heard by mortals, and – last but not least – 'a wee green man' seen in the Sma' Glen. Ghosts are feared, though there are but few tales of them harming living persons. Belief in witches and the black art is also common.

One rather curious item of tinker folklore deserves mention. A sort of mystical aura surrounds the name of the MacPhees, one of the Scots tinker clans. The MacPhees are regarded by some as the 'original' tinkers, the 'first on the road', but even so an undoubted 'hoodoo' seems to lie over their very name: it is bad luck to hear or speak the name MacPhee, and a substitute name such as MacFud, MacaFud or MacaTuttie is supposed to be used in place of it.

Although the 'flattie' (non-tinker) population for long feared that the tinkers were child-stealers (witness the lullaby 'Hush ye! Hush ye! Dinna fret ye! The black Tinkler winna get ye!'), the folklore of the tinkers shows clearly and even poignantly that they lived in much greater fear of the ordinary population than the 'flatties' did of them. This persecution complex found, and still finds, expression in gruesome folklore about 'burkers' (body-snatchers) who were supposed to be continually on the wait to waylay and murder travelling folk, and sell their bodies to the anatomy schools. Paraded by an accomplished story-teller at the camp-fire, the ghoulish trappings of the burker stories conjure up a phantasmagoric *grand guignol* world reminiscent of Dylan Thomas's 'The Doctor and the Devils'. Lum-hatted black-frockcoated 'noddies' (medical students) drive the 'burker's coach' into the countryside to try and find isolated tinker encampments; the coach is long and black-draped, looking like a hearse; bloodhounds lope silently beside it; the horse's harness is swathed in cloth to prevent it chinking; the horse's hooves have rubber pads on them. In some of the stories the tinker victim gets his throat cut, and his relatives discover too late that he is missing; in others, there are hair's-breadth escapes from the villainous doctors and 'noddies'.

Although we can well believe that defenceless ragged nomads were occasionally the victims of murderous body-snatchers, we must probably look further back in history in order to understand the deeper-lying reasons for this persecution complex. In the seventeenth century it was a capital crime in Scotland merely to be an 'Egyptian' – Egyptian, for the courts, meaning not merely a gypsy, but any sort of wanderer, vagabond minstrel or travelling tinsmith of no fixed abode. If it could be proved that a travelling man of uncertain occupation was 'halden and repute to be an Egyptian', he was as good as dead. Among the victims of this law was the famous fiddler James MacPherson, who was hanged at Banff in 1700; his name is immortalised in the folk-song 'MacPherson's Rant', which survives on the lips of present-day tinker singers.

A Companion to Scottish Culture, ed. David Daiches, Edward Arnold, 1981.

Bynames among the Tinkers

In common with all communities where the same surname is shared by hundreds of people, and where the number of Christian names in general use is fairly limited, the Scots tinkers make extensive use of 'bynames' or nicknames. An accurate knowledge of those in current use in a particular community is essential to anyone trying to thread his way through the labyrinth of tinker relationships. In many cases, the nickname pinpoints with epigrammatic precision the place of the individual concerned in his own family, and in the community at large, e.g. 'Burnt Bonnet's Maggie's Silly Jock'. In some cases an individual may have two nicknames, one used behind his back, and the other to his face. Tinkers often say, 'Ye never ken your ain byname.'

When the Scots tinkers bestow bynames, they exhibit a truly Rabelaisian (or Joycean) imaginative exuberance which makes more conventional nomenclature seem very prosaic. The following is a list of contemporary tinker bynames collected in Central Scotland and the North-East:

The Sheep's Heid
The Blue Doo
The Rockingham Teapot
The Evil-Eyed Piper
The Golden Kipper
The Hauf-hangit Minister
    (or: The Lang-neckit
    Minister)
12 Hairs from Dunkeld
Half a Sark
The Water Pelky (Kelpy)
The Scowdered Hedgehog
Wooden Sleeves
The Glad-Eyed Sailor
Het Skirtie
Toady's Orphan
The Mad Chemist
Henseed
Candy Heelies
Catchy Bussy

The Big Mahungry
Hare's Mouth
The Bald-heided Gypsy
Twa Burnt Holes in a Soakin' Weet
    Blanket
Lambie Laddie
Andra Hoochten
The Baby Austin
The Test Pilot
Scrappin' John
The Hangman
The Young Blackie
    (Blackbird)
Water-bottle
Big Roar
The Sheep's Pluck
The Baser (Ba' Heid)
Lucky Stocking
Cleaned Easy
Jimmie Joukies

The Sweepin' Brush   Electric Katie
Moonlight Moggie   Fried Een
Strawberry Nose   Alicky Doo
Twa Thumbs   Vinegar Bottle
The Plout   Tin Croon
Love-in-a-Close   Mr Clap

Scottish Studies, vol. 6, 1962.

Tales from Barra:
Told by the Coddy

With Foreword by Compton Mackenzie and Introduction and Notes by J. L. Campbell. W. & A. K. Johnston & G. W. Bacon Ltd, Edinburgh 1960.

The Coddy – John MacPherson, postmaster of Northbay, Barra, who died in 1955 – was a celebrated public figure on his native island. The boarding-house known as Taigh a' Choddy, built to accommodate the tourists who, between the wars, started coming to Barra from all the airts, was soon a centre from which the folklore and folk-tales of the island were disseminated orally through the length and breadth of Britain, and beyond. In Egypt, during the Second World War, I heard the story of the Weaver and the Little Weaver told in English by a Medical Officer who had heard it two or three years previously when out fishing with the Coddy.

Dr John Lorne Campbell, who has put Scotland greatly in his debt by his devoted and indefatigable pioneer folklore research in the Hebrides, has done commemorative justice to the Coddy's story-telling powers in this charmingly got-up little miscellany. Nearly all the material was told in English, and taken down in shorthand by Miss Sheila J. Lockett. Dr Campbell has written an Introduction which not only provides information about the Coddy's life and family tree but also gives the reader as much as he can conveniently digest of Barra's history and present problems.

The stories themselves range from international folk-tales to yarns about the famous *Polly*, the whisky ship which was wrecked off Eriskay in 1941. There are also tales and anecdotes about the MacNeils and other Highland chiefs which are a most entertaining blend of orally transmitted fact and fantasy. The concluding sections offer a fascinating gallimaufry of stories and beliefs about fairies, ghosts, second sight and witchcraft.

That the Coddy was an expert raconteur in English as well as in Gaelic is obvious even from the printed page. Indeed, for his English-speaking audience, either at *Taigh a' Choddy*, or around and about Barra during fishing expeditions, he seems to have developed a special style which one might term, without the least disrespect, a kind of dignified 'dragoman' style. This it is which gives the little book its distinctive bouquet.

At its best, the Coddy's style has a laconic deadpan humour which recalls Damon Runyon. Here is a prison guard talking to two Barramen who are languishing in French captivity during the Napoleonic wars:

> 'Well, boys,' he says, 'I am hearing you talking Gaelic, and I am hearing you also complaining about the food. Well, I have no other alternative but to agree with you that the food is very bad.'

Or here, MacNeil at the Battle of Bannockburn:

> he stripped down to his kilt only and his braces … he was mowing the English enemy down wholesale and retail.

At times he comes away with a remark of devastating epigrammatic simplicity:

> This is, of course, a traditional story which nobody could say whether it is right or wrong.

In the stories of supernatural folklore one feels that the Coddy's English is less adequate to his task than in the lighter tales. Occasionally he takes the easy way out, and omits passages which (if one happens to have come across Gaelic recordings of the same material) seem a genuine loss. For example, in *How Time was Lost in the Fairy Knoll* – a variant of No 470 in the Aarne/Thompson type-index – the Brevig man who goes to the shore to look for treasures washed up by the sea catches sight of a human jawbone. In the Gaelic version recorded by the late Dr Calum I. MacLean on 1 October 1946 (Irish Folklore Commission MS 1028, pp. 468–78), this version goes:

> Chan fhaca e dad sam bith ann ach claban duine a bha a' tionndadh an dràsda is a rithist 'nuair a bhristeadh a' rùid a staigh, agus dh'fhalbh e sios gu grunn a' phoirt, agus thog e an claban agus choimhead e air, agus thòisich e 'na inntinn fhéin air moladh, agus b'fhiach e sin a mholadh, àilleachd na fiaclan a bha 's a' chlaban, agus thubhairt e ris a' chlaban, 'Nach briagha an fhàilt a dh'fhàgadh tu ann am bonnach mór eòrna agus clapaire math do dh'ìm Gàidhealach air,' agus e a' sadadh bhuaithe a' chlabain
> (Translation: He saw nothing at all but a man's skull which turned over now and then when a swell burst in; he went down to the shore of the Port, and he lifted the skull and looked at it, and he began, in his own mind, to praise – and it was worthy of praise – the beauty of the skull's teeth. And he said to the skull, 'Wouldn't you leave a lovely mark in a big barley bannock with a good lump of Highland Butter on it!' – and with that he threw the skull away.)

Here is the same passage, told in English and taken down in shorthand:

> He stood above the Port, and seeing nothing except a human jawbone with beautiful white teeth. The jawbone drawing his attention very much, he went down to the sea, picked it up and examined it, and said to himself that it was the finest set of teeth that he had ever seen – and at that stage he threw it away, and walked up.
> The idiomatic difference is obvious.

For the interest of readers understanding Gaelic, Dr Campbell gives as an appendix a transcription of a wire recording of the Gaelic version of *MacNeil of Barra, the Widow's Son and the Shetland Buck*. The story is of considerable interest, because of the picture it ingenuously but convincingly presents of the wanton and arbitrary despotism which must all too often have underlain clan chief autocracy. MacNeil takes a fancy to the Mingulay widow's son, and carries him off to Barra, in spite of his mother's distress. When the boy grows up, and has strength enough to beat him in wrestling matches, the Chief attempts to murder him by ordering the crew of the *birlinn* to put to sea in a hurricane. Later in the story, the Chief treacherously attempts to use his *sgian dubh* on a wrestling champion he has failed to beat in a fair fight.

Whatever one may think of the subsequent coming of the 'Law' to *dùthaich mhic Nìll* – Dr Campbell has documented this in *The Book of Barra* – one cannot help feeling that the abolition of the heritable jurisdictions must have been greeted with some relief by the ordinary clansman. The Coddy explains the place-name *Cnoc a' Chrochadair* as follows:

> When MacNeil of Barra had somebody to hang he would notify the *crochadair* to come up, and his salary was, I understand, this: he had a little dominion there at Cnoc a' Chrochadair and it belonged to him. Hanging was his only job, and he got as salary a free croft for doing it.

Scottish Studies, vol. 7, 1963.

Exodus to Alford
by Stanley Robertson
Balnain Books, 1988

There are still a fair number of nomadic traveller families in Scotland who camp out all the year round in their tarpaulin-covered humpback tents, defying the worst that our weather can throw at them, but a much greater number hibernate in houses. Come the spring, these temporary house-dwellers feel an irresistible urge to get out on the road again, and the routes they follow are in many – perhaps most – cases ancestral traveller routes which have witnessed similar compulsive pilgrimages for hundreds of years. Leaving the alien world of the 'scaldies' (non-traveller townsfolk) behind, they feel *free* once again, and it is this magical feeling of liberation which Stanley Robertson, 'master storyteller of the traveller folk', conjures up with truly professional expertise in this entrancing book of reminiscences and folk-tales.

Stanley is a nephew of Jeannie Robertson, the great Aberdeen ballad-singer who died in 1975. Jeannie's mother Maria Stewart, who kept a wee shop – selling 'a'thing' – in the Gallowgate of Aberdeen, and was the source-singer for many of Jeannie's finest songs, could never wait to get out on the road when the yellow was on the broom. Sometimes she went 'up the Dee and doon the Don', and sometimes the other way round, but she never forgot the heady smell of freedom which Stanley conveys so marvellously, and which the late Betsy Whyte evoked with similar eloquence in the autobiography which she completed, and luckily saw published, well before her untimely death.

Until the School of Scottish Studies 'broke through' into the semi-hidden world of the travelling people in the early 1950s, remarkably few folk-tales in Lowland Scots had ever been put on record. This contrasted sharply with the great wealth of Gaelic folk-tales which were known to exist because of the pioneering work of John Francis Campbell of Islay, and others, in the last century. The maverick Peterhead printer-antiquary Peter Buchan had indeed made a collection of *Ancient Scottish Tales* in the 1820s, but these were somewhat wooden anglicised recensions which reproduced neither the language nor the flavour of the Scots originals. Because practically no field collectors had ever ventured among the travellers (or 'tinkler-gypsies') before, the enormous bulk of story-material uncovered among them, from 1954 onwards, came as a stunning surprise to folklorists the world over. It was in Jeannie Robertson's wee hoosie in Causewayend that the breakthrough took place, and once the floodgates were opened there was no stopping the onrush. Traveller after traveller contributed fine versions of *Märchen* (international wonder tales), and every type of traditional narrative, whether sung or spoken. Some of the visitors were close relatives of

Jeannie's, and one of these early tapes contains items recorded from Jeannie's elder brother Willie (Stanley's father), and Lizzie, Stanley's mother. The latter supplied a panoramic history of the Scots travelling people, claiming for them a very ancient lineage among Scottish ethnic groups, and she advanced shrewd cogent reasons to explain the travellers' attachment to Prince Charlie and the Jacobite cause.

Dipping into Stanley's book, I wondered what story he would give to Lizzie, and it came as no surprise to find that 'Mither's Tale' ('the Third Tale at Alford') was a real gem. This story is a version of the international tale given the number 812 in the Aarne/ Thompson compendium *The Types of Folktale*, and there called 'The Devil's Riddle'. In order to free a girl from bondage, Jack (the generic name of a young good-hearted hero) has to find the solutions to three conundrums set him by 'The Laird o' the Black Airts'. Jack is helped by an old woman, who tells him that the only person who can supply the answers is 'Hoddie', i.e. the Devil. She herself happens to be the Devil's auntie, so after hiding Jack under her petticoats, she opens a trapdoor and takes him down to Hell. The ensuing passage deserves to be reproduced in full:

> When she gangs in, Hoddie is pleased to see her, as auld Sissie is his favourite auntie. She looks at him an says 'Whit the deil ill ails ye, cos ye look awfy distraught.' 'Oh' says he, 'I seem tae hae some pullichers o hell in between mi horns an they are pittin me divvi.' 'Oh sit doon,' cries Sissie, 'an I'll look yer heid for ony parries.'
>
> [pullichers: fleas; divvi: crazy; parries: lice]
>
> Noo, Hoddie faas asleep in his auntie's airms an then she wakens him awfy quickly, an says 'Hoddie, I wis trying tae remember, we aa ken there's a mannie in the moon, but how dae we ken there's a wifie?' 'O dinnae be silly Sissie – di ye no remember there his tae be a wifie on the moon as weel as a mannie, cos whar else wid the sun (son it is orally) come frae!' Then he faas asleep again, and she wakens him up quickly and says 'Hoddie, I wis trying tae remember, if the *wee dwarfie o the north* wis chasin his big faither and mither, whit time o day wid it be?' 'O yer bein awfy daft the day Auntie – wid it no jist be *a little after two*'. 'O, so yer right Hoddie.'
>
> He sleeps again an she wakins him frae his slummin again, and she says 'Hoddie, a wis trying tae remember, how wid a man wi one ee see mair than a man wi twa yaks [eyes]?' 'Weel Auntie Sissie, ye must be gettin awfy dottled in yer auld age; dae ye no remember – a man wi one eye can see yer twa yaks, but ye can only see his one eye – so of course he can see mair than you.' 'O weel Hoddie yer a clever lad and I'm getting dinleyfied in mi auld years. Never mind, I'll hae tae be gan awa cos this is an awfy warm place ye hae here.' 'Weel, dinnae let it be sic a lang time till ye come back an see me.'

These affectionate exchanges between the Deil and his favourite auntie convey something of the delicious flavour of this fabulous book.

In writing down stories he has heard orally, the author – who reveals himself in the book as a most accomplished and sophisticated literary artist – uses a good deal of travellers' cant: more, on average, than appears in transcriptions of travellers' folk-tales recorded on tape. For example, he frequently uses the cant word 'nesmore' for mother, where his own auntie Jeannie, telling stories to other travellers, would use mother (or mither): 'and so Jack gaed awa hame tae his auld mither'. This feature of his style is without doubt a by-product of the cleverly executed transmutation of oral story-telling into self-conscious literary narration. However, the use of cant as a sort of colouring device struck me more than once as a rather questionable artifice. Cant is in essence a cover tongue, to be used when the speaker wants to disguise his meaning; in a folk-tale told inside the traveller community, a cover lingo is self-evidently not necessary.

A possible exception to this general rule might be the language of the 'burker' stories – the characteristic traveller horror stories which grew up in the aftermath of the Burke and Hare murders – but Stanley has not included burker stories in this volume. He has, however, included a number of ghost stories and supernatural legends narrated (most convincingly) as actual experiences, and in these the use of cant words like 'kenchins' (children) and 'peeve' (booze) seems a lot more natural.

The last third of the book ('Home with Jack', via Braemar, Ballater, Torphins and Garlogie) consists of ten splendidly told 'Jack Tales' – versions of international wonder tales which have found 'a local habitation and a name' in the Scottish North-East. Here Stanley's narrative skill comes into full bloom, not seldom recalling that of his auntie Jeannie: the idiomatic balance of the language seems easy and assured, like the 'ballad-Scots' of sung narrative, and there are long tracts with never a cant word. Here is the dénouement of Kittlie Katie's tale at Ballater – 'Jack and the Well of Life's Water':

> So the servant speaks, an tells the King how 'one day I wis intae the wid collecting wild berries, whin I hear the evil Black Knight plotting wi his freens: the craws, the ravens an the rooks … on how he will cast an evil spirit upon ye, the King, so that he can get the bonnie Princess all tae himsell and, if onybody tries tae get tae the Well o Life's water, (an wis lucky enough tae get past the sentinel Cat) then the black birds o death will dee for them! Weel! … then he catches mi in among the trees, (an he kent I hid heard his plans) so he turns mi intae a bird and starts tae get the evil black birds tae kill mi … I manages tae escape and then, luckily – I met in wi Jack here, an tried tae help him as I could – and I'm real glad tae see that Jack his bin successful!'
>
> Aa o the folks in the castle are happy … Jack marries the Princess (and they hiv a good family o bairns) … an he sends for his mither (who marries the faithful servant that hid helped Jack!) So, it aa goes tae show – that if ye dae things wi a pure heart and guid intent – then ye aye reap the best o rewards and blessings … jist like Jack!

The traveller whose by-name is Man's Brains tells a version of Aarne/Thompson 577 ('The King's Tasks') – undoubtedly one of the basic folk-tales of the human race, and one which has been recorded in variants of bewildering complexity throughout the world. Man's Brains is well aware of this:

> Every traveller in the land aa hae their ain versions o this tale o 'the three tasks'. As for masell I never ever found anything too hard for mi. Sometimes wi were ain stupidity we can mak easy things difficult. If only we deek [look] a wee bittie closer then we can see that the tasks o life are nae sae hard as they seem tae be.

The majority of Jack Tales are indeed moral tales, like the last story in the book – Maisie

Morloch's 'Jack and the Clever Man'. This is a version of the very widespread tale – 922 in Aarne/Thompson – which is related to No 152 in Grimm ('The Shepherd Boy'). The best known English analogue is the ballad 'King John and the Abbot of Canterbury' in the Percy MS, and is No 45 in Professor Child's *English and Scottish Popular Ballads*), where Jack stands in for a local 'wise man' when the latter cannot answer three riddles set him by 'cloven Hoddie'. Stanley is never sweir to make the moral absolutely explicit:

> Really and truly, some folks get an awfy great schooling and great learning and then think they ken everything, (and so forget the Deil) but there'll come a day again, whin aa their great learning disnae help them – an they may hae tae get help frae a peer ignorant tinker ...

It only remains to add that if this is not the most attractively decorated book of folk-tales ever produced, it is certainly up there contending. Simon Fraser – the 'bean rannie gadgie' (kind gent) who is Stanley's artistic collaborator – has painted a set of pictures which mesh with the text at several levels, and point up the tales' symbolic glamourie. The result is a delight to hold and look at.

Scottish Literary Journal, vol. 30, Spring 1989.

Magical Mysteries
Nyakim's Windows
by Stanley Robertson
Balnain Books, 1989

One of the most astonishing and potent phenomena on the present-day cultural scene is the emergence of gifted performers and tradition-bearers from the ranks of travelling people. Shunned and avoided by settled society, the travellers guarded their love of song and story almost as if it were a sacred charge, although this inherited treasure remained a closed book to outsiders right up to the 1950s, when field-work undertaken by the School of Scottish Studies began the 'dig' which was to bring so much brilliance and inventiveness to light.

In 1953, Jeannie Robertson revealed the wealth of classical balladry which was still retained in safe custody by traveller champions, and this revelation well and truly rocked the world of international folk-song scholars. But an even greater surprise was in store for students of the folk-tale. One evening Jeannie herself asked for a story, came away with an Aberdeenshire version of an international folk-tale, and since then thousands of Lallans *Märchen* (wonder tales) have come pouring into the archives of the School of Scottish Studies.

Several story-tellers have since become household names in folklore circles – Duncan Williamson and the late Betty Whyte spring to mind – but in many ways the most intriguing figure of all is Jeannie Robertson's nephew Stanley, the author of *Exodus to Alford* who has earned the title of 'master' story-teller of the travelling folk. Encouraged by the success of his first book, Stanley has now given us a truly entrancing sequel.

Credit for starting him off on this exceptionally interesting creative route must be given to the Traditional Music and Song Association of Scotland, which some years ago added story-telling to the list of competitions at the festivals it organised. Stanley was soon carrying off cups and prizes, and recordings of his splendidly told tales served as models for a new generation of 'revival' story-tellers, but fortunate chance led to his breaking new ground by personally giving his stories literary form. The result is what to all intents and purposes constitutes a novel type of art form.

There are, however, some quite striking differences between Stanley's first book and his second *Nyakim's Windows*. *Exodus to Alford* took as its framework the nostalgically remembered springtime wanderings of city-settled travellers who spent the winters cooped up in houses; as Betsy Whyte related in her fascinating autobiography *The Yellow on the Broom*, these temporary house-dwellers felt an irresistible urge, come the spring, to set out on the road again and in *Exodus to Alford* Stanley showed the magical feeling of liberation which all such travellers shared.

At each of the major stops on the ancestral traveller routes 'up the Dee and doon the Don' he gave a story to one or other of the wayfarers he remembered from earlier days, and most of these stories were versions of international folk-tales which had gained a local 'habitation and name' in the North-East. Thus, although the stories were full of supernatural magic, they were also tethered firmly to earth by virtue of the real-life setting.

In *Nyakim's Windows* Stanley adopts a very similar device, but this time he takes his readers on a sort of 'magical mystery tour' leaving Pitsligo and the Deil's Road o' Bennachie behind; he is soon touching down across the Atlantic, among the malignant ghosts of exploited and defrauded Red Indians, and before the end of the trip he has even embarked on 'astral travels'. The vehicle readers are invited to travel on is a magnificently decorated 'Vardo' – gypsy living caravan – drawn by a silver Arab stallion called Andaron, and with an ancient traveller guru called Nyakim as guide.

It is this mystical character, 'dressed like a Tibetan Lama', who selects the stories Stanley is instructed to tell at the various stopping-points. Owing to the author's real creative powers, this at times rather artificial-seeming device on the whole works pretty well.

The most noticeable single difference between the two books lies in the fact that in *Nyakim's Windows* the stories are in the main Stanley's own inventions and not recognisable international folk-tales (like the 'Jack tales' which occupy the final third of *Exodus to Alford*). Some are clearly reminiscences of Stanley's own experiences at various folk festivals like Kinross and Kirriemuir; others supply poignant evidence that he still feels very close to his Auntie Jeannie. What binds all the tales together and gives the book its inimitable cachetic flavour is the ever-present sense of threatening evil, and of the powers for good that can counteract it. Few who know them would deny that the gifts Sandy celebrates are a very real part of the traveller inheritance.

As in the earlier book, Stanley makes plentiful use of the Lowland travellers' cant, as well as of North-East Scots, and Romany and Gaelic expressions; he has constructed a highly idiosyncratic literary language, and although this is fairly easy to read for anyone who has heard the stories narrated at folk festivals and ceilidhs, there are patches here and there where the uninitiated may find the lingo rather hard going.

I have left to the last the feature which makes Stanley's story-books such a delight to handle and read. He has been lucky enough to secure a brilliant and congenial artistic collaborator in Simon Fraser. Fraser's work adds a new dimension to what are already works of formidable literary artistry.

Scotsman, 21 October 1989.

In the Open, a bitter-sweet life
Red Rowans and Wild Honey
by Betsy Whyte
Canongate, 1990

Until comparatively recently the 'hidden' world of the Scots travelling people remained a closed book to the settled population, and a mutual distrust and fear poisoned relations between them. This deep-rooted antagonism between two radically different ways of life expressed itself, for the travellers, in the Grand Guignol mythology of the 'burkers' – procurers of bodies for the medical schools – who were believed by many, right up to the middle of this century, to be still at their lethal game, with 'tinkler-gypsies' as a preferred target. By the same token the travellers have been credited by settled folk, at one time or another, with every crime imaginable.

That there has been a definite improvement in this ethnic war-situation is directly due to the present folk-revival. The enormous wealth of traveller folk-culture – songs, ballads, stories, music – was gradually revealed by collectors for the School of Scottish Studies from the 1950s onwards, and some of the major performers from among their ranks have become veritable folk-heroes – and heroines – for a wide circle of enthusiasts. Of these, no one enjoyed a more richly deserved popularity than the late Betsy Whyte, who died from a heart attack in August 1988 during the Auchtermuchty Folk Festival, deeply mourned by all who were there.

In 1979 the first instalment of Betsy's autobiography appeared, entitled *The Yellow on the Broom*, and it was at once apparent that this gifted travelling woman, who had first become noted as a champion story-teller and ballad-singer, the star of ceilidhs and folk festivals, was also a born writer, with a very distinctive style. Indeed, it is this style, and above all the use of language – the adroit but never overdone colouring of travellers' cant (the secret lingo of the fraternity), mixed with Perthshire Scots and a fluent sensitive English – which proves to be a really marvellous vehicle for this particular brand of printed-word story-telling and gives her two books a quite unique flavour.

Many passages recall the delicate linguistic balance of ballad-Scots: 'That night nature decided to chastise her clouds, and their mighty roars and sair weeping awoke me in the small hours of the morning.' The cant supplies plenty of wonderful phrases, e.g. 'in the doldrums o' drink' (for a massive hangover).

The two editors – Dr Peter Cooke and Ian Gould – have provided formal punctuation, spelling and paragraphing, but the end result is an accomplished narrative voice which many a professional writer might envy. Like her friend and 'fellow-traveller' Stanley Robertson, Betsy has been able to move without all too great effort out of the world of oral tradition into written literature. This speaks much both for the strength of the travellers' oral culture, and for the acumen of the headmaster who advised her to read widely.

The title of the second book, *Red Rowans and Wild Honey* – as poetic and evocative as *The Yellow on the Broom* – stems from a saying of old Maggie Townsley, Betsy's mother: 'Life is a mixture o' rowans and wild honey. We maun hae the bitter tae mak us appreciate the sweet' – and indeed the traveller life, as Betsy lived it, had plenty of both. She was acutely sensitive to the beauties of nature, and this second book is full of masterly passages of lyrical prose describing the pleasures of life on the move in the open air; even the hard darg of tattie-planting and howking, of flax-pulling and binding, and long hours among the dreels of the berryfields of Blair were sweetened for Betsy by the familiar smells of clove, burning wood and hay.

The brutal fact remains that the travellers' life was often hard and even agonising in the extreme – not least because of the heartless attitude towards the travellers frequently displayed by folk who should have known better. A typical example, recalled here by Betsy, concerns the nurse who attended her after the birth of her first child; a woman who emerges from this account as much more 'ignorant' than the people she despised. On the other hand, Betsy is always keen to give credit where credit is due; of the doctor who delivered the bairn she writes: 'Dr Lang, may his bed be in Heaven, was a jewel of a man.'

Red Rowans and Wild Honey takes Betsy's story from her father's death through the pains and pleasures of adolescence, to her first meeting with Bryce Whyte, her husband-to-be, and the difficult days of courtship. She is exceedingly frank about the personal problems that faced her – chiefly her initial distaste for sexual intimacy, which made her unwilling to marry – and the description of the traveller-style marriage service conducted by her mother is accordingly very moving:

> Mother sat on her knees and asked the Blessed Saviour to be with us … 'I am neither a minister nor a priest but I ken that you can work through any human soul. Whether they be only a cratur like me, or the king in a castle. This twa young folk should be married, and by the power o this blessed book let them be man and wife in your sight after they have sworn on it.'

The narrative continues into the early years of the Second World War, and provides a vivid chronicle of the vicissitudes of that period as experienced by the travellers, most of whom had close relatives in the Forces. There were the inevitable losses and bereavements, and Bryce was invalided out of the Army with an injured spine. However, in spite of all the sorrows and hardships, the overall impression left by this book is one of affirmation, even exhilaration: like the late Ewan MacColl, Betsy never lost touch with 'the joy of living'.

Her second book, like the first, has the authentic bloom of the open air on it; it carries the reader to the very centre of a way of life which, although profoundly alien to most industrialised Western society, has a permanent appeal, validity and attractiveness of its own. A fitting epigraph for it might be Lorca's lines:

O city of the gypsies, who
that saw you could forget you soon?
Let them seek you in my forehead
The playground of the sands and moon.

Scotsman, 31 March 1990.

LITERATURE AND POLITICS

The Women of the Glen:
Some Thoughts on Highland History

Historians who write about the Highland Clearances – the infamous mass evictions in which (as Karl Marx stated in *Das Kapital*) areas as big as German principalities were systematically and brutally cleared of their inhabitants – invariably refer to the extraordinary lack of resistance on the part of the victims during this cataclysmic period of capitalist 'social engineering'; yet none (as far as I know) has ever ventured anything like a convincing answer to the really baffling question which must surely occur to anyone reading the history on record: why was it the women, rather than the men, who offered such resistance as there was?

In his book on *The Highland Clearances*, John Prebble describes one such scene:

> Four miles down the glen, as they came through a wood by the march of Greenyard, their road was blocked by sixty or seventy women, with a dozen or less men standing behind them. The women had drawn their red shawls over their heads, and were waiting silently.
>
> Taylor, the Fiscal, and Stewart got down from the carriage and walked to the head of the police. Taylor shouted to the women in Gaelic and told them that they must clear the way for the Law, and when they did not move he took out the Riot Act and began to read it ...
>
> The constables went forward with their truncheons lifted, and, according to the *Inverness Courier* (which got the information from Taylor), the Strathcarron men immediately ran for the hills, leaving their women alone. Although some men must have remained, for two were injured and one was later charged, the absence of all the others is hard to condone, as it was at Culrain, Gruids, and elsewhere. The assault of the police was short, brutal, and bloody. The *Courier*, again reporting Taylor perhaps, said that there were three hundred women there, and that they were armed with sticks and stones. If they were, they were remarkably inefficient in the use of them. For no policeman suffered more than a bruise or a dented hat. (p. 244)

These events took place in 1854. No wonder the Highlanders were disinclined to turn out to fight the Russians. During the war against the French Revolution and Napoleon, the Isle of Skye had furnished thousands of men for the forces. By 1937 Skye had contributed to the British Army twenty-one Lieutenant-Generals and Major-Generals, forty-eight Lieutenant-Colonels, 600 Majors, Captains and Subalterns, 120 Pipers, and 10,000 NCOs and men.

The Sutherlanders had fought under Gustavus Adolphus, and become the fame of the armies of Europe. When one remembers the accounts of their martial spirit on the battlefields of Germany, Spain, and the Low Countries, one asks oneself with incredulity why they did not defend their own homesteads. Your guess is as good as mine, and the following tentative explanation is offered with the utmost diffidence. I do not think it is the whole truth, but it is part of the truth.

First of all, one must get the Jacobite period into perspective. It is often said that the ancient clan society was destroyed at Culloden, and in a sense this is true, although the process of disintegration had begun long before. However, it is easier to apply surgical methods to the body politic than to subvert the folkways of a millennium. Passing an Act to abolish the heritable jurisdictions does not mean that you get rid, automatically, of the mental attitudes involved, either on the victim's side, or on the side of the judges. Reading the accounts of some of the clearances, one gets an impression of the ritual of 'pit and gallows' still in operation, and the luckless clansman waiting to be topped by the chief's *crochadair* (executioner).

There was occasional resistance, when the people were goaded to utter desperation, or when a resolute leader was thrown up. In 1849, at Sollas, North Uist, there were wild riots, and here and there one finds reports of men such as Archibald Dubh Macdonell, who – threatened with eviction – 'called up his seven stalwart sons, armed himself with a broadsword his grandfather had carried at Culloden, and defied both the law and his Chief' (Prebble, p. 150).

But the general picture is one of almost masochistic apathy and defeatism. In 1832, evicted Chisholms living in Canada sent their chief an address of loyalty, although he had just finished throwing half his remaining clansmen out of Strathglass. It was not till the 1880s with the 'Battle of the Braes' in Skye, and the sending of warships to the Minch, that resistance assumed proportions serious enough to force Government action, and, ultimately, to secure the passing of the Crofters' Act of 1886.

Incidentally, the record of the evictions at Knoydart, Strathglass, and Glengarry makes it clear that there is no truth in the statement one occasionally encounters that there was more resistance in Catholic areas than in Protestant.

So why – you well may ask – were things so different in Ireland? To that the short answer must surely be that in Ireland the landlords were felt to be (as indeed in many cases they often were) foreigners: whereas in Scotland the expropriators and savagers were in the main the old ancestral clan chiefs themselves. In spite of their galloping anglicisation, and the inner erosion of their patriarchal status, the chiefs were still felt to be the clan fathers – *Mac Gille Chaluim or Mac Sheumais Chataich*, or whatever – to whom obedience and allegiance were owed.

It is when we examine the role of the women in resisting the evictors that the folklorist begins to feel he might be able to offer the historians some revealing evidence. One of the most noticeable and most easily documentable characteristics of Celtic tribal society, from the early Irish heroic sagas onwards, is the place in it of tough, strong-minded women.

This is the hidden world of matriarchy, exercising power indirectly, which existed over against the masculine authority of the chief. Curiously enough, it was when dealing with a subject from Celtic tribal history that Shakespeare drew the archetypal portrait of a hero who is outwardly all panache, pride and swagger, but who depends almost abjectly on his mettlesome wife at moments of crisis:

Infirm of purpose! Give me the daggers![1]

At this point we need to recapitulate what is known of the status of women, and of their military prowess, in early Celtic society. Polybius, writing in the second century BC, states that in time of war the women of the Celts accompanied the men to battle, following them in wagons.[2] The bellicose reputation of Gaulish women is attested by Ammianus Marcellinus in an often quoted passage:

Nearly all the Gauls are of a lofty stature, fair, and of ruddy complexion; terrible from the sternness of their eyes, very quarrelsome, and of great pride and insolence. A whole troop of foreigners would not be able to withstand a single Gaul if he called his wife to his assistance, who is usually very strong, and with blue eyes; especially when, swelling her neck, gnashing her teeth, and brandishing her sallow arms of enormous size, she begins to strike blows mingled with kicks, as if they were so many missiles sent from the string of a catapult.[3]

The most formidable single opponent encountered by the Romans in Britain – with the possible exception of the Caledonian chief Calgacus, who commanded the northern tribes against Agricola at Mons Graupius – was the 'warrior queen' Boudicca (Boadicea), who is thus described by Dio Cassius:

She was huge of frame, terrifying of aspect, and with a harsh voice. A great mass of bright red hair fell to her knees: she wore a great twisted golden necklace, and a tunic of many colours, over which was a thick mantle, fastened by a brooch. Now she grasped a long spear to strike fear into all those who watched her ...[4]

In *The Celtic Realms,* an excellent comprehensive survey by Myles Dillon and Nora Chadwick, the high status of women in the Celtic world is continually emphasised:

History and tradition alike echo the high prestige of women in Celtic mythology ... In the Heroic Age of Ireland Medb, Queen of Connacht, is the reigning sovereign. Ailill, her husband, is never more than her consort, and Medb is the greatest personality of any royal line of the Heroic Age.

In Irish and Welsh stories of Celtic Britain the great heroes are taught not only wisdom but also feats of arms by women. In the Irish saga known as 'The Wooing of Emer' Cuchulainn is trained in all warrior feats by two warlike queens – Scathach, who is also a *fáith*, i.e. a prophetess, an expert in supernatural wisdom – and Aife ... Among the ancient Picts matrilinear succession was the rule till the ninth century. Bede tells us that even in his own day whenever the royal succession among the Picts came in question their ruler was chosen by succession from the female line. (pp. 194–5)

The most famous allusion to Celtic fighting women occurs in Tacitus's description of the Roman assault on the island of Anglesey in AD 61. Women and Druids were among the British warriors drawn up to withstand the assault, and to protect the island's sacred groves. After the battle these groves were destroyed – an act untypical of Roman policy, and suggesting a real fear of the Druids as inspirers of opposition.[5] (As Julius Caesar had put it a hundred years previously, *natio est omnis Gallorum admodum dedita religionibus,* 'The whole Celtic people is greatly addicted to religion'.)[6]

The 'man's world' of the Celts was also a warrior world, and the descriptions of it given by several classical authors tie in remarkably well with the information contained in the Gaelic heroic sagas. Like many warrior societies, in which the young men are isolated from the women for long periods, trained from their earliest years in the use of arms, and brought up to vie with each other in battle and in the hunt, it was a society in which homosexuality seems to have been very widespread. The references of Greek and Latin historians to this subject are quite explicit, and have a remarkable consistency. They are not as well known as might be expected, for the whole idea seems to have embarrassed Celtic scholars, much as the speech of Alcibiades in *The Banquet* about his relations with Socrates is said to have embarrassed and troubled poor Jowett.

Diodorus Siculus, writing in the first century BC, has this to say:

> The Celtic women are not only as tall as the men, but are just as courageous ... But although they are attractive, the men are much keener on their own sex; they lie around on animal skins and enjoy themselves, with a lover on each side. The extraordinary thing is that they haven't the smallest regard for their own personal dignity or self-respect; they offer themselves to other men without the least compunction. Furthermore, this isn't looked down on, or regarded as in any way disgraceful; on the contrary, if one of them is rejected by another to whom he has offered himself, he takes offence.[7]

This information came to Diodorus from Posidonius, an historian who travelled through Southern Gaul, and observed Celtic folkways on the spot. Strabo, who died about AD 26, writes laconically that 'the young men in Gaul are shamelessly generous with their boyish charms', and Athenaeus, two centuries later, repeats the statement of Diodorus about the Celt's male bed-partners.[8] This evidence of homo-erotic practices in an enclosed warrior society is of course in no way surprising. It is confirmed in the most striking manner by several passages in the great Irish heroic saga, *Táin Bó Cuailnge* (The Cattle-Raid of Cooley).[9] In the versions contained in the *Yellow Book of Lecan* and (more completely) in the *Book of Leinster* the tale is told of the fight between Cuchullain and his 'ardent and adored foster-brother' Ferdia, who face each other in heroic single combat at the ford. Ferdia does not want to fight Cuchullain who has been his comrade-in-arms at the battle-school of Scathach in Alba (Scotland), but Medb, the queen of Connacht, sends 'poets and bards and satirists to bring the blushes to his cheek with mockery and insult and ridicule, so there would be nowhere in the world for him to lay his head in peace'. When Cuchullain learns that Ferdia is on the way to fight him, he says: 'I swear I don't want a meeting. Not because I fear him, but because I love him so much,' and before their first encounter he reminds him:

> Fast friends, forest-companions
> We made one bed and slept one sleep
> In foreign lands after the fray.
> Scathach's pupils, two together,
> We'd set forth to comb the forest.

In this verse, written down in Ireland more than a thousand years after Diodorus wrote the passage quoted above, we have an unmistakable echo in poetry of the rather ironic down-to-earth description of 'heroic love' in the Greek historian's prose.

The combat of Ferdia and Cuchullain has been compared (by Aodh de Blacam) to the duel between Hector and Achilles, and Cuchullain's lament over the body of his lover to David's lament for Saul and Jonathan. ('The beauty of Israel is slain upon thy high places.') On another level (more in tune, perhaps, with the native temperament) one feels like repeating of the two champions what Henry de Montherlant once wittily remarked of the heroes of the Satyricon, that they may be *bougres*, but at any rate they are not *de mauvais bougres*.

In view of the enormous time-gap to which we just alluded, it is maybe advisable, at this point, to recall Gordon Childe's remark in *Scotland before the Scots* that human history comes not so much in 'Ages' as in 'Stages'. It should always be remembered that because of Ireland's relative isolation, aboriginal Celtic folkways continued to flourish there right up until the early Middle Ages. Rudolf Pörtner puts it succinctly when he compares the 'protected' survivals in Ireland, the Off-Off Island, to life in a *Naturschutzpark* or nature reserve.[10]

The same general situation undoubtedly prevailed in many parts of the Scottish Highlands and Islands until even later, as voluminous folklore records testify. Ancestral memories of Celtic head-hunting are still to be encountered in parts of the Outer Hebrides – as are hang-overs of some of the other phenomena we have been discussing. The plot of a folk-tale 'MacNeil of Barra, the Widow's Son and the Shetland Buck', which was recorded from 'the Coddy' (the late John MacPherson, postmaster of Northbay) by John Lorne Campbell, contains some curious motifs.[11]

Much fascinating information about the sexual mores of medieval Celtic society is to be found in Kenneth Nicholls's *Gaelic and Gaelicised Ireland in the Middle Ages*. The rights enjoyed by women under Brehon law – which continued to be operative in most parts of Ireland until the seventeenth century, although 'officially' terminated by the Statutes of Kilkenny in 1366 – would be the envy of many women today. Women had the right of independent property ownership, could divorce and remarry with ease, and could be practitioners of the arts and sciences if they so desired. 'There was no such thing as an illegitimate child; a mother had simply to "name" the child and if it was a son, he would inherit part of his father's property. Marriage was one of the keys to Irish women's independence, based as it was upon a complex series of property relationships which did not automatically involve property transfer from women to men.'[12] Nicholls tells us that 'down to the end of the old order in 1603, what could be called Celtic secular marriage remained the norm in Ireland ... Christian matrimony was no more than the rare exception grafted on to this system' (p. 73).

According to Peter Trewhela, 'If a couple chose to part, all they had to do was to stand back to back on the hill of Tailteann near Tara, and walk away from each other. Trial marriages were very common.'[13]

Myles Dillon, in *The Celtic Realms*, confirms the statements of the writers already quoted:

> The law of marriage in early Ireland is of special interest, as it shows in great measure the persistence of ancient customs in spite of Christian teaching.

> Divorce is freely allowed. Indeed there is a trace of annual marriage. A marriage
> may always be ended by common consent ... The practice of placing one's
> children in the care of foster-parents was a normal feature of Irish society, and it
> was not confined to the noble class ... The time of fosterage ended for boys at
> seventeen, for girls at fourteen, and they returned home. Those who had been
> fostered together were bound in close relationship. This relationship with one's
> *comaltae* is a recurring motif in the sagas. (pp. 132–3)

Dr John MacInnes informs me that until the forfeiture of the Lordship of the Isles at
the end of the fifteenth century, a very similar judicial system must have prevailed over
much of the Highlands. We know of a family of hereditary law-givers – the Morrisons
of Ness in Lewis – who, after the Irish pattern, acted as jurists for the Lordship. There
can be no doubt that these *breitheamhan* were the far-off heirs of the learned men
reported among the Celts of Gaul by Julius Caesar and Posidonius.

That the women of Celtic Scotland were as combative as those of Ireland is attested
by Hector Boece:

> The wemen war of litil les vassalage and strenth than was the men; for al rank
> madinnis and wiffis, gif they war nocht with child, yeid als weill to battall as the
> men.[14]

In his splendid, erudite book, *A Midsummer Eve's Dream*, which is a discursive
commentary on William Dunbar's poem 'The Tretis of the Tua Mariit Wemen and the
Wedo', Professor A. D. Hope provides much information on the position of women in
Scottish society at various periods in our history. He quotes the statement of Thomas
Morer (who was chaplain to a Scottish regiment about 1689, and who wrote *a Short
Account of Scotland*) that 'the women of Scotland are capable of estates and honours,
and inherit both as well as the males and therefore after marriage may retain their
maiden name,' and adds:

> The way in which women retained their own names and often their own
> property in Scotland impressed many travellers. It was perhaps the last after-
> glow of an age in which the real power had been theirs to exercise and enjoy.

What light – if any – does all of this throw on the recurrent pattern of women's
resistance to the clearers which is so amply documented? If I am on the right track –
and I emphasise again that this is a theory, advanced tentatively – then there is more to
the presence of the women in the front line than the obvious considerations that they
were less likely to be clubbed by police and military; were in themselves (as wives and
mothers) the most direct human reproach to the callousness and inhumanity of the
evictors; and (to put it at its lowest) were less likely to be proceeded against than the
men. All these are valid points, but they are not enough to explain this very perceptible
pattern. Surely it is only completely explicable as another relic from the mental world
of the shattered tribal system. It was the 'women's world', which stood in, with all its
spirit, courage, and resilience, when the 'man's world' faltered.[15]

The swashbuckling 'man's world' of chief, gillie-wetfoot, and arms-toting *duine
uasal* had come unstuck – finally unstuck – on Drummossie Moor; not long after, it was
to be taken over, lock, stock and powder-horn, by the British Army. The hidden

'matriarchal' women's world, of whose splendid vigour we have so much evidence in Gaelic song-poetry, had remained intact, and when the men took to the brae in ignominous *sauve qui peut* on the appearance of the 'baton brigade', it provided a fragile last line of resistance before the fire-raisers moved in. It was as if they meant to show that if the men were not prepared to defend hearth and home, they were.

The male who does appear in baleful prepotent pride on the scene of the Clearances is, alas, on the oppressor's side. Haranguing his cowed subjects from a high wooden throne, and threatening them with hell-fire if they disobey those set in authority over them, he is the Calvinist minister. This sinister character can well and truly be regarded as the devil of the piece; while lambasting the people for their sins, and openly suggesting that they are being made to suffer because of them, he is quite capable at the same time of angling for an extension to his glebe. Donald MacLeod informs us in *Gloomy Memories* that during the famine of 1836 the Revd Hugh MacKenzie, moderator of the Presbytery of Tongue, exchanged part of his glebe for more extensive property. 'But in consenting to the change he made an express condition that the present occupiers, amounting to eight families, should be removed, and accordingly they were driven out in a body.'[16]

And so it was the women who – in accordance with aboriginal Celtic tradition – defied the invaders of their world: the venal Calvinist ministers, and the crowbar-wielding minions of 'the gentry with no pity'. However, their appearance in the front line raises a number of questions to which one would be glad to have the answer. Where were the children and babies during such scenes as that at Strathcarron? Who was looking after them?

In this connection one must also take into consideration several reports – factual news reports, as well as 'folk narratives' – that men dressed as women took part in episodes of resistance. One hesitates to believe that the heroes of Badajoz or Waterloo, or their relatives, would dress themselves in women's attire because they lacked 'civil courage'. In Ireland the 'Molly Maguires' were the most belligerent of transvestites. Was this an example of military camouflage, the better to do down the aggressor?

Be that as it may, one could wish – reading the accounts of some of the clearances, and their pitiful consequences – that the seven battalions of the Fingalians had been deployed in battle array against the rapacious chieftain-landlords, and their factors and minions, rather than this 'petticoat brigade'. Donald Ross, a Glasgow lawyer, went to Skye after the Boreraig and Suisinish evictions of 1853, carrying with him large quantities of food and clothing for the people. His account of his experiences was published in a pamphlet *Real Scottish Grievances* the following year:

> He saw seven children, all under the age of eleven, lying in a shed on a collection of rubbish, fern, meadow-hay, straw, pieces of old blanket, and rags of clothing. Rain and snow fell upon them. They were so thin, and so light, he said, that he could have carried them all in his arms for a quarter of a mile without feeling their weight.[17]

And what were the sanctimonious Calvinist mullahs doing when all these dreadful things were taking place on their manse doorsteps? The discreditable truth (with very few exceptions) is – nothing, or practically nothing. The record of the Free Kirk is better than that of the Established Church in this context.

One cannot avoid the conclusion, from much of the evidence available, that the 'judgement of the Lord' fulminations of the ministers tended to induce a hopeless apathetic subjection in the minds of their flocks, and sapped their will to resist their oppressors.

The moral is that no one surveying this whole subject can afford to leave out of the picture the peculiar psychology of Scots Calvinism – how it can both energise and hypnotise, and – at worst – make thoroughly apathetic. G. K. Chesterton gave gnomic expression to the inner truth of the matter when he wrote (in *The Honour of Israel Gow*): 'Scotland has a double dose of the poison called heredity; the sense of blood in the aristocrat, and the sense of doom in the Calvinist.'

When the people of Glencalvie were evicted (May 1845), they sought refuge in Croick Kirkyard, and they scratched a few messages for posterity on the window panes. The most pathetic, and in many ways the most revealing of these, reads as follows: *Glencalvie people, the wicked generation.*[18]

It seems clear that there were a lot of hidden – and open – persuaders who wanted the people to believe that what had hit them was a sort of divine scourge, and that resistance offered to the landlords was tantamount to resistance offered to the Lord. I suspect that women were less susceptible to the powers of this sinister hoodoo than were their menfolk; the women, as we have seen, were the bearers of very old traditions of custom and belief that were deeply antagonistic to the puritanical (and essentially 'father-figure') Church.

It was a woman – Mary MacPherson, *Màiri Mhór nan Oran* – who wrote the most poignant lament for the older Scotland shattered by the Clearances. However, in our own day a male poet, T. S. Law, has written in English a poem on the same subject which strikes a quite individual note of lyric elegy, and of truly Swiftian *saeva indignatio*. I conclude by quoting it in full:

The Clearances

Hear how the names sing,
      Macdonald, Clanranald,
hear how the names sing,
      Argyll and Lochiel.
Hear them, hear them,
      MacLeod and Glengarry,
hear them,
      Baillie, MacDonnell and Ross.
These are the names that ennobled their line,
these are the owercome in auld lang syne.

These are the names of the traitors and tinkers,
these are the merciless, murdering swine,
these the destroyers, the deaths heads, blood-drinkers,
these are the owercome in auld lang syne,
these are the names that ennobled their line.

Listen to
>   Drummond, Breadalbane, and Atholl,
listen to
>   Hamilton, Balfour, and Innes,
listen and hear,
>   Sutherland, Fraser,
listen,
>   Matheson, Seaforth, Robertson.
These are the names that ennobled their line,
these are the owercome in auld lang syne.

These are the cannibals, heart-cruel, savagers,
their Highlanders' bodies and souls meat and wine,
these the procurers of gentleness, ravishers.
These are the owercome in auld lang syne,
these are the names that ennobled their line.

Notes

1 *Macbeth*, Act II, Scene 2.
2 Polybius, *Histories*, V, 78.
3 XV, xii (Charles D. Yonge's translation).
4 *Roman Histories*, Epitome of Book LXII, 3–4.
5 Tacitus, *Annals*, XIV, xxx.
6 *De Bello Gallico*, VI.
7 Diodorus Siculus, *Bibliotheke Historike*, Book V. Diodorus is as frank about the drinking habits of the Celts: 'They take such inordinate pleasure in wine that when it is imported by merchants they drink it straight; and when they're intoxicated with excess of drink, they either go to sleep, or go crazy altogether.' (The Greeks customarily diluted their wine in one way or another.)
8 Strabo and Athenaeus, quoted in Gerhard Herm, *Die Kelten* (Düsseldorf 1975), p. 96.
9 The quotations from the *Táin* are taken from Thomas Kinsella's translation (Dublin 1969).
10 *Bevor die Römer Kamen*, p. 325.
11 See *Tales from Barra: Told by the Coddy*, ed. J. L. Campbell (Edinburgh 1960).
12 Tom Woodhouse, 'Lost Freedoms', *Gay Left*, No 8.
13 'How Celtic Women fell from Power', in *Celtic Theology*, an SCM pamphlet.
14 *Chronicles of Scotland*, Bellenden translation, I, 20.
15 Professor Kenneth Little tells me that the same sort of thing has happened in Africa, when a male warrior caste is broken by defeat, and the women for that reason 'have the edge' on the men. While the latter sit around, play cards and get drunk on cheap liquor, the women conduct public and commercial business, and are the purposeful representatives of the group *vis à vis* the outside world.
16 Donald MacLeod, *Gloomy Memories* (Glasgow 1888), p. 37.
17 Prebble, p. 292. Ross's account of the treatment meted out to a 96-year-widow is reprinted in full in Alexander Mackenzie's *Highland Clearances* (pp. 239–44).
18 P. A. MacNab, 'The Church at Croick', *Scots Magazine* (May 1963). MacNab's article epitomises so well the whole tragic history we have been recounting that I quote it here practically *in toto*:
>   Croick church was built in 1827. It is one of about a dozen churches built in Scotland by Thomas Telford, the famous road-maker. It was then the centre of worship attended by a weekly congregation of 200 from the little communities which won a living from the soil and grazings round about. Now they are gone. Nothing remains but old tracks radiating through

the heather to green oases on the hillsides, and an occasional rickle of stones which mark where the houses of a thriving people once stood, mute evidence of the Clearances and subsequent depopulation. Every year on the last Sunday in July a Communion Service is conducted in the Church by the Minister of Kincardine Parish, whose consolidated charges and wide district point to the once large population for whom all those churches were established.

... Everything is plain and well preserved inside the church. The centre of interest lies, of course, in the east window where a few words and names scratched on the diamond panes remind us of the whole sad story behind the depopulation, the outcome of one of the later clearances or 'Improvements' of the last century. The incidents which centred on Croick Church are as reprehensible as any of the more widely publicised Clearances, although, in justice to the landlord, Major Charles Robertson of Kindeace, it should be said that they took place on the initiative of his factor, James Gillanders, who lived in Tain. The object of his policy of Improvement was Glen Calvie, which lies quite near Croick, which itself had suffered in the same manner a few years earlier.

In 1843 the people of Glen Calvie, reduced in numbers to no more than ninety by earlier evictions, were described as a happy, self-contained community. Although the glen was poor and rocky it was rented at £55 10s, considered an exorbitant figure; yet the people paid it. Furthermore, they were free from debt, law-abiding and had sent many soldiers to the wars; they raised sheep and black cattle and grew potatoes and barley. They could trace their tenancies back for 500 years. The events which followed came to the notice of *The Times* who sent a special correspondent to the scene. He summarised the general position in the north, with special reference to Glen Calvie: 'through the actions of the factors in the lonely glens, hundreds of peaceable and generally industrious peasants have been driven from their means of support to become wanderers and starving beggars – a brave, valuable population lost'.

In 1843 Gillanders began his scheme to turn the glen into one large sheep farm at an even higher rent. The first step was to serve summonses of removal on the tenants. Anticipating this, however, and on watch just outside the boundary across the river, the women of the glen intercepted the constables and, seizing the wrists of the man holding the writs, they applied live coals to the papers until they were destroyed, seeking to prove they had neither been seen nor handled in the glen. Next year, not to be outdone, the crafty Gillanders invited the chief tenants to Tain for a 'friendly discussion'. Instead he placed the formal notices to quit in their hands. Decree for removal followed, and the law took its course. Stunned and bewildered, the people began to hunt feverishly for alternative holdings; but only six families could find a place, and poor ones at that. The others were at last evicted by force, and for a time, while their menfolk were continuing the hopeless search, they were allowed to shelter in Croick churchyard, exposed to the elements – wishing, as it is recorded, that death would come to allow them to join their forefathers beneath the sward. They were helped only by the minister, who did all in his power to ease their conditions. As the people passed the weary days among the tombs, someone among them, scratching idly on the diamond-shaped panes of the east window, left a short, pathetic message for posterity. In the unhurried copperplate writing of the last century, we can still decipher some of the names: C. Chalmers; John Ross, Shepherd, Parish of Ardgay; and others, and, bowing meekly to what was accepted by a God-fearing people as Divine chastisement – *Glencalvie people, the wicked generation. Glen Calvie people was in the Churchyard here May 24th, 1845.* The words Church Officer also appear under the name Ann McAlister but it is probable that the designation refers to an illegible name scratched below. It is highly unlikely that a woman would be acceptable as Church Officer in the middle of the last century, in a community such as this was. Why were they not allowed to shelter inside the Church? I suggest the answer is simple. In those days it would have been regarded as desecration of a holy place and even under such necessity, and if invited by the Minister, they would probably have refused.

The Celtic Consciousness, ed. O'Driscoll, Canongate, 1982.

Glencoe on our Minds

In a review of Professor George Pryde's *Scotland from 1603 to the Present Day*, A. J. P. Taylor wrote: 'What will keep Scotland alive now? The law is as strong as ever. Education now brings little advantage or difference. The Church still seems formidable on paper, but religion is declining everywhere as a popular cause. Perhaps the Scots will have to fall back on their history after all.'

I doubt if we are in quite such desperate straits as all that, but this may be no bad time, all the same, to ask how Scottish history is faring in the mid-1960s. The question is by no means merely an academic one. As a nation, we have what the Germans call *eine unbewältigte Vergangenheit* – a past with which we haven't completely come to terms. (In this we are quite unlike the English, who have come to terms with their history so well that they have largely forgotten it.) One of the splinters lodged in the Scottish consciousness, and one which troubles every now and again, is the Massacre of Glencoe. There can't be many Campbells in Scotland who do not feel a faint twinge of discomfort when Glencoe is mentioned, even though the myth of exclusive Campbell responsibility has long been exploded. It is instructive, therefore, to 'compare and contrast' three books about this famous atrocity – one which appeared thirty-three years ago, and a couple published within the last twelve months.

John Buchan's *The Massacre of Glencoe* (1933) is quite a short book; it sets the scene, delineates the principal characters, describes the background of seventeenth-century Highland life and moves on to the terrible dénouement, and its aftermath, in 130 pages. 'Popular' in the best sense, and comfortably readable at a sitting, it displays an unobtrusive but in its own way quite formidable scholarship. One hundred and fifty-two source reference notes are supplied at the end of the book, although the text itself is not interrupted by asterisks or other annotations. In technique, it is fresh and unorthodox. As a novelist, Buchan clearly felt the need for a certain amount of fictional narrative, and he prefaced his book with the following note:

> In this essay in reconstruction, I have tried to include no detail which has not a warrant from contemporary evidence, and is not a legitimate deduction from such evidence. The only liberty I have taken is now and then to state boldly as a fact what should strictly be qualified by a 'probably'.

Buchan is quite frank, therefore, about his 'essay in reconstruction'. Nevertheless, this method has its weaknesses. These are most apparent in the interview between MacIain and Colonel Hill at the Fort of Inverlochy (Fort William), parts of which read like an entry in an amateur drama one-act-play competition.

> 'I have many ill-wishers, and the chief of them is MacCailein Mor himself.'
> 'Argyle is not in the town at present, which is the better for you. Sir Colin
>   Campbell is the Sheriff-depute'.
> 'Ardkinglas, though a Campbell, is an honest man', said the chief.
> 'I am happy to agree with you. He is also my friend, and I will write him a letter'.
>   (p. 48)

There are also one or two exceedingly odd mistakes in Buchan's book. He makes
Duncanson's order to Glenlyon refer to 'the rabelle, the McDonalds of Glenco', when
the MS shows beyond a doubt the phrase should be 'the rebells, the McDonalds of
Glenco'. Also, he makes Hill insist on inviting MacIain to a meal, although Hill himself
stated, in a letter to the Earl of Tweeddale, written a few weeks after the Massacre:
'Glencoe came to me and I advised him to haste to the Sheriff, and I would not let him
stay so much as to drink, but he turned about and went to Glengarry and let the time
elapse.'

The reference to Glengarry has never been satisfactorily explained. MacIain cannot
possibly have made the journeys to Invergarry; it took him all his time to get to
Inveraray by 2 January 1692, as he had the bad luck to be arrested and detained for
twenty-four hours at Barcaldine by Captain Drummond of Argyll's regiment. Can it
be that Glengarry, most defiant of the 'unsworn' Jacobite chiefs, was waiting near
Inverlochy to get a personal report from MacIain about his interview with the
Governor? Or was Hill, the just man, lying for once? The old Colonel's passing
allusion to Glengarry is not the least puzzling thing in all this tortuous story, but in a
more recent work about the Massacre, John Prebble's panoramic *Glencoe*, (1966) it is
not so much as mentioned.

Prebble's book, although not free from serious defects, is a remarkable *tour de force*.
The author has been at pains to consult all the manuscript and other sources he could
trace, including the Argyll papers at Inveraray, never before consulted on the subject of
Glencoe. His description of the trials and tribulations, as well as the positive achievements, of the veteran Cromwellian Colonel Hill (in many ways the true hero of the
book) is first-rate. Realising that the Massacre, like the Battle of the Boyne, is only to
be comprehended against the background of the 'Great Revolution' and the wars of the
League of Augsburg, Prebble quite rightly devotes much of his book to narrating the
events which led up to the first major crisis in Highland history. He also has a good
chapter about the culture of a society which (like the Montenegro clan society
described by Djilas) was still, in its structure and values, amazingly Homeric. Unfortunately, the book is not free from disfiguring errors; detailed page references to
sources are conspicuous by their absence; and the imaginative reconstructions which
Buchan also attempted, has in Prebble's book absolutely run to seed.

Let us look at a few specific points in detail.Prebble's first chapter is called 'The
Gallows Herd'. On p. 45 he explains this epithet as follows: 'Lowlanders called them
(Highlanders) the herd-widdifous, the Gallows Herd, and were happy to pay them to
be on their way without molestation. An old Aberdeen ballad sang the general feeling:

> Gin ye be gentlemen, light and come in,
> There's meat and drink in my hall for every man.

Gin ye be herd-widdifous, ye may gang by,
Gang down to the Lowlands and steal horse and kye.'

The ballad to which Prebble refers, although he does not mention the source of his quotation, is 'The Baron of Brackley', which is No 203 in Professor F. J. Child's *English and Scottish Popular Ballads*. Child gives four versions of the ballad. His A version (Laing's, 1822) has the following lines:

Gin ye be gentlemen, licht an cum in,
Ther's meat an drink i my ha for every man.
Gin ye be hir'd widdifus, ye may gang by.
Gang doun to the lawlands, and steal horse and ky.

Other versions have 'a curn hir'd widdifus' and 'fifty heard widifus'. These texts make it clear that the reivers are referred to as 'hired widdifous', i.e. mercenary cut-throats or 'gallows-birds'. In any case, 'herd-widdifous', meaning 'gallows herd', is an impossible construction in Scots. Herd can mean herdsman, as well as 'herd' in the English sense, and at a stretch the phrase could mean cut-throat herdsmen; however, as we have seen from reference to the older texts, this is not the case here.

It seems a reasonable assumption that the phrase Gallows Herd, supposed to have been used by Lowlanders of Highlanders, exists only in Prebble's fertile imagination. (The irony is that on p. 22, he talks about Macaulay 'having no Gaelic, and trusting to his imagination when in doubt'.)

In spite of this dubious origin, the emotive chapter heading 'The Gallows Herd' stays with us, at the head of every second page, for nearly seventy pages. This 'ghost phrase' is supposed to be an example of *Mi-run mór nan Gall*, which Prebble translates (p. 11) as 'The Lowlander's great hatred'. The ordinary reader, finding this Gaelic phrase in the index, with four page references, might imagine that it was some sort of formalised concept, like Justification by Faith, or a phrase with a certain historic reverberation like the Salic Law. It is nothing of the kind. It is one line from a poem by the Clanranald bard Alexander MacDonald (Alasdair MacMhaighstir Alasdair), which was written half a century after the Massacre. In this poem Alasdair says that Gaelic has survived in spite of 'the great ill-will of the Lowlanders', and points out that it used to be the language of the '*Gall-bhodacha* (the Lowland carles) themselves.

One begins to see what Prebble is up to. Admittedly, there has been a lot of bilious xenophobia in Scottish history, but this has been by no means restricted to relations between Highlander and Lowlander. In 1745 an Oban poetess, from the Scottish Gaelic heartland, referred to the Jacobite Highlanders as *prasgan nan Garbh-chrioch* ('the rabble of the rough-bounds': see J. L. Campbell, *Highlands Songs of the Forty-Five*, p. 59).

The quartering of the Highland Host on the south-west Lowlands in 1678 led to similar recriminations, although Galloway had an ancient Gaelic tradition which survived on the lips of native speakers into the seventeenth century. Prebble refers to the Highland Host in the following terms: 'It was as if several thousand Afghan hillmen were to be billeted in Sussex' (p. 63). This is a striking and eminently quotable phrase (it has already been quoted several times in reviews). It is also utter balderdash.

The level of material culture and comfort was not markedly higher in the Galloway of 1678 than in the lands of the Earls of Strathmore and Airlie, whence many of the levies came. These Perthshire 'Afghans' didn't actually kill anyone, but they 'looted at will, and frightened old women into a decline' (p. 63). I wish the same could be said of most twentieth-century armies quartered among subject-populations.

It would be tedious to list all the examples of glamour-whimsy which make a technicolour gaudy-night of Glencoe – 'his pen, in pale fingers thrust from a cuff of lace, was the servant of his hatred, a living thing almost' ... 'there was a madness in the man' ... 'he was the instrument of *Mi-run Mór nan Gall*' – but here is an example of the sort of slip which irritates even where it amuses. On p. 99 we find a reference to the Jacobite army 'still sleeping below the Haughs of Cromdale'. Prebble does not mean that they are prematurely buried; he obviously imagines – by analogy with German *hoch*? – that 'haughs' means high ground. Actually haughs are low-lying meadows.

Prebble draws liberally on James Philip's epic poem 'The Grameid', especially for the flamboyant muster-roll of the Highland chiefs at Dalcomera, but while obviously valuing this work as a historic document, he doesn't appear to think much of it as poetry. On p. 75 he says of Philip: 'his enthusiasm, if not the tortured allegories of his prose, recreated a forgotten day when the grass was covered with steel and tartan, when the air was filled with the sound of pipes, and Graham of Dundee stood his horse before his army', etc. Can it be that this reference to prose is due to the fact that Prebble has been working from the faithful and unpretentious prose translation of Canon Alexander Murdoch, editor and translator of 'The Grameid', rather than from Philip's own elegant and stylish Latin hexameters? Two passages from Canon Murdoch's translation are quoted word for word by Prebble (Book III, 57–68, and Book IV, 94–102), but you will search *Glencoe* from end to end without finding a reference to the translator – which is to be regretted because Murdoch was in many ways a distinguished individual. He was a fine classical scholar, an erudite Scottish liturgist (he had a flyting with Dean Ramsay on the issue of the introduction of the Scottish liturgy in his own church) and a bonnie fechter for Scotland's 'rights and common', wherever and whenever he felt they needed to be defended.

In his preface, Murdoch wrote: 'When I was asked to edit "The Grameid" a translation was not contemplated, but only a running margin of contents and a few notes. I agreed towards the end of last year (1887) to make a translation which would give the English reader the matter of the book in a readable form, and to increase the notes so as to make one volume of the (Scottish History) Society's publications' (p. xvii). His notes, used by Prebble, bear witness to an encyclopedic historical and antiquarian knowledge of the period, while the quality of his translation, at its best, may be judged from one splendid passage in Book IV. This describes the march of Dundee's army (which included the hundred warriors of the Glencoe MacDonalds) on the first stage of the campaign which culminated in the Battle of Killiecrankie:

> Already squadron and battalion prepare to leave the camp. The army, brilliant with the varied weapons of Lochaber, moves the standard, while the pipe sounds, and the whole force in marching order advances into the open country. The bold Glengarry, as leader of the first line, marched in the van, accompanied by thirty horse in due order. Then the rest of the chiefs advanced each in his own station, and followed by his own people ... The Highland army, with its glitter

of brass and flash of bright musket, braves the sun, and with bristly spears affrights the air, as it moves forward. When at length it touched thy borders, O Badenoch! its wings were extended widely over the declivities of the hills. Far off the clans were seen shining in the light of the sun. A thousand helmets glitter as many quivers resound; a thousand spears, from their points bright with golden light, reflect the rays, and the fields feel the tread of the axe-bearing Gael, and the Grampians are terrible with the flaunting banners. ('The Grameid' pp. 167–8)

That his translation of Philip's heroic poem is not wholly 'prose' is perhaps shown by the fact that Hugh MacDiarmid printed an extract from it, arranged by him as verse, in the poem 'A Hosting of Heroes', which appeared in *A Kist of Whistles* (1947).

Maybe Murdoch is himself the sort of history the Scots should be concerned with, although (unlike *Mi-run mór nan Gall*) he does not achieve an entry in Prebble's index. Something has got badly distorted here, and we need to get it back into focus. One way we can do this is to take a leaf out of Brecht's book, and Neruda's, and realise that 'Juan the stonecutter' is more interesting than the dynastic wars and disputations – and even the language wars – which blow over and around him. If the name MacDonald and Campbell exert such a perennial fascination, why not take a look (for example) at Alexander MacDonald, the nineteenth-century miners' leader, and at John Francis Campbell of Islay, who initiated the first major research project into Gaelic oral tradition? Likewise, with the Macleans, we might devote some overdue attention to John Maclean, socialist thinker, man of action, and martyr, and to the late Dr Calum MacLean, Campbell of Islay's principal twentieth-century successor.

The great gory show-pieces such as Glencoe will be written about again, of course, but when they are, I hope we all have the sense to prefer a book such as Donald J. Macdonald's *Slaughter under Trust* (1965) to the glossier efforts of the romantic littérateur and pop historian, however well packaged. Mr Macdonald's book is a powerful short re-telling of the story; it eschews jerry-built reconstructionism of the 'smile on Hill's face faded' variety, but it loses nothing in readability because of this sensible self-denying ordinance. Basic source documents such as the 'Letter from a Gentleman in Edinburgh to his Friend in London after the Massacre' and the Report of the Commission of Enquiry are reprinted verbatim in a series of fifteen appendices. There is no costume-play posturing, but the writer has considerable powers of *Einfühlung*, and the narrative consequently makes a compelling effect of immediacy and verisimilitude.

In this century Scottish historiography has been climbing painfully out of an appalling morass of sentimental-romantic nonsense, and flighty wishful thinking. For every one book which lends it a helping hand, there are ten which seem intent on shouldering it back in again. 'The Man that Corrupted Hadleyburg', in the case of Prebble's *Glencoe*, is *Time-Life* journalism – the use of emotive captions and chapter-headings to provide colouring matter, and induce an artificially 'pepped-up' reader-reaction. It is all very well to claim that in the text you provide a character-study in depth of a complex personality, when, under a photograph of his portrait, you print the words BE EARNEST, BE SECRET AND SUDDEN, BE QUICK.

In spite of all the research that has gone into this, and a truly virtuoso skill in presentation, Prebble's *Glencoe* must serve as a warning. Artfully camouflaged pieces of romantic history just won't do any longer. The Scots will have to come to terms with their history if they are to survive as a nation, and secure the elementary civilised right of a nation to control over its own affairs.

Full version of a truncated article that appeared in *Scotsman*, 25 June 1966.

The Silver Bough
Vol. III. Hallowe'en to Yule
By F. Marian McNeill
pp. 180. Glasgow: William Maclellan. 1961.

In the second and third volumes of *The Silver Bough*, Miss McNeill covers much the same ground as did Mrs M. MacLeod Banks in the three Scottish volumes of *British Calendar Customs*, but her approach to the subject matter is quite different. Where Mrs Banks confined herself to simple presentation, grouping her selected items as logically as possible to form an orderly work of reference, Miss McNeill enters into the spirit of the customs and events she is describing, and (as it were) dons guising gear herself to communicate the fun of the fair. Her books convey vividly the eager joy of the participant, and it would be out of place to judge them solely by the canons of academic method. *The Silver Bough* has small hopes of supplanting *British Calendar Customs* as a handbook for folklore scholars, but it makes infinitely more diverting reading.

The initial chapters are devoted to Hallowe'en, and may fairly be taken as representative of the author's approach. On the very first page one is faced with the sort of uncompromising statement which Mrs Banks so resolutely eschewed – 'the Cult of the Dead was based upon the doctrine of the Immortality of the Soul' – but the succeeding pages on witches and warlocks, foys and bonefires are written with such infectious enthusiasm that they disarm criticism. The paragraphs on Hallowe'en pranks and divination rites are not so much documentation as incitements to participation; taking a leaf out of her own celebrated cookery books, Miss McNeill actually presents some of these in the style of recipes. Here, for example, is her description of *Burning the Reekie Mehr*:

> Take a cabbage or kail stock, scoop out the centre, and fill the hollow with tow … Choose your scene of action: then set fire to one end of the mehr, apply the lighted end to the key-hole of a door, blow lustily at the other end, and you will send a column of smoke into the house.

Similarly, Miss McNeill's choice of illustrative quotations does not stop short at items which provide social, folkloristic or historical documentation. She pulls in literary and sub-literary effusions from every airt, ranging from Hogg's splendid sinister 'Witch of Fife' to Lewis Spence's lush purple passage about James III in Trinity Kirk. The handsome plates which decorate the book include folksy Hallowe'en stills from a documentary made by the Walt Disney (London) Film Unit, as well as a 'fey' painting by John Duncan, and an admirable Cruickshank drawing of the Mock Abbot and his retinue.

In spite of this uninhibited eclecticism, the book makes a surprisingly unified and coherent impression. In some ways it resembles a master folk-singer's repertoire, which may include everything from tragic ballads to Edwardian music-hall songs. It moves between the silks and scarlets of medieval symbolism and the threadbare homespun of the cottar's weekday. Maybe it is no bad thing, once in a while, to have this glimpse of folklore 'from the inside' – the sort of folklore the ordinary man in the miners' Burns Supper recognises, however dubious the folklorist may be about some of its manifestations.

This said, I must list one or two bad shortcomings. Miss McNeill never supplies page references; 'see *The Golden Bough*' is a maddening instruction to anyone who seriously wants to follow up a reference. Even worse is this sort of thing (p. 146): 'From an old ballad. (See Child, note).' This, moreover, is the one solitary reference to Professor Child in the entire book, and cannot be much help to someone who has never heard of him. It is far from the only case where a little more care should have been taken.

Scottish Historical Review, April 1963.

McGonagall the What

I

William McGonagall and the Folk Scene

He's hey the road, ho the road, doon the road; the tods
ging tae their holes, and the wee birdies flee awa hame tae
their nests – but there's nae rest for Silly Jack.

Old Tale

I was much too far out all my life,
And not waving but drowning.

Stevie Smith

Is folk-song ever poetry? Can poetry learn from folk-song? Is there a zone where they overlap, or should we speak rather of co-existence? How and where does money come into the picture? (Or how can we just occasionally keep it out?) These are our themes, and our presiding genius is William McGonagall, poet and tragedian, and unchallenged prince of bad verse writers.

McGonagall is in the news again – indeed, he is very seldom out of it. Every now and then someone discovers that he sounds good with a jazz backing, or a pipe chanter accompaniment. Peter Sellers goes to town, with him, and on him. That whale gets thrown up again on the rocky shores of Associated Rediffusion. And David Winter & Son Ltd of Dundee – the firm which printed the original broadsheets which McGonagall hawked in the streets of that city, and of Auld Reekie, for a penny – have good reason to appreciate the value of the *Poetic Gems* which they continue to supply to an ever-welcoming public.

But – it may be objected – why bring McGonagall into a discussion of folk-song? Surely, when we discuss McGonagall, we are scraping the bucket of uninspired 'art-poetry'. What has he got to do with the poetry of the ballads, with the poetry of folk-song? Haud your horses – it's not as simple as that. If you have jumped to the conclusion – from the title, and these opening paras – that we are going to tie the battered tin-can of McGonagall to the tail of the folk-song revival, and thus knock its 'image' for good and all, you are quite wrong. However, we have got to face it that a careful scrutiny of the works of McGonagall can teach us a great deal about the nature of folk-poetry.

Not long back, *Folk Music*'s Jack Speedwell took a slap at Bob Dylan.* He quoted

---

* See also Ewan MacColl, *Sing Out!* September 1965, p. 12; and *Melody Maker,* 18 September 1965.

Pete Seeger's remark, 'Bob Dylan is a great poet,' and professed bafflement. Valéry, Rilke and Lorca were widely regarded as among the greatest twentieth-century poets – yet Speedwell could see little in common between their work and the songs of Bob Dylan. But all of a sudden, he sees the light – he takes from the shelf the well-thumbed works of the great McGonagall, and all is clear.

Well, is it? Speedwell had an interesting point there, but he failed to develop it, except in the most rudimentary fashion. Let us proceed a little further, and see where the trail leads us.

William McGonagall did not regard himself as a folk-poet but as an art-poet, and one of the greatest at that; he bowed the knee to Shakespeare and nobody else. However, although the bard himself would have been horrified to hear it – the folklorist can 'place' McGonagall more easily than can the literary historian.

The most famous of Scots 'worthies' was born in Edinburgh in 1830, of Irish parentage:

> My father was a handloom weaver, and wrought at cotton fabrics during his stay in Edinburgh, which was for about two years. Owing to the great depression in the cotton trade in Edinburgh, he removed to Paisley with his family, where work was abundant for a period of about three years; but then a crash taking place, he was forced to remove to Glasgow with his family with the hope of securing work there, and enable him to support his young and increasing family, as they were all young at that time, your humble servant included. In Glasgow he was fortunate in getting work as a cotton weaver; and as trade was in a prosperous state for about two years, I was sent to school, where I remained about eighteen months, but at the expiry of which, trade again becoming dull, my poor parents were compelled to take me from school, being unable to pay for schooling through adverse circumstances; so that all the education I received was before I was seven years of age. My father, being forced to leave Glasgow through want of work, came to Dundee, where plenty of work was to be had at the time – such as sacking, cloth, and other fabrics. It was at this time that your humble servant was sent to work in a mill in the Scouringburn. (*Poetic Gems*, p. 5)

When McGonagall was born, the Coogate of Edinburgh had a big Irish population (still has, in fact); the birthplaces of McGonagall and of James Connolly, the hero of Easter 1916, are not far apart. Orange and Green are both well represented. Also, the Coogate lies 'contagious' to the Burke-and-Hare axis, which runs in the direction of Surgeon's Hall. McGonagall must have heard, from his cradle onwards and upwards, a rich mixture of Irish and native Scots folklore. In Paisley and Glasgow especially, he must have heard umpteen songs with first lines like 'It was upon the 12th of July in 1690 famous'. Songs with this sort of stock opening are still being composed here and there, but in nineteenth-century Scotland and Ireland they were the common-place of ploughman's bothy and city gin-palace. The drawling 'come-all-ye' tunes brought over to Scotland by bands of Irish labourers must have been very familiar to McGonagall when he was a child, and when he started composing his own poems he quite naturally adopted the idiom of the pedestrian 'come-all-ye's'.

A large number of his poems begin with lines like:

> 'Twas in the year of 1842, and on the 27th of May ...

and quite a few can be fitted to these same come-all-ye tunes. Some of his rhymes show that he was thinking, if not talking, with an Irish accent all his life:

> ... the barque she sprang a leak.
> Still the crew wrought at the pumps till their hearts were like to break.
>
> (*Poetic Gems*, p 173)

And another:

> And as for the robbery and outrage at the hands of the ghouls,
> I must mention Clara Barton and her band of merciful souls ...
>
> (*Poetic Gems*, p. 213)

Also, he quite often uses the 'wrenched' accent of the ballad stanza, i.e. puts the stress on the second syllable when a trochaic dissyllable ends a line. For example:

> Ye sons of Mars, come join with me,
> And sing in praise of Sir Herbert Stewart's little army.
>
> (*Poetic Gems, p.* 53)

McGonagall did not compose many actual songs. One of the few on record is 'The Rattling Boy from Dublin' (*Poetic Gems*, p. 47) which has a 'Whack fal de da, fal de darelido' chorus, and which was apparently one of his most popular items.

It will be seen from the above that McGonagall's life and work form a pattern which is really quite familiar. The difference between McGonagall and scores of folk-poets (anonymous) using virtually the same idiom was that he had something – something unique – which the others hadn't got. It was a gift so extraordinary and so personal to himself that he remains one of the few virtually unparodiable poets. Completely devoid of the lyrical knack which would have set his productions on the road to becoming folk-songs, he had the compensating ability – or compulsion – to use *nothing but* the hobbling and broken-backed rhythms and verbiage of pedestrian folk-poetry, and to use these so consistently from end to end of poem after poem that in effect he created a new style. This style was formed out of the debris and detritus of folk-song – out of all the things which song composed in 'the idiom of the people' sheds in the process of *becoming* folk-song.

McGonagall's work was a sort of frowsy doss-house in which every wooden phrase, every gormless anti-climax was sure to find a bed.

If one listens to the productions of Irish 'come-all-ye' folk poets, one realises at once what McGonagall derived from them. The sinuous drawling tones which can accommodate umpteen words per line provided him with his characteristically elongated line; the stock subjects of battle, disaster, eulogy and lament provided him with his themes; the occasional delicious pancake drop into deadpan flatness provided him – unconsciously, I am sure – with his characteristic gimmick. It is this last feature of the 'come-ye-all' – the pantaloon fall with a thickening sud – which is present in McGonagall's work in classic form.

Indeed, if one were to search for a single designation for the bard of Dundee, one could not do better than dub him a poet of the 'belly-flop'. To perform this type of belly-flop continuously demands a certain type of talent, as anyone who ever tries to parody him soon finds out.

Who, for example, has ever succeeded in recapturing the sublime banality of the following:

> The authorities of Berlin in honour of the Emperor considered it no sin,
> To decorate with crape the beautiful city of Berlin:
> Therefore Berlin I declare was a city of crape,
> Because few buildings crape decoration did escape.

(Poetic Gems, p. 33)

Or this, from 'Lines in Defence of the Stage':

> No, in the theatre we see vice punished and virtue rewarded,
> The villain either hanged or shot, and his career retarded.

(More Poetic Gems, p. 38)

'Lawn Tennyson' and the other high-heid-yin poets of the Victorian age did not like soiling their lips with references to the smoky industrial life of the busy ports, cities and collieries. McGonagall had no such inhibitions – indeed, he may claim to have anticipated the 'Pylon' school of poetry by more than half a century. Also, he was a stickler for scientific exactitude:

> Then as for Leith Fort, it was erected in 1779, which is really grand,
> And which is now the artillery headquarters in Bonnie Scotland;
> And as for the Docks, they are magnificent to see,
> They comprise five docks, two piers, 1,141 yards long respectively ...
>
> Besides, there are sugar refineries and distilleries,
> Also engineer works, saw-mills, rope-works, and breweries,
> Where many of the inhabitants are daily employed,
> And the wages they receive make their hearts feel overjoyed.

Do we detect the very faintest bulge of a tongue-in-the-cheek at this point? Listen to this, a few verses later:

> Then there's Bailie Gibson's fish shop, most elegant to be seen,
> And the fish he sells there are beautiful and clean;
> And for himself, he is a very good man,
> And to deny it there's few people can.

(More Poetic Gems, p. 91)

McGonagall's paeans of praise to certain Scottish watering-places may also cause a number of eyebrows to be raised:

> Beautiful town of Montrose, I will now commence my lay,
> And I will write in praise of thee without dismay;
> And, in spite of all your foes,
> I will venture to call thee Bonnie Montrose.

(More Poetic Gems, p. 77)

Now let's take a trip to North Berwick:

> North Berwick is a watering-place with golfing links green,
> With a fine bathing beach most lovely to be seen;
> And there's a large number of handsome villas also,
> And often it's called the Scarborough of Scotland, as Portobello.
>
> *(More Poetic Gems*, p. 79)

Like Willie Gallacher, McGonagall was strongly against the booze, and in 'The Destroying Angel' (or 'The Poet's Dream') he paints a grandiose apocalyptic canvas, showing the Demon Drink being overcome by the direct method. The Angel cries:

> 'Now, friends of the Temperance cause, follow me:
> For remember it's God's high degree
> To destroy all the public-houses in this fair City;
> Therefore, friends of God, let's commence this war immediately' ...
>
> And when the Perth Road public-houses were fired, she cried,
>
>   'Follow me,
> And next I'll fire the Hawkhill public-houses instantly.'
> Then away we went with the Angel, without dread or woe,
> And she fired the Hawkhill public-houses as onward we did go.
>
> Then, she cried, 'Let's on to the Scouringburn, in God's name.'
> And away to the Scouringburn we went, with our hearts aflame,
> As the destroying Angel did command.
> And when there she fired the public-houses, which looked very grand.
>
> *(More Poetic Gems*, p. 36)

No one was ever able to tell the Bard that he had finally and ultimately plumbed the depths of bathos:

> Friends of humanity, of high and low degree,
> I pray ye all come listen to me;
> And truly I will relate to ye,
> The tragic fate of the Rev. Alexander Heriot Mackonochie.
>
> Who was on a visit to the Bishop of Argyle
> For the good of his health, for a short while;
> Because for the last three years his memory had been affected,
> Which prevented him from getting his thoughts collected.
>
> *(Poetic Gems* p. 185)

One can't escape the inevitable question. Lines like these have led some critics to ask, quite seriously – was it all an enormous leg-pull? They point out that McGonagall seems to have done quite well out of his innumerable appearances at parties, socials, soirées and convivial Rotary-type functions. Listen to his account of one such, among well-upholstered burgesses of the Highland capital:

> 'Twas on the 16th of October, in 1894,
> I was invited to Inverness, not far from the seashore,

To partake of a banquet prepared by the Heatherblend Club,
Gentlemen who honoured me without any hubbub.

The Banquet was held in the Gellion Hotel,
And the landlord, Mr Macpherson, treated me right well;
Also the servant maids were very kind to me,
Especially the girl who polished my boots most beautiful to see.

The Banquet consisted of roast beef, potatoes, and red wine,
Also hare soup and sherry, and grapes most fine,
And baked pudding and apples, lovely to be seen,
Also rich sweet milk and delicious cream.

Mr Gossip, a noble Highlander, acted as chairman,
And when the Banquet was finished the fun began;
And I was requested to give a poetic entertainment,
Which I gave, and which pleased them to their hearts' content.

And as for the entertainment they did me well reward
By entitling me the Heatherblend Club Bard;
Likewise I received an Illuminated Address,
Also a purse of silver, I honestly confess.

(*More Poetic Gems*, p. 108)

When McGonagall rose to do his act, on this occasion, he addressed the company as follows: 'Gentlemen, I feel proud tonight to be among such a select company of gentlemen.' These words at once underline the difference between McGonagall and his contemporaries, the spinner and weaver poets whose work became folk-song. The people who acclaimed McGonagall and made his name a household word were *not* his fellow-workers – *they* preferred 'The Dowie Dens o' Yarrow' and 'The Wark o' the Weavers' – but the well-off Victorian bourgeoisie, who laughed at McGonagall not only because of his inimitable gift for the bathetic but also (and perhaps mainly) because he was a haywire working-class rhymster who considered himself a poet.

Not only pillars of the state at home but empire-builders abroad joined with one accord in the mock-respectful derisive chorus. Here is a letter received by McGonagall in 1891 from an officer in the 1st Royal Scots, a battalion then on overseas service in Zululand: 'Your poems show a taste not to be met with in many of the writings of the present age, and one can only wonder how you could have produced such a selection of poems, commencing as you did at such a late stage in life … I am confident your book could command an extraordinary sale if you arranged for its being sent out to the Cape or Natal Colonies, where so many well-known men reside who hail from the "land o' cakes".'

That McGonagall was a butt for rather odious undergraduate snobbism is obvious from the record. In February 1891, three students of Glasgow University wrote him a letter, asking him, inter alia:

Would you recommend us to write direct to the Queen as a patron of poetry; or should we go to Balmoral to see her there?

What chances do you consider we have in knocking out Tennyson as Poet Laureate?

If we should resolve upon going to Balmoral, which route would you recommend? Also name any 'models' that may be known to you in that direction; stating landlady's name, and if married or single.

These clever young gents also addressed a 'poem' to the Bard, which includes the following lines:

> They will one day yet rear him monuments of brass, and weep upon
> his grave,
> Though when he was living they would hardly have given him the
> price of a shave.

McGonagall-baiting became one of the principal pastimes of the Edinburgh students. In the upper room of the 'Woolpack' – the same room where Dominic Behan and his supporting singers used to drink during the Edinburgh run of *Behan Bein' Behan* in 1963, and where Pete Shepheard and Jimmy Hutchinson of St Andrews had their folk-singing sessions during the Festival – the students loved to confer bogus orders and decorations on McGonagall, hymning his praises in McGonagallese, and generally taking the mickey. In 1894 he was made 'a Grand Knight of the Holy Order of the White Elephant, Burmah'. McGonagall seems to have stood it all with good humour, and because he was once observed leaving one of these functions with rather a curious satiric smile on his face, some have suggested that he secretly enjoyed his ignominious role, and was actually fooling his baiters. They recall the rejoinder of Jimmy Fleemin 'The Laird of Udny's Fool' to a wiseacre who had asked him – with a wink to the company – who he was. 'I'm the Laird o' Udny's feel – fa's feel are ye?'

There is an Irish connection here too. One of McGonagall's benefactors was the Dublin-born actor-playwright Dion (short for Dionysus) Boucicault, author of *The Colleen Bawn, Arrah na Pogue* (a play set in the year 1798) and *The Shaughraun*. Boucicault, who was as kind and generous as he was shrewd, on at least one occasion gave his 'fellow Thespian'; a handsome hand-out. The grateful McGonagall, given a buckshee seat, may have found something vaguely familiar in his benefactor's picaresque Silly Jack heroes, of whom David Krause has recently written: 'His hero is a wise fool, the master of the mischievous revels, who is the inevitable occasion of hilarity in others as well as natural humour in himself' (*Boucicault*, Dublin, 1964, p. 13).*

If McGonagall seems graver than the Irish *pagliacci* – so the proponents of this theory would argue – it is because he had to adjust to the ruling expression – the ruling elder expression of the 'elect' – of nineteenth-century Scotland: an unspeakable Calvinist mask of self-satisfied gravity. Burns hit it off in his day with the devastating line:

> Ye are sae grave, nae doot ye're wise.

---

*Readers unfamiliar with Boucicault's work will be surprised to find how much of the comic flamboyance of O'Casey and of Brendan Behan is foreshadowed in his characterisations.

There *may* be something in this general idea, and it is perfectly true that McGonagall was in effect earning his living as a sort of licensed buffoon; one suspects, however, that McGonagall, like many – perhaps most – of the professional zanies of history, was 'not waving but drowning'.

One must remember, too, that the attitude of the Scots bourgeoisie to the poet – *any* poet, not only the McGonagall type – has usually been one of amused contempt, not unmixed with hostility. Victorian Scotland was horrifyingly Philistine, and the mental attitudes of those days are still very much alive in the country today. When one comes across a portrait of McGonagall, and contemplates his sensitive histrionic features, which so strikingly recall Henry Irvine and Oscar Wilde, one can't help feeling that when that monstrous money-glutted Victorian society was laughing at McGonagall, it was to a certain extent laughing at poetry itself.

Not that McGonagall didn't conform. He conformed to the point of sycophancy. Apart from one poem in which he expresses admiration for Parnell, his flag-wagging jingoism was outrageous enough to scunner even an Empire Loyalist. Furthermore he seems in the main to have been quite successful, acting as his own agent, in extracting money, even from the practical jokers who had their fun codding him. If McGonagall failed on occasion to make the grade financially, it was usually more because of bad luck than lack of judgment. When he was in New York (1887), he tried to get work. 'I went three days after being in New York to look for engagements at the music-halls. I was told by all the managers I saw that they couldn't give me an engagement because there was a combination on foot against all British artistes' (*More Poetic Gems*, p. 17). In Dundee, after his return home, he appeared at Baron Zeigler's circus and Transfield's circus, and he had a great success in Glasgow. 'I gave three private entertainments to crowded audiences, and was treated like a prince by them.' All in all, he seems to have done every bit as well as many of the folk-singers earning a living from the clubs at the present day.

Nor does the resemblance end there. Like some modern folk-singers, McGonagall composed various pieces which connect with traditional items in the folk idiom. In such poems one can detect folk-motifs blown up or attenuated as if in the distorting mirrors of a fun-fair. Let us look at one, which – in the McPeake version at least – will be familiar to every reader. Among the top ten of the most popular (and deservedly popular) songs of the folk revival is 'Will ye go, lassie, go' (The Wild Mountain Thyme). This, as I pointed out in *Sing* some years back, is a Northern Irish folk variant of 'The Braes o' Balquhidder', one of the songs of the Paisley cotton-weaver poet Robert Tannahill (1774–1810). It will be remembered that in the early 1830s, when McGonagall was a wee bairn, his father 'wrought at cotton fabrics' in Paisley, and McGonagall junior must have been familiar with Tannahill's songs, which enjoyed enormous popularity, particularly in the west of Scotland. 'The Braes o' Balquhidder' is Tannahill's contribution to a well-established genre in European folk-song. It is the call of the town-bred boy to his girl to have a country holiday, and enjoy sex and scenery 'where glad innocence reigns'. The best of these songs have a wonderful and often poignant lyric freshness – especially those composed at the time the Industrial Revolution was turning many of our towns into smoky hell-holes. However, these songs have many antecedents in European literature, and the spirit that pervades them – that of young love triumphant – is the ecstatic cry of the *Pervigilium Veneris*:

Cras amet qui nunquam amavit, quique amavit cras amet
(Loveless hearts will love tomorrow, those that have loved will love again.)

It is a 'ver novum' – a 'new Spring', in every sense – which these songs celebrate.

Well, what will McGonagall make of this darling theme? Those who have a
penchant for the thickening sud will not be disappointed.

> Bonnie Clara, will you go to the bonnie Sidlaw hills
> And pu' the blooming heather, and drink from their rills?
> There the cranberries among the heather grow,
> Believe me, dear Clara, as black as the crow.
>
> Then, bonnie Clara, will you go
> And wander with me to and fro?
> And with joy our hearts will o'erflow
> When we go to the bonnie Sidlaws O.

(More Poetic Gems, p. 72)

And another:

> Then, bonnie Annie, will you go with me
> and leave the crowded city of Dundee,
> And breathe the pure, fragrant air
> In the Howe of Kilmany, so lovely and fair? ...
>
> And there's a wood sawmill by the roadway,
> And the noise can be heard by night and day,
> As the circular saw wheels round and round,
> Making the village with its echoes resound.

(More Poetic Gems, p. 75)

(This, surely, suggests a variant to the Ball of Kirriemuir:

> 'Ye couldnae hear the sawmill
> For the swishin' ...' etc.)

We only have room for one other example. Part of the first verse of 'The Bonnie Lass
o' Dundee' reads as follows:

> Her face is fair, broon is her hair,
> And dark blue is her e'e.

(More Poetic Gems, p. 101)

This echoes a ballad commonplace; cf. the first verse of a Perthshire version of Childe
Maurice (Child 83) which was recorded in the berryfields of Blairgowrie from Martha
Stewart, July 1955:

> His face was fair, lang was his hair,
> And the green was where he stood.

The next verse of McGonagall's poem contains the lines

And her face it is the fairest
That ever I did see.

This at once recalls Annie Laurie, the most famous version of which is itself a literary 'folk variant' of an older song, composed by William Douglas of Fingland (see Robert Ford, *Song Histories*, pp. 23–31).

Like many literary (or pseudo-literary) gents who have borrowed from the folk tradition, McGonagall himself became (in his own lifetime) a folk character. People say of him – in just the same way they say of Burns – 'there's mair o' him than's in the book.'

And there is, too. A large sub-literature exists of what one may call Mock-McGonagallese. Ask anyone in Scotland to quote a verse of McGonagall, and the chances are he will recite:

As I was walkin' doon the road,
I met a coo – a bull, by God!

This, as you can see at a glance, has been 'fathered' on the Bard – it was never written by him. For one thing, the couplet is in Scots (or as near it as makes no matter), and McGonagall very seldom used dialect, no doubt regarding it as vulgar. The chances are that he delivered his own poems with more than a touch of the shoddy genteel accent of 'ould dacency'.

It is highly unlikely, therefore, that McGonagall was the author of another amusing stanza, which is also fathered on him by popular attribution:

O water o' Leith, o water o' Leith,
Where the girls gang doon tae wash their teeth;
And ower the stream is a hoose, right knackie,
O' that grand auld man Professor Blackie.

Any verse mentioning such an exalted figure would have, of course, to be in English. And this thought obliges us to take a closer look at what McGonagall owed to his Irish vernacular heritage.

II
McGonagall and the Irish Question

O come all ye noble patriots, and listen to my song.
'Tis only forty verses, so I won't detain youse long.

Dublin street ballad

Bedad, he revives - see how he rises:
    Finnegan risin' in the bed.
Says, 'Whirl your whiskey around like blazes' –
    Thunderin' Jayzus, do you think I'm dead?'

Finnegans Wake

McGonagall's status as a larger-than-life folk character places him beyond question in the vanguard of a clearly identifiable Scoto-Irish goliardic tradition. As is only to be expected, he makes a periodic courtesy appearance in the press; indeed, one feels instinctively from time to time that he is waiting in the wings, and is just about to effect a well-timed mock-dignified re-entry into the news. Here for example, is one instance of his all-pervasive presence. A story which appeared in the *Scottish Daily Express* of 15 September 1965 afforded the following information:

> 'Wearing lum hats and claw-hammer 'jaikets', the loyal and ancient fraternity of Weavers in Ladybank, Fife, set out for Bo'ness, West Lothian, on Friday night carrying a coffin – with WHISKY in it.
>
> They are holding a celebration to perpetuate the memory of William McGonagall, Dundee's poet and tragedian. The coffin contains 'The Spirit of McGonagall', explained Mr Graham Bell, of the Royal Hotel, Ladybank, who holds the proud title 'Admiral of the Tay'.'

The spirit of McGonagall! This must have been the brew that circulated at Finnegan's Wake. Two drops, and the corpse is guaranteed to rise from the bed with a great roar of resurrection-elation. Here, anyway, is the point at which we clinch the Irish connection, and display some fruity examples of the type of verse which supplies the link between McGonagall and Erin's Isle. The first is by Michael O'Brien, the 'Wexford Bard', which I transcribed in 1949 from an old newspaper cutting in the library of the Irish Folklore Commission in Dublin.

> Lament for Canon Dunne
> On Friday the 18th day of June, in the year of '97
> Old Ireland's son, blessed Canon Dunne, was called away to heaven.
> A better *sagart* [priest] never lived in Blackwater in our time.
> Only 64, not one day more, he was only in his prime.

(The Canon's career is faithfully recorded, parish by parish.)

> From that he went to Litter and from there to Adamstown
> And when Father Walsh he had resigned, to Blackwater he was sent
>
> down,
>
> So that leaves him here about twelve year, perhaps a little more,
> Till God's angels came his soul to claim for blessed Jehovah shore.

(And here we come to the final belly-flop.)

> He was sinking fast for some time past, and though his end was near,
> His death was not expected by us so soon around here.

Admittedly this is rather more singable than the majority of McGonagall's efforts in the same style, but the connection is clear enough. In McGonagall's 'The Death of the Revd Dr Wilson' (*More Poetic Gems*, p.161) there is an internal rhyme in the last line of the first verse, much as in the Wexford Bard's threnody:

> 'Twas in the year of 1888 and on the 17th January
> That the late Rev. Dr Wilson's soul fled away;
> The generous-hearted Dr had been ailing for some time,
> But death, with his dart, did pierce the heart of the learned divine.

> He was a man of open countenance and of great ability,

And late minister of Free St Paul's Church, Dundee,
And during the twenty-nine years he remained as minister in Dundee
He struggled hard for the well-being of the community.

He was the author of several works concerning great men,
In particular the Memoirs of Dr Candlish and Christ turning his face
towards Jerusalem
Which is well worthy of perusal, I'm sure,
Because the style is concise and the thoughts clear and pure.

McGonagall has left us a revealing description of this calling to the privilege – or
malheur – of being a poet. He wrote:

> I seemed to feel as it were a strange kind of feeling stealing over me, and remained
> so for about five minutes. A flame, as Lord Byron has said, seemed to kindle up my
> entire frame, along with a strong desire to write poetry; and I felt so happy, so
> happy, that I was inclined to dance, then I began to pace backwards and forwards
> in the room, trying to shake off all thought of writing poetry; but the more I tried,
> the more strong the sensation came. It was so strong, I imagined that a pen was in
> my right hand, and a voice crying, 'Write, Write.' (*Poetic Gems*, p. 6)

Here we have a far-off echo of medieval Irish poetry, and it is possible to take it back
step by step to its original. In the National Library of Ireland there is preserved (in an
early nineteenth-century broadside) a song entitled 'The Young Man's Dream'. This is
the first verse:

> It happened one night as I lay on my bed,
> A vision appeared to me that filled my heart with dread.
> Why is your genius idle, it unto me did say,
> Arise, young man, and sing the praises of your country.

The McGonagall measure is unmistakable, although this is a *song* and can be *sung*.
Furthermore, the type of song can at once be identified; it is an 'Aisling', or vision
poem, one with very definite rules of structure, and (after 1690) with an obsessive all-
pervading ideological incubus – namely, hope for the resurrection of shattered Gaelic
Ireland with the help of the exiled House of Stuart. The most famous single poem in
this tradition is Egan O'Rahilly's 'Brightness of Brightness', a translation of which can
be found in Brendan Kennelly's *Penguin Book of Irish Verse*. There is a song in Irish
with virtually the same title as that of the broadside ballad quoted above: *Aisling an
Oigfhir*, The Young Man's Vision.

Nothing in literature could be more curious than the contrast between the excellence - and I mean excellence - of the best of the Gaelic poems in this tradition, and the
almost unnerving gormlessness and slaphappiness of the Anglo-Irish broadside versions which stem directly from them.

The episode in McGonagall's life which really clinches the Irish connection is his
forlorn journey to Balmoral to seek the personal patronage of Queen Victoria. This
echoes similar pilgrimages made by Gaelic poets in the seventeenth and eighteenth
centuries to the stately homes of jumped-up Anglo-Irish Protestant landowners;
deprived of their traditional patrons, these poets brought along panegyrics in honour

of the new owners: these were written not in Irish but in a curious brand of high-flown flowery English. An example of this is *Castlehyde*:

> There are fine horses, and stall-fed oxes,
> And dens for foxes to play and hide;
> Fine mares for breeding, and foreign sheep there,
>   With snowy fleeces in Castlehyde.
> The grand improvements, they would amuse you.
>   The trees are blossoming with fruit of all kinds.
> The bees perfuming the fields with music,
>   That brings more beauty to Castlehyde.

Here the internal assonances, characteristic of Gaelic verse, are imported quite deftly into the English stanza.

Having been refused largesse by Mr Hyde of Castlehyde, the poet reworked the final lines of the song - which originally read

> And in all my rangings and serenadings,
> I found no ayqual to Castlehyde -

turning them into the following contemptuous brush-off:

> And in all my rangings! and serenadings,
> I found no naygur like humpy Hyde.   (Naygur = niggard)

The 'Year of Liberty', 1798, caused an enormous eruption of street ballad versifying, both on the Orange and Green sides of the fence. Just before the rebellion, thirty-six men of a Yeomanry Corps who were suspected of being United Irishmen were shot on the Fair Green of Dunlavin, Co. Wicklow. Here are the first and last verses of a broadside ballad printed in Cork and preserved in the library of Trinity College, Dublin (J. D. White's collection of Irish ballads):

> In the year one thousand seven hundred and ninety eight,
> A sorrowful ditty to you I'm going to relate,
> Concerning those heroes both clever and rare to be seen,
> By false information were shot upon Dunlavin Green.
> ...
> Now to conclude and finish my mournful tale,
> I hope all good Christians to pray for their souls will not fail.
> Their souls in white pigeons a-flying to heaven were seen,
> On the very same day they were shot upon Dunlavin Green.

The Orangemen were naturally quick off the mark to counter all this underhand rebel tear-jerking, and some of their effusions come so near to the genuine McGonagall that one might almost regard them as a bridge between the Shankill and the Cowgate. Here are two verses from 'David Brown's Farewell to Kilmod Lodge 541':

> Farewell you Carrickmannon boys, adieu unto Forth Hill,
> No more I'll share your social joys - when I think on you my heart does
>   fill;

But when I land at Quebec a glass of water I will call,
And toast to those I do respect, my brethren in the Protestant Hall.

So brethren true be you ever so few, William the Third commemorate.
On the 12th July, be it wet or dry, that glorious day still celebrate,
And in the evening of the 12th you'll assemble there I hope,
As the glass goes round remember Brown, and raise your voice and
                                                    shout 'No Pope!'

The antics of the balladeers did not go unremarked by the Irish literati. In 1836, when McGonagall was six, J. D. Herbert printed in his *Irish Varieties* a delicious parody of the street-singer's wordy, meandering, nasal 'nyaaa'. The subject was George IV's state visit to Ireland in 1821.

The good sense of the Roman Catholics caused them to change their intentions of annoying, with their complaints, the royal ear;
And they propos'd having a public dinner to celebrate the coronation, at which was expected the very best of good cheer;
Then an unexpected proposal came from the Protestants to the Catholics so very distinct and clear.
That all hostilities and jealousies should cease, and both parties assemble at dinner without any doubt or fear
At the celebration, celebration, oh! the wonderful celebration!

G. D. Zimmerman has several good passages on the vocabulary and style of the Irish balladeers:

In the really popular ballads and songs the vocabulary is slender. A limited stock of epithets recur again and again. Ireland is 'poor', 'old', and 'distressed'. Her sons are 'gallant' and 'true-hearted'. Heroes are 'bold', 'undaunted', 'noble', 'clever' 'true' ...
The ballad-writers probably devoted little time to the composition of their texts. To fill up the lines they had at their disposal a stock of tags, of recurring phrases frequently employed to express similar ideas. The use of commonplace expressions is indeed common to folk poetry in general; it has been observed that sub-literary poetry preserved a mode of composition fundamentally different from that of more learned literature: it used as its elements whole passages rather than isolated words. For the authors of Irish street ballads this technique was not as essential and highly developed as it had been for epic singers and story-tellers belonging to an entirely oral tradition. Still, it had two advantages: it facilitated the writing and the memorising, and it also pleased the audience.

All this could equally well be said of McGonagall. However, the difference between his lucubrations, and those of his cousins across the water, resided in the fact that their productions were *sung* and his were not.

It should also be remembered that like the come-all-ye poets, and indeed like the medieval Irish court-poets too, McGonagall is a meticulous chronicler of events, local and national, and as such as in the grand central tradition of 'public' poets. From the death of a new unremembered Free Kirk minister to the melodramatic death of General Gordon in Khartoum, all was grist to his mill.

The Scottish and Irish popular traditions have innumerable points of contact, and those we are surveying are certainly not among the least interesting and curious. Perhaps I may be allowed at this point a word of personal reminiscence. When I was working in Ireland, in the late 1940s I invented (for the entertainment of friends) an imaginary MP – Mr Donegal McGonagall, T.D., leader of Clann Gombeen in Dail Eireann – whose exploits I hymned in McGonagallesque come-all-ye stanzas, sung with an attempt at authentic native nyaaa. These proved quite popular among a select circle in Belfast, Dublin and Dungannon – a circle, I might add, consisting impartially of diggers with the left and the right foot. One of these ditties – it began 'At Poguemohone, when the moon was shining' - was a satire against the T.D., and people like him, who sang anachronistic 'patriot' songs to divert the attention of the Irish people from the pressing social and economic problems confronting them.

However, the commerce was, as always, a two-way affair. At one of the Belfast hoolies, I heard such a spirited rendering of 'Johnston's Motor Car' (from Jean Connor) that the tune kept dancing in my memory. A few weeks later when I was returning from a short holiday in Scotland aboard one of the Burns-Laird steamers, I composed 'The Men of Knoydart' to that same air. The song began while we were lying at the Broomielaw, and was complete before the Clyde coast faded from sight. It had its premiere in Kelly's Cellars in Belfast the following lunch-time.

While we are still across the water, the reader may be interested to know that there was once a 'prose McGonagall' in Ireland – a lady-novelist called Amanda McKittrick Ros. If you aren't familiar with the works of the 'Irish Ouida', you should beg, borrow or steal a copy of *Delina Delaney* without delay. Funniest of all unconsciously funny prose-writers, Amanda was the wife of the station-master at Larne, so, in a sense, she commanded the sea and rail crossroads of Irish and Scottish folkways. After a few pages of Amanda, you will begin to wonder if we are not maybe dealing with a compulsive grotesquerie which is distinctively Scots-Irish.

On our side of the water, this singular urge reaches high altitudes of awesome absurdity in the writings of a few half-crazed Presbyterian zealots who seem to have been permanently high on the Bible. In 1837 John Hutton paid a Dumfries printer (J. McDiarmid, of Irish Street) to bring out a poem ludicrous-pedantic beyond belief: it is called 'The Seals, Trumpets and Thunders of Revelations'. This sort of thing:

> Four wandering tribes Euphrates
> Settled near. (What of them? What then?
> I expect ye to say, and ask: What then?)
> These had been bound by means of the Crusades.
>   ('Droll blades!'). I say the day,
> The day I say – the judgment day
> Is now before us – the judgment day -
> The day of judgment – 'tis the judgment day ...

And after every second or third line, a lumbering, top-heavy dray of notes on the planting of churches in Chaldea and Mesopotamia, on Alaric and the Visigoths, on Othman and Amurath, Titus and Vespasian, Peter the Great and Charles XII of

Sweden. The whole thing reaches a 'Justified Sinner'-like peak of hallucinatory Calvinist solipsism when the poet arrives at William of Orange's victories over the French and
their Jacobite allies at Aughrim and the Boyne:

> Louis was beat, and so shall ye
> Abide in me continually.

Reading this sad stuff has the paradoxical effect of making one grateful for
McGonagall; at any rate, he had guts, and a belly to flop on. However, although
McGonagall is the supreme practitioner of the art of the belly-flop, he turns out to have
some unexpected rivals. That extraordinary mixed-up genius, Hugh MacDiarmid,
who has written some of the best poetry Scotland has ever seen, and some of the worst,
has done a lot of notable belly-flopping in his time. One example is his incredible poem
'The Fingers of Baal contract in the Communist Salute', which was published in 1946
in *Poems of the East West Synthesis*. This is supposed to be a poem of ideas - the 'ideas'
being lifted bodily from a haywire tome, *6,000 Years of Gaelic Grandeur Unearthed*,
which was published in Berlin in 1936, during the Nazi regime - but the end product is
the purest 'babu' McGonagallese.

   Here are two sample stanzas:

> Infernal fantasies contrived to hide
> The simple unacceptable truth!
>   – Read Hommel's History of Babylonia,
> And Fink's Die Sprachstämme des Erdkreises, sooth.

> The Atlantis Fable is but a colossal exaggeration
> Of the natural catastrophe of 1031 BC
> Which broke in upon Cornwall – fantastically embellished,
> To hide the simple report of the Scilly Isles tragedy

In this truly fantastic production, which deserves to be read in full, MacDiarmid
displays all McGonagall's compulsive 'come-all-ye' desire to extend his line and get his
rhyme.

   I submit that only the sort of investigation we are undertaking in respect of
McGonagall could possibly furnish any meaningful explanation of how the author of
'The Second Hymn to Lenin' and 'Lament for the Great Music' could also write (and,
after writing, print) such lines as these:

> Black, yellow, white – just being human's
> The thing. And nothing now could be finer
> Than the rest of the world clapping Mao on the back
> And crying: 'What ho! my old China!'

> Militarism, Imperialism, Superstition.
> Exploitation. Oppression – heck!
> This is the great pay-off at last.
> Who'll square it – with a phoney Chiang-Kai-Shek?
>   ('The Chinese Genius Wakes Up', *Lines Review*, No 19)

McGonagallese poems which are not just parodies, and which display the clodhopping belly-flopping techniques of folk-poets at the very bottom of the echelons turn up occasionally here and there. One such is 'The Glen Cinema Disaster,' composed by an anonymous Paisley bard. Here are a few verses, transcribed from a MS collection of 1938:

> It was afternoon, in a Cinema called the Glen,
> No thoughts of death had anyone in the cinema then;
> The picture on the screen was a picture called the 'Crowd',
> And it got a rousing welcome, the children cheered it loud.

> There was nothing but happiness, inside that cinema hall,
> Until by mistake, there rose a dreadful call,
> It caused immediate havoc, it holds terror, even for men,
> What was the effect on children, that fateful day in the Glen.

> The hall was packed with children, the cream of our future generation,
> Whose one object in being there, was harmless recreation,
> To enjoy the last day of the year, was their main desire,
> But fate was very cruel, to them, when some-one shouted 'Fire'.

> Those poor innocent children, did what only others would do,
> They rushed for the nearest exit, but couldn't all get through.
> Some were trampled underneath, never to rise again,
> And their beautiful faces, were distorted with pain.

> Words cannot be found, to describe that horrible scene,
> To the whole of Paisley, such a tragedy never has been,
> It will be remembered in Paisley, for many a long day,
> As the Glen Cinema disaster, and the 'Black Hogmanay'.

> So in your thoughts of disaster, try if you can to pray,
> For those poor innocent children, who lost their lives that day,
> Think of the Fathers and Mothers, Relatives, wives and men,
> Who lost their Sons, Daughters, or Relatives, that awful day in the Glen.

Now let us look back at our opening questions. The hard truth is that folk-song becomes poetry – or has a chance of becoming poetry – as and when it gets rid of McGonagall. He is, as it were, the sump into which all that is least creative in folk-song is bound to drain. However, the work of McGonagall, anti-hero of the un-folk process, serves, paradoxically, to illuminate a wide stretch of the debatable land between art-poetry and folksong.

If we must admit that a song in the folk idiom is more likely – at any rate in its initial stages – to resemble McGonagall than to resemble Lorca, Rilke, Valéry, etc., it is also true that the work of the real folk-poet is never – or almost never – as insipid, nerveless and generally banal and moribund as the work of the great ruck of minor and minuscule art-poets. The dimwits among such art-poets often affect to despise oral folk-culture, usually for vulgar reasons of exclusiveness and preciosity, but the top-notchers usually have more sense. Writers such as Burns and Lorca have learned much from a lively and virile folk-culture, and have themselves written songs which were to become absorbed into local folk-traditions. The art of the people, says Davenson, is 'la curiosité permanente de l'élite'. Yeats and Auden have experimented, successfully, with the folk idiom, and Charles Causley, W. S. Graham, and Christopher Logue have carried these experiments a stage further. Organisers of poetry readings now regularly invite folk singers to participate; poetry and jazz have been cohabiting off and on, sometimes producing some by-ordinar offspring.

Sydney Carter has been a sort of Bishop of Woolwich of the revival, demonstrating with ecumenical bonhomie that religion and folk-song are not incompatible, while secular cross-currents from folk-song, art literature and the theatre converge turbulently in the work of Ewan MacColl.

The folk process is not only a matter of unconscious modification; it is also a matter, at many different levels, of *conscious creation*. The moment experienced by the creator of 'folk art' can be comparable with the moment experienced by the 'art' poet or composer. As in all forms of human activity, it is a question of time, of slow (often necessarily slow) maturing. Think of the people at a ceilidh who sit the night long hardly opening their mouths, and who emerge in two or three months – or years – as folk-artists. The absence of direct money stimuli seems to be very important, especially in the early stages. Professionals and professionalism are no new thing in folk-song, of course, but the high-powered American pop-folk set-up, with its escalating onslaught on the sensibilities, is quite definitely a new and highly disquieting phenomenon. One feels that the growing folk-artist should earn his or her living in almost any other way than by tying up the creative strain with the ordinary tin-pan alley cash nexus. Folksong has, in the past, been an 'underground,' against official or establishment culture. From now on, it will also (I reckon) be an 'underground' against money-minded pop-folk skulduggery, now rampant in 'folk' clubs all over the country.

The difference between the one thing and the other has been delineated in mordant prose by Gershon Legman (*The Horn Book*, p. 503):

> The final identifying rule is therefore this – and it has no exceptions. All folkniks, folk-songers, folklore-fakers … have one characteristic in common, and by it they can invariably be told from the real thing; *They are all out for the money*, plus a goodly bit of cheap public attention and acclaim … Folk-fakers will not sing, record or print one bloody word or note without a brassbound contract for a cut of the box-office take … The above unfailing stigmata are not only the most infallible characteristics of the breed, but also the most peculiar thing about them, since they are so completely at variance with the whole soul and character of folklore. Real folksingers, and for that matter real folk, whether they can carry a note or not, will occasionally give forth with a song, or tell a joke, spin a tale, crack a riddle, or cut a caper at a local dance or beer-joint, just on the basis of good spirits, or having had a couple of drinks, or trying to please a pretty girl, or all three combined; without requiring cash payment and a 56–year copyright made out to them in advance. This is not even considered praiseworthy or peculiar of them, but simply the way it is done – the way folklore is (to coin a phrase) orally transmitted.

Legman puts it in a nutshell when he says, referring to the commercial folk scene and its victims, the real folk-singers:

The lesser breeds without the Know How – the Northern Scots, Southern Italians, Deserted Arabs, etc., – who have been doing all the folksinging, will receive as their share: folk-all.

David Wright in *Moral Story II* thinks of Poetry as an old street-walker, but his words apply equally well to Folk-song, looking from the pavement at a carload of prosperous folk-fakers driving past:

> out of the corner of my eye I'd seen a Rolls Royce
> Purr by us with a back seat full of her old friends,
> Passing, like the gent in the song, the girl they'd ruined.
> They lifted a disdainful nostril at her noise,
> And continued, as you might expect, to pursue their ends,
> With cigars drawing, and the radio carefully tuned
>
> To a highbrow programme. So across the gutter
> We caught one another's look, and as their exhaust
> Echoed outside of the Ritz like a burst paper bag,
> Laughed like hyenas; she, with a shaking udder,
> Said, 'I was a lovely piece, when they met me first.'
> And lineaments of desire lit the old hag.

This being the rather depraved scene we are faced with, let us be grateful, at any rate, for the creators, the makars, the composers, those with a spark of the divine fire – and if anyone can leaven this unholy lump, they will. And before we start reaching for stones to chuck at Bob Dylan, as if he were a sort of folk-song equivalent of the woman taken in adultery, and before we join the hooting chorus when his 1965 Newport 'image' comes up for discussion, let us for heaven's sake remember that an unmistakable vein of genuine poetry runs through the best of his work. Which thought, of course, brings us back in reverse to McGonagall. We have noted that he is virtually unpariodable and this is true: parodists invariably overdo it.

At this point I hope I may be forgiven another personal reminiscence. After the second (and last) battle of El Alamein, I tried my hand at a victory ode in the style of the master; if nothing else, it may serve to show how very unlike McGonagall most of such efforts are. The title was 'McGonagallese Ode on our Re-entry into Tobruk'. Here are the first two verses:

> While proceeding to Tmimi, as ordered,
>   I turned aside to take a look,
> And see what cruel war had done to
>   bonny Tobruk.
> But now I'm here and have a shufty, all I can
>   say for this unprepossessing spot
> Is that today, the 16th November 1942,
>   the Eighth Army is in it, and the
>   bloody Jerry is not.
>
> That Rommel has regained his freedom
>   of movement, we one and all must agree,

> For a general moving with more liberated alacrity
> the town did never yet see.
> Iron Crosses and swastikas, tanks, guns and officers'
> Volkswagens, 88s and Light Howitzers,
> row upon fucking row,
> All buggering off in the direction of Tripoli
> as fast as they can go.

Robert Garioch quite liked this effort, but he pointed out that McGonagall would never have written 'bonny Tobruk'; it would inevitably have been 'the beautiful city of Tobruk'. And as for 'buggering off,'… quite unthinkable!

III

The McGonagalliode

It has been suggested by G. S. Fraser that McGonagall's work reflects the civic soul of Dundee, but this has always seemed to me an unjustified slight on that long-suffering city. In any case, I think we may claim to have shown that it isn't true. McGonagall certainly spent much of his life in the city of 'jute, jam and journalism', and he mostly spoke up for Dundee; however, he removed finally to his birthplace Edinburgh, and the last years of his life were played out against the backcloth of the great Calvinist capital itself, sombre, elegant, sinister. One thinks of him, soldiering on into the new century, his ulster buttoned up to his chin against the snell East wind, bound perhaps for the Woolpack (always his favourite howff), or else for the Parliament House, where he sold signed copies of his poems, written in pencil, to the bewigged advocates and their clients. The most theatrical-looking of European capitals provided a fitting stage-setting for the old trouper playing his final scene – and made him, in spite of all, one of the company of Burns and Fergusson, Herd and Hume, and the roystering boon-companions of the Crochallan Fencibles.

> Did Burns no read, or he micht taste
> LORD IN THEE IS AL MY TRAIST
>
> The lintel-stane o' Bacchus Court
> THE LORD IS ONLIE MY SUPORT

During the course of this article, we have said some harsh words – harsher words than McGonagall himself would probably have used – about the students who baited the old man. Let us make amends by quoting, as envoy, some lines from the 'McGonagalliode', written by a present-day student – Gordon Farquharson, Laureate Bard of the Edinburgh University McGonagall Society …

> O beautiful gilded statue of Eternal Youth, standing above the Old Quad
> in state,
> With your flaming torch, the darkness of ignorance to illuminate,
> Hear now my praise of one who knew you well,
> As he, for some considerable time, nearby did dwell.

He was none other than William McGonagall, the poet and tragedian of
      renown,
A citizen and worthy inhabitant of Edinburgh's fair town.
He was truly gifted as a great poet should be
With wisdom, imagination, innocence and sincerity.
Often have I felt as I have left a certain hostelry in South
College St, in which I have been quenching my drouth,
That I have seen the shade of the poet himself standing in the nearby
      close mouth,
Which has given me greater inspiration for the cause,
That is, of proclaiming the greatness of McGonagall to all without
      pause,
Wherefore, I now declare to all who read or hear my lay,
And solemnly avow that from now until I reach my hindmost day,
And I am lowered into my grave clad in my funeral robe,
That I shall wholeheartedly endeavour with all my might to
                  spread the knowledge and fame of the
                        works of William McGonagall
                              throughout the
                                  globe!

Chapbook, 1965.

Who Remembers R. B. Cunninghame Graham?

Who remembers R.B. Cunninghame Graham? And why? As in the case of Robert Burns many people honour Graham for wrong or at least for irrelevant reasons. They stressed the 'legendary figure', the intrepid horseman and explorer, the man who at the age of seventeen had been shipped to South America by his family and had grown up among gauchos. They were full of romantic praise for 'Don Roberto, descendant of Scottish kings and Spanish hidalgos', the adventurous laird who more than any other Scot in modern times seemed to combine in himself two traditional Scottish figures - the soldier of fortune and the wandering scholar.

Very little of this, oddly enough, was exaggeration. Graham had such an eventful life and bobbed up in so many strange places that it was only too easy to paint him in glamorous colours as a sort of modern Don Quixote of the pampas.

On the other hand, there were those who recalled his period as a radical MP for NW Lanarkshire from 1886 to 1892, his denunciation of liberal hypocrisy, his defence of Parnell, his championing of Socialism and the six weeks he spent in Clerkenwell jail after getting bashed over the head with a policeman's truncheon on Bloody Sunday 1887.

Which is the Graham that matters? Or is it wrong to disentangle them? With the appearance of *The Essential R. B. Cunninghame Graham,* an anthology of his stories and other writings, edited by Paul Bloomfield, we might as well have a shot at getting the thing straight.

In the first place, Graham the gaucho-laird and Graham the agitator of Bloody Sunday - not to mention Graham the man of letters - are not really incompatible figures if one sees them against a recognisable Scottish tradition, the tradition of James V the "gaberlunzie Man", and of penniless clansmen who regarded themselves as the equal of any king - not excluding 'Jamie' in Edinburgh.

Here Mr Bloomfield is of little help. He wants to see Cunninghame Graham as a 'British author and gentleman' and pays scant attention to the Scottish tradition to which Graham belonged.

However he does include a short story 'Beattock for Moffat?' which shows that Graham's mastery of the rhythm and idiom of Scots speech was sure.

But more important, Graham really does deserve his place in affectionate working-class memory. Listen to an extract from his maiden speech in Parliament (1 February 1887):

On glancing over the Queen's speech, I am struck with the evident desire to do nothing at all. Not one word to bridge over the awful chasm existing between the poor and the rich; not one word of kindly sympathy for the sufferers from the present commercial and agricultural depression - nothing but platitudes, nothing but views of society through a little bit of pink glass.

He went on to speak of Parnell and the Irish fight for freedom, and concluded with the tremendous onslaught on the imperial capital:

this dreary waste of mud and stucco - with its misery, its want and destitution, its degradation, its prostitution, and its glaring social inequalities - the society we call London - which by a refinement of irony, has placed the mainspring of human action, almost the power of life and death, and the absolute power to pay labour and to reward honour, behind the grey tweed veil which shrouds the greasy pocket of the capitalist.

In the 1880s Cradley Heath, the centre of the English nail industry, was aptly dubbed a 'hell-hole'. The average earnings of the nail and chain makers for fifteen hours' work a day were 6s a week, and the women employees, who worked naked to the waist, earned even less.

When the Prime Minister refused to let him go on discussing the plight of the chain makers, Graham denounced him with cutting words. The Speaker told him to withdraw them, and Graham refused. 'I never withdraw.' The Speaker therefore asked him to withdraw himself. 'Certainly, Sir - I will go to Cradley Heath!' And he at once took the train there to continue the agitation.

Another point that should be made, for Mr Bloomfield skates over it, is that, like all early Scottish socialists, Graham was a doughty fighter for Scottish Home Rule.

In spite of the defects I have mentioned, Mr Bloomfield's book is timely and useful. The stories are well chosen, and he has included extracts from the Latin-American histories - including a surgical study of the Paraguayan dictator, Lopez, who fancied himself as the Napoleon of La Plata, and died after unleashing a crazy war against Brazil, Uruguay and the Argentine.

Review of *The Essential R.B. Cunninghame Graham*, edited by Paul Bloomfield (London, 1952) in *The Daily Worker*, November, 1952.

Lorca and Cante Jondo

Federico García Lorca,
Deep Song and Other Prose,
edited and translated by Christopher Maurer;
Marion Boyars, 1986.

Federico García Lorca, the most famous poet of twentieth-century Spain, was only thirty-eight when he was murdered by a Fascist death squad soon after the outbreak of the Civil War. He was an Andalusian – an heir, therefore, of a tradition which is quite distinct from the majority Spanish tradition, being strongly coloured by ancestral Arab influences. The province had been 'al-Andalus', in the twelfth century probably the most civilised part of Europe. Lorca said in a newspaper interview, published not long before his murder, that the expulsion of the Moors in 1492 had been a 'disastrous event … An admirable civilisation, a poetry, architecture and delicacy unique in the world – all were lost, to give way to an impoverished, cowed town, a wasteland populated by the worst bourgeoisie in Spain today'. Earlier, in a lecture, he had expressed equally forthright sentiments: 'Being born in Granada has given me a sympathetic understanding of those who are persecuted – the Gypsy, the Black, the Jew, the Moor which all Granadans have inside them.' In his work he used forms like the *casida* and the *gacela* (ghazel), both Arabic poetical forms, and in the lecture on his *Romancero Gitano* he stated: 'I called it Gypsy because the Gypsy is the loftiest, most profound and aristocratic element of my country, the most deeply representative of its mode, the very keeper of the glowing embers, blood, and alphabet of Andalusian and universal truth.' No wonder the Spanish Fascists regarded him as a dangerous enemy, and took an early opportunity of getting him out of the way.

Deep Song brings together the lectures, poetry readings and radio talks given by Lorca between 1922 and 1936, the year of his death. The editor and translator, Christopher Maurer, stresses in his introduction the most important single fact about Lorca as a creative artist, namely that he consciously operated in an oral tradition, and mistrusted print. 'His creative powers were most stimulated in the presence of *listeners*, not future readers, and he was well known as a poet before he ever published a book. He once said, without exaggerating very much, that all of his manuscripts had been taken from him forcibly by editors and friends. When his poems and plays were printed he considered them "dead on the page", but when he read them to others he could make them live and protect them – "against incomprehension, dilettantism, and the benevolent smile".' These statements are confirmed by the testimony of J. L. Gili who put it on record that 'he was essentially averse to committing himself to print. His literary friends had to use countless stratagems in order to extract a poem from him for one of their periodicals … He preferred reading his poems, because as he said in his revealing essay on the *duende*, "poetry requires as interpreter a living body".'

The most revealing and suggestive lecture translated here is the one mentioned by Gili in the above passage: 'Play and Theory of the Duende', first given in Buenos Aires in 1933. The *duende* is the mysterious indefinable power in a singer or artist without which even the greatest technical prowess is of no avail. The Andalusians say: 'This has much duende.' Manuel Torre, a gypsy singer of whom Lorca wrote that he 'had more culture in his blood than any man I have ever known,' once told another singer, 'You have a voice, you know the styles, but you will never triumph, because you have no duende.' On another occasion Torre explained, after hearing de Falla play his own *Nocturno del Generalife*, 'All that has black sounds has duende.' It was of this chthonian spirit, this breath of Dionysian magic informing and transfiguring both song and singer, that Lorca himself was to write: 'The duende is a power, not a work: it is a struggle, not a thought ... it is not a question of ability, but of true, living style, of blood, of the most ancient culture, of spontaneous creation.' And later he gave gnomic expression to the mystery: 'The true fight is with the duende.'

Ben Belitt described this lyrical lecture as a *divertissement*, and asserted that it represented Lorca's 'case for the mantic in art'. Maurer demurs, rightly in my view: he says, 'Lorca's solution is a more dialectical one. He says that the artist must *fight* the *duende*, hand to hand – i.e., he must fight his own irrationality, his own demonism, and his own death. Inspired art is born of that struggle.'

It is not without interest that the Scots travelling people have an expression the 'conyach', which exactly corresponds to the *duende*. For Belle Stewart, a true singer has the conyach; without it even a splendid voice is powerless. Sheila, Belle's daughter, has more of the conyach than any singer I have ever heard with the solitary exception of the late Jeannie Robertson. The word conyach probably has some connection with the Gaelic *caoineadh*, 'weeping,' (the word from which 'keening' comes); Harry Makem, elder brother of Tommy Makem, the popular folk-singer from County Armagh, told me on one occasion in Keady that real singers 'whinge and cry the song'. Here another remark of Lorca's fits into place: talking of the *cante jondo*, deep song, he says: 'Another very special theme, one repeated in most of these songs, is weeping', and he quotes a verse of a song which is used in his play *Mariana Pineda*:

> If my heart had
> windowpanes of glass
> you would look in and see it
> cry drops of blood.

In *Casida del Llanto* he wrote:

> I have shut my balcony window because I do not want to hear the weeping ... the weeping is an immense dog, the weeping is an immense angel, the weeping is an immense violin, tears muffle the wind, and nothing else is heard but the weeping. (prose translation by J. L. Gili)

After this, the origin of the word duende itself seems quite prosaic – even faintly comic. It is derived from *duen de casa*, lord of the house; this character in Spanish folklore is a household spirit fond of hiding things, breaking dishes, causing noise and making a general nuisance of himself – in fact, a sort of cross between a poltergeist and a brownie.

It is no accident that one finds the equivalent of duende (in its extended meaning of creative-destructive daimon) on the lips and in the hearts of the Scots travelling folk, the 'tinkler-gypsies', because – as Lorca recognised – the Andalusian gypsies are the true heroes and custodians of *cante jondo*, deep song. And here it is vital to note that Lorca made a distinction between *cante jondo* and flamenco:

> The essential difference between deep song and flamenco is that the origin of the former must be sought in the primitive musical systems of India, in the very first manifestation of song, while flamenco, a consequence of deep song, did not acquire its definitive form until the eighteenth century.
>
> Deep song is imbued with the mysterious colour of primordial ages; flamenco is relatively modern song whose emotional interest fades before that of deep song. Local colour versus spiritual colour, that is the profound difference.

It was his meeting with Manuel de Falla when he was a student that marked a real leap forward in his development; de Falla gave him encouragement and guidance when he set about collecting traditional songs and recreating them in his own artistic image. In June 1922 master and pupil organised a festival of *cante jondo* in Granada; the explicit purpose of this was to save deep song from commercial adulteration and extinction. In words comparable to those of Gavin Greig when he wrote of his own collecting work: 'the project is in the first instance a patriotic one', Lorca exclaimed in the public lecture he gave at the festival: 'Gentlemen, the musical soul of our people is in great danger! The artistic treasure of an entire race is passing into oblivion. Each day another leaf falls from the admirable tree of Andalusian lyrics, old men carry off to the the grave priceless treasures of past generations, and a gross, stupid avalanche of cheap music clouds the delicious folk atmosphere of all Spain. We are trying to do something worthy and patriotic, a labour of salvation, friendship, and love.'

Any Scottish reader acquainted even peripherally with the texts of some of our marvellous anonyms, either Scots or Gaelic, will understand immediately what Lorca was getting at when he said, in the same lecture: 'It is wondrous and strange how in just three or four lines the anonymous popular poet can condense all the highest emotional moments in human life. There are songs where the lyric tremor reaches a point inaccessible to any but a few poets:

> The moon has a halo
> [or: the moon is fenced in],
> my love has died.'

Indeed, one can say of our own finest folk-song, in both languages, exactly the words used by Lorca in his peroration:

> Nothing can compare with the tenderness and delicacy of these songs, and I insist again that it is infamy to forget them or to prostitute them with base, sensual intention or gross caricature … The passionate wind of poetry will throw fuel on the dying fire, livening its flames and the people will continue to sing.

It is heart-rending to think of this truly fabulous poetic career being cut short by murder. And yet it would be dishonest not to recognise that in these lectures, as in so much of Lorca's poetry, we find constantly recurring the black and baleful Spanish obsession with death – even with insensate violent death. 'In all ages Spain is moved by the duende, for it is a country of ancient music and dance where the duende squeezes the lemons of dawn – a country of death. A country open to death … Everywhere else, death is an end. Death comes, and they draw the curtains. Not in Spain. In Spain they open them. Many Spaniards live indoors until the day they die and are taken out into the sunlight. A dead man in Spain is more alive as a dead man than any place else in the world. His profile wounds like the edge of a barber's razor … Throughout the country, everything finds its final, metallic value in death.'

And later, in the same lecture: 'The *duende* does not come at all unless he sees that death is possible. The *duende* must know beforehand that he can serenade death's house and rock those branches we all wear, branches that do not have, will never have, any consolation.'

So, in his most famous poem, the lament for the bullfighter Ignacio Sánchez Mejías, Lorca acclaims in his hero

> Tu apetencia de muerte y el gusto de so boca
> (Your appetite for death and the taste of its mouth).

Reading some of this sombre, glorious poetry, one cannot help recalling uneasily the favourite slogan of the Fascist general Millán Astray, *Viva la Muerte!* (Long live Death) – a slogan which he impudently flung at the Basque philosopher Miguel de Unamuno at a ceremony in the University of Salamanca on 12 October 1936 – the day of the Festival of the Race. Unamuno was in the Rector's chair. His brave reply to the crippled fanatic (who had one leg, one arm and one eye) lost him his freedom; it included the following words:

> Just now I heard a necrophilous and senseless cry: 'Long live death.' And I, who have spent my life shaping paradoxes which have aroused the uncomprehending anger of others, I must tell you, as an expert authority, that this outlandish paradox is repellent to me. General Millán Astray is a cripple. Let it be said without any slighting undertone. He is a war invalid. So was Cervantes. Unfortunately there are all too many cripples in Spain just now.

When Unamuno delivered this Augustan rebuke to the vicious prepotent vulgarian – who compounded the insult by shouting out *'Abajo la Inteligencia!'* (Down with the Intellect) – Lorca had already been dead for nearly two months. His body was lying in an unmarked mass grave in Viznar, in the hilly country outside Granada. Ian Gibson, the Dubliner who has meticulously chronicled the phases of English sado-masochism, has also given us the most accurate account that we are likely to get of the last days of Lorca. The poet's grave is near the spring of Ainadamar, the 'Fountain of Tear's' which was praised by Arab poets when Granada was still Moorish:

> Its water moans in sadness like the moaning of one who, enslaved by love, has lost his heart … and the moons of that place, beautiful as Joseph, would make every Moslem abandon his faith for that of love.

Gibson writes:

It seems appropriate that the *Fuente Grande*, praised by the Islamic poets of Granada, should continue, six hundred years later, to bubble up its clear waters only a few hundred yards from the unacknowledged resting place of Granada's greatest poet. For it was to this spot that the killers drove Federico García Lorca and his three fellow prisoners in the dawn of 19 August 1936; here they took the poet who had dared to say that the fall of Moorish Granada to Ferdinand and Isabella, the 'Catholic Monarchs', was a disaster.

Where the bungalows now stand by the roadside there was, in 1936, a grove of ancient olive trees. Here Valdés's men led their victims. When the grave-digger arrived shortly afterwards he found the four bodies lying on the ground. He remembers particularly having noticed that the schoolteacher had only one leg and Federico was wearing a loose tie – 'you know, one of those artist's ties.'

He buried them in a narrow trench, one on top of the other, beside an olive tree.

And why, then, was Federico murdered? All kinds of diverse theories have been floated, the most notorious being that it was 'un règlement de comptes entre invertis' (a settling of accounts between homosexual rivals). It is true, of course, that it was not only because of his birth in Granada that the poet had sympathy with persecuted minorities. In his *Ode to Walt Whitman* Lorca had excoriated *los maricas*, the 'impure' homosexuals who 'give boys drops of soiled death with bitter poison'. A fantastic myth began to take shape, actively promoted by one Jean-Louis Schonberg, whose book *Federico García Lorca: L'Homme – L'Oeuvre* was published in Paris in 1956; this was to the effect that Lorca's death was schemed and plotted by 'impure' homosexuals, who resented the *morgue supérieure*: the haughty contemptuous pride to which Lorca had given open disdainful expression in the *Ode to Walt Whitman*.

These speculations, resting on the flimsiest of evidence, were naturally grist to the mill for Franco's propagandists, because they helped to shift the blame from those responsible for the murder on to other shoulders. There can be no doubt that Lorca was killed because he was a Republican, and had defended the Republic in speech and print. Ian Gibson quotes another section of the same newspaper interview which I mentioned at the beginning of this article:

> I will always be on the side of those who have nothing, of those to whom even the peace of nothingness is denied. We – and by we I mean those of us who are intellectuals, educated in well-off middle-class families – are being called to make sacrifices. Let's accept the challenge.

And Gibson comments: 'Spoken only a few months after the massacre of the Asturian miners, at a time when the average income in Spain was pitifully low, the poet's words left little room for misunderstanding: he was for the poor against the rich, for the workers and peasants in their fight against oppressive and anti-democratic forces which were determined to maintain them in a position of economic subservience.'

Lorca was killed because the leaders of the *Escuadra Negra* in Granada knew perfectly well where his political sympathies lay. They knew that he was 'essentially of the Left' (Schonberg was right in that, at any rate), and that he was opposed to a clerical-Fascist dictatorship. That is why he had to die, together with the flower of the liberal intelligentsia of Granada – doctors, lawyers, professors, writers, journalists, artists, poets. Among the victims was a famous specialist in children's diseases, Rafael García Duarte. Another was Lorca's brother-in-law Dr Manuel Fernandez-Montesinos, Socialist Mayor of Granada, who was shot by the Fascists on 16 August – four days before the poet himself was taken on the road to Viznar.

I conclude with a passage from 'Elegy for Maria Branchard', one of the prose pieces in *Deep Song*. Maria was a painter who had the misfortune to be a hunchback; she made her home in Paris after remarking that 'Spain is the only country where somebody like me is made fun of.' Lorca, friend and ally of the persecuted and rejected, addressed her shade thus:

> All praise you now. Critics praise your work and friends praise your life. I would like to be gallant to you, both as a man and as a poet. I would like to make this modest elegy say something very old, as old as the word 'serenade', though naturally with no irony at all. And without using the language of the man who is sophisticated and 'modern'. In all sincerity. I have been calling you hunchback, but I have said nothing of your pretty eyes, which filled with tears as a thermometer pulses full of mercury. Nor have I mentioned your hands, the hands of a maestro. And I want to speak of your wonderful long hair. I want to praise it. You had a head of hair so beautiful and so generous that it wanted to cover your body as the palm tree covered the Child you loved on His flight into Egypt. You were a hunchback. But men understand little. I want to tell you, Maria Blanchard, as a friend of your shade: you had the most beautiful head of hair there has ever been in Spain.

Cencrastus, no. 26, Summer 1987.

The Laverock i' The Caller Lift

Ae weet forenicht i' the yow trummle
I saw yon antrin thing,
A watergaw wi' its chitterin' licht
Ayont the on-ding;
An' I thocht o' the last wild look ye gied
Afore ye deed!

There was nan reek i' the laverock's hoose
That nicht – an' nane i' mine;
But I hae thocht o' that foolish licht
Ever sin' syne;
An' I think that mebbe at last I ken
What your look meant then.

It was not long after I'd discovered, as a Dulwich College schoolboy, that a great Scottish poet – quite possibly, our greatest ever – was alive and writing in my native land, that I succeeded in running a copy of *Sangschaw* to earth in Foyle's bookshop in the Charing Cross Road, and was once more hit between the eyes by glorious immortal poetry.

Reading 'The Watergaw', all sorts of childhood memories invaded my mind, and when I discussed the poem with A S MacPherson, one of the Dulwich masters familiar with a fair amount of MacDiarmid's work – particularly the early poems – I heard that the lines

An' I thocht o' the last wild look ye gied
Afore ye deed!

were thought to refer to the death of the poet's own father. Macpherson had a copy of the 1931 number of *The Modern Scot* – the magazine founded by James H Whyte in St Andrews the year before – and showed me the lines in the poem 'Kinsfolk':

Afore he dee'd he turned and gied a lang
Last look at pictures o' my brither and me
Hung on the wa' aside the bed, I've heard
My mither say ...

(This seemed to me pretty conclusive proof, but it is only fair to add that in a letter to

Edwin Morgan dated 15 January 1975 MacDiarmid made the following positive
assertion: 'I must tell you that "The Watergaw" was not written about my dying father
– or the dying of any other person – and suffers I think because it can be read in that
way' (Alan Bold *The Letters of Hugh MacDiarmid*, p. 677).

As with 'The Bonnie Broukit Bairn', I found that I had memorised 'The Watergaw'
as soon as I'd read it, and the lines which to this day always induce a *frisson* when I
speak them are:

> There was nae reek i' the laverock's hoose
> That nicht – an' nane i' mine.

The year – a golden year in retrospect – that I 'discovered' MacDiarmid was 1936, but
it was not till much later that I became acquainted with the various statements he had
made about his first tentative steps in the writing of Scots, and about the sources of his
early poems. In 1922 – when Hugh MacDiarmid was only one of a quiverful of
pseudonyms – Chris had stated in the columns of the *Dunfermline Press* that 'The
Watergaw' had been constructed (by 'a friend') using words found in Sir James
Wilson's *Lowland Scotch as spoken in the Lower Strathearn District of Perthshire*, a
book published by Oxford University Press in 1915. Wilson had invented for himself
a rather ungainly-looking phonetic system to convey the local pronunciation of the
words and phrases in his book, and the saying in the section Proverbs and Sayings used
by Chris's 'friend' in his 'construction' reads as follows:

> Dhur'z nay reek ee laivruk's hoos dhe nikht

which Wilson translates as 'There's no smoke in the lark's house tonight' (said when
the night is cold and stormy).

When questioned about the meaning of the lines about the Laverock in 'The
Watergaw', MacDiarmid at least twice in letters echoed Wilson's gloss. For example,
in a letter from Montrose to Professor Herbert Grierson, written on 15 May 1925,
(Bold, *Letters*, p. 309) he wrote: 'The first line is an old Perthshire saying meaning
simply: "It was a dark and stormy night", so the two lines really mean: "A dark and
stormy night succeeded that wet forenight, and my heart was similarly dark and
stormy".'

Nine years later, on 20 July 1934, he supplied an extended explication in a letter to
the anthologist Maurice Wollman:

> There was nae reek i' the laverock's hoose
> That nicht – and nane i' mine.

Literally translated, this runs:

> There was no smoke coming from the lark's nest that night –
> and none from mine

which of course makes no sort of sense in English. Actually the first line is a metaphor
which means: It was a dark and stormy night.

'But the trouble with simply giving the line that gloss is that it does not explain the
actual words of the original, and, also, makes nonsense of the second line:

> It was a dark and stormy night
> That night – and none in mine.

'The end of that is, of course, exactly contrary to what I am really saying, viz.

> It was a dark and stormy night
> That night – and my heart was dark and stormy too.

'In view of these difficulties, perhaps the best gloss would be:

> The first line reads 'There was no smoke coming from the lark's nest that night',
> a proverbial figure of speech meaning that it was a dark and stormy night, while
> the second line must then be read as meaning 'and my heart was dark and stormy
> too'.

This is a good example of the virtual untranslateability into English of many highly-concentrated Scots phrases.'

Oddly enough, when I first read 'The Watergaw' as a schoolboy, these famous and much quoted lines about the laverock awoke a quite different echo in my head – an echo not of Lowland Scots but of Gaelic, and having nothing to do with a dark and stormy night. My grandmother had in her library a volume entitled *A Collection of Gaelic Proverbs and Familiar Phrases*, based on Macintosh's Collection and edited by Alexander Nicolson MA, LLD, Advocate. This notable work, usually referred to as 'Sheriff Nicolson's Collection', was published in 1881, and my grannie's copy had been given her, soon after publication, by the local 'Piskie' minister. As stated on the title-page, Sheriff Nicolson's collection was based on an earlier one made by the Revd Donald Macintosh (1743–1808), a native of Killiecrankie (and therefore a speaker of Perthshire Gaelic), who described himself in his will as 'a priest of the old Scots Episcopal Church, and last of the nonjurant clergy in Scotland'. The collection of this staunch old Jacobite was published in Edinburgh in 1785, and Nicolson paid tribute to it, in the preface to his own book, as 'a valuable contribution to Celtic Literature'.

Towards the end of this preface, Sheriff Nicolson provided a list of poetical sayings, translated into English, and he described them thus: 'Among purely poetical and pretty sayings the Gaelic ones take a high place. Here are a few examples:

> Blue are the hills that are far from us.
> Night is a good herdsman; she brings all creatures home. The three prettiest
> dead, a child, a salmon and a black cock. The sea likes to be visited. Thy heart's
> desire to thy pulse! There is no smoke in the lark's house.

It was doubtless this list that had stuck in my memory.

*   *   *

It was during my final year at Cambridge (1945–46), that I chanced on a copy of Sheriff Nicolson's book; this was in the Moat House, the home of a wonderful couple, Hugh and Jessie Stuart. Hugh, an authority on Pascal, was a lecturer in the French department; Jessie had been a disciple of the 'Grecian Anthropologist' Jane Ellen Harrison, the author of *Themis and Prolegomena to the Study of Greek Religion*, and their circle in the 1920s and '30s had included Prince D S Mirsky, to whom Hugh

MacDiarmid dedicated the *First Hymn to Lenin*. When I renewed acquaintance with them after World War II their house had become a sort of ceilidh house for musically-minded Scottish students, because Hugh Stuart – who came of an old Banffshire Jacobite family – possessed a priceless 18th-century manuscript book of Highland fiddle tunes, and his son Ludovick was a very talented performer on the instrument.

Thumbing through Nicolson's collection, I tried to find the Gaelic original of the saying about the lark's house, and fairly soon located it:

> *Cha 'n 'eil deathach 'an tigh na h-uiseige.* –
> There is no smoke in the lark's house.

Nicolson's comment I felt was singularly felicitous and well-expressed: 'The bird of most aspiring and happy song has untainted air in its lowly home.'

So here, I thought, must be the source of 'nae reek i' the laverock's hoose.' At that time I had never clapped eyes on Sir James Wilson's *Lowland Scotch*, and it was not until 1962, when the trustees of Malcolm Macfarlane presented a copy to the library of the School of Scottish Studies, that I hunted up the saying to which MacDiarmid had himself drawn attention, and mulled over Wilson's explanation: 'said when the night is cold and stormy'.

Frankly, I could make neither head nor tail of this. Why on earth should 'no smoke in the lark's house' betoken a 'cold and stormy' night? Sheriff Nicolson's note seemed to make much more sense. I was predisposed to suspect that the Scots saying was an echo of the Gaelic one – and was interested to note that Wilson had devoted a whole paragraph of his introduction to a discussion of the Highland presence in Strathearn:

> The Gaelic surnames which are common in Strathearn show that the ancestors of many of the inhabitants came from across the Highland line; and what happens now in our own experience has no doubt been going on for centuries. A Highlander, whose native tongue is Gaelic, and therefore quite unintelligible to his Scotch-speaking neighbours, comes down from his ancestral home north of the Grampians, and settles down in some Lowland village, perhaps marrying a Lowland wife. He gradually picks up the dialect of the people among whom he lives, but never entirely forgets the Gaelic he spoke when he was a boy, and speaks Scotch with a Gaelic accent and some Gaelic words and idioms (Wilson, *Lowland Scotch*, p. 11).

I was tempted to conjecture that the Scots version of a saying found also in Gaelic was, in this case, an example, in linguistic form, of just such an ethnic migration. But what about the 'cold and stormy' night (or 'dark and stormy', as MacDiarmid amended Wilson's note). The more I thought about it, the more it seemed to me likely that Wilson had scribbled down the saying, without understanding its full significance, and coming to edit the book, had decided to use his imagination. Either that, or one of his informants had parroted the saying without comprehending it, and thus had led Wilson up the garden path.

Needless to say, nothing of such speculation affects the powerful strong poetry of 'The Watergaw'. If, in fact, the Wilson gloss rested on a misapprehension, it would not be the first time that brilliant poetry had sprung from some sort of error or miscalculation.

By a curious synchronic coincidence, this Gaelic saying was quoted by Mary Beith in her column 'Porridge and Prunes' in *The Scotsman* (28 May 1994), at the exact time I was assembling material for the present article. Her remarks were occasioned by news reports of a skylark's song being heard 'at heaven's gate' while John Smith was being laid to rest among Scottish Kings at Reilig Odhrain on the Island of Iona ... After mentioning this, Mary added, as if in an aside: 'What is the meaning of the saying 'Cha'n eil deathach an tigh na h-uiseige'? – 'There is no smoke in the lark's house'?

She did not have to wait long for an answer. A few days later Chrissie Bannerman, writing from the Old Manse, Balmaha, gave virtually the same explanation as Sheriff Nicolson had, a hundred years previously: '*Deahach* means smoke, but it is smoke that does not go up the chimney, and instead leaks unpleasantly inside the house. The lark of soaring song has untainted air in its nest.'

This, I venture to suggest, graphically supplies the background to the Gaelic *seanfhacal* which Nicolson rightly included in his list of poetical sayings. It conjures up the picture of a 'black house', with the fire in the centre of the floor, and a hole above to let the smoke escape – an arrangement which naturally meant that smoke, as often as not, would linger inside the building, occasionally to the considerable discomfort of the occupants.

I have sometimes wondered whether an Irish Gaelic analogue of this saying might not have been one influence on Sir Samuel Ferguson's beautiful song *The Lark in the Clear Air*. This was one of my mother's favourite songs; she learned it from an officer in the Irish Guards whom she met when she was nursing wounded servicemen in Guy's Hospital in London after the armistice of 1918. (She had been doing similar work in France during the War). This officer I only know of as Michael – 'Michael had a lovely voice', she used to say, and she was well and truly entitled to express an opinion on the subject, because – although I say it as shouldn't – she had an outstandingly beautiful voice herself.

> Dear thoughts are in my mind
> And my soul soars enchanted
> As I hear the sweet lark sing
> In the clear air of day
> For a tender beaming smile
> To my hope has been granted,
> And tomorrow she shall hear
> All my fond heart would say.
>
> I shall tell her all my love
> All my soul's adoration
> And I think she will hear me
> And will not say me nay.
> It is this which gives my soul
> All its joyous elation,
> As I hear the sweet lark sing
> In the clear air of the day.

I never met Michael, who died in the early 1920s, but I did meet his sister Shelagh, when with my mother I paid my first visit to Ireland in 1929, at the age of nine. Shelagh was an amazing woman who looked as if she might have stepped straight out of a Somerville and Ross 'Irish RM' story. I still have a photo of her she gave my mother; it shows her striking 'an antic pose' – no doubt after a glass or two of Beaujolais (her favourite tipple). I'm not sure whose the plus-foured knee is she's using as a footstool – maybe Flurry Knox's!

Shelagh, to my recollection, was by no means a bad singer too, but her party pieces were always familiar Percy French songs like 'Father O'Flynn':

> O Father O'Flynn ye've a wonderful way with you,
> All the young childer are wishful to play with you –
> All the ould sinners are wishful to pray with you –
> Here's a health to ye. Father avic ...
> Once the bishop looked grave at your jest
> Till this remark set him off with the rest –
> 'Why lave gaity all to the laity –
> Cannot the clergy be Irishmen too?'

It may seem incongruous, but my most vivid memory of that Church of Ireland household – in which the liveliest current topic of conversation was the inquity of disbanding famous Irish regiments like the Royal Munsters and the Connaught Rangers, and whose heroes were not the men of 1916 but

> the mad Mulvaneys of the Line,
> – All that delirium of the brave –

is of my mother and Shelagh singing 'The Wearing of the Green' as a sort of duet. 'The most distressful country' ... they both sang it with genuine feeling; and indeed almost tearful pathos.

Other memories of that first Irish trip: a visit to the Dublin Zoo, and feeling sorry for the white rhinoceroses, because they seemed to spend hours standing on the one spot, and looking glum; and learning to ride a pony in the Phoenix Park – the thrill of my first trot, and how to rise in the saddle.

Oh, that Dublin Zoo ... what a wonder for a nine-year-old. How many people know that for over half a century – as a proud keeper informed Shelagh, my mother and me – that palatial zoo exported lion clubs to dozens of zoos around the world? There are Dublin lions – or their descendants – of impeccable lineage, in zoos as far afield as Adelaide and Toronto. This far-famed Dublin lion-stud was still producing pedigree lions until 1957 – so the curator, Mr Ron Willis informed me on the phone on 12 October 1994 – but now they are specialising in various threatened species like snow leopards. (On 24 September 1994 a male snow-leopard cub called Toibin was exported to the zoo at Cologne!)

And, maybe as an affectionate echo of achievements in the lion-stud of old – they are also breeding tiny golden lions, aka Tamarins.

*   *   *

Years later, when I was having a jar with Stephen and Kathleen Behan – Brendan and Dominic's parents – in their council house in Kildare Rd, Crumlin, I told them about

that first visit to the zoo, and Stephen launched without delay into one of his favourites
– 'The Zoological Gardens',

> Thunder and lightnin' it's no lark
> When Dublin city is in the dark.
> Would yeh care to go to the Phoenix Park
> And view the Zoological Gardens?
>
> I went up there on me honeymoon
> We saw the lions, and the ould baboon,
> And we strayed for a while neath the silv'ry moon
> Around the Zoological Gardens
> (chorus: Thunder and lightnin' etc)
>
> She says to me, me dear friend Jack
> Sure I'd like a ride on the elephant's back.
> If yeh don't go outa that, I'll give you such a smack
> Around the Zoological Gardens.
>
> But Jack, she says, to give you yer due
> There's nothin' jumps around as well as you.
> No, not even the big Australian Kangaroo
> Around the Zoological Gardens.
>
> Oh Lord, says I, now don't be daft
> She says it's true, and yer not to laugh.
> But yer lovely and long like the spotted giraffe
> Up in the Zoological Gardens.
>
> We left by the gate at Castleknock.
> She says, me dear, sure we'll court on the lock.
> Then I knew she was one of the rare oul' stock
> Outside the Zoological Gardens.

I showed the words of this song recently to two Irish friends, after telling them I was
writing about laverocks, and one pointed out, 'There's a lark in the first line of it.' To
which the other contrapuntally replied, 'Once you start, you can't keep them out of it.'

The distinguished poet and antiquary Sir Samuel Ferguson (1810–86), who wrote
'The Lark in the Clear Air', was a Belfast man; his family was of Scottish origin. As
Deputy Keeper of the Public Records of Ireland, he brought system and order into the
public archives, and was knighted for these services in 1878; His volume *Lays of the
Western Gael* was not published till 1865, when he was fifty-five, but he had already
inspired, and been inspired by, an important generation of Irish writers: above all,
Thomas Davis, the principal bard of Young Ireland.

According to R F Foster, Ferguson was 'a bridge between the flowering of national
studies in the 1830s, and the literary renaissance of the 1890s'.

His best known song was 'The Lark in the Clear Air', and it travelled with amazing
speed to every corner of Ireland.

Furthermore, it crossed the Moyle, and entered the repertoires of dozens of singers in Argyll, and beyond. Willie Mitchell of Campbeltown and his talented family delighted in it (Henderson, *Alias MacAlias*, pp 181–9), and it has been heard over the years at many of the folk festivals organised by the TMSA – the Traditional Music and Song Association of Scotland. However, it never suffered the sort of changes, textual and musical, that a folksong invariably does: it is always rendered exactly as Ferguson wrote it. In that sense, it should be called – to borrow Francis Collinson's terminology – a 'national' rather than a 'traditional' song: the 'nation' being in this case the whole far-flung legion of the 'sea-divided Gael'.

It will be obvious, from the above, that Ferguson had an enviable opportunity to become master of the entire archive, then existing, printed and manuscript, of Irish folk tradition, and if – as I suspect – an analogue of the Scots Gaelic saying recorded by Sheriff Nicolson was circulating in the mid-19th century in the smoky cabins of Connemara and/or the beehive huts of Achill Island, it is by no means impossible that Ferguson might have run across evidence of it.

Be that as it may, his marvellous song communicates with grace and eloquence, and with the utmost economy, the whole magical ambience of the West of Ireland. And is it not an intriguing thought that a Gaelic *sean-fhacal*, passed on by word of mouth, probably for centuries, on both sides of the *Struth na Maoile* (alias the North Channel), might possibly be the ultimate progenitor not only of 'The Lark in the Clear Air' but also – *mirabile dictu* – of 'The Watergaw'.

Cencrastus, 50, 1994

That Dolphin Torn, That Gong-Tormented Face
Dylan in Bloomsbury

In July 1940, expecting almost any day to be called up, I acceped an invitation from Paul Potts, self styled 'Canadian hick poet', to spend a week or two in London. Paul, whom I had met when he came to Cambridge three months earlier to lecture on Mayakovsky for CUSC (the University Socialist Club – though at that time the S would more appropriately – or honestly – have stood for Stalinist), had been lent a two-roomed flat in Great Ormond Street – one up, one down – by an Irish painter called Eric O'Dea; he had it for the summer, and I was one of several Socialist/Stalinist students he had invited to doss down in it, whenever the occasion offered.

During his Mayakovsky lecture, he had outraged some of the elect by declaring that – politics apart – Roy Campbell was a bloody good poet; and this I was heartened to hear, because shortly before in that same CUSC clubroom I had said much the same thing. (The following scene was rather like a Bateman cartoon – 'character says Adolf Hitler is not a bad chap'). All the well-heeled bourgeois CPers had tried to chew my balls off with their toothless gums, and Comrade 'Tickle arse More' (Nicholas Moore) being at that time redder than the deepest Reds, had informed the company that I was an incipient Fascist. Needless to say I'd given him a reply in kind, and relations between us were never quite the same again.

(All the same, I can truthfully say – from the vantage point of half a century later – that Nicholas was also a bloody good poet – in spite of rather bad-tempered hostile cracks by our contemporary John Heath Stubbs: see his recently published autobiography *Hindsight*.)

Well, on May Day two bus-loads of CUSCers went down to London to show the Red Flag in Hyde Park; after arrival there I went in search of Paul Potts, and I found him inside the park, near Speakers' Corner, trying to flog his *Poet's Testament* (alias *Lenin is our Mate*) to the newly arrived demonstrators. I offered to take a few to sell, and had disposed of about a couple when Paul and I were both arrested by the polis: it was illegal – at that time – to sell such literature as poetry broadsheets 'within the gates'. The coppers kept us inside for about three-quarters of an hour, and then dismissed us with a warning – after which we proceeded to give *Poet's Testaments* away (gifts were legal) and then retired to a pub in Soho.

Paul knew most of the inmates, and one of them asked, 'Who's this bloke?' (meaning me). 'Him,' said Paul, 'That's Hamish – he's one of the wandering kings of Scotland.'

Two months later, I was back in London, and soon found myself installed (thanks to Paul) in Eric O'Dea's chaotic studio (the 'one down' room of the two-roomed flat in Great Ormond Street); Paul's own conglomeration of chaos was housed immediately overhead. Masses of paintings were stacked all round the studio, which contained two permanently unmade beds. One of these paintings was a rather 'criminal type' impression of Paul Potts himself; another was a portrait of a rather insipidly good-looking young bloke, which had been commissioned by Stephen Spender. The only other furniture was a dilapidated chair. There was also a miscellaneous collection of 78 gramophone records, many broken; and there was also as heterogeneous an assortment of books I had – up to that date – ever seen; it reminded me of the time when – a year or two before – I had found, on a book stall on the Rive Gauche, a copy of Cobbett's *Rural Rides* cheek by jowl with a volume entitled *Le Vice chez les Femmes*.

July 1940 – these were the antediluvian pre-Blitz days (soon to be dramatically interrupted) when every London house was standing straight as a Grenadier on parade, and Paul could say, scratching his balls contentedly, that London was, and would be, the safest place in the whole country. While Paul lay ruminating in bed in the middle of the morning, I would go round to the shops to fetch in a sliced brown loaf for our breakfast, and if any of the neighbouring houses were already whited for the axe, I have to admit I never noticed it.

Living in adjacent houses were about 40 cheerful and friendly young homosexuals, who – together with the omnipresent big-bosomed Cockney matrons, who were shortly to be making endless pots of tea for the capital's firefighters – seemed to me just about the most good-natured people in the whole world. In Soho the loose-limbed lope of the youngish Quentin Crisp was a familiar sight (his flowing gaudy garb, then considered daring and outrageous, would in two decades have become the hippy norm). Is it only sentimental hindsight which makes me think of pre-Blitz Bloomsbury and Soho as an idyllic urban Aracady? I remember scribbling in a notebook, one lazy afternoon – Jours du York Minster – Nuits de Soho Square.

(Long after, reading Paddy Kavanagh's scattering of 'London' poems, I could sense the workings of a similar attraction; in one of these poems, he even mentions Paul:

> In these romantic lots
> I run into Paul Ports
> Noticing the pull of roots.
> I have taken roots of love
> And will find it pain to move.
>
> Betjeman, you've missed much of
> The secret of London while
> Old churches you beguile
> I'll show you a holier isle –
> The length of Gibson Square
> Caught in November's stare
> That would set you to prayer)

One evening Paul had gone out to the pub and I hadn't, because I had started rereading *The Playboy of the Western World*, and I wanted to read it to the end. I was sitting in the studio on one of the permanently unmade beds, and I had just got to the concluding scene, when Christy says: 'You'll have a gallus jaunt I'm thinkin', coachin' out through limbo wid me father's ghost' – and was wondering how that palpable Scots gallus had found its way into the dialect of Co. Mayo – when I heard a queer sort of a. scrabbling shindig going on below, and then Paul's voice shouting, 'Hey, turn on the light, will you.' I did so, and the next moment there was a heavy pounding on the staircase, and a small tubby man shot like a cannonball into the room. He stood just inside the studio, heaving and quivering, and I gave him the once over; he was a short-arsed paunchy fleshy bloke, with a big blob of a nose, heavy pouches under his watery eyes, and a slobbery red wash of mouth – not, at first sight, an over-prepossessing character. He was dressed in a blue tweed suit, the trousers secured with a stout thick belt like a cummerbund; round his neck was a red bow tie with white spots on it, and perched on his head was a jaunty little pork-pie or billycock hat. To. say that he was fou – or that he had drink taken – or that he was completely fluthered – would be a laughable understatement.

The next moment Paul appeared in the doorway, and just as I was wondering what in the name of holy mackerel he had brought home tonight, he said, in his casual way: 'Meet Dylan. He's as pissed as arse-holes.'

Dylan Thomas extended a soft flabby hand, which I shook.

Paul whispered to me that he had found Dylan sitting disconsolate and alone in the Café Royal – the waiter, maintaining heartlessly that he was drunk, had refused to serve him another drink; however, Paul had ordered a drink and given it to Dylan. Finally Paul had commandeered a taxi and brought him home, Dylan sleeping like a child in his lap all the way.

Meanwhile Dylan had staggered to the chair – the one and only – and collapsed into it. For a time he was silent; then he gave a deep sigh, and murmured: 'Jesus Christ. Christ Jesus. Jesus Christ.' His eye was glazed, and fixed in a look almost frightening. I wondered for a depressed moment what we would do if he died on our hands.

Shortly, however, he began to sit up and take notice. His eyes rolled round the studio, first aimlessly, and then with a sort of owlish approval. They came to rest on me.

'Nishe place,' he said, 'Yours?'

'No,' I said. 'I'm a visitor here, same as you.'

'O.' A grunt.

Then Paul spoke up. 'Say, Dylan, you'll sleep here, won't you.'

No reply.

'Sorry we haven't got a woman to give you.'

For the first time he smiled. 'Doesn't matter. I've had too much of that.'

'We've got no pyjamas for you either.'

'Good God,' said Dylan, 'I never wear them. Completely useless – unnecessary.'

Paul indicated the unmade bed which wasn't occupied. Dylan heaved himself out of the chair, tore off his clothes at high speed, and then plunged naked like a porpoise into bed and closed his eyes.

Paul gazed down at him affectionately, and then we both moved quietly away from the bed, imagining in our innocence that we had seen the last of Dylan for the night.

In this studio there were three windows, two overlooking Great Ormond Street, and the third – just above the bed Dylan was in – overlooking a jagged waste of gardens, sheds, fences, rubbish dumps and outhouses – and beyond, the hencoop roofs of London. Pinned in front of each of these windows there was naturally – this being wartime of a sort – a not exceedingly efficient blackout. It was to the third of these windows that our eyes suddenly turned, for Dylan had slung back the bedclothes, risen as dramatically as Finnegan at his wake, and hoisted his paunchy pink bulk on to the sill. His little fat legs clambered with astonishing agility from the bed to the window ledge; then the blackout was pulled aside, and light poured out into back street London. There stood Dylan, framed in the window, as naked as a Veronese Ganymede.

Paul gazed at him in transfigured horror as he stood poised over a 40 or 50 foot drop, his little pink bottom quivering. He started swaying slowly, backwards and forwards; slowly and rhythmically backwards and forwards; then with a little lurch he went forward for the last time, and disappeared from view. The blackout flapped back into position, and Paul collapsed into the chair, clapping his hands to his brow.

'O God,' he said, 'They'll say I killed Dylan because I was jealous of his poetry. O God, I'm in for it now.'

I had a momentary mental vision of a short-hearsed funeral procession disappearing into some remote Welsh boneyard, but – proving myself practical for at least once in my life – I rushed forward and hauled the blackout aside once more – disclosing Dylan's little fat rump still quivering gently in the night breeze. And at that moment there was the sound as of a mountain cataract in spate, or of the rains descending as the monsoon breaks. Dylan was pissing into the night.

He reappeared, clambered down from the window, and got back into bed, explaining: 'There's a balcony.' Then he went to sleep.

It was true. Though neither Paul nor I had noticed it there was a narrow little balcony outside the window, looking dangerously fragile and rickety – you would hardly have trusted a flowerpot on it. However, but for that balcony, the 'Ballad of the Long legged Bait' or, indeed, 'Fern Hill' – might never have been written. On Paul's face was a look of holy relief.

When I woke in the morning Dylan was awake already. He had got up and draped his nakedness with a blue blanket, and I watched him from my own bed, strolling round the studio in this toga-like garb, and looking like a Caesar of the decadence. I was too tired to start talking, so I dozed off again; when I awoke for the second time, he had gone upstairs still in his blanket, to say hello to Paul.

About an hour later when I had got up, washed and dressed, I went upstairs and found Dylan sitting on Paul's bed. He was describing the wedding of another Welsh literary figure – I think Keidrych Rhys – and making scurrilous remarks about things in general.

'Sorry about last night,' he said to me. 'It was my first night on the drink for eight weeks. Just up from the country – I'm a respectable married man now.'

There was a pause in the conversation.

I was intrigued to know what he thought of MacDiarmid and his 'pan Celtic' politics, and I asked him if he felt in tune with the sort of left-nationalist position MacDiarmid stood for. I could see immediately from his expression that he did not find the subject of much interest.

'I contributed stuff to the *Voice of Scotland*,' he said, 'but I'm not in sympathy with this nationalism of MacDiarmid's.'

'But,' I persisted, 'Surely you yourself owe quite a lot to the Welsh movement – and the Welsh literary tradition?'

'Nothing whatsoever. I don't speak Welsh. I have nothing in common with them. I like MacDiarmid though, and a lot of his stuff.'

I mentioned the so called New Apocalypse to see what his reaction would be.

'Beneath contempt' was Dylan's reaction. 'They got a story and a poem out of me by false pretences – haven't even paid me for them yet. But I have no intention of getting myself labelled as Apocalyptic – I don't want to hear people saying – Dylan Thomas – O he's a member of the Apocalyptic School.'

I made bold to quote a squib of my own, beginning

> Some apoplectic apocalyptics
> Were climbing a eucalyptus tree ...

and was rewarded with another smile from Dylan.

'And what do you think of the work of –' I mentioned a Cambridge acquaintance. (This was probably Nicholas Moore [1923])

'Negligible. Apart from borrowing from me or borrowing from other people, nothing. I like the things he's got from me of course, but that's no credit to him.'

Upstairs, dressing, he came across some photos of Stephen Spender, and shied back as if he had come on a pool of liquid Lewisite.

'Ugh. Doesn't he look awful' – and he broke into a sort of pseudo 'pansy' whine: 'O glorious boy, standing by the power house ...'

Finding the paintings, he looked through them, making a few comments. To one (which I thought the best), which was inspired by the Sadlers Wells Ballet, he gave limited praise; then he found the handsoe *Kouros*, commissioned by Spender, and said: 'Yes, of course, you would expect them to have no taste at all. Or rather, homosexual taste, which is no taste at all.'

This remark seemed to me to indicate a certain degree of homophobia – a word, incidentally, which didn't exist at that time – and I asked aggressively: 'What about Michelangelo?'

'Bugger Michelangelo,' said Dylan.

There was a pause for reflection – for both of us, I think – and then he declared, with some emphasis: 'Auden and Spender – their poetry's played out – played out completely.'

By this time he was dressed, and, sitting on the bed he had risen from during the night, he looked at me, for the first time, with what I felt was a certain interest.

'Are you a Pacifist?' he asked.

'No,' I said. 'I expect to be called up any day now. What about you?'

'O,' said Dylan, 'I'm one of the lucky sods. I'm off. I've got it here.' And he pointed with a sweeping vague gesture towards his diaphragm.

'Are you ready?' called Paul from upstairs. 'I'm hungry.'

Down he came, and we sallied out to pick up our breakfast; Dylan, looking quite natty in his pork-pie hat, accompanied us. He went into a telephone box to phone up a friend, and that was the last I saw of him – till after the war.

Of his *obiter dicta*, during this memorable first encounter, I only recall one other – he said of somebody, or something, 'It comes straight out of the early Pound.' I can't recollect now who or what it was that came straight out of the early Pound, but in comparison with most of his other literary judgements – it seemed to me a fairly mild indictment.

[Written on a troopship, 1941; completed and revised, Edinburgh 1993]

Cencrastus, 47, 1994.

Byspale in Benghazi

On 13 August 1942 Monty arrived in the desert. He wasn't supposed to take over command of the 8th Army until the 15th, but decided to jump the gun, and assumed command as from 2 p.m. that afternoon. He sent a telegram to GHQ Cairo, announcing his decision, and, as he says in his *Memoirs*, 'This was disobedience, but there was no come-back. I then cancelled all previous orders about withdrawal.'

Almost immediately stories began to circulate about the 'new broom'. I was at that time attached, as an IO, to the HQ of the 1st South African Division, and anecdotes filtered down to us from HQ 8th Army – no doubt picking up accretions on the way. Here is one (retailed to Dan Pienaar, our Div. General, by Brigadier Crystal); it purports to be a gobbet of Monty's table talk.

'I am the General. Nothing that Rommel can do can embarrass me. The other generals who were here before me have failed, because they weren't the right kind of general. I am the chap.'

This histrionic self-confident arrogance alienated some of the staff officers at GHQ, but it worked like magic among the – at that time – somewhat dejected and disillusioned swaddies in the desert. Here is another anecdote which circulated: before giving a pep talk to officers of 13 Corps HQ, Monty was reputed to have said: 'I am going to speak for half an hour. During this time, there will be no smoking or coughing. Then there will be a ten-minute interval, during which there will be smoking *and* coughing.'

Not long before Alamein – again, according to Brigadier Crystal – he informed officers of the 7th Armoured Division (the original 'Desert Rats'): 'I have got a good job waiting for me at home, so I am not going to be long over this one.'

These anecdotes have not been put on record before – as far as I know – but the following excerpt from his speech to 8th Army officers on the evening of 13 August 1942 *has* been; however, it bears repeating: 'I believe that one of the first duties of a commander is to create what I call atmosphere. I do not like the general atmosphere I find here – it is an atmosphere of doubt. All that must cease at once. Here we will stand and fight. There will be no further withdrawal. I have ordered that all plans and instructions dealing with further withdrawal are to be burnt – and at once. We will stand and fight here. If we can't stay here alive, then let us stay here dead.'

When he came to write his *Memoirs* (published by Collins, 1958), Monty admitted that when he uttered these words he was remembering Thermopylae, and the famous poem by Simonides which was Englished by William Lisle Bowles:

Go tell the Spartans, thou that passest by,
That here, obedient to their laws, we lie.

It was his way of telling the 8th Army: 'We will do the same, if need be.'

I had seen a little of fascism in action in Germany before the War, but I had naturally no idea of the extent of the horrors then being enacted in Nazi-occupied Europe. If I had known that, every single day of the battle we were about to fight, the Germans would be massacring thousands of innocent people in the extermination camps of the East, I would no doubt have felt, even more strongly, that we just had to win the forthcoming battle, come what may.

After Rommel's last stab at reaching the Delta was fought off (31 August 1942) by the tanks and guns dug in on the height of Alum Halfa – a model defensive battle, as Monty was later to describe it – the build-up continued for our offensive Battle of Alamein; this started at X-20 (20 minutes to 10) on the night of October 23rd. Our artillery opened up – 480 guns on the 30 Corps front of twelve kilometres, between the Ruweisat Ridge and the sea. There was approximately one gun to every 17.5 yards of ground; 250,000 rounds were fired.

I have tried to give some idea of what I felt at that moment in the Interlude (Opening of an Offensive) between the two halves of *Elegies for the Dead in Cyrenaica*, but nothing could possibly recapture the appalling din of that artillery barrage, which made the earth throb and shudder in what seemed a veritable 'apocalypse now' – or indeed a 'heart of darkness'. 'It (the barrage) stunned even our own troops,' wrote Major H Gillan, of the 9th Australian Division, 'and the ground vibrated under our feet like the skin of a kettle-drum.'

Indeed, the jaw-breaking battering of the guns seemed to me to be landing blow after blow on one of my molars, for by ten o'clock I had a raging toothache – which admittedly took my mind off everything else that was happening.

Needless to say, I had to thole it for days on end – until on the 27th I got leave to commandeer a truck and a driver, and make for the 'field dentist' four or five miles back from the line.

The field dentist's little *royaume* was a sight that, as the saying goes, would have daunted the stoutest heart. Sacking wound round four poles made it look like the dead spit of a field latrine. Inside, when I arrived, the field dentist was operating what looked like a Victorian knife-grinder's appliance, churning away with his right foot while he drilled a hole in a victim's tooth – the victim looking like a damned soul, straight out of Hieronymus Bosch. Beside him, his assistant was mixing a filling on a tin plate, while desert sand flew all over the place – no doubt adding some local colour to the filling. I remember thinking that this was one of the horrors of war that wouldn't find its way on to the newsreels.

Next please! I went in, and sat on a rickety 'field chair'. As always happens, my toothache had been banished completely by the sight described above – but there was nothing for it but to dree my weird. 'What's wrong, then?' I indicated a molar on the right-hand bottom tier of my jaw, and requested him to extract it.

After a brief inspection, the field dentist assured me that he could save it. This was the last thing I had wanted to hear, and I practically beseeched him to lug it out. But no – it would be a shame, it was eminently savable – and out of the corner of my eye I could

see his right foot moving towards the knife-grinder's appliance. Bloody Hell – but the
field dentist was OC of his own little show, and he had one more pip on his shoulder
than I had. Clearly, there was no alternative but to sit back, and think of Scotland.

However, he was as good as his word; he well and truly saved that molar, and I
retained it in my mouth until 1957, when I was up north recording the Highland
Stewarts. I asked the Inverness dentist to give it me as a souvenir, which he did – and I
still have it somewhere, no doubt with a few grains of desert sand, to authenticate it.

By November 4th the Axis forces were defeated; the Germans stole the Italians'
transport and beat it westwards. It was at 8 a.m. on that day I suffered my one war
wound (of sorts). The battle was over; we were out in the open desert, when suddenly
out of the blue a Stuka appeared, and strafed us – dive-bombed and machine-gunned –
and everyone threw himself forcefully on to the hard uneven stony desert. I realised, as
soon as I tried to get up, that I had injured my back, and later in the day reported sick
to Dr Van der Merwe, the first SA Div MO; he examined me, and said that what I
probably needed was a bone-setter, or osteopath – 'but unfortunately I don't think we
have one in the desert'.

He wanted to send me back to the Delta, but I knew already that I was supposed to
go forward with 10 Corps – the Armoured Corps – and didn't want to miss the
advance. (In any case, I felt that if I was going to have back trouble, I might as well have
it at the front rather than – excuse me! – in the rear.) I told the MO this and he said OK,
and wished me luck.

I remember Dr Van der Merwe with the greatest affection; he was a little
Pickwickian character who confessed to being very anti-English – I told him, 'Don't
worry, I'm not all that pro-English myself' – and sang songs like *Sarais Marais* that
dated back to the Boer War. As a parting present he 'lent' me his copy of Koestler's
Darkness at Noon saying – and I transcribed his words in my notebook:

> I haven't had a very eventful life, as some lives go; I was never out of South Africa
> till I came with the Union forces to Egypt. But I have had my difficulties to face
> and decisions to make, and this book recalled them all to me. I can't say I enjoyed
> it, because it gave me too much excitement and pain for that, but thought it one
> of the most important books I'd ever read. I have thought hard for a parallel to
> it, and honestly I have got to say that I can find it only in the agony of Christ in
> the garden … Anyway, as the hunted is part of the hunter, two in one, take it. It
> will be excellent PW camp reading.

Excerpts from a notebook diary:

> Tuesday 17 November. Prisoners from 5 Panzer Regiment, include a
> Swedenborgian member of a congregation of 80 from a room in Berlin (faith
> now outlawed). Evening: my first tropical storm: an angry thronging rumble,
> and then the first drops. Flight to the tent, where I had to act as Atlas sustaining
> the world, or King Kong clasping the bars of his cage. Tent flapping its wings like
> an albatross taking off. Gusts filling the bellying sails. – Soaking Ararat
> afterwards.

> 8th Army Folklore: The Ghost Naafi, which flits into Tobruk by moonlight,
> and flits out again just before the dawn. I had been following this nocturnal

legend since entering Libya, and had come to the conclusion it didn't exist, when on my second stay at El Adem – about 1800 hours – in the already gathering dusk I saw a solitary vehicle just outside the confines of the camp. There was just enough light to make out the letters NAAFI on the side of it – I moved towards it at speed, and when I got to it I asked, 'Got any chocolate?' The driver turned to me (no death's head but a breezy English face) and said, 'Sorry sir, we're opening up at Msus'. A moment later the engine was running – and it was gone.

Thursday November 26th: El Adem airstrip. Recalled to Cairo, to interrogate high ranking prisoners captured at El Alamein. Hitched a lift on a Hudson leaving at 1400 hours. The plane was seriously overloaded, because a number of other officers and OR's, allowed leave, had also thumbed a lift to Cairo. A few moments after take off, I came as near to death – I suppose – as at any time in the desert war, because the little plane suddenly seemed to judder, and then dropped (as it seemed) almost vertically towards the limestone desert. Luckily the pilot succeeded in righting it, when it was practically grazing the desert floor, and we climbed steeply out of danger.

Here are notes I scribbled on the plane:

Near the bounds of Libya, saw deep wadis like family trees gouged out on a sand table, and the toy shop spirals of Sollum and Halfaya. And depressions like the surface of the moon. No one who has been in the desert would feel strange if a Jules Verne expedition deposited him in a lunar qattara.

Cairo, the Nile, and the deep green Delta from the air, the Citadel on its Arthur's Seat, the pretentious modern city, the factory chimneys, the race track, the aerodrome and the warrens of Moslem Masr, the miniature mosques like the most fragile models – and in the distance, in grey fog bloodshot with sunset – the tiny pyramids, playthings, dusky emblems of the sun.

Then in the bus from Heliopolis I began again to smell the smell of Cairo – quintessence of filth, attar of excrement.

November 29th. Evening with Speirs and Ruth – discussing Scotland, Egypt, mad Mrs Groves and her cold in the womb – listened to Churchill's speech: 'springboard for attack on Italy'. (For Speirs, see *Cencrastus* 48).

In Cairo I had plenty of opportunities to size up the extraordinarily vigorous literary scene, which Olivia Manning later described in an article in Cyril Connolly's *Horizon* (October 1944): 'Poets in Exile'. Not long after this appeared, G S Fraser contributed a similar article 'Recent Verse: London and Cairo' for Tambimuttu's *Poetry London*; in this, he concentrated on the poets who featured in the magazine *Personal Landscape*. This latter was founded as a vehicle for the poetry of various non-military expatriates: Robin Fedden, Lawrence Durrell, Terence Tiller and Bernard Spencer, in particular, and was regarded by most blokes in uniform as a somewhat highbrow or 'mandarin' production. (For 'personal' read 'private', as one of the soldier poets who congregated in Music for All and the Victory Club put it. It appeared he had tried to 'gatecrash' it, and had received a gentle but all the same pretty firm rebuff.)

All the same, an inspection of the magazines more open to contributions from the troops (*Salamander*, *Citadel* and *Orientations*) shows that the standard in these was by no means low. *Citadel* was founded towards the end of 1941.

Its first editor was Reggie Smith, Olivia Manning's husband; the two had escaped from Bucharest earlier in the year, and then from Greece. Reggie eventually (October 1941) got a job as a lecturer in the English Department of the Fuad al Awal University; one of his colleagues was John Speirs.

Reggie was an enterprising editor; in the six months of his editorship he published poems by people like Robert Liddle – one of the contributors to *Personal Landscape* – as well as several poets in uniform: above all, Keith Douglas, now universally regarded as the outstanding soldier poet of the Second World War.

Another quite broadly-based mag. followed in 1942: this was *Orientations*, which was undoubtedly worth every one of the three piastres it cost (a beer cost two). Its fifth number appeared in December 1942, and I picked this up in the Victory Club, just before returning to the desert to rejoin the 51st Highland Division as an IO.

After submitting interrogation reports on some of the 'top brass' German prisoners who had fallen into our hands at Alamein, I was relieved to hear that Major-General Douglas ('Big Tam') Wimberley, GOC 51 Div., had requested GHQ Cairo to release me so that I could rejoin the Div. as a German- and Italian-speaking IO. This meant that I was able to take off on December 18th in a 15-cwt Dodge, with a driver, Private Kettle, and a bilingual German Jewish sergeant as assistant, to drive westwards to a rendezvous in Libya.

Private Kettle turned out to be a wonderful source of bawdy folklore, so I found myself in the agreeable position, sitting beside him, of collecting rhymes and recitations in place of enemy intentions and tank losses. Here is one of his favourites:

> Oysters is amorous, lampreys is lecherous, and whelks
> goes straight to the balls. But shrimps – *sheye rimps*!
> – thems the fuckin' awfullest things of all.

Mr 'Iggins comes 'ome the other night, been debauchin' 'isself wiv shrimps – says, Mrs 'Iggins, a loan of your cunt – *hif* you please. Whereupon, 'e proceeds to satisfy 'is dirty animal nature no less than three (three!) times, and then rolls over as if satisfied. But no – up 'e starts again, and says, Mrs 'Iggins, a loan of your cunt, *hif* you please. So I claps me 'and over me fundamental horifice, and says, No, nothin' doin'. Whereupon the dirty old fucker proceeds to toss 'isself off, right over the fuckin' ceiling, from which it drips – drip, drip, *deye-rip*, the whole fuckin' night through, never got a wink of sleep.

Yes, Mrs 'Obbs, as I was sayin' ...

This like a lot of his store, had a distinct period flavour – almost Dickensian, in fact. (I thought Dickens would have used it, if he'd thought he could get away with it – maybe attributing it to Mrs Gamp – who, in turn, would no doubt have attributed it to Mrs 'Arris!)

Another of Private Kettle's astounding collection seemed much older, and exhibited a quite different idiom:

I'll tell you a noble story
  Of the hero Alexander,
He had a prick nine inches thick
  And he called it his Commander.

He went to woo the fairy queen
  on a night as black as charcoal
But in the dark he missed his mark,
  And shoved it up her arsehole.

In the fullness of time the babe was born.
  Now listen to this marvel!
It had no prick, it had no balls,
  But a double-barrelled arsehole.

This seems related to Tom o'Bedlan's song ('From the hag and hungry goblin That into rags would rend ye'), which is generally regarded as the ancestor of the limerick: the 'feel' of it is definitely Shakespearian ... Anyway, I had to have recourse to limericks, to try to keep my end up. Private Kettle hadn't heard the following, and much appreciated it:

There was a young man of Calcutta
Who tried to write cunt on a shutter.
  He had written CU
  – When a pious Hindu
Knocked him arse over tip in the gutter.

As for 'The Bastard King of England' and 'The Good Ship Venus', they kept us going from Mersa Matruh to the Halfaya Pass (from that time on my secret name for Private Kettle was Thersites, and I found myself whispering under my breath: 'Lechery, lechery – wars and lechery – all incontinent varlets!')

Every December, since the desert war began, there had been a catch phrase in the 8th Army, 'Christmas in Benghazi'; Wavell got there in 1940, and we were back – though not for long – in '41. Although the HQ of the Highland Div. which was my destination was away out in the direction of Agheila, I resolved I would definitely enjoy a 1942 'Christmas in Benghazi', and – with Private Kettle's vociferous encouragement – this is exactly what I did. Unbeknown to me the late Neil McCallum – whom I got to know very well in Edinburgh after the War – had made the same decision, and his memory of a Christmas entry into the town accords so well with mine that I transcribe his account (published in *Journey with a Pistol* Gollancz 1959) word for word:

We reached Benghazi quite late. The town was lit by the moon, a smooth white light that lay like a powdering of frost. The streets were very quiet, and the buildings were like cool marble. The moonlight fell on arches and balconies, terraces and cupolas, towers and minarets. Sitting in front of the truck was like driving into the Arabian Nights. We came too late to find accommodation, and we slept, once again, beside our vehicle on a piece of waste ground.
  It was very cold, and the sky was rich with stars. The moon was so bright it lay

glaringly upon the town, and only in the distance did it soften the features of the land. It was the quietness that was startling. It seemed no one was in Benghazi except ourselves. Even the hairless pi-dogs were silent. It was a quietness apart from the war, a white tranquillity. I fell asleep looking at a cypress in the moonlight. It was Christmas Eve …

Christmas, Boxing Day and a few more days were spent in the small paradise of Benghazi. A storm arose and did immense damage to the harbour, [This was on Jan. 4th. H H]. Our sleeping tents, in the garden behind the pink house, were surrounded by a sticky red mud. There was a large ornamental garden nearby … After a week of bumping through the desert, on the way from Egypt, this cultivated garden was very civilising. There were palms and eucalyptus trees, and ponds with goldfish. There was an irrigation system drawing its water from two deep wells. Above, all, there was a sense of the orderliness the Arabs have for the things they revere, especially their horses and the cultivation of gardens.

On Christmas Eve, I looked out the December copy of *Orientations* I had brought with me from Cairo; and settled down in one of these truly civilised gardens to read it. I opened it – as one often does – at the final pages – and realised, almost with a sense of shock, that the Langholm Byspale had accompanied me out to Benghazi. There he was – in the shape of an article 'Hugh MacDiarmid – People's Poet' by Kenneth Hartley.

Hugh MacDiarmid is the people's poet. He is a realist in the sense that he believes in the objective reality of external nature, and our ideas of truth are formed by looking out through our senses, and by devices which science can provide to extend the evidence of our senses, at this reality. Moreover, he accepts not only nature itself, but all the relationships which man as a conscious part of it has created with other parts, and the forms of society which he has created with other men, and the whole of his attempt to understand and to master that external nature, as the subject for his poetry.

Since in subject he accepts everything so in technique he accepts every means of saying – all language from the slang of the American movies to the compact jargon of the medical man and the geologist, the engineer and the scholar. Few writers have had the scholarship necessary to use so mighty a technical apparatus, and of those few, many have been at pains merely to exhibit it as amends for lack of content, or even as an end to itself. Others again have been content to make sensory music with the strange words and phrases. MacDiarmid does none of these things. Only a man in whom this formidable scholarship was so completely assimilated as to flow unconsciously at the bidding of ideas, could handle the things he chooses. Conversely, only a poet whose message is of such fundamental things requires to build for himself such a machinery of expression.

What then is his message? His view of people and human society arises so inevitably from his vision of nature, that had he never written a line of political verse his writing would still be an inspiration to those who believe in the infinite diversity, and the rightness of the diversity of man, and of man's relations to man. And this is something we must understand if we are ever to understand MacDiarmid, this delight in the diversity of nature, and the hatred of all forms of falsehood which try to impose order from above, and ignore or break down natural differences. We must understand, too, that nature to him is never static, that he studies phenomena through the processes of development and change which they undergo.

> Come let us transfer all moral issues
> And social relations to a higher plane
> Where men may agree, but if they don't
> Can never be forced to submit again
> To the will of others by hunger and want.
> It's time to end that sadistic cant
> Come let us put a premium then
> On pure example and persuasive force.
> Not that they're likely to carry far
> In maintaining present conventions, of course,
> Since these all depend on the belly grip
> And will change completely when that's let slip.

A person who did know his work, reading the foregoing might suppose that MacDiarmid attempted to be a kind of all-seeing eye, perceiving nature spread out below him from some exterior vantage point. Nothing is less true. Essentially MacDiarmid's view of nature includes himself as a part of it – as a perceptive midget describing the mighty world around it, which all the time is acting spiritually, mentally, physically, socially, upon him. We never lose sight of himself as a human being in his poems, but we realise that here is a completely adult man, one whose vision of reality is so intense and so complete that he has neither the time nor the desire to turn his eyes inwards and write about his own mental processes. Instead his mind is so constructed that he uses it as a catalyst to make known his experiences to us. Like D H Lawrence, he understands phenomena by projecting himself into them, and when the phenomena are non-human, the technical difficulty is to translate this wordless identity into human concepts.

> Nay, I feel
> I know your music best when as it were an island pool
> Away here I hold a glass of water between me and the sun
> And can only tell the one from the other by the lint-white quiver.
> The trembling life of the water – like a man bending his head
> As from outside as a man can, to look at his whole mind
> As if it did not belong to him though he knows
> It is yet that by which he knows all that he knows.

It has been said that poets are the real leaders of their age. MacDiarmid is a Scottish Nationalist, one of the leaders of the movement and of the Scottish Renaissance which is its counterpart in letters. Even to one who is not a Scotsman and who has no deep understanding of the political issues involved, the reason is easily apprehended. Passionate belief in the individual, and hatred of external coercion, a unique understanding of the cultural heritage of his race, could make him nothing less. Only when Scotland is no longer stretched upon the Procrustes bed of English forms of government, he claims, will it be able to make to a voluntary union of nations that contribution which is its genius.

We never lose sight of MacDiarmid, the man. What manner of man is he? He is a man with all the heritage of the Scottish working class in his blood, the humour and experience, the toil and struggle. When he turns from a study of the Norse sagas or the great pibrochs to write a biting epitaph on Walter Elliott, or a comment on a Cockney soldier looking at Edinburgh we accept it as another facet of this spiritual giant's character.

> Here lies Walter Elliott
> Under a stone to tell, you that
> You needn't restrict
> Agricultural supplies
> Any longer – now he's here
> To help them rise;
> In his right place at last.
> Making up for his past.

MacDiarmid is the voice of the people from which he sprang. It is reasonable therefore to expect to find in his work those qualities most characteristic of the vanguard of the workers – courage, strength, forthrightness, hatred of all forms of compromise, and that simplification of issues usually found in a fighting class, which is summed up in the phrase 'who is not for me is against me'. One might expect to find these developed at the expense of subtlety of thought and feeling, tenderness and other less militant qualities. But one reckons without the character of the man. We are well acquainted, through the work of so many of the minor poets of today, with pity and the tenderness arrived at through personal weakness, of subtlety and delicacy born of necessity in a man unable by experience and endowments to handle great themes. Here we find the tenderness and pity of great strength, the kindliness and understanding of a strong champion fighting in the fierceness of his love for those whom conditions have battered and drugged into a state when they are no longer able to fight for themselves.

MacDiarmid is a giant certainly, a giant of the future. He writes for the present, and his poems are the operations of a radical surgeon on the rotten flesh of contemporary society.

And in the shadow of this colossus the so-called Left Wing poets of today – half declassed and wholly introverted, wrapped up in the saving of their own neurotic little spiritual skins – will collapse unheeded to dust, the seeds of their own destruction being already within them. For as MacDiarmid himself says:

> It is easy to cry
> I am one with the working classes
> But no task in this world surpasses
> In difficulty his who would try,
> Must try since he is not, succeed or die.
> Miseducated and more articulate,
> Sensitised by what numbs their fate
> And raised up by what keeps them down,
> Only by the severest intellectual discipline
> Can one of the bourgeois intelligentsia win

Up to the level of the proletariat
On this side of the grave or that
– The only goal worth aiming at.

Here is a writer very different from the fashionable poets of the playing fields of Eton.

I have no idea who Kenneth Hartley was or is –for I had no time or opportunity to make enquiries when the war was still on, and none of the surviving *literati* who were in Egypt have been able to enlighten me. From internal evidence it seems he was not a Scot – and as Hartley is quite a well-known Irish name I made what has been generously termed an 'inspired guess' that he was a Liverpool Irishman – and probably (again from internal evidence) a freewheeling member of the Communist Party who either did not know – or did not care – that MacDiarmid had been expelled from the Party for Nationalist deviations a few years previously.

The quotations he used in his article made it clear that the book Kenneth Hartley had stuffed into his kitbag, when leaving for Egypt, was *Stony Limits*, published by Victor Gollancz in 1934 – arguably his finest single collection. The first quote is from 'The Belly-Grip' – stanzas 3 and 4 of a masterpiece of 'direct utterance'. This is one of the poems much admired by Prince Dmitri S Mirsky, who joined the Communist Party of Great Britain in 1931, before returning to the Soviet Union in 1932 – and, eventually, to incarceration in the camps of the Gulag – and death in despair.

The second quotation is from what is surely one of the finest poems in MacDiarmid's entire *oeuvre*, 'Lament for the Great Music'. The lines quoted by Hartley awoke in my memory several other passages from this great poem, which is a hymn to *ceol mor* – the towering pibrochs of the MacCrimmons – and a celebration of the Gaelic genius – as well as a bitter excoriation of what he saw as Scotland's latter-day cultural abdication. The lines that first came into my head were the following:

Your pibrochs that are like the glimpses
Of reality transcending all reason
Every supreme thinker has, and spends the rest of his life
Trying to express in terms of reason;
Your pibrochs that in the grey life of these islands
Are like the metaphysic of light in the style of Plotinus,
The great one-word metaphors of the Enneads,
Gleaming godlike in the dry and formal diction,
The light that *has* been on sea and land ...

I must have sat there for long and long, while other lines came irresistibly into my mind – especially the final passage which I had word for word:

... All ever born crowd the islands and the West Coast of Scotland
Which has standing room for them all, and the air curdled with angels,
And everywhere that feeling seldom felt on the earth before
Save in the hearts of parents or in youth untouched by tragedy
That in its very search for personal experience often found
A like impersonality and self-forgetfulness,
And you playing 'Farewell to Scotland, and the rest of the Earth'
The only fit music there can be for that day

> – And I will leap then and hide behind one of you.
> *A's caismeachd phìob mòra bras-shròiceadh am puirt.*
>
> Look! Is that only the setting sun again?
> Or a piper coming from far away?

After arriving in the desert I had seen some terrible things dry-eyed – for example, the 'brewed-up' tanks, some with their occupants semi-cremated in them, which I had had to count after the battle of Alum Halfa – but I'm not ashamed to say that as I sat there in Benghazi, murmuring these final lines of wonderful strong poetry, I felt the pricking of tears in my eyes.

(It was 'Lament for the Great Music', in fact which made sue resolve to complete my book of Wartime Elegies on the island of South Uist.)

The final quote is the opening stanza of *Etika Preobrazhennavo Erosa* (The Ethics of Brotherly Love), minus the last four lines:

> O remorseless spirit that guides me
>   The way seems infinite;
> What endless distance divides me
>   From the people yet –

As we loaded up the Dodge, before setting off to report to 'Big Tain' Wimberley, I remember reflecting that Chris Grieve would undoubtedly be pleased to know that an article acclaiming him as 'People's Poet' included a quote from a long philosophical poem stacked to the gunwales with recondite allusions to classical Gaelic literature!

And so, indeed, it turned out, although I had to wait till after the war, when he and Valda were living at 32 Victoria Crescent Road, Glasgow, before I had a chance of showing it to him.

The Poetry of War in the Middle East, 1939–1945

Like most of the poets I'm going to talk about, I grew for war. Born on 11 November 1919, exactly a year after the armistice which marked the end of the 'first round', I was eighteen at the time of the Munich crisis, and nineteen when war was declared. At the time of the Battle of El Alamein, which marked the turning point of the war, as far as Britain was concerned, I was still only twenty-two. This battle was one of the major formative events of my life, and I still feel myself very close to it.

The citizen army which was gradually built up in the Middle East to face Rommel was a literate army, its soldiers the beneficiaries of the 1918 Education Act. In this it certainly differed greatly from the set-up a quarter of a century earlier which their fathers had known. In the First World War the voice of the ordinary swaddy was the soldier's folk-song, documented in collections such as John Brophy and Eric Partridge's *The Long Trail,* and although the Second World War also produced quite a copious folk-song, the striking new thing was an amazing flowering of written poetry, some of it of quite a high standard. And of this poetry, a good deal of the most interesting undoubtedly emerged from the historic crossroads of the Middle East.

A new approach was taken by Victor Selwyn and his colleagues of the Salamander Oasis Trust when they began to gather material for *Return to Oasis* (1980), a volume based on a poetry anthology produced in Cairo in 1943 by three volunteer editors whose highest rank was corporal. (Cairo saw an astonishing profileration of poetry magazines and booklets during the war; others were *Citadel, Orientations* and *Personal Landscape.*) *Return to Oasis* included not only the original book, and added to it a large number of poems which arrived in answer to advertisements; its success was such that they followed it up with a second volume called *From Oasis into Italy.* In 1985 a further collection, entitled *Poems of the Second World War,* was published by Dent in their Everyman's Library series.

In his introduction Victor Selwyn draws a necessary distinction between the '*Oasis* approach to war poetry' and that of other editors. 'Whereas Ian Hamilton … says that he looked for what the poets wrote when they went to war, our concern has been the converse: to seek the writings of those who *became* poets as a result of going to war. Naturally we select from the established poets, too. But to get the feel of war we have deliberately sought unpublished manuscripts, the verses written by unknowns from the airfields of Britain to the POW camps of South-East Asia – many of which have lain hidden in desks and drawers for forty years, or were left to widows and children, along with the medals.'

A striking example of this method at its most effective is undoubtedly the disinterment of poems written in Libya and in Greece by J. E. Brookes. Brookes served as a private in the 2/5 Battalion Australian Infantry Force (AIF). Before the war he had worked his passage from Liverpool to Australia, landing with 2s 6d. On the outbreak of war he walked from Broken Hill to Melbourne to enlist. In a letter to me written on 9 September 1985, he states: 'The war poems (which my wife rescued from our 'glory hole' under the stairs on seeing Victor Selwyn's advertisement asking for war poems in 1979 were all written in 1941, and all described true incidents.'

As an example of their quality, here are extracts from 'Thermopylae 1941':

> No purpose served consulting horoscopes
> at Delphi; students of Herodotus
> would know withdrawal to Thermopylae
> and putting up barbed wire could only mean
> fighting a rearguard action QED,
> as Euclid would have put it. We had been
> deposited into the warlike lap
> of ancient deities. I said to Blue,
> my Aussie mate, 'There was this famous chap
> Leonidas, he was the Spartan who
> defended it with just 300 men
> against an army.' Bluey took a draw
> upon his cigarette. 'Well stuff 'im then!'
> a pungent comment on the art of war ...
>
>   ... I said 'They wore
> long hair the Spartans, a visible proof
> that they were free, not helots, and before
> the battle they would gravely sit aloof
> and garland it with flowers.' Bluey spat.
> Continuing to watch the empty road
> across the plain he took off his tin-hat
> (a proof that he was bald) and said 'A load
> of bloody pooftahs!' Thus he laid the ghost
> of brave Leonidas. ...
>
> ... And later with our cigarettes concealed
> behind cupped hands we peered into the night
> across the darkened plain and it revealed
> first one and then another point of light,
> and then a hundred of them, moving down
> the distant backcloth, shining off and on
> like tiny jewels sparkling on a crown
> of moonlit mountains, a phenomenon
> caused by the winding path of their descent
> round hair-pin bends cascading from the heights
> beyond Lamia, our first presentiment

of evil genius – they were the lights
of Hitler's war machines! ...

        '... Time to pick
the flowers, Blue, that bloom upon the steep
hillside' I said 'make daisy-chains and stick
the buggers in our hair!' He was asleep.

After listing his poems 'Bardia 1941', 'Tobruk 1941', 'Waltzing Matilda' and 'Burial Party', John Brookes adds 'Thermopylae and Waltzing Matilda work best if they are read with a pronounced Australian accent ("Strine")'. This statement provides us with a revealing clue to the reason for the success of many of these good poems by 'unknowns' – they are harbingers of the 'spoken poetry' movements of post-war years, examples of poetry that to be at its most effective *has* to be spoken. It is no accident that so many of Brookes's poems have place-names in their titles; they are intensely *local* poems – poems belonging to a well defined and healthily self-conscious community.

One of the 'desert war poets' who did not survive the war was W. H. Burt, whose ballad-like 'Stane Jock' was first published in *Citadel*. At the time he wrote it, he was a Lieutenant in the 51st Highland Recce Regiment, and the poem is sub-titled: *For the glory of the Highland Division on the night of 23 October 1942*.

        Atween the mune an' the yird
            There is quick steel:
        Atween the steel and the yird
            There is quick stane!

        the man-trap is fu' o' men
            Walking saftly.
        The man-eating mandrakes scream
            As they bite.

        The stane Jock O' Beaumont Hamel
            Is f'en doon.
        There's nae mair pipes in France –
            Nae mair sweet croon.

        But this nicht stane Jock,
            Walks in the sand!
        this nicht I hear the pipes,
            I hear the band!

        There's nane deid but his dead e'en
            Glower at the west.
        There's nane living but stepping hard
            Towards the west. ...

        ... Gallus laddies a'!
            Stanes o' destiny!
        Stane Jock in the mantrap field
            Walking saftly.

W. H. Burt was killed in Germany on 10 April 1945.

The Gaelic poet George Campbell Hay also served in the Middle East and North Africa. In 1983 he was awarded An Comunn Gaidhealach's prize for the best Gaelic book published that year: this was for *Mochtàr is Dùghall*, which is about the Tunisian campaign. Here is a short excerpt from Hay's English version of the introductory poem:

> The man who fired the shot, he was no cheerful, eager warrior.
> His belly driving him to weep with the bad, tepid water of the flats.
> His eyes red and watering with want of sleep and the schnapps he had
> > drunk.
> He blaspheming, and cursing the dust, the heat and the Colonel.
>
> Who knows what dark power brought you together on this pinnacle.
> That guided you over mountains and oceans, hardening you with
> > misery.
> The three of you – you two who formed your brotherhood, and the hand that
> bound you together in acquaintance,
> Sneaking, crawling on all fours, snaking like beasts of prey.
> The Gefreiter who gave you your death, and pulled out, leaving you
> > together ...
> He was captured with the scream in his throat, a madman on Cape Bon.

If I may seem to be concentrating unduly on the Scottish writers, it is because they *have* been to a certain extent neglected in this particular context – and also the ones I have on parade were without doubt very accomplished poets indeed. The late Robert Garioch is widely regarded as the best poet of the post-MacDiarmid generation to use the old Lallan or Scots language – the language of Dunbar, Fergusson and Burns. He was put in the bag near Tobruk while serving as a signalman in 201 Guards Motor Brigade headquarters: he and his mate were looking after a battery-charger mounted on a Ford V8 truck, and were victims of the confusion which reigned on 20 June 1942, when Ritchie lost his grip, and the Germans breached the defences of what had been, the previous year, an encircled but never taken fortress. After the war Garioch wrote of his years as a POW in Italy and Germany in *Two Men and a Blanket* (1975), but during the war he had composed a spirited ditty called 'Kriegy Ballad' (Kriegy = Kriegsgefangener = POW) to the tune of 'We're sailing to Botany Bay'. A couple of verses will give the flavour of this:

> Yes, this is the place we were took, sir,
> And landed right into the bag,
> Right outside the town of Tobruk, sir,
> So now for some bloody stalag.
>
> There was plenty of water in Derna,
> But that camp was not very well kept,
> For either you slept in the piss-hole,
> Or pissed in the place where you slept.

This artful pastiche of a 'folk song' – which apparently caught on among some of the

Kriegies – was in 'British Army demotic', not in Scots, for Garioch always had a good ear for the idiom of his chosen audience. As his poems in Scots are far better known than his work in English, I'd like to quote from his 'Letter from Italy', to show how well he could write in the 'sister tongue':

> Late summer darkness comes, and now
> I see again the homely Plough
> and wonder: do you also see
> the seven stars as well as I?
> And it is good to find a tie
> of seven stars from you to me.
> Lying on deck, on friendly seas
> I used to watch, with no delight,
> new unsuggestive stars that light
> the tedious Antipodes.
> Now in a hostile land I lie,
> but share with you these ancient high
> familiar named divinities.
> Perimeters have bounded me,
> sad rims of desert and of sea,
> the famous one around Tobruk,
> and now barbed wire, which way I look,
> except above – the Pleiades.

Somhairle MacGill-eain (Sorley MacLean) was a close friend of Garioch's; his first published work appeared in *17 Poems for Sixpence* (hand printed by 'Geerie' on his Chalmers Press in 1940). Unlike most of the other poets mentioned, Sorley was a militant pre-war anti-Fascist who, but for intractable family circumstances, would have volunteered to fight in Spain with the International Brigades. He was a native Gaelic speaker from the island of Raasay; his people were singers and tradition-bearers, and consequently he was a heritor of the splendid song-tradition of the Hebrides – arguably the greatest glory of all of Scottish culture. At the same time he and his people were repositories of bitter ancestral memories of the Highland Clearances. But he was also an heir of the ancient Gaelic tradition of *gaisge* (valour) and so was able to write without self-consciousness, in *Dol an Iar* (Going Westwards):

> There is no rancour in my heart
> against the hardy soldiers of the Enemy,
> but the kinship that there is among
> men in prison on a tidal rock
>
> waiting for the sea flowing
> and making cold the warm stone;
> and the coldness of life
> in the hot sun of the Desert.
>
> But this is the struggle not to be avoided,
> the sore extreme of human-kind,

and though I do not hate Rommel's army
the brain's eye is not squinting.

And be what was as it was,
I am of the big men of Braes,
of the heroic Raasay MacLeods,
of the sharp-sword Mathesons of Lochalsh;
and the men of my name – who were braver
when their ruinous pride was kindled?

The most quoted – and best remembered – of Sorley's desert war poems is *Glac a Bhàis* (Death Valley), a poem which has as epigraph: 'Some Nazi or other has said that the Fuehrer had restored to German manhood the "right and joy of dying in battle".' A very moving poem is *Curaidhean* (Heroes), Sorley's tribute to a soldier from South of the Border:

I did not see Lannes at Ratisbon
nor MacLennan at Auldearn
nor Gillies MacBain at Culloden
but I saw an Englishman in Egypt. ...

His hour came with the shells;
with the notched iron splinters,
in the smoke and flame,
in the shaking and terror of the battlefield.

Word came to him in the bullet shower
that he should be a hero briskly,
and he was that while he lasted
but it wasn't much time he got. ...

I saw a great warrior of England,
a poor manikin on whom no eye would rest;
no Alasdair of Glen Garry;
and he took a little weeping to my eyes.

Sorley was quite badly wounded at El Alamein, and saw no further action after the battle.

Looking through the *Oasis* anthology, I have reread several notable poems which should rate more than a mention – F. T. Prince's 'Soldiers Bathing', Drummond Allison's 'Verity', Vernon Scannell's 'Walking Wounded' and G. S. Fraser's 'Egypt' – but the poems which would stand out in any company are undeniably those of Keith Douglas, who 'scarpered' from a safe job at base to take command of an armoured troop at El Alamein, was wounded at Wadi Zem Zem and, after returning to England to take part in the invasion of Normandy, was killed in action on 9 June 1944.

When I first saw his name, in one of the Cairo poetry mags (*Citadel*, I think), wondered if he was a Scot – and as he bore a resounding Scottish name, it was a reasonable assumption. However, from all I heard about him later, from Tambimuttu and others, it became very clear to me that he was intensely, indeed almost militantly,

English. From people who had met him at various times I began to build up a picture
of him, and I have to admit that some of his attitudes, as people described them, frankly
puzzled me; the dedicated, almost childish 'spit-and-polish' militarism to which his
friends bear witness, reminded me uncomfortably of the mental attitudes of another
non-Scottish poet with a Scottish name: Roy Dunnichie Campbell. But it was a long
time before I tumbled to his real spiritual kinsman. With his pugnacity, occasional
brusque intolerance and generally 'cross-grained' nature – but also in his ability to
reveal, when he wanted to, an immense reservoir of gentleness and courtesy – he
undoubtedly bore a strong temperamental resemblance to Hugh MacDiarmid.

Like MacDiarmid, too, he was obviously a man of blazing genius, sticking out a
mile from among the ruck of his contemporaries; furthermore – and here the resemblance is at its closest – he had no compunction about casting himself in the role of a
'great poet'. In a fascinating account of his time at No 1 General Hospital at El Ballah,
Palestine (printed in *PN Review* 47), Lt Col John Stubbs reports conversations with
him: 'He made it quite clear: "I'm going to be a major poet" end of message. He said
that time and time again to me and "There are lots of people who dabble with poetry,
they don't really understand it, but I insist, I'm going to be a major poet come what
may".'

And who can doubt, reading the cluster of poems that have survived, that Keith
Douglas – who did not even live as long as Keats – was telling the literal truth. Some of
these poems, like Wilfred Owen's after the First World War, are now established as
classics – I am thinking particularly of 'Desert Flowers', 'How to Kill', Cairo Jag' and
'Elegy for an 88 Gunner'

('*Vergissmeinnicht*'). I have room to quote only one of his poems – partly because it
is my own favourite, and partly because it nicely counterpoints Sorley's *Curaidhean*
(quoted earlier):

> 'I think I am Becoming a God'
>
> The noble horse with courage in his eye
> clean in the bone, looks up at a shellburst.
> Away fly the images of the shires
> But he puts the pipe back in his mouth.
>
> Peter was unfortunately killed by an 88:
> it took his leg away – he died in the ambulance.
> When I saw him crawling he said:
> 'It's most unfair – they've shot my foot off.'
>
> How can I live among this gentle
> obsolescent breed of heroes, and not weep?
> Unicorns, almost,
> for they are fading into two legends
> in which their stupidity and chivalry
> are celebrated. Each, fool and hero, will be an immortal.
>
> These plains were their cricket pitch
> and in the mountains the tremendous drop fences

brought down some of the runners. Here
under the stones and earth they dispose themselves
in famous attitudes of unconcern.

Finally – although it may seem trite to say so – I can't forbear adding that the lasting impression left after reading the poems in the *Oasis* anthology is of the fundamental 'decency' and good-heartedness of the writers: not exactly 'literary' values, admittedly, but very impressive for all that. I close with a poem by Douglas Street called 'Love Letters of the Dead' – subtitled 'A Commando Intelligence Briefing' – a poem as clearly based on a true incident as J. E. Brookes's 'Thermopylae'.

'Go through the pockets of the enemy wounded,
Go through the pockets of the enemy dead –
There's a lot of good stuff to be found there –
That's of course if you've time', I said.
'Love letters are specially useful,
It's amazing what couples let slip –
Effects of our bombs for example,
The size and type of a ship.
These'll all give us bits of our jigsaw.
Any questions?' I asked as per rule-book;

A close-cropped sergeant from Glasgow,
With an obstinate jut to his jaw,
Got up, and at me he pointed;
Then very slowly he said:
'Do you think it right, well I don't,
For any bloody stranger to snitch
What's special and sacred and secret,
Love letters of the dead?'

Aquarius, 17/18, 1986–7.

Puir Bluidy Swaddies are Weary

In his book *Sicily* – it is not a guide book, but a cool dispassionate account of the Sicilian campaign of July–August 1943 – Major Hugh Pond has this to say about the impression the 51st Highland Division made on other units of the Allied Armies:

> The Highland Division, down from its tall gangling Commander 'Lang Tam' Wimberley down to the humblest Jock private, was very much a law unto itself. One often had a feeling that they were fighting a Holy Crusade, and at the end of the war, they would return to Scotland, take Edinburgh by storm, put a Scottish King on the throne, and form an independent country' ... Wimberley was an untiring, see-for-himself commander; he did not believe in 'bumph', and the closer he was to the fighting, the better he liked it. The high morale and spirit of the Division was largely due to their leader, whom the men all loved and respected.

At the first light of day, in the early morning of 10 July 1943 – D. Day! – the fisherfolk of Portopalo, the most south-easterly village in Sicily, woke up to find the normally sparsely populated sea-roads congested with a vast armada of landing craft and other vessels of all shapes and sizes. it must have been a stunning sight for them! ... On 'Amber Beach' – Rada di Portopalo – tanks and vehicles of 154 Brigade of the Highland Div. were being unloaded, and the only Sicilians to be seen were at pains to identify themselves as *borghesi* (civilians). (Some, as it turned out, were in fact members of the 'autonomous' Italian coastal battalions who had taken the first opportunity of changing into 'civvies'!)

Leading elements of the Division were soon in Pachino, the first little town of any size in the area, and they were greeted with white flags and even – here and there – with what looked like a welcome on the part of the locals. The first enemy reaction was an air-raid by planes of the Luftwaffe on the beaches, but they caused comparatively little damage, and remarkably few casualties ... My first job, as IO (Intelligence Officer) was to interrogate four German deserters, who were waiting to be picked up by our troops, and who assured me that there were no Germans south of the plain of Catania.

I decided to see for myself, and after borrowing a motor bike from a CMP (Military Policeman) who had just disembarked, I rode north in the gathering light, with a tremendous feeling of exhilaration: we were out of Africa, and back in Europe! ... Admittedly the scenery and vegetation were not particularly 'European' – white dusty roads, prickly pears, stone walls about a metre high, vineyards on either side of the road

– but all the same, this was Europe, and I had a heady euphoric feeling that I could ride north for ever! There was no sign of enemy troops, or indeed of any military activity whatsoever. The *contadini* – the peasants who were working in the fields – hardly gave me a glance, although when I waved to them one or two actually waved back! ... After I had ridden north for several miles I reluctantly turned the bike round and rode back the way I had come; fairly soon I encountered sections of a Black Watch company, recognisable at once by the red hackles in their bonnets, proceeding cannily northwards, strung out on both sides of the road. I was able to tell the first senior NCO I came across that they could afford to take it a bit more easy: there were no enemy troops for miles ahead.

Indeed, the first German troops whom we encountered were paratroops – three battalions of the First Parachute Division, sent from the Avignon area in the south of France, which landed in Sicily on the 12th and 13th July, mostly on the airfields near the river Simeto. The job they had been allotted was to hold up our troops before they could reach the plain of Catania, in order to allow the defences there to be better prepared and co-ordinated. This meant that 152 Brigade of the, 51st – a Camerons battalion, and two Seaforths battalions – had to deal with them, and after some very fierce fighting, mainly against No. 2 battalion of these paratroops, the Camerons sorted them out near Francofonte (16 July), and they were pretty soon encircled and completely cut off.

The officer commanding the 2nd battalion was one Captain Albrecht Guenther, and – against the rules of war – this officer ordered his men to discard their uniforms, and collect civilian clothes of some sort from the terrified citizens of Francofonte. This they did at gunpoint, and a number did manage to get through to the German lines, disguised – though not very convincingly – as Sicilian peasants.

On the morning of 17 July I was proceeding in a jeep up a road near Buccheri when I noticed two characters in ragged civvies standing close to the side of the road. They did not look much like Sicilians – one was a shortish tubby little man, and the other a tall lanky galoot – and I decided to have a word with them. I got my driver to stop, and walked over to this odd couple. As I approached them, the taller of the two involuntarily drew himself up, and came to attention in the German fashion, clapping his hands on his hips.

'Sind Sie Deutscher?' I asked him, and he replied 'Jawohl'. I asked him his name, rank and number, which he gave – and as indeed he was bound to give under the terms of the Geneva Convention; then I asked him what his unit was – this he was not bound to give – but he at once identified it as No.2 battalion, 1st Fallschirmjaeger (parachute) regiment.

So far so good. Then I turned my attention to the other German; he at first refused to say anything, but after a moment or two of thought he decided he might as well divulge his own identity and I was surprised to learn that he was the same Captain Guenther who was OC of the battalion which had held us up – though not for long – two days previously! – So here I had two valuable prisoners, and was alone with the driver of my jeep, in the middle of a vast expanse of mountainous Sicily – and no other troops of either army in sight. It was obviously necessary to get these prisoners back to Corps HQ so that they could be interrogated, but there were obvious dangers involved.

I had a pistol, and the two Germans had discarded their arms when they discarded their uniforms, but there is not much room in a jeep, and my driver would be occupied driving, so I felt for a moment or two in a real quandary. If the Germans started anything when we got under way I might be able to shoot one of them – but hardly two.

I asked Guenther if he would give his parole not to try to escape on the journey back to Corps, but he not unnaturally refused. Consequently, there was nothing for it but to risk it; I put Guenther in the front seat next to the driver, and his batman/orderly – for that is what he was – in the back seat on the right; I sat, myself, as far back as possible on the left, and covered them both – but mainly the officer! – with my pistol.

Luckily other vehicles appeared, coming up the road from the direction we were travelling, and I managed to get my captives back to Corps without mishap – but I still feel a 'cauld grue' when I think what might easily have happened if Lieutenant (Acting Captain) Guenther had decided to try to disarm me and make a bolt for it.

One reason he didn't – I thought then, and still think – was that he was highly embarassed, as a German officer, to have been captured wearing a pair of dirty ragged civvie breeks, and did not fancy roaming around any further in an area where genuine Sicilian males might easily have given him short shrift!

At Corps HQ I delivered the Jerries to the GI – remarking, incidentally, that I was pretty sure that Guenther would at some point try to escape. I was just about to get into my jeep to return to 51 Div., when who appears on the scene but a photographer from AFPU (the Army Film and Photographic Unit), who had been told by someone in the ACV (Armoured Command Vehicle) about my exploit in capturing the OC of No.2 Battalion 1st Parachute Regiment, and wanted to take a picture of the two of us ... And this is the one (reproduced here) which has reappeared over the years in book after book, and film after film, about the Italian campaign!

According to Major Pond – *Sicily* pp. 142–3 – Albrecht Guenther continued to attract interest in various quarters as he was moved back down the line: 'Many of the captured German parachutists, taken back to rear areas for treatment and questioning, remained arrogant and hostile in the face of all threats and interrogation ... One of them, 28 year old Lieutenant Albrecht Guenther, captured behind the lines in civilian clothes, was taken to 8th Army Headquarters, and interviewed by Major General Francis de Guingand, where he was warned that under International Law he could be taken out and shot as a spy.

'Quite calmly the young man replied: "That is quite understood. But as a para-chutist who has fought in Holland, France and Russia, it does not alarm me. I took the risk and I failed – I deserve it. Heil Hitler!"

'De Guingand ordered him to be taken to a prisoner of war camp, and released the story to the BBC in the hope that it might lead to better treatment for some of the Allied prisoners.'

*   *   *

When I reported back to Div. HQ I was told to proceed immediately to the HQ of the 152 Brigade – this was the brigade which had had to deal with the paratroops from Avignon – and try to placate Brigadier Gordon MacMillan of MacMillan, who was threatening to shoot another batch of paratroops in plain clothes, captured that morning. To mollify him – and I could see there was a genuine danger that he would actually carry out his threat – I explained that all captured German personnel were needed for interrogation at Army HQ, and that he might well be denying valuable operational information to Monty. So, to make the point, and mollify the irascible clan chief still further, I paraded the Germans in front of him, and tore strips off them – telling them that under International Law we would be quite justified in executing them summarily, and that they were darned lucky to fall in to the hands of this particular civilised Highland gentleman.

The Brigadier complimented me on my command of vituperative German, and offered me a glass of vino.

*　*　*

There is a sequel to this particular story. Sixteen months later, in December 1944, I was attached as an IO to 1st British Infantry Div. on the northern slopes of the Apennines. We held Monte Grande, overlooking the Po plain, and facing us was the German 1st Parachute Division – the same outfit which had been dropped over the hills around Francofonte, and had been well and truly sorted out by the Camerons and Seaforths. (At that time we were preparing for the final offensive which – in collaboration with the great Partisan insurrection of April '45 – was going to wrap up the war in Italy.)

On 12 December, these paratroops of 1 Div. launched a crazy frontal attack on Monte Cerere, with the clear intention of using it as a springboard to Monte Grande – the idea being to squeeze out our own troops at neighbouring Montecalderaro. The attack was a ghastly fiasco: 19 Brigade of 8th Indian Division, which was on our left flank, properly gave them the works; they suffered heavy losses, and their dead littered the hillside. They did manage to take Casa Nuova, but got thrown out of it again almost immediately, because our troops in Frassineto were able to shoot up their left flank. On Monte Cerere they bit the dust, and never got into our positions at all.

It was not long before prisoners arrived in our lines – some frankly deserters – and I remember reflecting grimly that at any rate they were all still wearing their uniforms! … All seemed keenly desirous to tell all they knew to the interrogator, and one and all combined to cuss the battalion commander who had sent them on this senseless enterprise. One of these prisoners was a company sergeant-major, and he bitterly accused that battalion commander of having *Halsschmerzen* (throat pains) – in other words of sacrificing his men, in order to win a *Ritterkreuz* (Knight's Cross), which was worn in front of the throat.

And what was the name of this ambitious *condottiere*? It was none other than Guenther – Major Guenther – and although that's a common enough surname in Germany, I could not help wondering if – by some extraordinary far-out chance – this bloke could possibly be the same Guenther I had captured in Sicily. I asked the sergeant-major if he knew anything about the background of this officer, and he said everyone in the battalion knew something about it, because the major could never stop boasting about his exploits. He had been in the campaign in France and Holland in 1940; had fought in Russia in '41 and '42; and although he had had the bad luck to be captured in Sicily, had managed to escape from a prisoner of war camp in southern Italy and had made his way through southern France to Germany; and that was how he had come to get his present job.

So … I was forced to face up to it – the blighter I had captured in Sicily was now facing me again on our section of the northern Apennines. I did not divulge this to the Oberfeldwebel, but I could not help reflecting – there was nothing for it now but for me to capture him again!

However, I was not to have that pleasure. When the final offensive got under way, he was captured and bumped off by one of the Emilian partisans.

* * *

Back to Sicily. The Campaign officially ended on 17 August 1943 when – the 'Italian and German High Commands having successfully completed the evacuation of their troops to the completed Italian mainland – a GI patrol entered Messina; Later the same day, General George S Patton Jr accepted the formal surrender of the city in the town hall. A few moments later – according to Major Pond – a British armoured car patrol drove in to Messina from the south;, .

In response to a GI query: 'Where youse guys been?' they greeted their Allies with a friendly 'Hullo, you lousy bastards!' – which was misunderstood by the Americans who were unaccustomed to such crude banter and thought they were being insulted.

* * *

A couple of days later I was proceeding in a jeep from Zafferana Etnea – a badly bomb-blasted village on the east side of Etna – to the little town of Linguaglossa (tongue in two lingos!), when I heard coming from a little piazza on the outskirts of the town the unmistakable sound of a massed pipe band. I hadn't heard a massed pipe band since Libya – since the big parade for Churchill in Tripoli, in fact – and although I was supposed to report to Big Tam Wimberley at Main Div. HQ – I decided to take five or ten minutes off, saying to myself: 'The bloody campaign's over – Big Tam will just hae to wait!'

Getting my driver to park the jeep, and asking him to stay with it, I moved forward with some difficulty through a dense crowd of enthusiastic Sicilians, shouting things like 'Viva la Scozia' and 'Viva gli Scozzesi', till I got to the top of the approach road leading to the piazza, and saw there a magnificent and heart-warming sight. It was the massed pipe band of 153 Brigade – two Gordons battalions, and one Black Watch battalion – and they were playing the beautiful retreat air *Magersfontein*. Presiding over the occasion was the immense bulk of Etna, with a plume of smoke drifting lazily from its crater.

In the silence after the retreat air finished I stood wondering what the Pipe Major was going to get his boys to play for a March, Strathspey and Reel. When they struck up again, the March turned out to be one of my favourite pipe tunes – 'Farewell to the Creeks', a tune composed during World War I by Pipe Major James Robertson of Banff. And while I listened to it, words began to form in my head – particularly one recurrent line 'Puir bluidy swaddies are weary'.

And they were too! Since Alamein some of the companies of that splendid division had been more or less totally 'made up' due to heavy losses – and I knew that shortly they were going home, presumably to take part in yet another D. day in north-west Europe. By the time I had elbowed my way through the crowd back to the jeep, I had the beginnings of a song half completed; that night it had its first airing in a Gordons

Officers' Mess, and I was soon scribbling the words out in pencil for all ranks. It took off with amazing speed – and in the event, preceded me back to Scotland. When I was collecting songs with Alan Lomax in the North East in 1951, we were occasionally offered it – sandwiched between classic ballads, lyric love songs and comic ditties –by ex-soldiers who had been in Sicily!

And now we backtrack again – this time to Tunisia, where – after the fall of Tunis and Bizerta on 7 May '43, and the capitulation of the Axis armies under Von Arnim – the Highland Div. had been training hard for the invasion of 'somewhere' in Southern Europe. Three Greek officers were allotted to the Div., as part of an elaborate cover plan to deceive the enemy as to where we were going to invade. And when they were informed, once they had embarked, that they were heading for Sicily, they naturally became more than a little disgruntled, and I was given the task, on 9 July, of calming them down. I assured them that it would not be long before they were all back in Alexandria – the great Greek city of the ancient world!

On the evening of 6 July 1943 I had embarked at Sfax, on the south-east coast of Tunisia on LST (Landing Ship Tanks) No. 8, which was to carry us back to Europe. On deck, the following morning, I counted some 60 vessels visible to me, riding in the Sfax sea-roads. This was only a smallish percentage of our convoy, which was only a small percentage of the whole. The atmosphere was quite calm: rather like a Mediterranian cruise!

Our deck was crammed with vehicles; you could hardly move edgeways. We got an issue of Yank lifebelts,, to go with the LST, which had only recently left the shipyards of Mr Kaiser.

About 1720 hours on 8 July we up-anchored, and sailed north in a well dispersed convoy of 600 vessels. Later that evening, Brigadier Davey, Chief Engineer of 30 Corps gave us a pep talk on the forthcoming battle, and read us Monty's message. Up to then the weather had been calm, but on 9 July a juicy roll developed, which got juicier through the day. I surveyed the convoy from the upper deck, and read up once again the enemy order of battle, as we knew it at that time; I idly committed to memory the units of 206 Coastal Division, which were due to enter the bag the following day.

During the night – the last night before D. day! – the roll got worse and the whole ship shuddered. I stayed awake, and two lines of poetry – of sorts – started circulating in my head:

> To Sicily, to Sicily
> Over the dark moving waters.

Shortly I had my first stanza:

> Armour, vehicles and bodies
> Make heavy cargo that is checked and away
> To Sicily, to Sicily
> Over the dark moving waters.

This turned out to be the first stanza of the first part of what developed gradually into a quadripartite poem; I worked on it in a desultory fashion over the next few months, but did not get it finished to my satisfaction until the 8th Army was up on the Sangro Front, on the east side of Italy, and I was temporarily attached to 8th Indian Division, as an Italian- and German-speaking Intelligence Officer. My first title for it was *Ballad of Sicily.*

Some months later, when I was on the Anzio beachhead, I was surprised to get a letter from Nicholas Moore – the same Nicholas who had called me 'an incipient fascist', because I had said in the CUSC clubroom in Cambridge that, irrespective of his politics, Roy Campbell was a bloody good poet – and this letter included a request for contributions to a mag. he was editing called *New Poetry.* (He had got my umquhile address – care of the Highland Div. – from G S Fraser, who by that time was working in Asmara, in the offices of the *Eritrean Daily News.*)

I decided to send *Ballad of Sicily* to Nicholas, and posted it almost by return; later in 1944 I received a copy of *New Poetry* No. 2, (and found myself, for the first time, in the company of Conrad Aiken, Wallace Stevens and other poets whom I had long admired from afar).

Incidentally, I have now rechristened it *Ballad of the Simeto,* to avoid confusion with the *Highland Division's Farewell to Sicily* aka *Banks of Sicily.* Primasole Bridge, over the river Simeto, was the scene of the fiercest and bloodiest fighting of the Sicilian campaign.

The Highland Division's Farewell to Sicily

The pipie is dozie, the pipie is fey –
He winna come roon for his vino the day.
The sky ow'r Messina is unco an' grey,
And a' the bricht chaulmers are eerie.

Then fareweel ye banks o' Sicily
Fare ye weel, ye valley an' shaw.
There's nae Jock will mourn the kyles o' ye –
Puir bluidy swaddies are weary.

Fare weel, ye banks o' Sicily
Fare ye weel, ye valley an' shaw.
There's nae hame can smoor the wiles o' ye.
Puir bluidy swaddies are weary.

Then doon the stair an' line the waterside
Wait your turn, the ferry's awa.
Then doon the stair an' line the waterside
A' the bricht chaulmers are eerie.

The drummie is polisht, the drummie is braw –
He cannae be seen for his webbin' ava.
He's beezed himsel' up for a photy an a'
Tae leave wi' his Lola, his dearie.

Sae fare weel, ye dives o' Sicily,
(Fare ye weel, ye shielding an' ha')
We'll a' mind shebeens and bothies
Whaur kind signorinas were cheerie.

Fare weel, ye banks o' Sicily
(Fare ye weel, ye shieling an' ha');
We'll a' mind shebeens and bothies
Whar Jock made a dat wi' his dearie.

Then tune the pipes an' drub the tenor drum
(Leave your kit this side o' the wa').
Then tune the pipes an' drub the tenor drum.
A' the bricht chaulmers are earie.

Ballad Of The Simeto
(For the Highland Division)

I

ARMAMENT, vehicles and bodies
make heavy cargo that is checked and away
   to Sicily, to Sicily
   over the dark moving waters.

The battalions came back
   to Sousse and Tunis
through the barrens, and the indifferent
   squatting villages.

Red flower in the cap
   of Arab fiesta!
and five-fold domes
   on the mosque of swords!

We snuffled and coughed
   through tourbillions of dust
and were homesick and wae
   for the streams of Europe.

But the others were blind
   to our alien trouble
they remembered the merciful
   the Lord of daybreak.

Launches put out
   from palm fuzzed coastline
to where landing craft lay
   in the glittering sea-roads.

Och, our playboy Jocks
The ships revolved
   through horizons of dust –
then foregathered like revenants
   from the earth near fresh graves.

Cleaned machine guns and swore
in their pantagruelian
   language of Bothies
and they sang their unkillable
   blustering songs,
ignoring, the moon's
   contemptuous malice.

All the apprehensions, all the resolves
and the terrors
and all the longings are up and away
   to Sicily, to Sicily
   over the dark moving waters.

II

Take me to see the vines
   take me to see the vines of Sicily
for my eyes out of the desert
   are moths singed on a candle.

Let me watch the lighthouse
   rise out of shore mist. Let me seek
on uplands the grey-silver
   elegy of olives.

Eating ripe blue figs
   in the lee of a dyke
I'll mind the quiet of the reef
   near the lonely cape-island

and by the swerve of the pass
   climb the scooped beds of torrents
see grey churches like keeps
   on the terraced mountains.

The frontier of the trees
   is a pathway for goats
and convenient sanctuary
   of lascive Priapus.

Over gouged-out gorge
   are green pricks of the pines:
like strict alexandrines
   stand the verticle cypresses.

O, with prophetic grief
   mourn that village that clings
to the crags of the west
   a high gat-toothed eyrie

for the tension in the rocks
    before sunset will have formed
a landscape of unrest
    that anticipates terror.

A charge has been concealed
    in the sockets of these hills.
It explodes in the heat
    of July and howitzers.

We are caught in the millennial
    conflict of Sicily.
Look! Bright shards of marble
    and the broken comice.

III

On the plain of dry water courses
    on the plain of harvest and death
the reek of cordite
    and the blazing stooks!

Like a lascar keeking
    through the green prickly pears
the livid moon kindled
    gunpowder of the dust

and whipped to white heat
    the highland battalions
who stormed, savaged and died
    across ditches called rivers.

Battle was joined
    for crossing of the Simeto.
Pain shuddered and shrieked
    through the night-long tumult.

But aloof from the rage
    of projectiles and armour
our titan dreamed on
    into brilliant morning.

And suspended from clouds
    was asleep like a bat
in the ocean of summer
    a blue leviathan.

Yes, Etna was symbol
    of the fury and agony.
His heart was smouldering
    with our human torment.

– Drink up your fill
   parched trough of the Simeto
for blood has streamed
   in too wanton libations

and tell of the hills
   hard mastered Dittaino
where broke with our onslaught
   the German iron.

A bonnet on two sticks
   is tomb for the Gael.
Calum Mor, mak
   mane for Argyll.

IV

Through doon-tuminelt clachans
   platoons of scozzesi
with tongues like fir cones
   and eyes like hidalgos.

Panache of pipes
   and the tasselled swagger
doddle of drums
   and a jig for danger!

The balconies, fountains
   and children greet them:
the hungry, the hating
   the weak will know them.

Who lift in their arms
   the sloe-eyed bambini
whose laugh crosses gulfs
   of the lapse of language.

Their dirks in the wames
   of sniftering bonzes
the lusty Jocks
   who desire signorine

and castrating tyrants
   in search of vino
our drouty billyboys
   in tartan filibegs!

– Gay pierrot plumes
   on the horses greet them:
guitarists and hawkers
   and hoors will know them.

Where faro armed
   keeps an eye on the straits
they'll strip for a swim
   in debatable waters

then loose on Calabria
   the sons of the hounds
to exult in red fangs
   of vicious artillery.

Ballads and bullets
   and reels to fire them!
The hangmen, the hornies,
   the deils will fear them!

Gramsci and the Partisans

Bandiera Rossa

After the fall of Rome, in June 1944, Partisan activity in Central Italy increased by leaps and bounds. In the area south of Florence the formation of partisan bands became a serious worry for the German Command. In Umbria these Garibaldini – as they became known – succeeded in creating the first of the liberated zones. Between Val Nerina and Reatino, a formation known as the Brigata Gramsci liberated over 1,000 kilometres of territory. A document defining its boundaries was one of the first of its kind to be drawn up during the struggle for freedom.

Kesselring, who had earlier not taken very seriously the possibility of Italian partisan assaults behind the line, now changed his tune, and ordered an all-out war against the patriots, the majority of whom in Tuscany were fighting under the *Bandiera Rossa* – the Red Banner: that is to say they were affiliated to the Communist Party of Italy.

His order read: 'It is the duty of all troops and police under my command to adopt the severest measures. Every act of violence committed by the partisans … must … be … punished immediately … wherever there is evidence of a considerable number of partisan groups, a portion of the male population of the area will be arrested, and in the event of an act of violence being committed, these men will be shot.'

When I heard about this from prisoners, I naturally remembered the appalling atrocity of the Ardeatine caves – the Germans shot 335 hostages in March 1944, after a partisan attack in Rome, while we were still on the Anzio beach-head – and I realised that the anti-Fascists of the Centre and North were taking on a totally ruthless enemy. Indeed, Kesselring's invitation to the troops under him to commit acts of savage inhumanity was quite unambiguous; he stated that he would 'protect any commander who exceeded the usual restraints in the choice of the severity of measures undertaken'.

Partisan Brigades

Nevertheless, there was no shortage of volunteers to join the partisan brigades on Monte Scalari and on Monte Giovi, and there they had the luck to find as leader one of the most charismatic paladins of the whole Italian Resistance – Aligi Barducci, whose battle-name was Potente. It was this hero who was to command the four brigades of the partisan Division of the Arno – Sinigaglia, Lanciotto, Caiani, Fanciullacci – which on 3 August came down from the Pratomagno, and proceeded to take part in the liberation of the Tuscan capital.

As the front drew ever nearer to the city, the High Command on both sides found itself faced with the appalling problem: what on earth was to be done about Florence? Was is possible to declare Florence 'an open city' and would the other side respect the declaration, if it were made? The same problem naturally faced Cardinal Elia Dalla Costa, who for months had been pressing the Germans to declare Florence an open city. On 12 May 1944 he received the following message from Hitler's HQ:

> The German Wehrmacht will continue to exert every possible effort to avoid giving the enemy any excuse to carry the war into this jewel of Europe.

On 6 July Kesselring addressed the Cardinal as follows: 'I appeal to you, Your Eminence, to try to obtain a clear and valid declaration from the Allies that they will respect Florence as an open city, and therefore will not exploit the territory of the city for military advantage.'

In his reply, the Cardinal asked Kesselring to consent to the despatch of a delegation of citizens of Florence to make contact with the Allied High Command, but no satisfactory reply came from the Germans.

Meanwhile, Field-Marshal Alexander had been conferring with Allied Intelligence officers about the same problems, and it was decided to enlist the aid of the partisans on the mountains, for two main reasons: one was the desirability of allowing Italian anti-Fascists to be given the honour of playing a major part in the liberation of the city; and the other was the necessity to secure the withdrawal of the Germans from the city. This meant that the partisans were to be given the task first and foremost of liberating the south bank of the Arno.

On July 30 the clandestine newspaper *l'Azione Comunista* published the following declaration:

> Marshal Kesselring.
> Having robbed us of our wealth, of our industries, after deporting and killing thousands of our brothers; having deprived us of water, gas, electricity, transport, auto-ambulances and every other public service; having destroyed our factories, our mills, our public buildings; having condemned us thus to the torments of an existence lower than that of the brute beasts, you now have the utter shamelessness to assert that you and your Nazis have conducted your-selves correctly towards us, and to accuse Alexander and the British soldiers who have done everything possible to respect our city, of being the cause of our misfortunes!

On the same day, the CTLN – the Committee of National Liberation for the whole of Tuscany – sent the following message to 8th Army HQ: 'The Tuscan Committee of National Liberation with all its political, administrative and military services remains at the complete disposal of the Allied Command, and desires to establish a liaison with a view to effective collaboration.'

The Battle For Florence

On the night of 3rd to 4th August the Germans blew up the bridges over the Arno, including the Ponte Santa Trinita – frequently described as the most beautiful bridge in Europe. The only bridge they left was the Ponte Vecchio, the picturesque bridge, with shops over it, beloved of tourists, but they ravaged both ends of it, and the houses on its approaches were completely destroyed. Furthermore, the German demolition experts placed hundreds of mines and booby traps in the wreckage, effectively destroying use of the bridge to our forces.

The first job Potente's boys had to tackle when they occupied the streets and riverside avenues – 'Lungarni' – on the left (south) bank of the river, was to deal with the sniper problem, which was acute (to say the least of it). The Germans, retreating across the Arno, had left behind a number of well-trained snipers, who – co-operating with a number of Italian Fascist snipers – accounted for quite a number of our troops. The streets of Florence – narrow, curved, twisty, shadowy – were ideal lurking-places for these characters – particularly top-storey windows – and the partisans themselves suffered numerous casualties. The civilian population – starving, and deprived for weeks on end of basic services – assisted the partisans in dealing with the sniper menace – the worst of these *franco-tiratori* being undoubtedly the Italian Fascists themselves – and when they got hold of one of these characters, he was summarily despatched – and indeed was lucky if he wasn't torn limb from limb.

The Garibaldi Division of the Arno under Potente's command established its HQ in the Villa Cora on the left bank, and proceeded to make contact with the HQ 8th Army. It soon became clear to Potente that right-wing elements on the Allied side, far from wanting to enlist the support of the partisans in the forthcoming battle to push the Jerries out of Florence, had as their first priority the disarming of the partisans, and the dissolution of the Communist Brigades.

In tackling this difficult problem Potente showed qualities of agile democracy. Too energetic opposition might have cost the forces of the Resistance dear, and compromised the policies being pursued by the anti-Fascist parties. On the evening of 5 August indeed, partisans of the Sinigaglia Brigade set up armed check-points around their HQ and sent word to representatives of the Allies that they would regard as enemies any forces which attempted to disarm them.

In the event, Potente's diplomacy triumphed. On 6 August 8th Army HQ sent a message that it had decided to utilise all the 1,600 partisans of the Garibaldi Division of the Arno in the forthcoming operation for the liberation of the whole of Florence. The following day a senior British officer, accompanied by Potente, inspected the brigades of the Division, and it was arranged that the Sinigaglia Brigade, accompanied by two companies of the Lanciotto, should take part in an operation to deal with the gunners on the north bank, who were harassing the avant-garde of the British and Canadian forces across the river.

One of the casualties of these unremitting bombardments was a young Scots Guards officer, Lieutenant Hugh M Snell, who was killed on 4 August. (After the war, a plaque was placed on the wall of a house in the Via Lupo, close to where he died, by some of his partisan comrades. He had been held in high esteem by the Garibaldini, one of whom paid tribute to his 'noble imperturbable. bravery').

From the time Garibaldini came down from the mountains, Potente had lived for the moment that the partisans under his command would be authorised to cross the Arno, and to take on the hated Nazi-Fascists in the Tuscan capital. On the 6th of August the order came. I remember as if it were yesterday the handsome blonde partisan general, in his red shirt and khaki breeks, poring over a sheet map of Florence, and issuing orders to his red-neckerchiefed subordinates and to the Canadians who were under his command.

Some 50 Canadian soldiers were to join 400 partisans in the operation on the following morning (the 9th). However, the Germans seem to have got wind of the forthcoming attack, and that evening a ferocious mortar bombardment raked the areas where the partisans were concentrated (San Frediano and San Spirito). Potente, and the British officer – Captain Wilmot – who was assigned to him, were wounded by the same shell. Potente suffered a terrible stomach wound and another wound in his thigh, and he bled to death from these wounds.

When British ambulance men arrived they went first to the British officer, but he refused attention until Potente had been attended to – a chivalrous gesture remembered to this day by the surviving Garibaldini who were present.

Immediately after Potente's death, the brigade commanders decided to re-christen the division: the 'Division Potente of the Arno'.

Furthermore, his passionately expressed wish that the division should not be dissolved – as was intended at 8th Army HQ – was to a certain extent fulfilled, for I succeeded in persuading our Div. commander to allow me to organise a small stream-lined partisan corps of our own, recruited from volunteers from among the partisans: a command section of five at Div. HQ, and with each brigade and the recce a group of five under a section leader. They were to act principally as guides in the Borgo San Lorenzo area, and accompany our troops on the advance towards the German 'Gothic Line'. Their elected leader was a partisan whose battle-name was Lazio – he had been vice-commander of the Lanciotto.

Gramsci – Un Grande Pensatore

It was while organising this little show, which was to prove its worth over and over again in the weeks ahead, that I first heard the name of Gramsci. Reference had been made by one of the partisans of the Lanciotto to a 'Brigata Gramsci', and I asked him who Gramsci was. 'Gramsci era capo del nostro Partito' was the reply. 'Era un grande pensatore.' (Gramsci was the leader of our Party – he was a great thinker.) It was not until after the war that I realised how apt the description was.

It is noteworthy that the great works quarried in the late 1940s and early 1950s from the prison notebooks saved for posterity by Tatiana Schucht, Gramsci's sister-in-law – *Historic Materialism and the Philosophy of Benedetto Croce*; *The Risorgimento*; *Intellectuals and the Organisation of Culture*; *Notes on Machiavelli, Politics and the Modern State* etc. – were not of course available as yet to the public; nevertheless, the idea of Gramsci as a 'great thinker' was already 'floating in the air'. This was probably a result, not only of Gramsci's brilliant prolific journalism in the early 1920s, but also – and maybe principally – of the classes he conducted in prison for the benefit of the other inmates.

Antonio Gramsci, the future leader of Italian Communism, was a Sardinian – and therefore a *meridionale* (Southerner); a commitment to Sardinian nationalism was his first political cause. It was when he was studying at a *liceo* in Cagliari, the provincial capital, that he published his first article, in *L'unione sarda* (the Sardinian Union), and 'out of intellectual curiosity' read his first Marxist texts. After winning a scholarship to the University of Turin, Gramsci left Sardinia, to return only four times before his death. He took with him an acute awareness of the misery and poverty endured by the peasants and workers of the island, and a lasting pride in the cultural heritage of Sardinia; particularly its dialect, folklore and traditional poems and songs.

Turin in 1911 was throbbing with the pulse of nascent and expanding Italian capitalism. It was the headquarters of FIAT; Itala, Diatto, Spa and Lancia all operated there. It was a period of expansion for the workers' movement, and of intense political debate as World War I approached. While a student, Gramsci experienced terrible poverty. From prison in 1927, he would write about this period to his younger brother Carlo:

> At home, they delayed about two months before sending me the application papers for the university. Since my enrolment was suspended, I couldn't yet receive the 70-lire monthly instalment of the scholarship. One of the university servitors saved me by finding a *pensione* costing 70 lire where they allowed me credit. I was reduced to such a point that I considered going to the police to ask them to send me home. When I received the 70 lire, I spent it all on a really wretched *pensione*. That winter I went around without an overcoat, wearing a light suit more appropriate for Cagliari. In March 1912 I was so depressed that I stopped speaking for some months; whenever I spoke the words got all jumbled up. Furthermore I was living near the banks of the River Dora, and the freezing fog got into my bones.

Gramsci completed a number of courses before dropping out in 1915 to become a full-time political activist. At the university he had met and befriended Togliatti and Angelo Tasca – future members of the executive of the Italian Communist Party. (Tasca gave Gramsci a French translation of *War and Peace* inscribed 'To today's school companion and to tomorrow's comrade in battle, I hope').

Togliatti remembered Gramsci joining the Psi – the Socialist Party of Italy – in 1913. The Psi was still under the influence of Mussolini, who would leave the next year because he advocated intervention in the war. Gramsci, influenced by this position, published an article in *Il grido del popolo* (the People's Cry), advocating an 'active and tactical' neutrality instead of an absolute one.

Russian Revolution

At the beginning of 1917, tomorrow's battle was on his doorstep. February saw the beginnings of revolution in Russia; October brought the Bolshevik Party under Lenin's leadership to power. The International Socialist Movement now had a focal point. As Gramsci was to write later in his prison notebooks, referring to Machiavelli's famous treatise *The Prince* (1532):

> The modern Prince, the myth Prince – cannot be a real person, a concrete individual. It can only be an organism, a complex element of society, in which a collective will, which has already been recognised and has to some extent asserted itself in action, begins to take concrete form. History has already provided this organism, and it is the political party – the first cell in which there come together germs of a collective will tending to become universal and total (*Prison Notebook*, ed. Hoare and Nowell Smith, p. 129).

In Gramsci's thinking a new 'collective will' had successfully imposed itself: the Bolshevik party was the 'Modern Prince' ... at one and the same time the organiser and active operative expression of the collective will.

Throughout Europe the war resulted in overwhelming suffering. The Turin working class, the heir of a militant history, rose up and spent four days on the barricades. The outcome was death, arrests and punitive shipments to the front. The demand had been for bread, but for the first time the name of Lenin was shouted, accompanied by chants for peace. Repression was swift and harsh, and the leadership of the local Psi was arrested. Gramsci, who had not directly participated, was left in charge. The national leadership of the Psi was criticised for not having supported the Turin proletariat after inciting it with its rhetoric. *The Confederazione Generale dei Lavoratori* (CGL), the socialist-affiliated union, was attacked for its collaborationism. These polemics would only grow, and would lead to the founding of the Italian Communist Party (Pci). At a secret national meeting of the 'revolutionary intransigent faction' of the Psi, convened in November 1917, Gramsci met Amadeo Bordiga, the first leader of the future Pci.

During 1918 Gramsci continued to write for *Il grido del popolo,* promoting the necessity for and organisation of a 'revolutionary culture' based on the belief that 'all men are intellectuals ... but not all men have in society the functions of intellectuals'. He spoke of a culture that would attack the division between worker and thinker: 'There is no human activity from which every form of intellectual participation can be excluded: *homo faber* cannot be separated from *homo sapiens.*'

Acknowledgments

I would like to express my indebtedness to the following for comradely help and encouragement over the years: Piero Sraffa, Carlo Gramsci, 'Al' Aldovrandi, Alfonso ('Bill') Vinci, Marian Sugden, Silvia Baraldini, Jessie Stewart.

Cencrastus, 54, 1996.

Introduction to *Prison Letters* of Antonio Gramsci (translated by Hamish Henderson)

One of the most striking pictures in the exhibition *The Vigorous Imagination: New Scottish Art*, which opened at the Scottish National Gallery of Modern Art on 9 August 1987, was 'The Self-Taught Man' by Ken Currie. This – like another of Currie's pictures, 'Ship-Yard Poet' – shows a Clydeside worker with a book in his hand. The poet is holding his own manuscript notebook; the 'self-taught man', sitting at a table, with the dove of peace on a poster behind him and a notebook open in front of him, is holding a volume on the cover of which, plainly visible, is the name GRAMSCI.

That a Scottish working-class intellectual – a stubborn survivor in Thatcher's Britain – should be interested in Gramsci's political thought in the 1980s is readily comprehensible. Indeed, he and folk like him might well have thought the fare through to 'East-windy West-endy' Edinburgh well worth the money if they had managed to get tickets for a film called *Gramsci* – sub-titled 'Everything that concerns people' – which was premiered at the Filmhouse a week after that same exhibition opened. In this film, made by Pelicula of Glasgow, a sort of Scottish connection was quite noticeably underlined, in that the Sardinian characters who are Gramsci's mates in Turi prison speak with recognisable Scots accents.

What, one wonders, would the ordinary filmgoer make of this arguably rather dubious ploy? Does the implied parallel hold water, or are we faced with mere jokey self-indulgence on the part of a young Scottish filmmaker?

To the student of European history Sardinia and Scotland might not seem very plausible yoke-fellows – a much closer parallel might seem that between Sardinia and Ireland, both victims of centennial foreign domination – but a closer examination suggests that there are similarities which lend body and substance to the film-maker's contrivance.

First and foremost, both communities (?countries. ?nations) have maintained, against the odds, dourly intransigent ethnic folkways which still exhibit a marked idiosyncratic 'national' character. The island of Sardinia has had to combat, from Carthaginian and Roman times onwards, the ruthless exploitation of its natural resources by a series of foreign invaders, and consequently its heroes, through the ages, have been what Eric Hobsbawm called 'primitive rebels': outlaws, brigands and freebooters who took it upon themselves to defend a last-ditch desperado independence against the ceaseless encroachments of self-seeking profiteering central authority. In one of the letters (no. 79) printed in this selection, Gramsci mentions a couple of these celebrities, and suggests that twentieth-century Sard children would have a more natural patriotic interest in them than in the tuppence-coloured heroes and heroines of 'official' history.

If Sardinia has had its Francesco Derosas and its Giovanni Tolu, Scotland has had its Rob Roy, its Gilderoy and its James Macpherson (hero of the famous 'Rant') – undoubtedly more 'real' (and 'patriotic') for Scottish children than the somewhat cartoon-like figure of Robin Hood.

There is another trait, common to Scots and Sards, which again seems a legitimate point of contact. The Sards, who for many generations provided soldiers and policemen for the service of Piedmont (and later for the Kingdom of Italy itself) have developed a very understandable respect for education, and all the advantages it can bring: Gramsci's own scholastic career bears eloquent testimony to this, as do many of his letters home, written when he was in prison (cf. letter 61, with its comments on how his niece Mea was being brought up). It is hardly necessary to underline the well-documented Scottish reverence for education and book-learning, particularly among the militant workers, who threw up a very special breed of working-class intellectual from the second half of the eighteenth century onwards. The Glasgow weavers – as the balladeer and playwright Freddy Anderson has recently written (*Scottish Trade Union Review*, no. 35, Summer 1987) had

> a great hankering for 'learning', and came to be the most educated and advanced of the working people of Scotland. Poets and scholars in various sciences arose from their ranks ... in the middle of the 19th century the banner of the vanguard of working-class struggle passed from the weavers into the hands of the iron and steel workers, the shipbuilders of Clydeside, and thus into another great period of intense struggle, which culminated in the early part of this century in the real legend, not myth, of Red Clydeside, with its famous shop stewards' committee, its brave women like Mrs Barbour of Govan. and Helen Crawford Anderson, and the thousands of others who have carried on the struggle of the Calton martyrs [striking weavers who were shot down by the military at Drygate Brig on 3 September 1787].

Finally, like other *meridionali* (southerners), the Sards are credited with being a dour, laconic, stubborn, self-analytical people – cf. note to letter 192 – and the formidable sinewy toughness to which many travellers have borne witness is not the least noticeable attribute of Antonio Gramsci himself.

This great Marxist – of whom Eric Hobsbawm has written that he was 'an extraordinary philosopher, perhaps a genius, probably the most original communist thinker of the twentieth century in Western Europe' – was born at Ales, in central Sardinia, the fourth of seven children; his father Francesco (who came of a well-to-do Neapolitan family of Albanian origin: *his* father had been a colonel in the Bourbon gendarmerie) was Director of the Office of Land Registry in the small town of Ghilarza. His mother, Guiseppina Marcias, a native of the island, was the daughter of a local tax inspector; she seems to have been a quite exceptional woman – and not only because, in the midst of a largely illiterate population, she was able to read and write. In brief, this was a petty bourgeois family which considered itself a cut above the peasants who made up the bulk of the local population.

When Antonio was 18 months old a servant girl who was holding him allowed him to fall from her arms, and as a result he gradually developed a bad spinal cuivature.[1] When he reached adulthood his deformity gave him the appearance of a hunch-backed dwarf: he was less than 5 ft in height.

In letter 90 he describes a childhood illness which nearly did for him, and adds that 'until round about 1914 my mother kept the little coffin and the special little shroud that they were going to bury me in'. As for school life, his first experiences of it were bitter in the extreme, because the other boys, with the cruelty of children, made merciless game of him and never admitted him to their games. Small wonder that he is remembered by the more honest of his schoolmates as a pitifully withdrawn little boy, the victim of constant bullying and persecution.

In 1897 an atrocious misfortune struck the Gramsci family. Francesco, father and wage-earner, was suspended without pay on suspicion of 'improper conduct' of the local administration; eventually he was sentenced to nearly six years' imprisonment. In all probability the wretched man had been framed for political reasons: he had supported the losing party in the elections of 1897. Peppina, the mother, had to bring up her seven children on her own, with no other money coming in to the family but the exiguous sums she earned as a seamstress. These years must have been appalling ones for the family; little Nino learned the horrors of dire poverty when he was at his most vulnerable through illness, and the experience stayed with him for the rest of his life. When he was eleven he had to go to work in the registry office, shifting large ledgers, and letter 150 gives us a heart-piercing account of the excruciating pains he suffered through doing work which was much too heavy for him.

His first years of schooling were badly disrupted by these misfortunes, but in spite of all this he managed in 1908 to pass the examination to enter the senior *liceo* in Cagliari; while in the island capital he lodged with his elder brother Gennaro, who had found work there after returning from military service. Gennaro had become a Socialist during his time in Piedmont, and he naturally lost no time in trying to indoctrinate Antonio, whose first political leanings were nevertheless towards Sardinian nationalism. After two years at the *liceo*, Antonio won a scholarship (for 'financially deprived students') to the University of Turin: he sat the exam at the same time as his colleague-to-be Palmiro Togliatti. At Turin, as at Cagliari, Gramsci was in miserable straits, physically and financially; his sister Teresina (in the same interview in *Gramsci Vivo* already quoted) puts on record letters home which are mainly continual pleas for comparatively small sums of money – 10, 15, 25 lire – and which, according to her, became a veritable incubus for the poverty-stricken parents themselves. Some of the prison letters describe the fearful conditions of extreme cold and malnutrition which Gramsci had to suffer as a student; during his first winter he did not even have an overcoat, and his suit was a summer suit more fitted for Cagliari than Turin. Most of the time he was an invalid, and eventually 'dropped out' of university life for the most comprehensible reasons – and also because, from mid-1915, he had moved over, as a committed Socialist, to political journalism.

If I stress the hardships of his youth, it is to make the point that, almost alone among the major Marxist thinkers of the twentieth century, Gramsci – although not of working-class origin – was subjected all through his early years to a poverty fully as corrosive as any contemporary proletarian could have had to endure, and this was compounded with health problems which would have driven most other men to the wall. Instead, he drew on the traditional fortitude and toughness of his Sard ancestors, which he himself extols in a letter to his sister Grazietta (156); in the same letter he recalls his mother's self-sacrificing heroism after the disaster which hit the family. One feels that his intransigent moral fortitude must have been largely due to his affection for her, and his memory of her unyielding tenacity.

There was, however, another element in his character which Teresina stresses in *Gramsci Vivo*: when liberated from the mockery and bullying of other school children, and when among his own brothers and sisters, he showed that behind the defences he had to put up he possessed a lively sense of humour (Teresina uses the English word).[2] She says repeatedly that he was 'merry, witty, ironical', and supplies several anecdotes to prove it; some of these are amusing fantasies about the supposed adventures of his younger brother Carlo. Although one must take into account Teresina's natural wish to counter the picture drawn by others of a withdrawn and melancholy child, there is plenty of independent evidence as to Gramsci's wit, and his satirical gifts. As for his storytelling capacities, also vouched for by others, we can readily recognise another well-attested Sard trait: the island storytellers are given to weaving fantastically convoluted folktales, adapting the stock of international *Märchen*, and giving them a 'local habitation and a name'. Writing to his wife Giulia on 1 June 1931 (letter 81) he gives an outline of a Sard folktale, and asks her to 'flesh it out' for his sons Delio and Giuliano. The Sards are also devoted to their very ancient ancestral types of folksong and music, and there are frequent references in Gramsci's letters to his childhood memories of the island's distinctive and attractive 'folk life'. There can be little doubt that, along with Gramsci's ironic spirit and his heroic political commitment to the betterment of the lot of the world's lowly, it was the memory of the popular culture of his native island which helped to sustain him during the darkest days of the 'long prison Calvary' (Guiseppe Fiori's phrase). Although he never completed his university studies – and his teachers, especially Matteo Bartoli, had foreseen a brilliant future for him in the realm of glottology and linguistics – Gramsci owed much to Turin University. It was there that he sharpened his love for exactness, precision and logical reasoning; there that he brought to full bloom his contempt for woolly superficiality, so often apparent in the prison letters. And there, too, that he met men like Umberto Cosmo, the renowned Dante scholar, who appears as a 'character' in the letters, and whom Gramsci remembered with affection – cf. letter 74 – in spite of a serious rift in their relations when Gramsci reproached his mentor for a dilettante approach to the workers' movement.

To Cosmo, too, Gramsci was indebted for his first introduction to the friend who was to play an enormous part in making more bearable his prison years: this was Piero Sraffa, the economist who was teaching at Cambridge when Gramsci was sentenced to 20 years' imprisonment in 1928. (A brief biography appears under the heading 'People in the Letters'.) Sraffa, from his secure and prestigious academic base in a famed redoubt of 'bourgeois' culture, was able to exert considerable moral pressure on the Fascist authorities, and he used this privileged position to the full. At the same time he was completely trusted by Togliatti, and other Communist leaders, and was therefore an invaluable personal and epistolary go-between in the prison years. That he maintained this position *vis à vis* the party without wavering, even after Gramsci's death, was ingenuously made clear by Maria-Antonietta Macciocchi in a rather baffled and acerbic account of her 1973 visit to Cambridge which she included in *Pour Gramsci* (Paris, 1974).[3]

It cannot be too strongly stressed that Gramsci was the inheritor of meridional high culture, as well as meridional hardship and poverty. Among the thinkers to whom there are frequent references in his writings is the philosopher Giambattista Vico (1668–1744), author of *La Scienza Nuova*, who, born like him in the backward tail-end of Italy, was nevertheless an important forerunner in a line which includes Marx himself. Writing about Vico, Gramsci usually prefaces his reference with the epithet 'the Neapolitan', and one senses that the word immediately brought another more recent Neapolitan philosopher to his mind. As Tom Nairn has written:

> Gramsci's cultural formation remained decisively marked by Southern Italian idealist humanism – the dominant school of thought among the educated classes of a still recently united Italy embodied in the personality and wide influence of the Neapolitan philosopher Benedetto Croce (1866–1952). This intellectual high culture was linked to a political liberalism which proved itself first corrupt and then, in the 1920s, ineffective against the rise of Fascism. There was to be no more penetrating critic of Italian Idealism than Gramsci himself; however, it should also be recognised that its influence furnished him with a degree of intellectual insulation, first against the determined economic Marxism of the Socialist Second International and then later against Stalinism. His own mature outlook was a sustained and quite self-conscious attempt to rethink Marxism in a kind of critical dialogue with the native philosophical and political idiom, and something can be seen from the title of the famous 1917 article with which he greeted the Bolshevik seizure of power in the Socialist Party daily *Avanti!*: 'Revolution against Capital'.

Among the most interesting letters written by Gramsci in prison are those containing reflections on Croce's historical writings, and his 'revisionism' (of Marxism); these re-phrase in often more accessible terms the same thoughts which occur in sections of the prison notebooks. For this we must surely thank his devoted sister-in-law Tatiana, who had clearly – in the gentlest possible fashion – laid out a bait for him after reading *A History of Europe in the Nineteenth Century*. The letters in question are 125, 126, 128, 129 and 133.

The effects of the October Revolution in Russia were felt immediately throughout the world, and nowhere more than in Italy, where a few months earlier the proletariat of Turin, 'Italy's Petrograd', had risen in a fierce spontaneous insurrection. After its suppression many of the most militant workers were sent to the front by the courts, and nearly all the most important Socialist leaders were arrested. Gramsci, who had joined the PSI in 1913, quickly emerged as the effective leader of a party in disarray; he took over the editorship of *Il Grido del Popolo*, the party weekly, at the end of August 1917, and was soon pointing to the Soviet model of workers' and soldiers' councils as the way forward to a proletarian revolution. (The inspirational figures in other European countries who most closely resemble him, at this point in history, are Karl Liebknecht, Rosa Luxemburg and John Maclean.) In April 1919, with Angelo Tasca, Palmiro Togliatti and Umberto Terracini, Gramsci founded a new weekly 'review of Socialist Culture' called *L'Ordine Nuovo* (The New Order): this journal soon acquired immense influence among the Torinese workers, and it was in it that Gramsci mapped out the plan of action which was to lead to the development of the shop stewards' committees (*commissioni interne*) – 'an embryonic form of worker government' – into factory councils, and eventually to the high point of Socialist militancy in September 1920, when the workers' occupation of northern Italian factories broke out in Milan, and soon spread to other industrial towns. However, the canny policies of the Liberal Prime Minister Giolitti (soubriquet: 'the old fox') ultimately prevailed; he refused to send in the troops – as some of the employers were demanding – and offered a compromise of 'industrial co-partnership' which never of course came to fruition, once the factory occupations were called off. As Gramsci was the first to recognise, this militant action could never have led to actual revolution; it was premature and uncoordinated.

Even before the occupation of the factories, Fascist squads had begun to use strong-arm tactics against Socialist centres and publishing houses, and the employers were soon pouring massive funds into Fascist organisations. The forces of reaction grew apace, and in October 1922, with Mussolini's 'March on Rome', the hopes of the Italian proletariat for a revolution on the Soviet model were obliterated.

At the PSI national congress in Livorno (January 1921), the Communist fraction at last rebelled against the supine 'centrist' leadership of the traditional ruling groups in the party, and the Partito Comunista d'Italia (predecessor of the present day PCI) was formed. Gramsci was among its founders, but the unquestioned leader – and the dominant figure in those early days – was Amadeo Bordiga, whose 'left sectarian' views were attacked in Lenin's famous polemical treatise *Infantile Extremism*, written in May 1920. It was one of the curiosities of the first edition of *Lettere dal Carcere* (published by Einaudi in 1947) that all references to the personal friendship that existed between Gramsci and this charismatic character were carefully excised.

In the Spring of 1922 Gramsci was sent to Moscow as representative of the PCI on the Executive Committee of the Communist Third International (Comintern), and could thus observe from a 'ringside seat' the beginnings of the power struggle which, well before Lenin's death, was already revealing itself, boding ill for the future well-being of the CPSU (Bolsheviks). However, the serious nervous illness which soon prostrated Gramsci and led, at the insistence of Zinoviev, to a lengthy stay in a sanatorium, was already in evidence before he left Italy; the defeat of the premature revolution must have been a serious blow to his morale, and undoubtedly exacerbated the crippling health problems from which he had suffered all his life. It was while he was recovering in the sanatorium that he met his future wife, Giulia (or Julka) Schucht, a member of a 'bourgeois' anti-Tsarist family which had spent prolonged periods in Italy. Julka was the one love of Gramsci's life, and she bore him two sons, one of whom (Giuliano) he never saw. Exceedingly sensitive and highly-strung, Julka seems never to have come to terms with the cruel fate which befell her husband, and eventually she suffered a severe nervous breakdown. The evidence of their gradual estrangement, becoming increasingly obvious from the first months of 1931 onwards, makes tragic reading in these letters.

Giulia's elder sister Tatiana had remained in Italy when the rest of the family returned to Russia not long before the outbreak of the First World War, and she it was who devoted the rest of her life to succouring her brother-in-law. (See 'People in the

Letters'.) The precious *Quaderni del Carcere* (Prison Notebooks), which are now regarded as one of the major Marxist classics of the century, were saved for posterity by the agency of two people: one was the Bolognese cell-mate of Gramsci, Gustavo Trombetti, who tended him during the paroxysms of one of his worst illnesses, and who succeeded in secreting the notebooks in a trunk when Gramsci was moved (in November 1933) from Turi prison to Dr Cosumano's clinic at Formia; the other was Tatiana, who after Gramsci's death took charge of his effects, lodged the notebooks in the safe of the Banca Commerciale in Rome, and eventually – a year later – sent them to Moscow in a trunk (cf. P. Spriano, *Gramsci in Carcere e il Partito*, Rome 1977, Chapter VII).

Although poor Tatiana had to bear the brunt of Gramsci's black moods of desperation, induced by 'prisonitis' as well as by harsh, unendurable physical pain – at one point we even hear from him the cry *'Ho rovinato la mia existenza'* ('I have made a ruin of my life'), which (for me) tragically recalls Rimbaud's agonising words, in his last letter to his sister *'Enfin, notre vie est une misère, une misère sans fin. Pourquoi donc existons-nous?'* – she never faltered in her devotion to her brother-in-law, and was with him as much as possible right up to the early morning of 27 April 1937, when he breathed his last. 'I watched over him all the time, doing what I could, moistening his lips, trying to restore his breathing by artificial means when it seemed to want to stop; but then there was one last loud breath, and an irreversible silence. I called the doctor, who confirmed my fears. It was 4.10 a.m. on the 27th.' (Tatiana's letter to Piero Sraffa in Cambridge, printed as an appendix to *Lettere dal Carcere*, 1965, pp. 917–18).[4]

We must now turn back in time for a brief account of Gramsci's life from the time he married Julka in Moscow, up to the day of his arrest in 1926. Towards the end of 1923 he was sent to Vienna, where he spent five months in charge of a Comintern 'information bureau' whose aim was to coordinate anti-Fascist action. In April 1924 he stood as a parliamentary candidate – Mussolini was still tolerating an elected parliament, although the election took place in a climate of violent strong-arm harassment throughout the peninsula – and was elected a deputy by a constituency of the Veneto. Relying on parliamentary immunity, he returned to Italy the following month, and for the rest of his time as a free agent he attempted to combat the ever-tightening grip of Fascism on the life of Italy by constructing alliances with other socialist or democratic forces. This entailed a sharp fight against the 'élitist' left sectarianism of Amadeo Bordiga, and at the Third Congress of the Party (held at Lyons in January 1926) his leadership was decisively confirmed, his policies obtaining 90 per cent of the vote.

The power struggle in Moscow was increasingly preoccupying him, and in October 1926 – only a month before his arrest – he sent a hard-hitting letter on behalf of the Political Bureau of the PCI to the Central Committee of the CPSU – care of Togliatti, who was embarrassed by it, and did his best to keep it dark, showing it only, it seems, to Bukharin and Manuilski. He attempted to justify this course of inaction in a letter to Gramsci, which the latter indignantly rebuffed. In his letter to the Central Committee Gramsci made it clear that the Italian Party leadership supported the Stalin/Bukharin majority in the Russian party, and blamed the 'Left' – Trotsky, Zinoviev and Kamenev – for the deep cleavage which had opened up, but he made no bones about his concern lest the Russian leadership tear itself apart. Indeed, he was bold and forthright enough to remind the CC of its responsibilities to the international proletariat. 'Today you are in the process of destroying your own work ... you are running the risk of compromising the directing role which the Communist Party of the Soviet Union had acquired under the impulse of Lenin ... Unity and discipline cannot be mechanical and coercive; they must be loyal, and the result of conviction, and not those of an enemy unit imprisoned or besieged – thinking all the time of how to escape, or make an unexpected counter attack ... comrades Zinoviev, Trotsky and Kamenev have contributed powerfully to our revolutionary education; they have sometimes corrected us with a good deal of rigour and severity; they have been counted among our masters.' One does not have to read between the lines to realise that Gramsci foresaw a bureaucratic degeneration in the Soviet Party which would lead inexorably to the elimination/liquidation of the opposition, and to the absolute personal power of the victor – in a word, to Stalinist dictatorship. Maria-Antonietta Macciocchi is undoubtedly right when she comments (*Per Gramsci*, Bologna 1974, p. 125): 'Could Stalin ever have forgotten or forgiven Gramsci, the leader of the Communist Party, for this firm act of criticism, directed openly to the International, and admonishing it in such terms?'[5]

Here one confronts the appalling paradox clearly enunciated by the painter Renzo Galeotti when he remarked (in a conversation with the present writer): 'By shutting him up, and keeping him shut up, Mussolini saved him' (*Mussolini l'ha salvato*).

On 8 November 1926 Gramsci was arrested in Rome, and after six weeks in political exile on the island of Ustica, 30 miles off the north coast of Sicily, he was taken to San Vittore prison in Milan, where he remained until May 1928. Put on trial in Rome on the 28th of that month, he was sentenced to 20 years, 4 months and 5 days' imprisonment, after being found guilty of conspiracy, and of agitation, provoking class war, insurrection and alteration of the Constitution and the form of the State through violence. Some of the prosecutor's words – reputedly echoing a demand of Mussolini himself – have become famous (or rather infamous): 'We must prevent this brain from functioning for 20 years.' On 19 July he arrived at the 'Penitentiary for Physically Handicapped Prisoners' at Turi, near Bari, and there he remained for the next five years in conditions which ensured that this physically ailing man had in effect received a death sentence. The progress of his destruction is revealed in cruel detail in these prison letters.

It was not until 1929 that he received permission to write anything other than letters in his cell; on 8 February of that year he began making notes in the first of the *Quaderni del Carcere* (Prison Notebooks). When he left Turi for the clinic at Formia (19 November 1933), there were 21 of these, and we have already related how they were saved for posterity. Gramsci was prevented by illness in 1935 from writing any more, but by that time there were 2,848 tightly packed pages in no less than 33 notebooks. They undoubtedly constitute a prodigy of will, intellect and indomitable staying power. I have no space here to attempt even a bald summary of the major strands of Gramsci's thought, as they can be discerned in these amazing manuscripts. His concepts of hegemony, civil society, 'national-popular', passive revolution, organic intellectuals, historic bloc, 'integral state' and war of position – to name only a few of the principal headings – are now the common currency of Marxist discussion.[6] The reader is referred to the annotated booklist which can be found at the end of the Introduction.

The three numbers of the *New Edinburgh Review* devoted to Gramsci in 1974 included the papers read to, and discussed at, the First National Day Conference on Gramsci, held in June 1974 at Edinburgh University (two papers were also included which were not read). The following is a list of the contributions: Stephen White, 'Gramsci and Proletarian Power'; Ann Showstack, 'Gramsci's Interpretation of Italian Fascism'; Gwyn A. Williams, 'The Making and Unmaking of Antonio Gramsci'; Stephen White, 'Gramsci in Soviet Historiography'; V. G. Kiernan, 'Gramsci and the Other Continents'; C. K. Maisels, 'Gramsci between Two Internationals'.

As will be seen from this list, the emphasis at the Conference was very much on Gramsci's political thought, and his part in Italian history. However, it is his writings on cultural matters – and in particular on popular culture, folklore and linguistics – which have increasingly occupied commentators in recent years. The compendium *Selections from Cultural Writings*, edited by David Forgacs and Geoffrey Nowell-Smith, and translated by William Boelhower, provides many of the basic texts. These display, more eloquently, perhaps, than any other sections of the prison notebooks, the astounding breadth of Gramsci's reading; his omnivorous interest (recalling Rabelais and Joyce) in words and all those things of which they are symbols; his penetrating powers of analysis when dealing with the different modes of perceiving society and the world to be found in different human groups and classes; and, last but not least, his real literary gifts when dealing with subjects which stimulated and challenged his imagination.

The Open University has greatly assisted in a wider diffusion of Gramsci's ideas on popular culture. In their second level course (U203), his name makes regular appearances, and there is a useful summary of his ideas on how the cultures and ideologies of different classes are related to one another in Tony Bennett's booklet accompanying 'Popular Culture' Block 1, Unit 3. Bennett draws to a considerable extent on the writings of Stuart Hall.

Mention should also be made of the role of *Marxism Today* in applying Gramscian methods of political and cultural analysis to the concrete situation in Thatcher's Britain.

In Vol. 2 of *International Folklore Review* (1983) Moyra Byrne has an excellent article on 'Antonio Gramsci's Contribution to Italian Folklore Studies'. She begins by surveying his notions of multiple levels of culture and society within and also linking and even transcending the broad designations of subaltern and hegemonic classes. She stresses the fact that the categories of thought and behaviour which Gramsci identifies as 'common sense' and 'good sense' ('good sense' being already more self-aware and therefore on a somewhat higher level than 'common sense') are found at all levels of culture and society. She then goes on to examine the apparent paradox which seems inherent in Gramsci's view of folklore: on the one hand he elevates folklore to the status of a world-view which demands serious study, and on the other hand he defines it as an incoherent heap of detritus which must be swept away by the class-conscious broom of a future working-class hegemonic culture.

It is this fruitful thought-provoking dialectical confrontation which has incited several warring factions in Italy and elsewhere into controversy; these have, over the years, tried to make sense of and synthesise the seemingly ambivalent and contra-dictory Gramscian views of folk culture.

At this point, I hope I may be allowed a personal reminiscence. When Alan Lomax arrived in Britain in 1950, at the start of an ambitious marathon of recordings for the Columbia World Albums of Folk and Primitive Music, I was working on the translation of Gramsci's prison letters which forms the basis of this new edition. He contacted me, and I interrupted the work to discuss Scottish and Italian folk culture with him. On the table lay *Letteratura e Vita Nationale*, which had just been sent to me from Italy, and I took the opportunity of introducing Lomax to the name of Gramsci, saying he was undoubtedly a major philosopher. Being a practical American, Lomax asked: 'What has he got to say to us?', and I told him, 'Quite a lot about folklore.' Also, to be practical, I gave him the name and address of Roberto Leydi, whom I had met in Milan a few months earlier.

In 1981 Moyra Byrne interviewed Leydi, who paid tribute to Gramsci's influence on Italian folklorists, and he explained to her his own role in the Italian folksong revival. He told her: 'I couldn't identify with the Italy of Victor Emmanuel, the history of wars, the battle of Solferino, generals, and so on and yet each of us has the need for patriotism of some sort.' He then went on to discuss a phenomenon which, many years earlier, Cesare Pavese had already described to me: namely the fascination of young intellectuals in Italy with the 'other America' of the poor and the outcasts as discovered through novelists like Steinbeck, Faulkner and Dos Passos; or through American neo-realist films, New Orleans Jazz and the Roosevelt era's Farm Security Administration documentation. (It was, of course, exactly this sort of complex of influences – plus Woody Guthrie, the Weavers, Pete Seeger and the Pioneer Revival Singers in the USA – which helped to spark off the now flourishing folk revival in Britain and other parts of Europe.)

Pioneering work in the field of 'oral history' was taking place before the outbreak of the Second World War – the Mass Observation project in Britain was part of the same movement – but the very phrase 'oral history' seems to have been an American invention. In Joseph Mitchell's *McSorley's Wonderful Saloon* (New York 1938) there is a rather moving description of one Joe Gould – 'Professor Sea-gull' – a maverick Yankee Bohemian of impeccable New England ancestry, who devoted his life to amassing materials for an enormous book to be called *An Oral History of Our Time*. Joe wrote and slept in parks, doorways, flop-houses, lobbies, cafeterias, on benches, on 'L' platforms, in subway trains and in public libraries. He described what he was aiming to do in the following terms: 'What we used to think was history – all that chitty-chat about Caesar, Napoleon, treaties, inventions, big battles – is only formal history and largely false. I'll put down the informal history of the shirt-sleeved multitude – what they had to say about their jobs, love affairs, vittles, sprees, scrapes, and sorrows – or I'll perish in the attempt.'

Joe Gould makes a fleeting appearance in early twentieth-century American poetry, by courtesy of e.e. cummings, who wrote (*Collected Poems*, no. 261): 'a myth is as good as a smile but little joe gould's quote oral history unquote might (publishers note) be entitled a wraith's progress or mainly awash while chiefly submerged or an amoral morality sort-of-aliving by innumerable kind-of-deaths.' (This must be one of the earliest references in literature to a now popular academic discipline.)

An essay of Gould's, printed in the April 1929 issue of *The Dial* had (according to Mitchell) a curious effect on American literature. A second-hand copy of the review was bought a few months later by the 20-year-old William Saroyan, who was greatly struck by Gould's work.

> To this day, I have not read anything else by Joe Gould. And yet to me he remains one of the few genuine and original American writers. He was easy and uncluttered, and almost all other American writing was uneasy and cluttered. It was not at home anywhere; it was trying too hard; it was miserable; it was a little sickly; it was literary; and it couldn't say anything simply.

These words of Saroyan's bear a curious resemblance – as we shall see – to a passage in Togliatti's 1938 tribute to Gramsci, when he refers to the sterile inflated rhetoric of much Italian literature and speechifying.

While Gramsci in prison was writing – and sometimes (as the variations in successive drafts of the Variorum edition show) revising and elaborating his thoughts on high art and folk culture – Joe Gould was amassing at high speed his huge unpublishable Rabelaisian/Urquhartian report on the 'subaltern culture' of the USA. One can well imagine what Gramsci would have thought of a good deal of this, if it had come to his notice. And yet, in the solitude of his barely furnished cell, his thoughts constantly returned to the gorgeous resilient folk-culture of his native Sardinia, and he plied his correspondents (mother and sisters) with questions about festas, folksongs, banners and ballads. Can one doubt that this was a conscious effort to add sap and savour to a life given point only by indomitable cerebral obduracy: to counter the rigours of an existence whose staying power was based (as he put it in one letter) exclusively on the will.

Indeed the conviction grows, as one reads and re-reads his cultural writings, that these memories constituted one of the principal holds on reality which sustained him as the agonising years dragged on; that he felt the exorbitant human need, as Diego Carpitella expressed it, to define and occupy 'one's own territory'. The gradual building up by others of a micro-history of the nation – 'of all that concerns people' – might also surely come to seem a 'communist and revolutionary act'!

However, the 'negative' attributes of folk culture, which Gramsci clinically examined, were what initially worried and sometimes antagonised Italian folklorists. When the late Ernesto de Martino 'went out there to see what was happening' (Leydi's words) – in other words, to undertake invaluable anthropological fieldwork in southern Italy – he felt himself to a certain extent 'put on the spot' by these same 'disparaging' passages . In his book *La Terra del Rimorso* (Milan 1968) he provides a curious and frank account of the moral and methodological dilemma that, in effect, Gramsci's view of folklore posed for him and his co-workers.

Ernesto de Martino died in 1965. Younger scholars, building on his self-questionings, as well as on his researches, confronted the problem by examining 'the persistence and "refunctionalization" of traditional folklore forms ... in the context of the change towards industrialisation' and the modern consumer society (Clara Gallini, *Un filone specifico degli studi antropologici Italiani*: manuscript of paper delivered in Alexandria, Egypt in 1980). These scholars 'saw the need to get away from a too radical application of the dichotomy "hegemonic" and "subaltern" which would define the world-view of subaltern classes mainly in terms of the positive attributes which a hegemonic world-view has and which it lacks. In ways and degrees that varied from one scholar to another, they sought in Gramsci's philosophy, or in their development of it, a belief in the alternative value of subaltern culture and society' (Byrne, *International Folklore Review*, p. 73).

In short, the possibilities of a political utilisation of folklore – of the fostering of an *alternative* to official bourgeois culture, seeking out the positive and 'progressive' aspects of folk culture – were explored energetically by Italian folklorists. Some explicitly rejected the Gramscian concept 'national popular' – the idea that the masses could achieve a 'higher' national socio-cultural unity on the basis of a rejection of folkloric and 'provincial' values. Combating this general idea, Gianni Bosio contended that working people's culture had the quality of 'autonomy', 'otherness', alternative values, and continuity with the older peasant culture, and was not to be contaminated by the qualities of bourgeois 'higher' culture. Pointing to models in the USA and in Britain, Roberto Leydi (in successive numbers of *Il Nuovo Canzioniere Italiano* in the early 1960s) stressed the value to the working-class movement of songs taking their inspiration from folk traditions, and highlighted especially the anti-Polaris songs like 'Ding Dong Dollar' which were sung on the Holy Loch marches. His example sparked off a new wave of field collecting, and young singer-songwriters contributed some excellent new protest songs to the Italian folksong revival. Inside and outside the universities, research into oral history proceeded apace. Summarising these developments, Ms Byrne describes Gramscian theory as 'a complex system – a system which raises questions and stimulates a constant identification of one's "reasons" and "means". Identification, and continual reexamination, of reasons and means is particularly essential to any folklore studies which address a contemporary reality marked by a new complexity of rapidly changing interrelationships between different levels of culture.'

Reading again the scattered remarks on folklore in the prison notebooks, one realises afresh that there is an unresolved but creative clash of contradictions in Gramsci's approach. If 'all that concerns people' is the rightful preoccupation of the working-class intellectual, of the 'self-taught man', then this must surely include the most ancient patrimony of human exploit and dream.[7]

In the *Guardian* of 1 September 1987 there is a moving account of a woman lawyer's struggle in Canada to defend Indian rights. According to Leslie Pinder, the lawyer,

> The judge had never met an Indian person, and I think he was a bit scared about being taken into a different world. At the beginning we explained that they were a huntergatherer society, who hunted through their dreams, and that their dreams became maps. The judge stopped me and said, 'Every society must have leaders. Are you telling me this society doesn't have leaders?' I explained that they have experts, but that it's not a hierarchical society. He said, 'That's not possible.'

The *Guardian* report continues:

> Incomprehension mounted as elderly Indians delivered testimony in their own language, describing how the world was created, and the relationship between man, the animals and spirits. 'They talked about their prophets. The judge asked whether that was spelled "profits". It was an incredible struggle from beginning to end'.

Ms Pinder, who is still awaiting the outcome, has worked almost exclusively on Indian cases for the past decade. She is much taken with Laurens van der Post's view that the tribulations of aboriginal people represent the destruction of our 'darker' side. 'Our rational, materialistic side has tried to kill an aspect of ourselves that is natural, intuitive, spiritual and creative. When you go beyond government policies, that's the heart of the matter.'

This news item recalls passages in Bruce Chatwin's fascinating book *The Songlines* (London 1987). 'In theory, at least', says Chatwin, 'the whole of Australia could be read as a musical score.' A musical score of stunning complexity and numinous significance, of which the learning is the most imperative business in the world for the aboriginal inhabitants of that continent. Chatwin quotes Heidegger (*What are Poets For?*): 'the song still remains which names the land over which it sings'. He concludes his last section of 'Journey Notes' as follows:

> Trade means friendship and co operation; and for the Aboriginal the principal object of trade was song. Song, therefore, brought peace … I have a vision of the Songlines stretching across the continents and ages; that wherever men have trodden they have left a trail of songs (of which we may, now and then, catch an echo); and that these trails must reach back, in time and space, to an isolated pocket in the African savannah, where the First Man opening his mouth in defiance of the terrors that surrounded him, shouted the opening stanza of the World Song, 'I AM!'

Small wonder that Gramsci, fighting to assert his continued existence, and his will to execute a lasting work, *für ewig*, should have asked his mother (in a letter sent from Milan prison on 3 October 1927):

> When you are able, send me some of the Sardinian songs that the descendants of Pirisi Pirione of Bolotana sing in the streets; and if they have poetry competitions at some festa or other, write and tell me what the set themes are. What about the festa of San Costantino at Sedilo and the festa of San Palmerio? Are they still celebrated, and if so, what are they like nowadays? Is the festa of San Isidoro still a big occasion? Do they carry in procession the flag with the four Moors' heads on it,[8] and are there still captains dressed in the uniforms of bygone days? You know these things have always interested me a lot, so please give me the information I need, and don't think they are silly things unworthy of attention.

Gramsci would no doubt have been interested (and probably delighted) if he could have been accorded a precognitive glimpse into the future, and known that a song *Quadernos Iscrittos in d'una Cella Oscura* ('Notebooks written in a dark cell') would be recorded in Sardinia under the auspices of the Istituto Ernesto de Martino 32 years after his death. The text of this song was composed by Peppino Marotto. Here is a rough prose translation:

> Notebooks written in a dark cell by a wise man light up the world. Life is still hard because exploited people don't yet fight to the end for their sacred rights. Gramsci left his mother in Sardinia, his master in Turin, his wife in Russia. With

immortal fame, more than any star, shines forth the light of unity that he established. Through the merit of Lenin, every nation wants communism to lead them to glory. Against the aggression of imperialism, the victory will lie with the forces of Ho Chi Minh.

The recording was made in Orgosolo, Nuoro district, Barbagia province. The singers were Peppino Marotto himself and Umberto Goddi, Sebestiano Piras, and Pasquale Marotto. The manner of performance was a kind of polyphony traditional in the central plateau of Sardinia. It is presumed to be ancient. It consists of a lead voice ('*sa boghe*'), a bass, a 'contra', and a middle voice. While *sa boghe* sings the words, the choir comes in on the last note with a series of 'nonsense' syllables intoned rhythmically, and harmonises on the foundation laid down by the bass.

The poems, called *Mutettus*, are made up of a first part on an ABCD/BCDA scheme, and a second part in which some of these lines are repeated in a different order, but which – and this demonstrates the skill of the author or improvisor – come together to make complete sense.

The background to the song is not without interest. Till about 1965 the Orgosolo region was extremely backward, poverty was extreme and life was deeply conservative and traditional. The economy was pastoral. Then the great cheese-making concern of Galbani, in search of cheap sources of supply and labour, set up factories in and around Orgosolo. The life of the shepherds and goatherds was violently altered, and they found themselves pitchforked into the twentieth century, into a world of time-clocks, production lines and labour disputes. The political consciousness of the neighbour-hood developed very rapidly, and the changes in the content of the folklore quite outstripped the changes in form. Hence the appearance of entirely modern texts set in remarkably archaic frameworks, as illustrated by the Gramsci song.[9]

The passage from the letter to Gramsci's mother quoted above, and others like it, served to a large extent to neutralise the effect of the long series of negative attributes which passages in the *Quaderni* attribute to folklore. In the past decade a certain equilibrium, a synthesis of speculation and experience, has been achieved in this whole disputed area, and some of the lesser-known remarks of Gramsci have acquired a fresh relevance. In addition, folklorists outside Italy have begun to tackle the job of examining their field of study from a class perspective, and the fresh controversies and 'flytings' which will inevitably surface can only benefit from the vigorous intellectual battles already fought.

Before his death, Benedetto Croce wrote, in a tribute to Gramsci, that he ranked with Giordano Bruno, with Machiavelli, with Vico – and, by implication, with Croce himself – as one of the greatest of Italian thinkers. Certainly, nearly all major writers, artists and film-makers of post Second World War Italy were to a greater or lesser extent influenced by his mighty presence in the recent past. To mention only a few: Pier Paolo Pasolini wrote *Le Ceneri di Gramsci* (The Ashes of Gramsci);[10] Elio Vittorini celebrated the Gramscian cultural heritage in the pages of *Il Politecnico*; Riccardo Bacchelli, writing *Il figlio di Stalin* (The Son of Stalin) tackled the dreadful subject of totalitarian contempt for humanity, of which Gramsci was an outstanding victim; and Renzo Galeotti painted his extraordinary series of Gramsci studies – *Omaggio a Gramsci* – 'Homage to Gramsci: the life of a martyr for the working class represented in the manner of Sacred Art'. As for post-war Italian film-makers, from Roberto Rossellini ('the patron saint of neo-realism') onwards, there cannot be one who has not, to a greater or lesser extent, come under the spell of Gramsci's memory and intellectual heritage.

To be sure, many of these intellectuals were only marginally Marxist, but Gramsci's influence drew them irresistibly in the direction of the same hegemonic umbrella. As James Joll put it in his excellent short study *Gramsci*:

> Because of their variety as well as their fragmentary nature [the notebooks] provide texts to support many different views of Gramsci's message, as well as raising unnumerable questions to which, on account of the circumstances of his life, Gramsci could not give an answer. His range of interests, the extraordinary breadth of his own reading and of his historical and philosophical culture, as well as the enforced detachment with which he was writing his more theoretic work make him unique among Marxists. At the same time the fact that he remained rooted in the Italian and the European idealist cultural tradition so that, however much he reacted against them, Vico and Hegel, Sorel and Croce were in some ways as important for him as Marx and Lenin, means that it is easier for the non-Marxist to conduct a dialogue with Gramsci than with any other Marxist writer of the twentieth century.

This reflection brings us up against one of the charges which were being levelled against Gramsci by his prisonmates in his own lifetime – that he was a 'Crocean idealist and a social democrat'. When this was reported to him by Mario Garuglieri, he replied,

> I respect Croce as we should respect men who are high intellectuals (*di alto pensiero*); Croce is a serious scholar; in his historical criticism he proves how solid his thought is, and how profound his culture. As a philosopher he marks the highest development in Italian thought, but as a politician he is the latest expression of a liberal doctrine which defends a society which is at the end of its tether. My comrades will realise how Crocean I am when they see the work about Croce that I am going to produce.

However, as Alastair Davidson recounts (*Antonio Gramsci: Towards an Intellectual Biography*, p. 251) he was sufficiently upset by a campaign waged against him by some comrades to suspend the series of discussions he had been conducting in the exercise yard.

> Henceforth the prison was divided into two groups: those for and those against Gramsci. Gramsci showed no readiness to break off contact with the Socialist, Pertini, with whom he had cordial relations, much as he had refused to be anything but friendly with Bordiga when they were confined at Ustica three years earlier.

The feelings against Gramsci among members of the hostile group did not express themselves in words only: on at least two occasions there were despicable acts of attempted physical violence. Nevertheless, he did not succumb to pressure, for there was no way he could go along with the sterile, myopic and totally unrealistic dogmatism of 'The Third Period', from 1928 onwards: the fable, that is, that in the immediate future the imperialist world would enter a new period of crisis and economic collapse, and that this would lead automatically to a renewed series of revolutions in Europe. Gramsci maintained that the idea of an imminent insurrectionary outbreak against Fascism was a dangerous illusion, and he also seems to have expressed reservations about the equating of social democracy with 'social-fascism' – the self-destructive line which in Germany undoubtedly facilitated Hitler's rise to power. These disagreements would almost certainly have led to his expulsion from the Party if he had been a free man, but – as Victor Serge (a supporter of Trotsky) wrote sardonically – 'reclusion saved him from exclusion'.[11] (C. L. R. James's book *World Revolution 1917–1936*, published in 1937, is still one of the most concise expositions of the deformations and distortions that a principled Marxist revolutionary had to combat in the period when Stalin was consolidating his power. Unfortunately, it contains very little about the repercussions of the power struggle in Italy.)

For almost a year and a half – June 1931 till December 1933 – there were no political-theoretical references to Gramsci in the publications of the Italian Communist Party in exile. As Spriano explains:

> Ernesto Ragioneri correctly linked this silence with the whole atmosphere of the Comintern during the Stalinist emphasis on the struggle against 'social-fascism', and with Stalin's famous piece on the historiography of the Bolshevik Party in November 1931, which laid down criteria wholly different from those which Togliatti had endeavoured to provide for an historical rethinking of the experience of the party. (*Antonio Gramsci and the Party: the Prison Years*, p. 73)

It is hard to resist the conclusion that if Gramsci had indeed been released in this period, and had been able to make his way to the Soviet Union, he would eventually have been the target for suppression or 'liquidation'. Even if he had escaped with his life, it is highly unlikely that he would have been able to continue work on his prison notebooks in Vorkuta.

With the outbreak of the Spanish Civil War, and the coming of the new 'line' on Popular Fronts against Fascism, this whole picture changed dramatically. In Tom Nairn's words, 'Gramsci's stubborn anti-sectarianism and openness had altered in retrospect; from near treason it had become clear-eyed prophecy.' In the article 'Antonio Gramsci, Leader of the Italian Working Class', which Togliatti wrote in May/June 1937, and contributed to the 1938 collection of tributes and recollections published in Paris under the title *Gramsci*, he painted an unforgettable picture of his great comrade as the thinker to whom Italian socialism owed the most profound modification it had undergone in the course of its history. One of the passages in his article became famous:

> Not strong physically, gravely wounded in his physical being by nature, Gramsci had an incomparable fighter's spirit. His whole life was subject to his iron will. He radiated energy, peace, optimism; he was able to impose on himself the toughest work discipline, but could enjoy life in all its aspects. As a man he was a pagan – a relentless scourge of all imposture, of all false sentimentality, of all flabby weakness. He used the weapon of laughter and derision in an unrivalled way, to expose the vanity and duplicity of those preaching morality to

the people in the interests of the ruling class. He had a profound knowledge of the life and customs of the Italian people, of the legends and stories which have been created by the people, and in which the people have expressed in ingenuous and intuitive form their needs, their aspirations, their dreams of liberty and justice, their hatred of the possessor classes. From this intimate contact with the people he drew inexhaustible and ever new elements of polemical power in the struggle against every form of oppression, not only in the economic-political field, but in the field of intellectual and moral life. The great Italians – from Giuseppe Boccaccio and Giordano Bruno to Giuseppe Giusti and Garibaldi – who fought to liberate the people from the chains of hypocrisy, servility and cant which an age-old tradition of domination by the Catholic church and foreign overlords had imposed on them, found in him an heir and a continuer. He was a bitter enemy of the inflated tinselly eloquence which vitiates such a large part of Italian literature and culture, and has choked in so many literate Italians the fresh bubbling sources of popular inspriration.

Having mentioned Ken Currie's 'The Self-taught Man' at the outset, I would like to conclude by quoting two or three stanzas of what is (in my view) one of the finest Communist poems of the century: 'The Seamless Garment' by Hugh MacDiarmid, which was published in *First Hymn to Lenin* in 1931. Gramsci could not have got to know of this masterpiece, which is a mortal shame, for we can be sure he would have recognised its worth. (MacDiarmid himself grasped immediately the world-significance of Gramsci when I read parts of the present translation to him in 1949; he was later to refer – in *In Memoriam James Joyce* to

> That heroic genius, Antonio Gramsci,
> Studying comparative linguistics in prison,
> For, as he said in his *Lettere dal Carcere*,
> 'Nothing less! What could be more
> Disinterested and *für ewig?*'

He also intuitively recognised the similarity between Gramsci's ironic use of language and the techniques of the great Austrian satirist Karl Kraus, mentioned a little later in the same poem.)

In 'The Seamless Garment', the poet is talking, in easy colloquial style, to a cousin of his who works in a tweed-mill in the Border town of Langholm (Langholm, the 'Muckle Toon', was MacDiarmid's birthplace).

> You are a cousin of mine
>   Here in the mill.
> It's queer that born in the Langholm
>   It's no' until
> Juist noo I see what it means
> To work in the mill like my freens.
>
> I was tryin' to say something
>   In a recent poem
> Aboot Lenin. You've read a guid lot

In the news but ken the less o'm?
Look, Wullie, here is his secret noo
In a way I can share it wi' you.

MacDiarmid compares Lenin's political sure-footedness

A' he'd to dae wi' moved intact,
Clean, clear, and exact

to Rilke's 'Seamless Garment o' music and thought', and calls on the Border weavers to pay heed to the produce of these other looms. The language of the poem is, for the most part, lightly sketched in Scots dialect readily comprehensible to an English-speaking reader, but at one point the great makar reverts to a richer canon of old Scots speech much as Gramsci might have needed a full measure of Sardinian to express his deepest feelings. This passage occurs in the penultimate stanza, and means (approximately): 'Lord, how the old "glad rags" of the past are cast off and discarded.'

Hundreds to the inch the threids lie in,
Like the men in a communist cell.
There's a play o' licht frae the factory windas.
Could you no' mak' mair yoursel'?
Mony a loom mair alive than the weaver seems
For the sun's still nearer than Rilke's dreams.

Ailie Bally's tongue's keepin' time
To the vibration a' richt.
Clear through the maze you een signal to Jean
What's for naebody else's sicht.
Short skirts, silk stockin's – fegs, hoo the auld
Emmle deugs o' the past are curjute and devauld.

And as for me in my fricative work
I ken fu' weel
Sic an integrity's what I maun ha'e
Indivisible, real,
Woven owre close for the point o' a pin
Onywhere to win in.

Notes

1 This, at any rate, is the reason for his hump-back given by his younger sister Teresina in an interview published in *Gramsci Vivo* (Milan, 1977); the same explanation was given to the present writer by Antonio's younger brother Carlo in 1950. However, It has been suggested that this condition was due at least partly to the attack of rickets he suffered as a small child.
2 But Piero Gobetfi saw things somewhat differently; see his 1924 Profile of Gramsci reprinted here.
3 I'd like at this point to express a personal debt of gratitude to Piero, who gave me a lot of help when I was translating the prison letters in 1949 and 1950 – as did Carlo, Antonio's younger brother, when I visited him in Milan.
4 'Savage indignation' stilled for ever, Gramsci was laid to rest in the Protestant 'cemetery of the English' in Rome, under the shadow of the pyramid of Caius Cestius; the remains of Keats and Shelley lie not far away.

5   *Per Gramsci* is the Italian version of her *Pour Gramsci*, published in the same year in Paris; the passage quoted is expressed with considerably more force in the Italian version than in the French.
6   Rather too common currency, sometimes, one might think, seeing 'hegemony' scattered around in blithe ubiquity over article after article, rather like 'Islamic' on the lips of Muslim fundamentalists. An article 'Italy's Fading Dream', about the PCI losses in the June 1987 election, appeared in *Marxism Today* of August 1987; it was sub-titled 'Hegemony in Tatters'.
7   Many of these problems are likely to be discussed at the International Seminar on 'Tribal Culture in a Changing World' organised by the Institute of Oriental and Orissan Studies, Orissa, India (9–12 December 1988). The Institute has already published *Folk Culture* (5 vols), which presents 200 papers on Folk Culture and Literature; Folkways, Religion, God, Spirit and Men; Folk Arts and Crafts; Folk Music and Dances and Folk Culture and the Great Tradition.
8   In the 1965 edition of *Lettere dal Carcere* the word *Mori* (Moors) is wrongly transcribed *Mari* (seas).
9   I am indebted for much of the above information to the late A L Lloyd.
10 An English translation of the title poem by Christopher Whyte appeared in *Bananas*, no. 23 (London, October 1980).
11 According to Fiori (p. 253), Gramsci's brother Gennaro, who visited him in prison in June 1930, reported to Togliatti in Paris that Gramsci agreed with the new 'line' and supported the expulsion of three dissident comrades, but this was not the truth. 'Had I told a different story, not even Nino would have been saved from expulsion.' However, Spriano (*Antonio Gramsci and the Party: The Prison Years*, pp. 56–9) quotes a statement by Luigi Longo (*Gramsci Vivo*, p. 76) that tells a somewhat different story; according to Longo, Gennaro 'told us that Antonio had not wished to say anything regarding the political communications transmitted to him.'
    There is certainly a difference of emphasis, but the implications of his refusal to express an opinion are nevertheless quite clear.

Further Reading

The reader is referred to the following works which the present writer has found useful:

Selections from the Prison Notebooks, edited and translated by Quintin Hoare and Geoffrey Nowell-Smith, London 1971. (Still an indispensable introduction for the English-speaking reader.)
Joseph V. Femia, *Gramsci's Political Thought*, Oxford 1981.
Jacques Texier, *Gramsci et la Philosophie du Marxisme*, Paris 1966.
Anne Showstack Sassoon, *Gramsci's Politics*, London 1980; *Approaches to Gramsci*, London 1982.
Roger Simon, *Gramsci's Political Thought*, London 1982.
James Joll, *Gramsci*, London 1977. (The best short introduction for a reader coming new to Gramsci.)
Christine Buci-Gluckmann, *Gramsci and the State*, London 1980.

For Gramsci's early life, introduction to politics and political development, the reader is referred to the following:

Guiseppi Fiori, *Antonio Gramsci* (translated Tom Nairn), London 1970.
Alastair Davidson, *Antonio Gramsci. Towards an Intellectual Biography*, London 1977.
John M. Cammett, *Antonio Gramsci and the Origins of Italian Communism*, Stanford, California 1967.
Martin Clark, *Antonio Gramsci and the Revolution that Failed*, Yale 1977.
Gwyn A. Williams, *Proletarian Order. Antonio Gramsci, Factory Councils and the Origin of Italian Communism*, London 1975. (Much of this appeared alongside the present translation of the *Lettere* in the Gramsci numbers of the *New Edinburgh Review* in 1974.)

Maria Antonietta Macciocchi, *Pour Gramsci*, Paris 1974.

Ed. Giuseppe Prestipino, *Antonio Gramsci. Arte e folklore*, Rome 1976.

Paolo Spriano, *The Occupation of the Factories*, translated and introduced by Gwyn A. Williams, London 1975; *Antonio Gramsci and the Party: The Prison Years*, translated by John Fraser, London 1979. (This latter is a book of the first importance; it clears up a number of difficult questions raised over the years since Gramsci's death.)

Since the appearance of the *Prison Notebooks* in 1971, three further volumes of Gramsci's writings have appeared in English translation: *Political Writings 1910–1920* (1977); *Political Writings 1921–1926* (1978); and *Cultural Writings* (1985), all published by Lawrence and Wishart in London. The definitive Italian Variorum edition of the *Quaderni del Carcere*, spendidly edited by Valentino Gerratana, came out in 1975 (Editori Riuniti, Rome). The 1965 edition of *Lettere dal Carcere*, edited by Sergio Caprioglio and Elsa Fubini, is a monument of modern Italian literature, and supersedes the earlier 1947 selection (which won the Viareggio Prize when it appeared). An enormous literature of comment and criticism has grown up in Italy relating to Gramsci's career, thought and influence: I have space to mention only the volume of papers given at the first Gramsci Studies Conference, held at Rome from 11 January to 13 January 1958: *Studi Gramsciani*, published by Editori Riuniti, Rome 1958. Articles about Gramsci appear with increasing frequency in British reviews and journals; a concise thought-provoking survey of his political thought by Paul Tritschler appeared in *Radical Scotland*, 20th issue, April/May 1986. A two-volume edition of the prison letters appeared as a supplement to *L'Unità* of 14 February 1988; this edition, not commercially available, was reserved for subscribers to and readers of *L'Unità*. It contained 28 new letters and prefaces by Paolo Spriano (Vol. 1) and Valentino Gerretana (Vol. 2), but carried only a bare minimum of notes.

Prison letters of Antonio Gramsci
First published by Zwan and Edinburgh Review (1988)
reprinted by Pluto Press (1996)

Germany in Defeat

I

Agony, agony, dream, ferment and dream
That is the world, my friend, agony, agony.

Lorca

The story goes that during the Nazi occupation of France Otto Abetz paid Picasso a courtesy call in his Paris studio. During the conversation Abetz caught sight of *Guernica* and exclaimed incredulously: 'Good God, did *you* do that?' 'No,' replied Picasso, '*you* did that.'

As one goes stravaiging through the ugly deserts of rubble which now clutter the German plain, one remembers little stories like that which point the moral. But the mind is left vexed and uneasy. No talk of X=O makes sense any longer. It was an ill wind they sowed, certainly: but one has to be silent before the ghastly relics of our whirlwind.

And another thing becomes clear, a thing that had occurred to me in the North African deadland, namely that many of the Surrealist painters of the 1930s were merely prophetic. The débris of a desert battle-field, every conceivable object in creation thrown out of the world's lumber room on to a 'nostalgic landscape' of Paul Nash; the skeletal silhouette of a crashed Stuka leading the eye away into an infinity of sterile desolation; the earliest littoral life, and wrecked upon it some grotesque memento of human mortality – all these one had seen before. Nowadays there is the same effect in the ruined cities of the Rhineland, an incredible remoteness, an impression of idiot stultification. Blunted edges, the ludicrous juxtaposition of worthless objects and things once valued. And Lorca's tremendous indictment of the West's spiritual dead end takes on a new meaning if you wander through the wreckage of Cologne:

Corpses decompose under the clock of cities.

What sort of life is it which thrusts its way through the rubble? When I was speaking at a Summer School at Bad Godesberg I met a young student, Heinz Vogt, who seemed more than ordinarily intelligent. He told me a little of his family history: his father, a Social Democratic deputy in the pre-Nazi Reichstag and afterwards head of the illegal German Mineworkers Union, had been captured and killed by the Gestapo in the Netherlands after the 1940 invasion. His mother had been put to death back in 1933, at the very start of the Fascist dictatorship. He himself, while an officer cadet, had formed an anti-Nazi cell in the German OCTU where he was stationed. Now he was trying to get himself orientated in the chaos of Bizonia.

I promised him that on my return from Berlin I would look him up in his home, and three weeks later I managed to do so. Leaving the Berlin-Rhineland train at Oberhausen, I thumbed a ride with a Black Watch lorry to Duisburg, and from there went by tram to Meiderich, the place where he lived. It was dark by the time I found the right street; no houses seemed to be whole in it from one end to the other. The scene presented a curious baroque exuberance of ruin, with outflung arms of masonry at the strangest angles. There was no light that I could see in any corner of that wilderness.

At last I located the house. It was in a rather worse case than most; the entrance was like a cave's, and pitch-black. I groped my way down a corridor, stumbling over all kinds of miscellaneous wreckage; without knowing it, I skirted a flight of steps leading downwards. Finally I emerged into a little backyard and saw a light across the way. Here I found the family – Heinz, his younger brother and a grandmother, all living in what had once been a coal-cellar.

They welcomed me in, and in a few minutes Heinz was overwhelming me again with his enthusiasms and interests – we discussed the Berlin reviews I had brought with me, talked of Jaspers and the pseudo-existentialists of Paris, argued again about Stalin and the National question; exchanged ideas about the world strategy of America's cold war, took to pieces a poet newly published in Heidelberg, and so on into the night, finishing up by singing folk-songs – among them my favourite *Und in dem Schneegebirge*:

> *Up in the snowy highlands there flows a cold stream: and he who drinks of it does not age, he remains young. I have drunk out of it, many a good dram: I have not grown old, I stay young.*

The 'Faustian man', the man who wants to achieve everything and suffer everything, to know everything and experience everything is a German ideal, and Heinz embodies it better than anyone else I know. Among other things he's learning Gaelic, and has already translated some of Sorley MacLean's poems into German. As for Scots, he has thrown himself into MacDiarmid and translated a lot of *Pennywheep*. In economics he is busy refuting the ideas of Sylvio Gessell, which are founded on those of Keynes. He wanted to learn Swedish, in order to read Björk and others. Psychology has occupied much of his time, and he's well read in Freud, Adler and Jung: Jung's excursion (complete with archetypes) into the disputed field of German collective guilt excites his scorn. He is also an athlete, a good dancer and an excellent shot.

It was strange, in that midsummer nightmare of ruin, material and human, to talk to an 'Admirable Crichton'. Revealing, too: because, though few young Germans are as gifted as Heinz, thousands and thousands share his Faustian longing.

With most, unfortunately, it works out at pure escapism. They throw themselves into the study of new languages, old heresies, recondite philosophasters and every form of transcendental nonsense with the express purpose of leaving unstudied the appalling (and challenging) situation which confronts them. But whatever task they assign themselves, they buckle down to it with astounding energy – all the more astounding because the food situation makes heavy inroads into the surplus energy of even the youngest. Adult Education authorities in several Western German cities report that courses on the appreciation of music, on Hume or Hegel, even on Sartre and *Huis clos* are filled to capacity; those in economics and social history are about as full as Camlachie election meetings. (A few months earlier I had been speaking for Robert Blair Wilkie, Independent Scottish Nationalist candidate, at the Camlachie by-election.)

And yet one finds it hard to take any German to task for escapism. The human ruin is worse than the material. Another student I met at Godesberg started the conversation by saying: 'You wouldn't believe how bad the Germans have become.' The younger people are filled with revulsion against the universal corruption they see around them. Ubiquitous black market, cigarette currency, shameless *sauve-qui-peut* of the hungry in which the fit and strong push the weak and infirm to the wall – everything seems to them a racket and an endless meanness. They think of it as the prostitution of a whole nation.

At Neuss a young man fought his way into a crowded train with a heavy sack of potatoes and hoisted it into the rack. An old woman sitting underneath feebly protested. 'Why, ye donnert auld runt,' the lad shouted – his Plattdeutsch goes straight into Lallans – 'if I'd ony coals I'd pit *them* on the rack tae!'

Is it any wonder that many secretly long for a word (or arm) of authority to bring order into this chaos?

It is that secret wish to be dominated that one senses in the halls of the great railway stations where black marketeers foregather, and adolescents roam around until the small hours of the morning waiting for a pick-up, or for a deal with some wandering Jock or well-oiled GI. It is that which makes menacing the scrawl in the lavatory of a German civilians' train: 'The East will be ours again. Hail to the Führer!'

Stefan George's later work (such as *Das Neue Reich*) is still banned, because it clearly glorifies what was to become the Führer Prinzip, and because it gives tongue to this secret desire for ruthlessly imposed order. In *Ein Dichter in Zeiten der Wirrnis* (A Poet in Troubled Times), written not long before his death in 1933, George looks forward to the arrival of a hero who will clear the temple, and build a 'new Reich' in which 'Master will be master again, and discipline discipline'. George marks too in these later poems the change in German homosexual taste: it is no longer the floating-haired lute-playing Heidelberg student who is his ideal, but the Storm Trooper or Hitler Youth leader, of whom he writes: 'Sein Kuss ist kurz und brennend' (His kiss is quick and burning). Now the fashion has changed again, and when the pendulum swings in Germany there's never any doubt about it: yesterday the Army and Hitler Youth imposed a savage square-head crop – today no German bobby-soxer but wears his hair like a Mélisande.

A reaction against militarism? Maybe. But unless I'm much mistaken there's hardly a lad of this long-haired brigade who would not be glad in his heart to hear the snip of the scissors. Sado-masochism – a desire to order, and even more to be ordered around – is a German constant which has to be taken into account. It lies at the root of the baffling contradictions in German group psychology which have made that formidable nation's name a by-word for achievement and degradation. Ulrich von Hassell, in his recently published diary, frequently alludes to it: 'What a people we are,' he exclaims in it 'what a people we are of heroes and slaves!'

How this works out in the formative years of schooling was illustrated for me by an episode which took place in Brambauer, near Dortmund. I was visiting the local school, and 'sat in' during a lesson. The class consisted of under-nourished ten-year-olds twittering in their seats with eagerness to show their knowledge, and competing against each other for the master's favour. Half-way through the lesson a little boy in the front row fired a pellet at one in the back with the aid of a piece of elastic. I rejoiced in this exhibition of healthy normality, but my pleasure was short-lived. The 'target' stood up, and with the brusque matter-of-factness of a Wehrmacht corporal making a report he denounced the culprit. The wrong one, as it happened, but it came to the same thing, because the accused laddie indignantly pointed out to the class the real criminal. The latter was sentenced to detention, and the self-righteous target sat down, a public hero.

It was clear that the class had little of the group solidarity of a typical Scottish school. Their allegiance was to the master, and the master demanded a military submissiveness. A German friend who was with me said afterwards: 'What an interesting example of our *Drang* to denunciation.' One could believe rather better after that the stories current in Hitler Germany about children denouncing their parents.

Befehl ist Befehl. Orders are orders. *Kadavergehorsam.* Corpse obedience. 'I don't believe', a Berlin engineer said to me 'that you'd find in any other nation in the world such an exhibition as I saw yesterday. Two policemen at the city boundary confiscated a few miserable sticks that an old woman had gathered for herself beyond it, because – orders are orders. We are the real Slavs, it's not the Czechs and Poles and Russians. *We* are the real Slavs: it's the worst misnomer in Europe'.

And now after a few angles on the occupied, let's take a keek at the occupiers.

In the entrance hall of York House, one of the administrative centres in Berlin, I saw an immense chart, giving the names and listing the offices of the host of occupants.

'Good God', I said to the Scots sentry, 'what are all these doing?'

'Och,' he said 'dodgin' the column, as usual.'

If the 'German' problem is serious, the 'English' problem is desperate. In an economic set-up in which the Americans are increasingly calling the tune, the bewilderment and lack of direction among the English officials is plain to see. They are now largely purged of the playboys who disgraced themselves in the period immediately after the war, but one can't say that the prevailing atmosphere among them is vastly improved. Conversations in a rapidly refining cockney which go on for hours and are exclusively about deals on the black market still reveal minuscule minds. More full-blooded social revolutions put paid to these people. The English apology for same (1945) sends its social misfits out to govern Germany.

In Hanover I heard from a reliable source that every day a driver goes out with his truck into the countryside and brings back fourteen litres of milk to supplement the ration – seven for the Commander's Mess and seven for the next senior Mess. On Saturday he fetches twenty litres, ten for each, to last over the weekend. This example may sound rather tame, but it's symptomatic. How the devil can one expect German farmers to collaborate and give foodstuffs for distribution on the ration to the folk in the towns, if the high CCG officials set an example like this?

But, let me give a brief account of a lecture I attended in the Soviet sector of Berlin. It was open to the public. The speaker was a Major Rudnik of the Red Army and the subject was Soviet foreign policy from 1918 to 1941. Rudnik spoke good German, but with a heavy rolling Russian accent. He outlined in great detail the events of 1939, as seen from the Soviet angle, and attempted to prove that the famous Non-Aggression Pact was a necessity in view of Western duplicity.

After the lecture was over, questions were invited. Some in the audience had no inhibitions. A student sitting just in front of me got up and asked: 'What about the secret clauses to the Non-Aggression Pact?' Rudnik asked 'What do you mean?' The student, supported by a friend, recalled ambiguous statements made during the Nuremberg trials. Eventually Rudnik snapped: 'Secret diplomacy ceased to exist in 1919 – as far as the Soviet Union is concerned.' He then gave an account of German-Soviet negotiations in 1939 as they effected the Russian areas of Poland acquired by Pilsudski in 1920.

Afterwards I followed the students out into the street. They strolled away together, still talking and laughing, and I left them having a beer at the local. No NKVD action seemed to be impending, as far as I could see.

And whatever the truth of the argument on either side, one thing was quite clear: freedom of speech was not denied *that* particular audience behind the Iron Curtain.

I broke my journey from Berlin at Hanover in the early hours of the morning, for I wanted to re-visit some friends at Göttingen. After the snowy-breasted sleeper I had left, the platform where a skirmishing throng was waiting for the Kassel train would have put fear into the Fingalians. As soon as the train drew in, a free fight started among the poor blokes trying to gain entry, and there was nothing for it but to join in too. Calling to the porter to follow me I cleared a lane into the nearest carriage, and wedging myself in the doorway I collected my bags from the porter over the heads of the combatants. About an hour after the train left I succeeded in getting a tolerable standing position.

The reason for all this? Fewer trains due to shortage of locomotives (reparations and requisitions); the coal problem, fewer rolling stock; the civilian railway system gradually falling to bits.

In Göttingen I found the family. The father, a Jewish doctor with whom I had stayed in 1939, had survived the war (although he'd spent a good deal of it in a camp), but his mother had been slaughtered in Theresienstadt. And Karlheinz the elder son, who had got out of Germany and joined the American army, was dead too.

II

Strolling around the University town of Göttingen, which is pretty well undamaged, I tried to find out about the students I had known before the war. In nearly every case the answer was 'Killed on the Eastern Front'. Among those killed on the Central Sector had been the young Herr von Goetz, who in August 1939 said to me: 'Politics is all a Schweinerei. I'd rather make the world kaputt with troops than play this political Schweinerei.'

My journey back to Hanover was a song compared to the trip south I described earlier. With a bit of bullshine I managed to persuade a US corporal to let me travel first-class in the American Leave Train. As I settled back in the cushions, a German porter surveyed me with a puzzled expression on his face; I was wearing a dyed battledress with no badges of rank, so he took me for one of his own countrymen. For a few minutes he continued to inspect me, and then turning to a mate of his, he asked (and I heard him quite clearly through the open window): 'What's he – a Nazi?'

> If the great Dutch language disappeared from literary usage and a Dutchman wrote in German a story of the Lekside peasants, one may hazard he would ask and receive a certain latitude and forbearance in his usage of German. He might import into his pages some score or so of untranslatable words and idioms – untranslatable except in their context and setting: he might mould in some fashion his German to the rhythms and cadence of the kindred speech that his peasants speak. Beyond that, in fairness to his hosts, he hardly could go: to seek effect by a spray of apostrophes would be both impertinence and mistranslation.

This prefatory note of Lewis Grassic Gibbon's to *Sunset Song* came into my mind as the diesel train from Hanover skimmed through Westphalia, because the homely Platt of the Rhineland – an ancient tongue much more closely allied to Dutch than to High German – is itself beginning to yield ground before the assault of school, film and radio. A girl student I talked to on a Rhine steamer stated that in her area the playground language of the children was now High German. And some of the old people were to be heard complaining that when they talked to their grandchildren in good Platt, they got an answer back in uncouth Hochdeutsch.

However, I found plenty of evidence of the vitality of the 'auld leid'. In Düsseldorf the CDU (Christian Democratic Union) had printed an election poster in Platt. It showed 'Jan Wellem' (Duke Johann Wilhelm, whose equestrian statue is one of the sights of the city) getting down from his mount. The text read: *Selfs Jan Wellem klömmt vom Päd, CDU hä wähle jeht!* (Even Jan Wellem climbs down from his horse, he's going to vote for CDU).

This appeal to popular sentiment was too dangerous to be disregarded, so the Social Democrats replied by invoking the patronage of another public figure. They posted the following slogan (also in Platt) under their rivals' poster:

Hedoch de Giesserjong säht Nee, Dat Volk wöhlt richtig SPD (But the pissing boy says 'No: The right vote is SPD'),

Furthermore, there's one pretty obvious use for Platt that the Rhinelanders have found, and that's as a vehicle for cracks at the expense of the occupying powers. At Annen, a place near Witten in the Ruhr, I found openly displayed for sale a song number in Kölner Platt (Cologne dialect) called 'Op dem Schwatze Maat' (On the Black Market). The pseudonym of its author was Hans Englisch (John English)! Here's the chorus:

> Op dem schwatze Maat, pass op, pass op!
> es et usgelaht, pass op, pass op!
> Wat deer deit fähle
> Kanns do he wähle –
> et sin Maggler do
> vun fäh un noh,
> Op dem schwatze Maat pass op, pass op!
> Do meht Geld un Kram – galopp, galopp.

'On the Black Market (mind out, mind out!), it's all there for sale (mind out,

mind out!), you can get everything here you're needing; there's spivs from far
and near. On the Black Market, (mind out, mind out!), you can make dough
pretty quick.'

All things considered, I began to feel that the Rhenish intellectuals are maybe a little
pessimistic about the fate of the old speech. Like their counterparts in some other
countries, they fail to realise how intimately the lingo is bound up still with the life of
the common people. I suppose the real answer both to them and to our Gibbons of the
future is that neither Dutch nor Scots have disappeared as languages from the map of
European letters. While they remain, the teachers of the Rhineland and the Mearns
might profitably consider whether it wouldn't be better to stop doing violence to their
own mental processes and to those of the children under their care. Once they start
thinking along these lines, they'll surely contemplate springing the dams that impede
the course of the speech which has come down to them from their fathers.

Why on earth should the megalopolitan dialects of bourgeois nation-states continue to rule the roost for good and all? Infinitely better would be the development of
an international auxiliary taught in all schools from Vladivostok to Valencia Island,
and the encouragement of all national and regional cultures, even the smallest.

The Soviet Union's treatment of the nationalities problem has signposted the way.
The minority languages of Siberia and the Caucasus enjoy the fullest rights and
protection, being used for commerce, for administration, and in the Law Courts, while
in this country Gaelic (one of the great historic languages of Europe) continues to be
treated as if it were a mere 'impediment to progress'.

Berlin is still beyond doubt the cultural capital of Germany. This is probably the
one solitary advantage of four-power government. It's possible on one day to hear
Benjamin Britten sung in German, in the British Sector, and the following day to take
the Underground to the Soviet Sector and pay a visit to Simonov's witty piece, *The
Russian Question*. The German Theatre itself is still very lively, although that remarkable actor Gustav Gründgens (whom I saw as Hamlet in 1937: he was billed as a truly
Nordic Hamlet) has gone to Düsseldorf to be Generalintendant. I saw him again last
autumn, when I had returned to the Rhineland – this time as Oedipus Rex. His
interpretation of the part was interesting, more Martin Harvey than Olivier; but after
an hour or so the hysterical semi-feminine whine got on my nerves. A German
Oedipus, his nostrils quivering with self-pity! My God, I thought, give me Mihailovic,
whose 'gale of the world' had at any rate the virtue of being laconic.

One of the chief British contributions to Berlin culture when I was there was a
grand military Tattoo. This drew enormous crowds, and was the occasion for much
caustic comment on the part of the Russians in the Kommandantura about the methods
used by Bevin to wean the Germans away from militarism. A student, who was a
member of the Socialist Unity Party, came with me to the Tattoo; he shook his head
over the revving armoured demonstration of Western might, but the massed pipe
bands delighted him as much as three years previously they had delighted the Romans.
'Ach Gott,' he said, 'if only Adolf could see this!'

To a lot of Berliners, however, this marching and countermarching meant just one
thing: that the *Ostgebiete* (territories in the East awarded to Poland at Potsdam) might
one day be German land again. Karl, the blue-eyed boy of our local education officer,

was asked one day by a denazified diplomat what he thought of the situation 'in the
east'. Karl, who led Youth Discussion Groups on democracy for the British Education
Officials, made the following cryptic reply, not realising that I was listening: 'Ich
arbeite im Rahmen der jetzt existierenden Möglichkeiten.' ('I'm working within the
framework of the possibilities which exist at present.')

'The Mongol East.' 'The encroachment of Asia.' 'Flinging back the Tartars.'
Goebbels can sleep sound in his grave; he need not stir. The propaganda of the capitalist
West has taken over one by one every single anti-Soviet slogan in the Nazi armoury.
Even the Iron Curtain is of Nazi origin – it was coined by Count Schwerin von
Krosigk, Finance Minister in Doenitz's short-lived Government, and given world
wide currency by Churchill in his speech at Fulton.

But what's far worse, these phrases tend to colour the political thinking of even
fairly enlightened people. In Berlin one frequently sees little Kalmuck or Uzbek
swaddies strolling along in front of the ruined Opera House, which still bears on its
façade the proud inscription: *Fridericus Rex Apolloni et Musis*. It's only too easy to
dramatise such an incongruous juxtaposition in terms of East and West. But what if
one sees (which is also possible) a black GI gazing up at the same inscription; is one to
invent a similar array of emotive slogans? Or isn't it simpler (and wiser) to see the
whole shoot in terms of the human comedy?

Anyway, millions of Germans have felt in their flesh what this devilish nonsense
means in the long run to the ordinary man, and at the great memorial ceremony for the
Opfer des Fascismus (Victims of Fascism) one could see clearly that the Berlin
proletariat is still in the forefront of the European working-class movement. From all
sectors of the city processions came marching, the place of honour being given to the
survivors of the concentration camps, and to the veterans of the Thaelmann Battalion
of the International Brigade. In the thronged Lustgarten, where hundreds of red
banners were blurred in a heat haze which was almost Sicilian, contingent after
contingent came to mingle with friends and comrades; many carried posters which
bore the names of the martyred – world-famous or unknown, the levelled in death's
proletariat. I saw *Luxemburg ... Wallisch ... Ossietsky ... Thaelmann ... Liebknecht*.
In front of the tribune from which Frau Louise Schroeder, the Social Democratic
Mayoress, addressed the rally stood three veteran anti-Fascists, motionless in blazing
sunshine which might have felled a guardsman. They wore, as an honoured uniform,
the black-and-white striped pyjama outfit of Dachau and Buchenwald.

But far more impressive to me, because a great deal simpler, was the short ceremony
I visited the following day – also in memory of the victims of Fascism. It was at the
Elisabeth Mittelschule, a girls' school in the Scharrenstrasse. A choir of about twenty
senior girls had learned a sequence of famous quotations, all bearing on loyalty and
self-sacrifice, and they reeled these off quite capably. Then I thought the show was
finished. But no. A single note on the piano, and the choir started to sing unaccompanied the old concentration camp song 'Wir sind die Moorsoldaten'.

> Far and wide as eye can wander
> Heath and bog are everywhere.
> Not a bird sings out to cheer us,
> Oaks are standing gaunt and bare.

We are the peat bog soldiers:
We're marching with our spades
To the moor.

Up and down the guards are pacing,
No one, no one can get through.
Flight would mean a sure death facing,
Guns and barbed wire greet our view.
We are the peat bog soldiers;
We're marching with our spades
To the moor ...

As I listened to this song, and thought back over the years that had gone by: my friends who had gone out to Spain, the Jewish doctor joking with his mother who was to die in Theresienstadt, battalions of the Highland Division leaving in lorries for the front at El Alamein, the shambles of the Ardeatine caves with their murdered hostages, and the whole ghastly tragedy of modern Germany in which I had found myself inextricably mixed up, I came within an ace of showing ungoverned emotion. Luckily the ceremony ended, and I could put a good face on my compliments and congratulations.

The Voice of Scotland, ed. Hugh MacDiarmid, March and June 1948.

Flower and Iron of the Truth
A Survey of Contemporary Scottish Writing

In the first decade of this century Scotland presented a daunting spectacle of cultural ruin. To many observers it seemed unlikely that the country could much longer maintain even a façade of national identity. The English imperialist Ascendancy had consolidated itself, with the full acquiescence of the Scottish bourgeoisie, during the course of the nineteenth century, and its domination in academic circles was virtually complete. The indigenous traditions of the people, both Gaelic and Lallans, seemed to have been left tattered and defenceless before the big battalions of alien aggression.

This apparent abdication was merely underlined by the blowsy vocal patriotism of the Scottish burgesses. These vied with each other in extolling the beauties of a countryside they had savaged, and in eulogising the works of a poet whose poems they no longer properly understood.

Yet today, as even hostile critics are obliged to admit, the picture is quite different. Although the 'official' crust of anglicising authority is still very much in evidence, forces have emerged in the last twenty-five years vigorous enough to change the whole atmosphere of Scottish life. A generation of younger poets and intellectuals has grown up which would be the just pride of any country in Europe. Let us examine more fully this curious phenomenon.

In the first place, the cultural revival cannot be disassociated from the growth to political maturity of the Scottish working class during World War I. In the great campaign against increased rents in the first years of the war and in the mass fights against conscription from 1916 onwards, the Scottish people rediscovered an élan which had carried it into action in 1848 and in the Crofters' War. And it threw up a leader of genius, the Glasgow schoolmaster John Maclean, of whose indomitable battle in the interests of the workers Gallacher has written so movingly in *Revolt on the Clyde*, and to whose revolutionary inspiration Lenin himself paid tribute. It would be hard to overestimate Maclean's service to Scotland; not only did he use his profound knowledge of Marxism to train a whole generation of activists, not only did he transform the workers' struggle in the industrial belt of Scotland and make the Clyde an embattled outpost of the European proletariat – he also, by a correct interpretation of the national problem, showed the workers and crofters of our country that the Scottish past was their rightful heritage.

Understanding from his own background and from his parents' stories the reality of the class war in the Highlands, he recalled to the people such episodes from their recent history as the Land League, and such documents as the following manifesto of

Highland resistance:

> The enemy is the landlord, the agent the capitalist – and the Parliament which makes and maintains inhuman and iniquitous laws.
>
> Cut down the telegraph wires and posts, carry away the wires and instruments! Stop the mailcarts, destroy the letters.
>
> Burn the property of all obnoxious landlords and agents. Set fire to the heather to destroy the game: disturb the deer: poison game-dogs!
>
> The oppressed toilers of England and the millions of disinherited people are watching your actions. Their hearts are with you in your battle for right and liberty.
>
> *God save the people!*

The achievement of Maclean was almost as great in the field of culture as it was in the field of active struggle. The legend of him was beyond question one of the principal formative influences which went to shape Hugh MacDiarmid, the giant of the Scottish Renaissance. MacDiarmid's *Hymns to Lenin* are in a certain sense his own tribute to Maclean, and many of the younger poets influenced by him have celebrated Scotland's greatest revolutionary figure in lyrics and ballads. Among these are Sydney Goodsir Smith, John Kincaid, Maurice Blythman ('Thurso Berwick'), and the Gaelic poet Sorley MacLean.

In the second place, Scotland, having played an important role in this international movement, began once again to look at Europe and to feel herself part of it. The manifest intellectual indigence of the great bulk of 'conforming' pro-English Ascendancy wowsers in the Scottish universities increasingly alienated the livelier spirits in Scottish academic life, and brought about between the wars a re-orientation of our intellectual contacts in the direction of the continent – a resumption, therefore, of the traditional Scottish alignments which had tended to be forgotten during the course of the nineteenth century. Thus it could come about that MacDiamid was translating Blok and Rilke years before the 'New Signatures' group in Oxford made such a song and dance about 'discovering' them. Gradually an intellectual climate came into being which favoured still more interesting experiments, and eventually Douglas Young could present in Scottish dress the verse of a dozen assorted languages.

The doyen of the Scottish movement is a Borderer, Hugh MacDiarmid. This redoubtable adversary of reaction in literature and in life has exerted an incalculable influence on the development of letters north of the Cheviots. A poet of the first order in Lallans, a coruscating polemicist in English and (for the last decade) an intrepid explorer with his own plastic multilingo, he has served as a rallying point for every forward-looking movement in the country since the publication of *Sangschaw* in 1925. Rescuing the Scots tongue from the slough of havering provincialism into which it had fallen, he demonstrated incontrovertibly by his own example that it was still capable of carrying art poetry: his *Drunk Man Looks At A Thistle*, a masterpiece which with unique bravado mixed a score of glorious lyrics with pantagruelian dollops of audacious philosophical banter, set the seal on this achievement.

For the benefit of readers not conversant with Lallans, here is a prose translation into English of the 'Eemis Stane', one of the early lyrics which remain his most celebrated poems – unreasonably, perhaps, because they were followed by 'the magnificent *To Circumjack Cencrastus* and the sweeping majesty of the *Hymns to Lenin'* (Lewis Grassic Gibbon):

> In the very dead of the cold harvest night the world like a loose tomb-stone sways in the sky, and my eerie memories fall like a downdrive of snow.
>
> Like a downdrive of snow, so that I could not see the words cut out in the stone – even if the moss of fame and the lichen of history had not overgrown them.

This revelation of the potentialities of the 'auld leid' had an effect on his younger contemporaries that one can properly call electric. But MacDiarmid's most positive service does not lie in his championship of the Scots language: it is rather to be found in the single-minded devotion he has shown in furthering the great cause of the proletariat in Scotland, and in clarifying the relation of the cultural revival to the political struggle. He realised clearly, and stressed over and over again that no literary revival is worth a damn if it fails to identify itself with the *present* difficulties and tasks of the people. And conversely, that no poetry which desires to be actual can afford to neglect the ramifications of exploit and dream in the people's past. In short, that Scottish poetry, if it is to contribute anything of value to the international complex, must first of all throw off the alien mummy-wrappings we have heard of, and recover its true identity.

MacDiarmid's stand in defence of these ideas against every kind of defamation and calumny has been little short of heroic. Now, having won through, he towers in rugged monolithic eminence above the contemporary Scottish scene.

The poets that have followed MacDiamid's lead can be divided for convenience's sake into two schools. The first includes those poets known as the 'Lallans Makars' – Albert Mackie, Sydney Goodsir Smith, Maurice Lindsay and Douglas Young. These are all considerable artists, and one of them (Sydney Smith, author of *The Devil's Waltz* and *Under the Eildon Tree*) is a poet of real power. Although their work shows pronounced differences, they have one major aim in common: a desire to extend and enrich the capacities of the revitalised Scots tongue as a vehicle for literature. Hence, constituting themselves a kind of unofficial Academy, they have done useful spadework in a number of fields, such as the standardisation of Lallans spelling; they have also joined issue polemically with the literary reaction. One of their company, Maurice Lindsay, has performed a function rather similar to that of Allan Ramsay in the eighteenth century: an indefatigable editor and anthologist, he has succeeded in making the Scottish public definitely Lallans-conscious.

The second of the two schools I referred to is gradually emerging. The poets belonging to it are not primarily interested in the language question, though they have turned one by one from English to Scots or Gaelic. They are resolved to carry a stage further MacDiarmid's application of Marxism to the Scottish predicament, and are eager to produce work which will interpret more immediately the reality of the Scottish people – of the commons of Alba, the industrial proletariat, the dockers, miners and shipyard workers, the Highland remnant. In a word, they have comprehended the need for a literature of *presentification*. Reacting strongly against the seeming archaism of the Makars – an archaism more of subject-matter than of language – they lay at their door the tendency of the Scottish public to equate Lallans poetry with a predilection for the grotesque: a taking wing on Jamieson's battered broomstick to riotous, non-stop Walpurgisnacht.

The poets of this second school (sometimes called the Clyde Group) want more Maclean and less Mahoun[1] in Scottish poetry. They are inclined to ask (and the question is relevant) what contact Lindsay's 'lanely wishan-wells' are supposed to have with the reality of life in Govan or Hamilton – or for that matter with the reality of life in Comrie or Lochboisdale. Conscious of the enormous untapped potentialities of Scots poetry, they fear that, left to the Mahoun-mongers, it may turn into a mere academic exercise, a field for Alexandrian virtuosity – a 'pluralism of superstructures' above a life with which it has lost all contact. And therefore they are in a mood to give Mahoun a kick on his ample dowp that will send him limping out of Lallans verse for a twelvemonth.

One of the most interesting of these writers is John Kincaid, whose *Setterday Nicht Symphonie* has just been published by the Caledonian Press. This poem comes nearer than anything I have yet seen to a successful evocation of the beauty that can be struck from the forbidding grey whinstone of Glasgow tenement life.

> Ay, birl awa citie, mak a gob at the mune,
> fling a haunfu o' stars at the heids o' the priests,
> tak the Clyde i' your airms ...
> Ay citie, ma citie, skirl awa citie,
> skretch oot your lauchin til waas faain doon;
> your flair is aa stampin wi' lads an' wi' lasses
> wi' joy i' their banes an' daunce i' their bluid.
> > O citie, ma citie
> > to Freedom be leal!
> > Tak haud o' the nicht!
> > Wha's for a quadrille?

Kincaid calls Glasgow 'ma douce raucle citie'. In the startling juxtaposition of these two untranslatable Scots words one recognises the brilliant single phrase that one was waiting for ... Another of the Clyde Group who promises well is Kincaid's friend and comrade 'Thurso Berwick'. This young writer has produced several love poems which show great insight and tenderness. The best of these is 'The Twa Wynds', published in the March *Voice of Scotland*. He has also written some excellent satirical verse.

The Caledonian Press has to its credit furthermore the publication of *Whit Tyme in the Day*, which is the first book of a difficult but (I think) rewarding poet, T.S. Law.

Our Time, 10 September, 1948.

---

1. Mahoun: One of the many names for that darling of Scottish literature – the Devil.

Lallans and all that

The correspondence columns of *The Scotsman* have recently been resounding with shrill cries and muffled grunts on the subject of Lallans. What is it, the scrievers asked – language or dialect, Celtic or Anglian, speech of our ancestors or linguistic aberration? The tug-o'-war went on for weeks. But in most of the letters the argumentative bitterness of the writers was only equalled by their dingy ignorance concerning the one point which really matters: namely, has our generation produced in Braid Scots any poetry worthy of the name?

For, after all, no one who walks through Scotland with his ears washed can doubt that the speech of the people is still a helluva lot nearer to the language of Burns than to the stringy metropolitan argot of the BBC announcer. Which means that there is still a living foundation for poetry in 'the raucle tongue'. And if that's conceded, what the devil does it matter whether the Jutes were the first speakers of it, or the Frisians? Surely no man of sense will waste his time speculating which exactly of the blubber-lipped buccaneers who invaded our shores were the first to call a cuddie a cuddie.

So I propose to cut out all the literary-historical cross-talk so beloved of Mr Douglas Young, which in the main I regard as so much nonsense-value. What we might ask ourselves is this: can evidence be found of a vital, contemporary and popular literature in the Scottish tongue?

Well, I doubt if any reader of this will not by now have made himself familiar with such famous poetry as the *Hymns to Lenin* of Hugh MacDiarmid. These poems are a landmark in European literature of the period between the wars, and have been translated into many languages – including (I am told) some of the minority languages of the Soviet Union. The speech in which they are written is for the most part a flexible modern Scots, the great bulk of the vocabulary still being in common use among our people today. Where MacDiarmid does admit a word which may have fallen into disuse he does it with the sure instinct of a master of language – the word is usually at once comprehensible in the setting of the poem, and because of that has legitimately regained entry into the canon of Scots literary speech. Often such words (e.g. 'clanjamphrie' for 'the whole lot') have found their way with astonishing rapidity into the journalistic columns of the *Evening Times* or the *Daily Record*.

This approach to language, at once revolutionary, traditionalist and creative, is exactly the approach postulated by the forerunner of Marxist aesthetics, Belinsky. Anyone wishing to see how perfectly colloquial speech and a fifty-fathom profundity can be blended in the best of MacDiarmid should read that poem in the *First Hymn to*

Lenin which is called *The Seamless Garment*. Here are two of the final verses:

> Hundreds tae the inch the threids lie in,
>   Like the men in a communist cell.
> There's a play o' licht frae the fact'ry windas—
>   Cuid you no mak mair yoursel?
> Mony a loom mair alive than the weaver seems
> For the sun's aye nearer than Rilke's dreams ...
>
> And as for me in my fricative wark
>   I ken fu' weel
> Sic an integrity's whit I maun hae,
>   Indivisible, real,
> Woven owre close for the point o' a pin
> Onywhere tae win in.

Since these lines of MacDiarmid's were written, more than two dozen poets of more than negligible performance have appeared in print, writing in Lallans. This is in itself an eloquent tribute to the liberating influence of this remarkable figure.

The first of the 'new boys' on the scene (largely because they had readier access to the organs of publicity) were the so-called 'Lallans Makars' – Maurice Lindsay and his maudlin mates. These bourgeois nationalists, hopelessly hobbled from the start by their political gormlessness, nevertheless performed a certain function in that they attacked and laid waste the last strongpoints of the nineteenth-century 'Kailyaird' school. But they are now in their turn being assailed and worsted by the younger Scottish Marxists of the Clyde Group, and it is quite clear already that (poetically as well as politically) they have had it.

The lead having thus passed from Edinburgh and Kelvinside to proletarian Clydebank, one is next bound to ask 'Who are these new Marxist makars? Will they make the grade?'

On present showing I am inclined to think that they will. Their task will be pre-eminently that of gaining direct contact with the people, and one of them – Maurice Blythman, who writes under the pseudonym 'Thurso Berwick' – has a knack of putting his stuff over to audiences of every size which reminds me of Mayakovsky. At the John Maclean Memorial Meeting there was a thrilling example of this, when his poem was interrupted at one point (*A Maclean is at yuir banquet!*) by loud spontaneous applause from the huge audience. This is the only time in my life that I can remember such a thing happening!

In the later poems of John Kincaid, too, there are signs that this vigorous poet is finding his way towards a diction which will command immediate response from working-class gatherings. Already he has shown in such poems as the *Setterday Nicht Symphonie* that no writer is better qualified to tackle in his work a valid presentation of the reality of the Scottish scene.

The Fife miner, T S Law, has also eschewed short cuts and has not been afraid in his first book *Whit Tyme in the Day* to grapple in the grand manner with the massy Scots tradition. Poems in this book such as *The Clenched Fist* mark a formidable achievement ... One of the latest recruits to the Clyde Group is a student, George Todd, who has struck one of the shrewdest blows in the anti-'Lallans Makar' polemic – *Embro Makars.*

　　Alexander Scott, the newly appointed Lecturer in Scottish Language and Literature in the University of Glasgow, is a poet whose natural affiliations are with the Clyde Group. The other members have been quick to realise this – Thurso Berwick, for example, wrote in a recent poem:

> And schours o' mortal hail sall stott
> Frae aff the shield o' Alex Scott
> Baldur o' aa oor blazonrie.

Let me end this abreviated survey with a word about the poet whom Todd singles out as a natural ally of the Clyde Group – Sydney Goodsir Smith. In his *Under the Eildon Tree* Smith has produced what – to my mind – is certainly the finest Scots poetry since the early MacDiarmid. This is no accident, because his development has been organic and entire – in contradistinction to that of the typical 'Lallans Makar'. But the most significant thing about his work is that (like that of Sorley Maclean, the Gaelic poet) it has alway shown a generous and rebellious sympathy with the forces of political progress. Sydney Smith is of the Left, and for that reason the writers of the Clyde Group have found in his poetry an inspiration second only to that of MacDiarmid. *The Ballant o' John Maclean* puts it succinctly:

> But they brakna his words o' flame
> Nor dowsit his memorie.
> Turn ower in your sleep, MacLean
> – Scotland has need o' ye!

Conflict, Glasgow University Socialist Club, March 1949.

Tangling with the Langholm Byspale

Mars is braw in crammasy,
Venus in a green silk goun,
The auld mune shak's her gowden feathers,
Their starry talk's a wheen o' blethers,
Nane for thee a thochtie sparin',
Earth, thou bonnie broukit bairn!
– But greet, an' in your tears ye'll droun
The haill clanjamfrie!

I remember clearly the exact moment I first read this amazing poem, and antisyzygy first took me by the thrapple. I was 16 years of age, a Dulwich College schoolboy, and was sitting in the Dulwich picture gallery, which I had completely to myself. I was there, partly because I intended, at some later date, to go in for the Lady Evan Spicer prize for Art (a prize anyone in the school could go in for, and which you could win with an essay on one of the pictures in the Gallery), and partly because it was an oasis of peace and quiet in the midst of the hurly-burly of school life.

Imagine walking for 15 minutes from a classroom, and finding yourself among Poussin, Claude, Rubens, Van Dyck, Murillo, Rembrandt, Hogarth, Reynolds and Gainsborough – not to mention Watteau, Tiepolo and Canaletto. Occasionally, I composed the odd irreverent rhyme about some of these, e.g.

Where is Watteau?
Lying blotto
In a grotto
With his queyn.

I had with me a book I had just taken out of the school library: this was *The Northern Muse*, an anthology of Scottish poetry compiled by John Buchan, and containing a fairly predictable mélange of ballads, Burns, 'Scots Chaucerians' and 19th-century sentimentalists. However, it also contained one astounding poem, that was quite unlike anything else in the book – and that, of course, was 'The Bonny Broukit Bairn'. (Incidentally, it was attributed not to Hugh MacDiarmid but to C M Grieve, and I wondered who on earth C M Grieve was. Later, when I had learned the truth, that C M Grieve and HMcD were one man, and that the poem had already been published, in *Sangschaw*, under Hugh MacDiarmid's name, I wondered whether Buchan, a good

Borderer, might not have preferred the forthright, no-nonsense Border monicker to the vaguely romantic tartan-clad Perthshire MacDiarmid – and still think this was probably the case!)

I read 'The Bonnie Broukit Bairn' surrounded by Europe's great masters, and I found I had effortlessly committed it to memory within a minute or two of that first reading – this ability I had probably inherited from my grannie, who had an extraordinary verbal memory for poems and songs: one of the poems she could recite from end to end was Sir Walter Scott's lengthy *Glenfinlas.* But in the case of 'The Bonnie Broukit Bairn' I have always felt that you *apprehended* it as a complete poem immediately, in the same way you apprehend some of the shorter poems of Blake's.

Now, in case anyone is wondering how a fairly recently published anthology of Scottish poetry could come to rest on the shelves of the library of an English public school, it should be made clear that Dulwich College – founded by the Elizabethan actor-manager (and 'Chief Master Ruler and Overseer of … Bears, Bulls, Mastive Doggs and Bitches'), Edward Alleyn, has had since its foundation in 1619, a very close connection with Scots and Scotland – above all, a military connection. After buying the Manor of Dulwich, not long after the accession to the English throne of James VI, Alleyn got the idea of establishing a college or hospital for poor people, and the education of poor boys, and he stipulated that the Master and Warden of 'Alleyn's College of God's Gift' should be 'of my blood and surname' – or, if the former was impossible, at any rate should bear his surname. The Scots name Allan being a permissible variant of Alleyn, there was a succession of mostly Scots Masters – the headmaster of Dulwich is 'the Master' – called Allan.

The military (and naval) connection also goes back quite a long way; one of its most famous 20th-century celebrities was Captain Gordon Campbell, VC – one of eight Highland brothers, all of whom had their schooling at Dulwich. (Other kenspeckle characters were briefly mentioned in Andrew Hunter's article in the last *Cencrastus*, no. 47.) Gordon Campbell served in 'Q boats', 'the heavily disguised submarine hunters which accounted for quite a number of enemy U-boats. Anyway, I used to contend that I, and one or two other young Scots, were the authentic 'poor scholars' for whom Edward Alleyn had aimed to provide an education!

Again, it might be regarded as somewhat out of the ordinary for a London suburban school to be the proud possessor of one of the most famous art galleries in the world. As the history of the Dulwich Gallery is almost as odd as my own, I should maybe add a word or two about its curious history. Towards the end of the 18th century, Noel Joseph Desenfans, a French poet and dramatist, came to England as a language teacher, and with the aid of the dowry that came to him from a wealthy wife, he embarked on a lucrative career as a picture dealer. In 1790 King Stanislaus II Poniatowski – the last king of Poland – commissioned Desenfans to buy pictures that were to form the nucleus of a Polish National Gallery in Warsaw. Desenfans accumulated nearly 200 paintings, but in 1795 the third partition (between Austria, Prussia and Russia) wiped Poland off the map for the time being; Stanislaus abdicated, and Desenfans was left with the whole collection on his hands.

After his death in 1807, it passed to Sir Francis Bourgeois, the son of a Swiss who had settled for a time in England; Bourgeois was a painter, and an assiduous art collector, and it was he who decided that after the death of Desenfans' widow the collection should go to Dulwich College. A gallery was built to house the collection, the architect being Sir John Soane, and the aesthetes among the Dulwich schoolboys of the thirties used to say that Soane's gallery was a greater work of art than any of the pictures it housed. Unfortunately the gallery was badly damaged by a flying bomb in World War II, but it has now been rebuilt.

It was in this building, and alone among these famous dead companions, that I first sustained the impact of that amazing being of bright genius who descended on the Muckle Toon o' the Langholm in August 1892; and it was not long before I had managed – rummaging in Foyle's, and in Gordon Fraser's in Cambridge – to pick up copies of *Sangschaw*, *Pennywheep* and A *Drunk Man Looks at the Thistle*. I also found out that Grieve/MacDiarmid's name – although not much of his work – was known to one or two of the Dulwich masters; to 'Guts' Gayford – the same master from whom I first heard of Gavin Greig's folksong collecting work in the North East – and to Arthur Stewart MacPherson, the German master, who in one conversation said of MacDiarmid's out-of-the ordinary political-literary divagations (quoting *Faust*, the 'Prologue in Heaven')

> Ein guter Mensch in seinem dunklen Drange
> Ist sich des rechten Weges wohl bewusst.
> (A good human being, in the midst of dark turmoil,
> knows in himself the right way to go).

These are the words the Lord addresses to Mephistopheles, when – as in the Book of Job – he has given him permission to tempt Faust from the straight and narrow!

(Long afterwards, it struck me as rich irony that someone, surveying MacDiarmid's often self-contradictory life-paths, should quote lines written by the 'Oon Olympian'. Almost as ironical, in fact, as that MacDiarmid should dedicate the *First Hymn to Lenin* – with the lines asking 'whit maitters't wha we kill' – to Prince D S Mirsky).

Fired with enthusiasm for MacDiarmid and his superb Lallan poetry, I began to proselytise among my schoolmates, and eventually gave a talk on his work to the Literary Society; there is a report mentioning this in the Summer 1938 number of the *Alleynian* (the school magazine).

The scene in the picture gallery, described above, was in 1936, and at that time MacDiarmid had been based mainly in the Shetlands, on the island of Whalsay, for over three years – although with occasional visits to the mainland – and he was to remain there until 1942, when he was obliged to move to Glasgow and accept work at an engineering company in Scotstoun.

In the Michaelmas term of 1938 I went up to Downing College, Cambridge, to read Modern Languages. As I had rooms in College, I was soon introduced to F R Leavis, who also, I found, had an interest in MacDiarmid; Leavis directed me to the articles in *Scrutiny* about various aspects of Scottish literature by the Aberdonian scholar, John Speirs (whom I was to meet when on leave in Cairo during World War II). Leavis also drew my attention to the chapter entitled 'The Present and C M Grieve' which rounded off these articles when they appeared in book form in the middle of my second year *(The Scots Literary Tradition*, Chatto & Windus, London 1940).

At first, however, it was not the chapter on MacDiarmid – interesting and provocative though that was – which first made me want to get to grips with Speirs's general position; it was – as few who know me will be surprised to hear – his chapter on the Scottish ballads. The first paragraph of this piece properly took my breath away; it seemed such an inadmissibly print-bound deliverance:

> As we have them in the Collections, the Scottish Ballads are poems chiefly of the eighteenth century. That they are quite different from other poems of that century may at first occasion surprise, but has its explanation. On the other hand it has been denied (by the primitivists) that they are poems of that century at all. It has been argued that there is no reason to suppose they did not come into being centuries earlier than the century in which they were written down. It has also been observed that a good deal of the 'material' used is 'mediaeval'. But a poem and the language it is in are one and the same. Translated, it either becomes a new poem or ceases to be a poem at all. It is sufficient therefore to point to the language the ballads are in, which in most cases is at the point of development it was in the eighteenth century. (This is not merely a matter of language, but of sensibility. The ballads taken down after the beginning of the nineteenth century show a distinct modification of sensibility). Certainly the ballads are traditional. But so also is every poem – in its own degree.

This paragraph made me long to beard Speirs face to face, and I was delighted to find, when I finally met up with him in Egypt – he had a teaching post at the Fuad el Awal University – that he was more than willing to discuss his views on the subject with me. We spent the best part of a night, in his Maadi flat, jousting together on the subject of folklore and the oral tradition, and before I left, to return to less intellectual warfare in the desert, I had the satisfaction of noting a certain perceptible weakening in his general position. Indeed, I think I can claim a modicum of credit for the fact that when *The Scots Literary Tradition* was reprinted – with additions – in 1962, by Faber & Faber, Speirs added a footnote to the above quoted paragraph:

> I would now (1961) say that I got the emphasis wrong in this paragraph. The Ballads *are* a residue from medieval poetry – therefore, with a long oral tradition behind them.

The chapter's peroration (in both editions of the book) still seems to me to provide food for thought:

> The ballads are concerned, it is true, almost entirely with the circle of the life of the body, with birth, instinctive action, death (often violent death), and the decay of the body. Again, they present on the one hand (as W P Ker and others noted) images of a princely grandeur erected out of earth, and on the other hand, its counterpart, the earthiness of death and decay ... They embody, in any case, very fragmentarily indeed, but with startling immediacy, a vision of human life which sprang apparently from the imagination of the 'folk'.

Another modification in which our arguments may have played a part, was in a footnote which (in the 1940 edition) goes as follows:

> Mr Robert Graves is interested in the 'ballads' that came into existence among the British troops during the war of 1914, but these are the merest drivel, as he would agree.

In the 1962 edition the end of this footnote reads as follows:

– but these have little intrinsic or permanent value, as he would agree.

About MacDiarmid we did not talk nearly so much, largely because I had felt myself in agreement with much of what he had written in his book – for example, his statement: 'He does not in actual fact (in spite of what he wrote of the necessity for doing so) begin from Dunbar but (in *Sangschaw*) from the folk ballad.' However, I think I argued successfully that in my opinion the statement that followed this remark was quite wrong ('The little that is in the Scottish folk-ballad mode is almost the only successful portion of *A Drunk Man Looks at the Thistle*). But I had agreed 100 per cent with his statement later in the book:

> ... Of the volume *Second Hymn* to *Lenin and Other Poems* (1935) I should be prepared to hazard the opinion that Grieve has at last really found himself. The best poems in this volume *resemble* certain occasional aspects of Blake and also of the Shelley of the *Mask of Anarchy* (compare their use of the political broadsheet technique), particularly in an anger finding direct, naïve expression. This particular naïvete is a much more difficult achievement than may at first appear. It marks the attainment of a difficult sincerity.

When we had more or less – after much of a night's argy bargy – talked ourselves to a standstill, John's wife Ruth ended the session with a reading of some of her admirable translations of Rilke's *Duino Elegies* (later published by Tambimuttu in *Poetry London*).

Before leaving for Africa, I had made an arrangement with a young sales assistant in Heifer's bookshop in Cambridge to send me (care of MEF – Middle East Forces) any books or periodicals he thought I would particularly like to have, and to charge them up – hopefully – to my account. The result was that copies of *Horizon* and books like MacDiarmid's *Lucky Poet* were duly launched on an extraordinary pilgrimage which carried some of them backwards and forwards from Cairo to Benghazi, and Tunis to the Sangro, with dozens of intermediate pirouettings. *Lucky Poet*, published by Methuen, London, in 1943, took nearly a year to reach me and was finally delivered when I was on the Anzio beachhead. I started to read it just after the fall of Rome, when I was esconced in reasonable comfort in the Pensione Eletta, in the Piazza del Gesù, but was unable to settle down with it until the war in Italy was over, and I was enjoying my first leave for over two years at Meran (Merano) in the South Tyrol.

Sitting on a bench among the green slopes of a spacious park which looked as if it was all set to climb upwards and onwards until it reached the snowy Alps, I read *Lucky Poet*, and sat reflecting on MacDiarmid's bewildering poetic and political career, and all the paradoxical and self-contradictory things I had heard about him, which seemed to me not so much a fruitful interplay – or clash – of opposites as hopelessly disparate ideas and contentions collapsing into an incoherent jumble. I remembered the acerbic comments of A S Macpherson at Dulwich about his supermanic flirtations with Fascism; what Paul Potts had told me about his friendship with the rabid anti-Semitic Count Potocki of Montalk (claimant to the throne of Poland) from whom he had rented a cottage in Sussex in 1932, and who was Paul Port's *bête noire*. Then, counterbalancing such thoughts, I remembered his brilliant satirical onslaughts on Burns Suppers and the 'high mucky-mucks' – and above all, the coruscating marvel of his early lyrics in

Sangschaw and *Pennywheep*, which had made me realise, as a schoolboy, that much remained to be quarried in the roch granity antres of the Scots language. I soon found myself writing a poem which I called 'To Hugh MacDiarmid on reading *Lucky Poet*', and the first draft of it was finished before I returned to Rome. Here it is, as I eventually revised it for inclusion in *Poems Addressed to Hugh MacDiarmid*, and presented to him on his 75th birthday (Akros Publications, 11 August 1967):

> You admit acting out a superb comedy
> Before the Scots burghers, that blubbing company.
> Panache weel cockit, sharp sgian in stocking,
> But conscious of something (your fighting tail?) lacking,
> You strut and you gaelivant before them.
> Powerless with your piping fancies to fire them
> You spurn their blind-alley ways their shuttered faces
> And gar your muse kick high her paces.
>
> If there were just two choices
> mine would be yours, MacDiarmid!
>
> You tilt against 'Englishism': the words sleek and slick,
> The smoothing fingers that add trick to trick;
> The admirable refusal to be moved unduly
> By the screaming pipe. The desire to speak truly
> With a middle voice; the acceptance of protection;
> The scorn for enthusiasm, that crude infection ...
>
> That's all very well.
>   But what about 'Scotchiness',
> This awful dingy bleary blotchiness?
> You list 'Anglophobia' as your recreation,
> But it's Scotland that's driven you to ruination!
>
> Why not admit it? The meanness, the rancour,
> The philistine baseness, the divisive canker,
> The sly Susanna's elder-ism,
>   McGrundyish muck-raking,
> Are maladies of Scottish, not of English making.
> If we think all our ills come from 'ower the Border'
> We'll never, but never, march ahead 'in guid order'.
>
> I try to make sense of your tortured logomachy,
> For there is a sense in which England's our enemy.
> Though to her we seem boorish or just plain funny
> She can buy 'the wee Jocks', and get value for money.
> (Although 'let us prey' is the text the Scots glory in
> (It's the paper we'll wrap up our blood-boltered story in)
> The licence to roam through the world for plunder
> We received on a plat from the big boss down under.

And does *that* let us out? Why, not on your life, sir!
We've fought England's battles to the dreepin knife, sir!
And after the gougings, the thumpings, the kickings,
We've never been averse to the jackal's pickings.
And, when we're gabbing, and have a drink to spout with,
'Here's tae us, wha's like us' is the toast we come out with.
I know you've been living in the Isles like a hermit,
But you know bloody well this is true, MacDiarmid!

And have said it all before. So we're back where we started.
Yes, you've said it all before.
And are broken hearted?
You've shown up the shame of our idiot Burns Suppers
Which – when poetry's skint, stonybroke, on its uppers –
Spend more on a night of befuddled bard-buggering
Than a poet can earn in a year's hugger-muggering.
The couthy Wee McGregors can still goad you to fury.
You tear coloured strips off their twee tasselled toories.
And as for our brass-hats, and their anti-Red slaverings
You've done more than most to put paid to their haverings.
So why all this other junk? Man, I don't get it.
This problem would soon lay me low – if I let it.
Amidst all the posturings, tantrums and rages,
Is there something you haven't said, in all these pages?
Is there some secret room, and you don't want to show it?
Did an unlucky break befall the Lucky Poet?

Just what do you stand for, MacDiarmid? I'm still not certain.
I don' wanna step behin' dat tartan curtain ...

When I wrote this poem, I had not read the bitter-black 'Letter to RMB' (Robin Black, editor of the *Free Man*) written not long after MacDiarmid's arrival in the Shetlands in 1933:

> There is nae ither country 'neath the sun
> That's betrayed the human spirit as Scotland's done ...
> (From 'Hitherto Uncollected Poems' in *Complete Poems*, ed. Michael Grieve and W R Aitken, London 1978, Vol. 2. A brief excerpt was printed in *Stony Limits* (1934), but did not contain the lines quoted.)

If I had, I might have phrased the passage beginning 'Why not admit it?' rather differently.

When Duncan Glen's book arrived, it seemed to me my poem did really stick out from among the others, if only because it represented a shot – even if a bosh shot – at grappling with the truth. At the other end of the spectrum were poems like Maurice Lindsay's somewhat lightweight effort of 1943 – written one year after he discovered Chris Grieve's existence:

> The English see you as an angry eagle
> Who tears at them with sharp and furious claws ...

A statement which I thought unlikely to correspond to the reality of the situation. Quite apart from the fact that eagles are more likely to tear at their prey with their beaks rather than with their claws, I felt, rightly or wrongly, that this was a wholly incongruous image. (Nearer the mark, to my way of thinking, had been Speirs's comment on MacDiarmid's desperate assault on Scottish Philistinism: 'he turns/and turns like a caged tiger'). Anyway, my first response to the anthology was to write a parody of Lindsay's poem beginning:

> The English see you as an ancient beagle
> That limps along on mangy calloused paws

but I decided to suppress this, as being too cruel to both parties concerned!

A month after finishing 'On Reading Lucky Poet' – which was in mid-October 1945 – I was on a plane home, to be demobilised. My first priority was to work on the series of desert war elegies – eventually published as *Elegies for the Dead in Cyrenaica*; and this I did in Cambridge and in Lochboisdale, where the owner of the hotel, Finlay MacKenzie (who liked my poetry) was kind enough to let me have a room for free, while I was completing them. Although I corresponded occasionally with Chris Grieve – the first letters from Lochboisdale are addressed with decorous formality, to 'Dear Hugh MacDiarmid' – I did not actually meet him until 24 March 1947, when I took pot luck and paid him a visit at 32 Victoria Crescent Road, Dowanhill, Glasgow. At that time he and Valda were living in the basement of a house owned by Walter and Sadie Pritchard, both art teachers; it was a nice commodious basement and the Grieves were happily ensconced in it. Unfortunately, my visit coincided with some sort of problem Chris had to deal with – I guessed there had been an argument with his landlord, or with Sadie – and he could only spare me a moment or two; he apologised, and told me to return when I was back in Glasgow.

However, when I next came down south on my motorbike – from Arisaig, to which I had moved from Lochboisdale – Chris had in the meantime accepted a job south (though not far south!) of the Border: he had joined the staff of the *Carlisle Journal*, whose offices were in English Street, and he was living in a local temperance hotel – not the most auspicious set-up for a poet who listed his recreations in *Who's Who* as Anglophobia! Valda was alone in the basement flat, for their son Michael was at school at Kilquhanity, in Galloway; when I arrived, she was clearly in an exceedingly agitated state, and told me straight away about her dire financial plight; she said Chris hadn't sent her a promised sub from Carlisle, and asked if I could lend her some money. This put me on the spot, because since leaving my free accommodation on South Uist I had been making an exiguous living giving lectures for the WEA in Lochaber, and had more or less reached the end of my tether financially; I knew that if I got back to Cambridge I could raise some dough, and I had intended to ride my bike through the night down the east-coast route to see Irish friends in the Cambridgeshire village of Dry Drayton.

So, lending her six bob, and apologising it was so little, I suggested that I should instead ride down to Carlisle, tell Chris that she needed dough urgently and see to it that he did something about it without delay. Before I left, Valda added a second commission to give to Chris, and it still appears poignantly on the flyleaf of my 1947 diary:

> 'Mike wants a parcel.'

So, later on that fine summer's afternoon – this was the beginning of June 1947 – I found myself driving JMD 85 – my Rudge Special's name was its registration number – straight down south among the Border hills in the direction of Carlisle. I got there about 5 p.m. and parking the bike outside the offices of the *Carlisle Journal* in English Street, I went inside in search of Hugh MacDiarmid.

'You want Mr Grieve?' asked the doorman, and he pointed the way. A moment later I was in the main office, and the man I was looking for was right there in front of me. I have never forgotten the expression on his face, as I first caught a glimpse of it in that newspaper office; it was the expression perfectly caught on R H Westwater's well-known painting: a wary sideways look, like that of a café-owner in some dangerous dockside area, half expecting trouble, and already sizing up what chance he had of coping with it. As soon as Chris was free – he was obviously completing work on some story as I walked in – he took me aside, and asked my business.

I gave him Valda's message, and after a moment's thought he asked me if I could lend him some money. I explained that I had already lent Valda as much as I could spare, and explained my own financial position. He then said that he could raise money if he could get back to Glasgow, and after sizing up the situation, I offered to give him a lift back on the pillion of the motor-bike. By this time it was too late to start back that day, so we arranged to take off the following morning at 10 a.m. Our evening meals were fish suppers, picked up at an adjacent chipper, and I went in search of a cheap B&B; Chris then retired to his temperance hotel.

The following morning we set off, as planned, and were in Glasgow by lunchtime. The journey was without incident – except for one awkward moment, when I was suddenly confronted with quite a deep circular rut in the road. I could allow for it, and rose in the saddle as we went over it, but Chris, of course, being behind me couldn't see it, so he was hoisted high, and came down with a thump. However, he took this very well – only remarking, later in the day: 'I thought you'd broken my os coccyx.'

The day had been fine when we started off, but it began to rain when we were nearing the city, and by the time we were crossing the Clyde it was coming down in buckets. Chris directed me to 793 Argyle Street, the offices of the Caledonian Press (printers of the *Voice of Scotland* and sundry other Nationalist publications) and introduced me to Kenny and Calum Campbell, brothers from Easter Ross, who ran the business. (Kenny was at that time known as Kenny MacKenzie, because – being a militant Scottish Republican – he had successfully avoided the call-up.) The firm was being subsidised by Robin Black, and MacDiarmid obviously hoped to get the necessary sub from Kenny and Calum – but they were in difficulties themselves, and told him to look elsewhere.

Consequently, we took off again, in the rain, on JMD 85, and for the next couple of hours MacDiarmid was engaged on a fruitless search for funds, becoming more and more crestfallen as every new hopeful turned out to be either unable or unwilling to provide any subsidy whatsoever. I have the clearest memory of that doleful pilgrimage because tramlines running amidst rain-soaked cobbles do not constitute the ideal surface for anyone riding a motor bike, and most of the streets we traversed had this double disadvantage. Once or twice, in, fact, we nearly came to grief – the bike was slithering all over the place – but we eventually landed up without physical mishap back at 793 Argyle Street. However, MacDiarmid had been unable to raise a penny, and it was obvious he was going to try again with Kenny and Calum.

To let them get on with it, I retreated into the back room – the printing presses were in the front compartment of the shop – and stood there awaiting developments. Although they were speaking practically *sotto voce*, I could hear scraps of conversation, and Kenny in particular was repeatedly asserting the total impossibility of the firm advancing Chris any more money. There was a lull, and then my heart sank as I heard Calum say 'What about this fellow?' (meaning me). A moment or two later Chris came into the back room and asked me whether – seeing he was in such awful straits – it was not possible for me to draw on my reserves and lend him some money – 'Ten pounds, if you possibly can'.

I quite literally did not know what to say. As an impecunious scholarship boy at Cambridge I had had to husband my money with extreme care, and had never allowed myself an overdraft. Although my years in the army had enabled me to build up a certain reserve, I had been obliged to draw on this quite heavily in my final (post-war) year at Downing; also, I had been digging into it up north while trying to complete my *Elegies*. Furthermore, I had had to pay for osteopathic treatment from a London specialist for a back injury incurred during the desert war – and indeed would have to pay for 'back-up' treatment for years to come – treatment which to this day is not available on the National Health Service. Last, but not least, I had bought JMD 85, which – although second-hand – had been quite expensive. Who can blame me if I did not reply to MacDiarmid's request immediately?

And then an overwhelming thought hit me – this man, who is going through all these balls-aching contortions to try and raise money for his wife and son is the same man who has written the most wonderful Scottish poetry for over a century – if not ever; he's the man who wrote 'Empty vessel' and 'Wha's been here afore me, lass?', and the 'Second Hymn to Lenin'. He is the man who has sacrificed everything to purge Scotland of its deadening Philistinism and who – in John Speirs's words – 'still stands for health and life and sincerity in Scotland against complacency and indifference'. I took out my cheque-book, and wrote C M Grieve a cheque for £10. I then took all three friends into a nearby pub and stood them all a pint.

(It was during this session that Chris told Kenny and Calum about my collection of soldiers' songs in various languages – which I had described to him over fish suppers the night before, in Carlisle – and suggested that – as not a few of them were bawdy – a fictitious club could be founded on the model of Sydney Goodsir Smith's Auk Society to print these ballads unbowdlerised and circulate news of this to prospective members – i.e. purchasers. The Campbells liked the idea, and before the end of the year, *Ballads of World War II* was available to paid-up members of the Lili Marlene Club of Glasgow.)

That night Chris let me doss down on a mattress in the basement flat, and in the morning I gave him a lift on the motor-bike to Glasgow Central Station, for he had decided – and I don't blame him – to use part of my tenner for a train journey back to Carlisle. (Kenny had advanced him the money on the strength of my cheque.)

Before boarding the train, he suddenly said: 'Don't tell Valda' (by which I took him to mean about the loan). Nor did I ever, to her dying day, even at the cost of her completely misunderstanding what had happened.

After boarding the train, Chris stood at the window of his carriage, and I wished him a happy journey. As the train started to move he smiled a rather curious enigmatic smile, and his farewell words to me were: 'You did what you had to do.'

* * *

Years later, in 1993, a party of folk went up to Aberdeen from Edinburgh to attend the
funeral of the magnificent ballad singer Lizzie Higgins (daughter of an even more
famous ballad singer, the great Jeanie Robertson whom A L Lloyd called 'a singer
sweet and heroic'). At the graveside of the *cimetière marin* where Lizzie was laid to rest
near her mother and father, we were joined by Tim Neat, who only a year before had
filmed Lingie singing the witch ballad 'Alison Gross' – an immortal piece of filming
which came just in time to perpetuate on video her extraordinary artistry. We then
repaired to the Atholl Hotel for a few drinks, and there – for some reason which now
escapes me – I told Tim all about that motor-bike ride in the rain, on a fruitless quest for
funds. A few days later, when I was back in Auld Reekie, I received the following poem
from him:

> 'You Did What You Had To Do'
>
> You did what you had to do, he said – brutal but true.
> From him it showed contempt, conceit, largesse.
> He
> In those words flung down and at once took up the glove;
> Chose to act as though he were some chosen one and
> Put me in my place – but the words came forth Divine –
> What had I done? Ferried round a man ahunt for money
> Aback my motorbike – and written out a ten pound cheque
> Hand on my heart and half my mind – to him whom now
>
> A train carried off the poet Hugh MacDiarmid.
> Glasgow
> Central Stration – dome to his cross and to the People's Doom!
>
> What I had done came first from pride. Who asked for
> Money can refuse? Second manners bred across the bed
> Of years – third sheer wish to help. Fourth all debt
> Is good – Fifth given a recognition his folk withheld –
> And last – the love-deep knowledge that in us two piers
>
> Had met in steam and smoke and hammer-beams conjoined
> Above the lowest and the highest fate that men can know
> Sweet poverty and need. Divine Dante and the Keystone Cops
> Were ours that day. Mr Grieve had passed round his hat
> His glass, his cup – to Peter, James and John – to me!

As I rode south on the east coast route to Cambridge on JMD 85, those farewell words
– 'brutal but true' – stayed with me and it was round about Stamford that a curious
thought occurred to me, that maybe they were quite literally true – that for reasons
outwith my power or control I had just had to enter MacDiarmid's life at that point –
and that he had accepted this, probably with the benefit of previous experience.

It was not so much a metaphysical apprehension as the sort of ineluctable necessity one faces up to before battle: I felt in the grip of a truly brutal reality, and that there was not much to be done about it ... Years later, reading *MacDiarmid in Shetland*, edited by Laurence Graham and Brian Smith, and published by the Shetland Library, Lerwick, in 1992, I recognised a similar incident, and responded to it with a similar *frisson*. At the end of 1937 MacDiarmid was 'in an infernal muddle of multiple composition', and his plight, both financial and spiritual, was getting desperate. I quote, with permission, some passages from Brian Smith's account of this period, which complements and amplifies that in Alan Bold's copious – but necessarily incomplete – biography:

> ... The prospects were bleaker than ever. He had had scarcely anything pub-
> lished for several years, and the local merchants, who had generously given the
> Grieves credit over the years, were getting restive ...

There was one hope. Grieve had heard about a young man, Grant Taylor, who was willing to come to Whalsay to act as the poet's secretary/typist in return for bed and board ...

Valda was desperate. Writing to Helen Cruikshank at New Year, she confided that they were 'utterly destitute – even without soap for washing'. They had had to cut their milk order by half. Mrs Bruce at Symbister House had showered them with gifts and food at Christmas, but Valda was terrified of the privations 1938 might bring. 'If we cannot pull through when Taylor comes up,' she wrote, 'it's the end – and I'll end the whole thing and us as well, rather than let Scotland break him and crow over it.'

> In the event Grant Taylor saved the Grieves.
> (Brian Smith, 1992).

The link between this young man, whom one can call without hyperbole, the pro-vidential *deus ex machina*, and the beleagured Grieve family, was the poet Robert Garioch, who bumped into Taylor one day and told him that Grieve was 'living in Whalsay and on his uppers, as you might say, pretty well broke' ... Bob was therefore self-evidently a potent agent of benefaction, and through his intervention he secured for MacDiarmid two and a half years of devoted service from Grant Taylor. However, it is sad to have to relate that MacDiarmid seemingly had a blind spot as far as Bob's poetic capabilities were concerned. In a letter to Tom Scott of 5 November 1965, he wrote (of Bob's poetry): '... in so far as I know his work there is very little of it of value. His strength lies in his knowledge of Scots, and particularly of demotic Edinburgh dialect, but he has no elevation and in general I think not only dull but vulgar in the worst sense' (Bold, *The Letters* of *Hugh MacDiarmid*, p. 703).

(My first reaction on reading these words was one of incredulity: how could anyone with any sensitivity assert, of the poet who had written 'At Robert Fergusson's Grave' and 'On Seeing an Aik-Tree Sprent wi Galls', that he was lacking in elevation?)

He gave vent to similar sentiments – in April 1952 or thereabouts – at an informal meeting in the Greyfriars Bobby Bar, when I had introduced him to Charles Stewart, the then Secretary of Edinburgh University. The purpose of the little gathering was to interest Stewart in the idea of lectures on modern Scottish poetry, to be given by Chris and myself, and we were backed in this project by Professor S T M Newman, the professor of music, and David Abercrombie, the head of the Phonetics Department. (This was the period of infancy of the School of Scottish Studies; I had just completed my first recording tour, paid for with University money, and the academics mentioned wanting to retain me on the spot until such time as more money might be forthcoming to pay for further trips.)

The venue was chosen, according to David, 'to put the poets at their ease' – an aim I thought eminently sensible and civilised. At some point in the conversation Bob's name came up – Stewart knew some of his work already – but Chris's comments on him were unexpectedly curt and dismissive – 'and', he added, 'he's a soft centre'. This remark annoyed me, because I had been a close friend of Bob's ever since demobilisation after World War II, and knew something of what he had been through as a POW. So I said, 'I rather think he's as tough a nut to crack as you are, Chris.'

It's possible that a certain deterioration in our relations, which became gradually more pronounced in the following years, dates from that moment of truth, in the Greyfriars Bobby.

*   *   *

Again it is sad to have to relate that MacDiarmid was misinformed by some person unknown about Bob's contribution to the MacDiarmid Symposium on 27 May 1972 – (this event was in honour of MacDiarmid's 80th birthday). Bob was supposed to have referred to Grant Taylor's help in the Shetland years in a manner which exhibited 'malice' towards MacDiarmid. In a letter to MacDiarmid written on 16 July 1972 (and now in Edinburgh University Library) I tried to put the record straight. I said in it: 'The friend or friends of yours who have suggested that Bob's remarks were "malicious" have themselves been guilty in my opinion of seriously misleading you. I don't want to start bandying around adjectives of that sort myself, but I can think of one which would describe their conduct! I have no use, and never have had, for this internecine nonsense, and try to knock it on the head whenever I come across it.'

This letter was enclosed with an 80th birthday present, sent off early: this was a new translation of Hesse's *Das Glasperlenspiel* (*The Glass Bead Game*) which first appeared in English in 1948 with the title *Magister Ludi*.

I was sure he would be interested in that book because it is – in one aspect of it, at least – a very sophisticated Karl Kraus-type satire on the whole idea of a super aesthetic intellectual élite.

*   *   *

When I arrived in the Cambridgeshire village of Dry Drayton, after those hectic days in Carlisle and Glasgow, and the long motor-bike ride south, I received ready hospitality from my Irish friends the Armstrongs, and set about the immediate task of typing out *Ballads of World War II* for Kenny and Calum Campbell. I also looked in at Downing College, two or three days later, and was not surprised to find that a statement from Barclays Bank, Benet Street, had arrived with my other mail at the porter's lodge. This contained the information that on 12 June 1947 a cheque for £10, made out to 'Grieve', had landed me in the red for the first time since I had opened an account there, at the age of 18, in 1938. l was three pounds, eight and five pence overdrawn! I decided to retain this priceless document as a souvenir, and it is still in my possession.

Luckily the assistant manager at the bank was an affable and friendly Welshman; when I went round the back to see him, he told me I needn't worry: he knew that I had always managed my affairs prudently, and would no doubt shortly be back in the black … However, like any canny Scots scholarship boy, I had a horror of being in the red, and began to look around energetically for gainful employment. Luck was with me, and in the Cambridge Union – of which I was a life member – I ran into an old friend who worked for the Army Education Corps; he invited me – because I was able to lecture in German of sorts – to take part in a conference for *Volkshochschullehrer* (People's High School Teachers) in Bad Godesberg, which would run for most of August: his suggestion was that I should organise a course on Scottish literature and folklore. I also got immediate employment lecturing on the same subjects to German prisoners of war in various camps – one as far north as Watten in Caithness – so that I was able before very long to re-enter the black in Barclays, Benet Street. (Incidentally, I retained an account there until the mid-1950s, for it seemed madness to remove my money – or overdraft – from a bank whose assistant manager was such a decent chap.)

One reason why my own life was, from a financial point of view, rather an uphill struggle at that time, was because organisations like Lord Reith's pious BBC had more or less blacklisted me for political reasons; another was undoubtedly the appearance of the shamelessly unexpurgated texts of *Ballads* of *World War II*. Even so the bank statements show that throughout the final years of the 1940s, I continued to do what I could to give the Grieves a helping hand – although after that initial tenner to Chris the cheques were all made out, not to him, but to 'V. Grieve' or 'Valda Grieve', and were all for fivers. This became possible after I got a job in Belfast as District Secretary of the Northern Ireland WEA, and quite soon afterwards, won the Somerset Maugham Award for my *Elegies for the Dead in Cyrenaica.* (Luckily I was able to supplement the £310 I got from the award with a win on the horses. I backed Russian Hero in the 1949 Grand National, and it came in at 66 to 1.)

John Lehmann, my publisher, invited me to London that spring to discuss future plans – I had told him of my intention to translate Gramsci's *Letters from Prison,* not long published in Italy – and I took the opportunity to visit a number of old friends, including G S Fraser and Tambimuttu. In a pub in New Oxford Street called The Hog in the Pound I ran into Keidrych Rhys, who about a year before had published a mini-anthology of modern Scottish poetry called *Albannach.* (This contained one of the early poems of Norman MacCaig – one of the sort for which, according to him, he was requested to provide an 'answer' !) Keidrych quizzed me about the Scottish scene, and I told him what I knew of the recent ongoings of Sydney Goodsir Smith and others. He asked me particularly about Chris, and I told him of my being able – due to the luck of the draw – to give the Grieves a little occasional practical assistance. He was quiet for a wee while and then said, quite vehemently: 'Watch out! That man is a specialist in the gentle art of biting the hand that feeds him.' This was a remark I was subsequently to remember ruefully, as will become obvious as the story unfolds.

Not long after the informal confab of April 1952 in the Greyfriars Bobby, described above, there took place a meeting of the committee by the Labour Movement People's Festival. This was an organisation suppprted by the Labour Party which the previous year had run an alternative Edinburgh Festival; this latter can now be seen in retrospect as the earliest ancestor of what became the Fringe. The star event of the 1951 People's Festival had been a ceilidh of traditional folk singers, both Gaelic and Lowland Scots, and it was proposed that we should repeat this outstanding success by laying on a second traditional ceilidh in the Oddfellows' Hall in Forrest Road (just opposite Sandy Bell's)! I then raised the question of what the committee should undertake to celebrate the 60th birthday of Hugh MacDiarmid, the principal patron of the People's Festival and it was agreed, after some discussion, that that year's ceilidh should be held in his honour.

In the event, the second ceilidh was an even more resounding success than the first one. The veteran Barra singer Calum Johnston again sang and played the pipes; the famous Gaelic singers from Lewis, Kitty MacLeod and her sister Marietta enthralled the audience with 'Cairistiona' and 'Agus Ho Mhorag'; an excellent bothy-ballad singer from the North East, Frank Steele, sang 'Come All Ye Lonely Lovers'; the young Arthur Argo, great-grandson of Gavin Greig, sang 'The Souter's Feist' in a boyish treble, and Jimmy McBeath gave of his best with 'Come all ye Tramps and Hawkers' and 'The Moss o' Burreldale'. Hugh MacDiarmid, in whose honour they were performing, was invited to sit on the platform, and at the beginning the entire audience rose, while Calum Johnston played 'Blue Bonnets over the Border' as a tribute to Scotland's greatest living poet – and most famous Borderer.

Chris was obviously deeply moved, and at the end of the ceilidh he rose to propose a vote of thanks to the performers. Here are one or two excerpts from his speech:

> Mr Chairman, Ladies and Gentlemen – As you all know, my personal vanity has always been notorious – but it is quite unequal to the present occasion. I've been absolutely overwhelmed by the honour that has been done me, and by the honour that the various artists, and this magnificent audience, have done to themselves, and to Scotland, in doing it.
>
> It would be wrong of me, even in proposing a vote of thanks, if I didn't point out that our tremendous treasury of folksong in Scotland, whether in Lallans or in Gaelic, is a treasury that has been occluded, very largely for political reasons, from the knowledge of the majority of our people. This Edinburgh People's Festival, and the movements in which my friends on the platform and others in the audience are concerned, is a re-assertion of that tradition, against the tide of all the things ... all the cultural enemies that are besetting us at the present time ...
>
> One thing must have struck you, I think, in the programme tonight – that is, the extent to which all the items in the programme have been correlated to the lives of the common people, to the work of the common people, the daily darg of the common people.
>
> We are not going to be taken from that – we're not going to be persuaded by the advocates of snob art; that some mystical palaver is better than that which comes from the working life of our own people.

That this fabulous ceilidh made a deep impression on MacDiarmid is conclusively proved by the text of an address which he delivered the following year to the Porch Philosophical Club in Doune Terrace, Edinburgh. (This latter organisation had been founded by Edward Haliburton, son of the Countess of Mayo, and it ran a number of off-beat cultural events in the early 1950s, as well as providing a roulette table for its members.) MacDiarmid's address was entitled *To Hell with Culture* and sub-titled *The Real Versus the Pseudo*; the full text of it was published in the *National Weekly* of 23 May 1953. He said, *inter alia*,

I have known Edinburgh intimately for nearly half-a-century, and I could count the cultured Edinburgh citizens I have met in it on fewer than the fingers of one hand. Most of them are now dead.

I did meet certain really cultured people at the Festival time last year – at a concert that wasn't on the official Festival Programme. It was a ceilidh at which the programme was sustained by Gaelic and Lallans folk-singers. There was a young boy from Turriff who sang like a lintie songs that had been orally transmitted for generations in his family. There was an old farm-wife of over 70. There was a tramp singer who has been travelling the roads of Scotland all his days. The Scottish Trade Union Congress and the Labour Party have just banned the whole thing because some of those concerned were not sufficiently respectful to (save the mark!) American culture. It was one of the finest concerts I ever attended. *The Scotsman* and other papers didn't print a word about it. These Scottish folk-singers were real artists. Every one of them was culturally worth all the famous artistes, conductors, actors and actresses of the official Festival a thousand times over. These folk-singers will never be decorated or named to an academy. When their voices fail, they will probably starve to death. But whenever you hear one of them singing you have there before you the aesthetic impulse of all times (genuine even if often on a merely elemental level) – and another exemplification of the way in which in Scotland we have bartered our birthright for a mess of commercialised cosmopolitan pottage.

(I am indebted to Dr Alan Riach for supplying me with a photostat of the article in question.)

A week or two before the *National Weekly* published this address I had set off for the North East on the third of my university-backed recording tours, and this time I concentrated on the travelling people in the city of Aberdeen itself; it was on that tour that I 'discovered' the greatest of all my finds – the immortal ballad singer Jeannie Robertson. When he first heard her later that year MacDiarmid was most enthusiastic; however, as will be revealed in due course, he did a quite astonishing *volte face* in 1964, when a heated controversy about the folksong revival erupted in the pages of *The Scotsman*.

The middle and late 1950s were for me a decade of intensive fieldwork among the bothy singers of Aberdeenshire, and among the Gaelic-speaking traveller folk of Sutherland, and I saw much less of MacDiarmid than in th 1940s. It seems possible – in view of the later worsening in our relations – that he felt that I was neglecting him in favour of tinker folk-singers, and that he resented this. In any case a sort of geographical divide had begun to open up in Edinburgh, separating the literary gents and their onhangers – who frequented the Abbotsford in Rose Street, and Milne's Bar at the corner of Rose Street and Hanover Street – and the 'folkies' who from 1951 onwards gravitated towards Sandy Bell's.

'Sandy's' was also, of course, the 'local' of the School of Scottish Studies, and became the favourite rendezvous of groups like the Dubliners, and characters like Pete Seeger, when they were in Auld Reekie. Not that MacDiarmid never showed up in Sandy Bell's – he was in his glory there after that famous Ceilidh of 1952, surrounded by the singers and musicians who had made such an impression on him – but Milne's gradually became his acknowledged 'howff', and he was to be seen there periodically in the company of Norman MacCaig, with whom he had formed a close friendship, and the egregious Sydney Goodsir Smith. These three formed, in fact, a sort of literary triumvirate, and for columnists in *The Scotsman* and *The Edinburgh Evening News,* they became – in journalistic shortspeak – the 'Rose St Poets'.

I was not often to be seen in Milne's myself, partly for the geographical reasons already alluded to – it takes considerably longer to walk from George Square to Rose Street than it does to walk to Forrest Road – but when I did look in there I was not seldom made conscious of not really belonging to its particular 'set'. Even so, I have to admit that I was unpleasantly surprised when, in January 1959, I was rather pointedly not invited to the inaugural Burns Supper of the 200 Burns Club, which was held in the Peacock Hotel, Newhaven; the club had been founded by Jimmy Crichton and Dr David Orr (MacDiarmid's benefactor on Whalsay) to celebrate the bicentenary of Burns's birth. This Burns Supper was doubtless a great occasion, and MacDiarmid, Norman MacCaig and Sydney Goodsir Smith were invited to become the Club bards.

The much respected Edinburgh firm Chambers had commissioned Norman to edit a collection of contemporary Scottish poetry, in honour of the bicentenary; this was to be entitled *Honour'd Shade.* Norman wrote to me, that same January, inviting me to submit poems for possible inclusion. Unluckily, this letter arrived when my thoughts and preoccupations were tied up with marriage preparations, and I did not get round to answering it until I returned to Scotland after a honeymoon in Provence. I had to face up to the fact that had not written much poetry – apart from songs – in recent years, as all my energies had been devoted to my collecting work; I wrote to Norman, telling him this, and adding that in any case I was rather doubtful if the poetry I had written was really good enough to be included in what was likely to be an anthology of top-notchers. And there the matter rested, as far as I was concerned, until the book itself was published in November, and an anonymous reviewer in *The Scotsman* asked why I wasn't included. He added: 'The anthology itself ... might perhaps almost have been called, like one of the poems it contains, "The Muse in Rose Street"'.

MacDiarmid's comment (published 21 November 1959) took up the last point with spritely alacrity:

> Well, why not? The Rose St group of contributors are certainly head and shoulders above all the contemporary Scottish versifiers, and several of them, in the opinion of leading critics in England and other countries, are of very high rank indeed.
>
> Probably what lies behind your reviewer's suggestion, however, is the common and utterly stupid objection to a 'clique'. Why, however, should poets be excluded from the rule that 'birds of a feather flock together'? Most of the best work in literature and the other arts has generally been done by such groups – and has always been bitterly resented by the inferiors excluded from such groups.

A correspondence was sparked off by this letter of MacDiarmid's, and continued for several weeks (cf. Bold, *The Letters of Hugh MacDiarmid,* pp. 799–805), – but I missed the first lot, being in London to discuss methods of preserving tape-recorded collections with the director of the British Institute of Recorded Sound. However, I arrived back on 28 November, and after reading up the backlog of letters I had missed, I wrote the following:

November 28, 1959

Sir

Returning to Scotland after a short absence, I am amused to find the Rose Street tattoo going great guns in your columns.

Hugh MacDiarmid defends the 'right of association' of like-minded men of letters. No one who remembers the fruitful results for literature of similar associations in the past can doubt that in the main his contention is perfectly justified. It is also true, of course, that sometimes such groups can make life difficult for the lone wolves of literature, but probably no poet of the Western world needs less reminding of this than Mr MacDiarmid.

Stewart Conn is quite right to give the other side of the medal a close inspection. Mutual admiration can be helpful and well-merited, but it has obvious drawbacks. The trouble is that half the clique is sometimes nothing more than a claque. Again, nobody is more familiar with the facts here than Mr MacDiarmid, for he has frequently referred to the 'safe' Scottish cultural Establishment as a conspiracy of mediocrity against genius – and against his own undoubted genius, in particular.

Since your reviewer has displayed solicitude on behalf of my muse, I should perhaps make it clear, in justice to Norman MacCaig, that I do not believe that my patronage of bars outwith the magic Rose Street circle had anything to do with my exclusion from the present volume. Mr MacCaig did, in fact, do me the courtesy of asking me for a contribution, and it was nobody's fault but my own that I did not submit one till it was too late. However, even if I had sent a sheaf by return of post, and Mr MacCaig had rejected them holus bolus, it would not have upset me unduly. It is my opinion that few of the shorter poems I have written of late measure up to the standard that I should have felt obliged to impose if I had myself been in Mr MacCaig's position; also the final shape of a new long poem I have been working on still eludes me.

In any case I have come to set greater store by my songs 'in the idiom of the people' than by other kinds of poetry that I have tried to write. By working in the folksong revival, therefore, I am paying what is probably congenial tribute to the 'honour'd shade' of the most famous Crochallan Fencible.

My experience may have been misleading, but I have not found Scots writers to be particularly strong on self-criticism. Naturally, self-criticism of any kind is seldom a popular pastime, but in countries like Scotland with special literary problems – I am thinking primarily of the language question – it is all the more necessary. It would help, of course, if more Scots read poetry, and developed an informed criticism … Here one is reminded of Hugh MacDiarmid's homely adage, 'birds of a feather flock together' for of no craturs in the world is this truer than of those popularly known as 'culture vultures'.

I am etc

Hamish Henderson

Ironically, it was on the same day that I wrote this letter that MacDiarmid decided to make a direct frontal assault on my poetry. In a letter written on 28 November, and published in the newspaper on 7 December, he enquired:

Why is your reviewer so insistent on the merits of Alan Riddell and Hamish Henderson? Although he does not hesitate to accuse me of 'inaccuracies', your reviewer says I have persistently implied that Mr Hamish Henderson is an 'inferior' poet. I challenge him to cite any comments I have ever published on Mr Henderson's poems. 'Silence gives consent', perhaps, and I will not deny that Mr Henderson's work is hardly 'my cup of tea'. But the matter is beside the point so far as *Honour'd Shade* is concerned. Mr Henderson was invited to contribute but ignored the invitation until months later, by which time the anthology was already at the printer's. If Mr Henderson was one of the 'notable poets' omitted, the editor was certainly not to blame in this case. (Parenthetically, since questions have been asked about it, I think and hope the phrase in question about 'notable poets' was used ironically, meaning poets omitted who might think themselves notable!)

I am unaware – and do not believe – that any critic of international repute has praised Mr Henderson's poetry (unless Mr G S Fraser is to be so accounted, as I certainly do not account him!). Anyhow, whatever may be said about Messrs Riddell and Henderson, I do not think they are poets of such consequence that it matters one way or the other whether they appear or do not appear in any selection.

This undoubtedly called for a response in kind, and I wrote one on 9 December:

Sir

Any reader unacquainted with the facts might be forgiven for assuming that Mr Hugh MacDiarmid had for years maintained a tacitly disapproving silence with regard to my *Elegies* and my poetry generally. This is not the case.

Between 1948 and 1953 Mr MacDiarmid contributed literary criticism and political articles to *The National Weekly,* the journal which was the liveliest carrier of Scottish Nationalist ideas during the period of the Covenant, the 'Stone' and the events leading up to the conspiracy trial. On 9 April 1949, there appeared in its columns a review by Mr MacDiarmid of my recently published *Elegies for the Dead in Cyrenaica.* In this review, he said, *inter alia:*

'Edwin Muir pointed out that the distinctive vision of Scottish poetry "is profoundly alien to the spirit of English poetry – it is the product of a realistic imagination". It is this vision which informs all Henderson's work ... In form and substance it [my book] compares with most of the war poetry of Rupert Brooke, Sassoon and even Wilfred Owen, to say nothing of the hordes of lesser war-poets then and since, as the logistics, and political implications, and global character of the last war compare with old fashioned militaristic sentiments about, say, the Boer War. It is, in fact, one of the few books – and the only volume of poems in English which has come my way – that expresses an adult attitude to the whole appalling business, and thoroughly deserves the honour of securing the first award of the Somerset Maugham prize.'

As for my songs in the folk idiom, Mr MacDiarmid referred to the 'John Maclean March' (*National Weekly*, 28 June 1952) as a 'splendid song'. (However, this doubtless comes under the heading of 'urban crambo-clink' and presumably doesn't count in the present argument.)

I do not hold it against Mr MacDiarmid that he has forgotten these remarks, committed to print years ago in a defunct periodical. One grows older, and one forgets things. Furthermore, it has been well said that consistency has nothing to do with genius. What does disturb me, whiles, is the whole tone and tenor of Mr MacDiarmid's approach to argument, which positively reeks of that very same self-centred provincialism which he is for ever and a day claiming to combat – he is 'satisfied' that 'no poet deserving inclusion has been excluded'. Does he really think that there was no place in 1959 under Burns' 'honour'd shade' for a single one out of the eight poets of *Fowrsom Reel* and *Four Part Song*?

According to Helen B Cruikshank, MacDiarmid's long-term friend and benefactor, the writer Moray Maclaren was greatly impressed with these two letters of mine, and running into MacDiarmid in one of the Rose Street pubs, he had come right out and asked him, 'Don't you think Hamish's letters show rare magnanimity, Chris?' To which MacDiarmid had replied – and I relate this with considerable diffidence, and even possibly a momentary blush – 'Hamish is a gentleman. I am not a gentleman.'

A letter in verse from Helen B. appeared on 11 December; its second stanza went as follows:

> Noo wha' dis Hughie think he can impress
> Wi's fremit learnin'? Fegs, wha is't unless
> It's Chambers Brithers, whase braw Dictionar'
> Supplied the borrowed words he writes wi' vir.

In his next letter (written on 12 December) MacDiarmid came down heavily on Helen's letter, as well as doing his best to counter my own:

Sir

I had not forgotten – nor have I altered in my opinion – what I wrote about Hamish Henderson's *Elegies for the Dead in Cyrenaica* ten years ago in the *National Weekly* and, later, about his 'John Maclean March' in the same papers and elsewhere. But *Honour'd Shade* could not use anything from the former in accordance with the express condition of the anthology, and the merits of the latter as a song, and the question of its quality as poetry are two very different matters. Like Mr Henderson, the other poets in *Fow'rsom Reel* seem to have petered out, unfortunately.

At the time I hailed their work because it seemed to me to herald a long-overdue development in Scottish poetry. That has not materialised, however. I am glad to hear that Mr Henderson is engaged on another long poem and hope it will justify my anticipations poetically and politically. All this, however, is irrevelant to *Honour'd Shade*. Mr Henderson's exclusion from which was, as he has told us, his own fault.

Miss Cruikshank's letter expresses a point of view which I have been fighting against as strenuously as I could for the past 40 years. The foreign writers and artists I listed may be 'caviare to the general' but they have had a great deal to do with modern achievements and tendencies in literature and the other arts in Europe, and to cite them in substantiation of my claim regarding cliques was certainly relevant. Scottish literature has suffered sufficiently from restriction to the kailyard and I need make no apology for my internationalism. In any case, all my work has been activated by the principle enunciated by J R Lowe when he wrote: 'Not failure but low aim is crime.'

As to Chamber's 'Dictionary' all our words are borrowed from somewhere or other – we do not invent them – and all that matters is how and to what end we use them. It is a pity more people do not have recourse to dictionaries for the extension and subtilisation of their vocabularies. Miss Cruikshank asks for whom I write and the answer is: Certainly not for those who, in discussing literary matters, are proud of their ignorance and fain to use it as a Procrustean bed, or for those (and Scotland is full of them) who reduce discussions on artistic matters to a question of 'scoring cheap laughs' or think they can dispose of great issues by remarks on the level of a gamin's cry: 'Get your hair cut' and ignore all the real problems raised in a lengthy correspondence in favour of an inane giggle which lets loose more than a whiff of sour grapes.

As Helen was an old friend of my own, as well as of Chris Grieve's, I disliked this crack about an 'inane giggle' and wrote the following on 21 December:

Sir

In his, to my taste, somewhat over ponderous answer to Miss Cruikshank's persiflage Hugh MacDiarmid objects to the 'gamin cry' being heard in lieu of argument.

Although as a professional folklorist, I have no small sympathy with (as well as interest in) the razory epigrammatic derision which this phrase connotes, I quite see the force of Mr MacDiarmid's objection. There is a witless philistinism of the streets which can be very galling. But there is also a philistinism of the boudoir (and even of the Rose Street pub!) which can be considerably more dangerous since it more often than not camouflages itself as a protective interest in literature and the arts.

Every country gets the 'culture vultures' it deserves; in Scotland, they are familiar figures, sticking around with necrophilous animation, and waiting to feast on the body of the stricken Bard. Hugh MacDiarmid has lived long enough north of the Tweed to know the glint of a beady eye when he sees one.

MacDiarmid's next letter contained a direct attack on the collecting work carried out by the School of Scottish Studies; it was, he averred, 'a waste of time and money'.

January 19, 1960
Sir

In 1938, one of the earliest commentators on my poetry wrote in the *Aberdeen University Review*: 'Always he (Hugh MacDiarmid) sees man "filled with lightness and exaltation", living to the full reach of his potentialities. In that clear word "all that has been born deserved birth".

> Man "will flash with the immortal fire", will "rise
> To the full height of the imaginative act
> That wins to the reality in the fact"
> until all life flames in the vision of

"the light that breaks
from the whole earth seen a star again
In the general life of man."

'The actuality is different. Men are obtuse, dull, complacent, vulgar. They love
the third-rate, live on the cheapest terms with themselves, "the engagement
betwixt man and being forsaken", their "incredible variation nipped in the bud".
They refuse to explore the largeness of life. This refusal he sees as a cowardice. If
for the mass of men this picture is true, he believes that human society is wrongly
ordered. Therefore the poet demands a political change that will give men such
living conditions as may make the finer potentialities actual:

"And have one glimpse of my beloved Scotland yet
As the land I have dreamt of where the supreme values
which our people recognise are states of mind,
Their ruling passion the attainment of higher consciousness."'

In the intervening twenty-two years that has continued to be the animating spirit
of my poetry. Mr Henderson, on the contrary, seems to find his ideal man in the
'muckle sumph', and to wish to scrap all learning and all literature as hitherto
defined in favour of the boring doggerel of analphabetic and ineducable farm-
labourers, tinkers, and the like. He is presumably at home among beatniks and
beatchiks. Personally, I continue to think Dante, for example, or Goethe greater
poets – and more creditable specimens of homo sapiens – than McGonagall or
the authors of any – and all – of the 'folk songs' Mr Henderson and his colleagues
so assiduously collect. I do not envy the task of whoever may ultimately have to
go through the great mass of indiscriminate tape recordings accumulated by the
School of Scottish Studies in order to find any elements of real value. Looking
for a needle in a haystack will be a far easier job. Such collecting is a waste of time
and money.

   The degree of literacy in most people as a result of our educational system may
leave a great deal to be desired, but there is some hope for the future surely in the
fact that although trashy newspapers and periodicals still command immense
sales there has recently been a considerable turning away from tabloids and 'the
yellow Press' in favour of more serious journals; or, again, in the production and
wide circulation of paperbacks of excellent quality.

   Mr Henderson quotes a few lines from my Second Hymn to Lenin, but to
wrest a small portion of a poem out of context in this way can be made to prove
anything, and Mr Henderson ought to have considered the significance of the
fact that the lines he quotes occur in a poem of an essentially non-popular kind,
the main burden of which is, in the question of the primacy of 'life' or literature,
to come down emphatically on the side of the latter. The lines he quotes simply
express a counsel of perfection – an ultimate (and perhaps unrealisable) aim, and
certainly one no poet anywhere, at any time, has succeeded in achieving,

   In addition to that, 'highbrow' although my work may be, and certainly at the
furthest remove from 'folk-poetry', it ought to be pointed out that no Scottish
poet since Burns has commanded anything like the sales and recognition I have

done, while through radio and TV I have reached many millions of listeners in this and several other countries.

But, Mr Henderson may say, my readers must have been mainly if not wholly in the 'upper classes'. That is not the case. When ultimately my correspondence is lodged with the National Library of Scotland he may be surprised to find that a very considerable proportion of my correspondents are working men and women in this and other countries who testify, often in the most moving terms, to the inspiration and encouragement they have derived from my poems. That influence has been directed all along to an'unqualifled onward and upward', whereas Mr Henderson evidently wants to stabilise people at a low level corresponding to a state of society which has virtually ceased to exist, and which will disappear completely and finally with the increasing introduction of automation, with its demand for ever more highly skilled workers, and its concomitant of vastly increased leisure which will certainly not be profitably filled listening to unlettered ballad-singers yowling like so many cats on the tiles in moonlight. Mr Henderson's claim is preposterous at this time of vastly accelerated change and increasing complexity in all connections.

This correspondence began apropos the anthology *Honour'd Shade.* Let me remind Mr Henderson and others of something written by John Davidson with which I completely agree, viz., 'The want of poetical power is the impelling force in the case of most versifiers. They would fain be poets, and imagine that the best way is to try to write poetry, and to publish what they write. They will never see their mistake. Equus asinus still believes that the possession of an organ of noise is sufficient, with a little practice, to enable him to sing like a nightingale.'
I am etc Hugh MacDiarmid

At this point the correspondence was brought to a temporary halt by an admirable letter from Tom Crawford, who had recently returned to Scotland after some years teaching in New Zealand:

Sir
It is perhaps ill-mannered for a visitor to intervene in a debate between two such masters of 'flyting' (surely a folk-art in itself) as Mr Henderson and Mr MacDiarmid. I am, however, surprised to find the greatest makar of modern times questioning the value of the School of Scottish Studies.

Far from being a parochial affair, the School of Scottish Studies is an institution of world importance and influence. As a New Zealand university teacher of English literature, I have known of its work, for years past, and have made considerable use of its periodical *Scottish Studies,* as have also my colleagues in the departments of history, geography, anthropology, and modern languages at the University of Auckland. Obviously, what is true of Auckland is probably true of every other university in the English-speaking world. We all have a deep respect for the School of Scottish Studies, which we regard as a pioneering body from which we can learn a great deal.

For example, the work of the school has stimulated some New Zealanders to press for the establishment of a School of Pacific Studies, which would co-ordinate research into Maori and Polynesian customs, folk-art and linguistics.

One of the most interesting things that has happened in New Zealand in the last two or three years has been the emergence of a group of Maori writers. These young men and women write their poems, short stories and novels in English, not Maori – and, for the most part, on contemporary, not traditional, subjects; but the academic collection and recording of Maori chants and customs (corresponding to the sort of impulse which produced the School of Scottish Studies here) has in practice sharpened the Maori writer's awareness of the world of today, rather than the reverse.

Mr MacDiarmid calls 'indiscriminate' folk-song collecting a waste of time and money. But the School of Scottish Studies works on a shoe-string, as compared with the institutes of Romania, Bulgaria, and Hungary where expenditure on such collecting is really lavish. Perhaps Mr MacDiarmid would answer that in those countries folk-song collecting is 'discriminate', in which case I would reply that it is safer to gather in all available specimens before evaluating them, than to begin with the arbitrary assumption that only such-and-such songs are worth recording: Any other procedure allows too much scope to the researcher's prejudices and unconscious preconceptions.

Folk song and some 'high poetry' may be more closely connected than Mr MacDiarmid thinks. Is there not a relationship between the songs in Shakespeare's plays and previously existing folk-songs? Were not the lyrics of Goethe's *Faust* influenced by the folk-song revival of the late eighteenth century? Does not Blake's imagery owe something to the symbolic traditions of English folk-song, which have recently been investigated by members of the English Folk Song and Dance Society? Did not Wordsworth inaugurate a poetic revolution by studying the art and literature of the 'muckle sumph', and was he not reviled for it in his own day? Finally, did not the greatest English-speaking poet of the present century, W B Yeats, a poet for highbrows if ever there was one, owe a great deal to the singing habits of the Irish peasantry?

I am etc

Thomas Crawford

This argy bargy about *Honour'd Shade* was by way of being a curtain-raiser to the much longer flyting session, also in the columns of *The Scotsman* – about the Scottish folk-song revival. But a description of this – from inside the ring – will have to wait until the next issue of *Cencrastus*.

Cencrastus, 48, 1994.

Flytings Galore:
MacDiarmid v. The Folkies

International House, at the corner of Princes Street and Castle Street, was a club founded during World War II by the British Council to cater for the intellectual and social needs of Polish and other Allied officers, and, after the war, it expanded its membership to include those citizens of Auld Reekie who appreciated artistic and cosmopolitan company. I was introduced to it by Edward Haliburton – the model for Monsewer in Brendan Behan's play *The Hostage* – who was later to found an even more libertarian outfit in Doune Terrace called the Porch Club. International House was one of the few places in Edinburgh in the immediate post-war period where one could be sure of finding people interested in *avant garde* poetry, and the arts generally, and this cultural oasis became for me a convenient rendezvous when I had visitors from outwith the city; I also used it, for years, as a *poste restante*.

To convey something of its flavour – I was having a drink one afternoon with an elderly Polish ex-officer, one of the regulars, and at one point in the conversation this gent remarked: 'This is the sort of place where you are for ever expecting someone truly beautiful to walk in, and it never happens.' At that moment an absurdly good-looking young Brazilian, with a bag of golf clubs over his shoulder, strolled in and Alcibiades himself could not have timed his entrance better.

One day, in the summer of 1949, I was standing at the bar when a rather worried-looking thin-faced young chap came up and introduced himself. He told me his name was Alan Riddell – 'from Australia and Greenock' – and that he occasionally wrote poetry. He also told me something of his background, including some hilarious anecdotes from his time studying navigation in Southampton during the war. He wondered if I could suggest outlets for his poetry, and I suggested he might try John Lehmann's *Penguin New Writing*, which had recently published some stuff of my own.

I didn't see much of him again until July 1951, when I was back in Edinburgh after acting as a guide (and coolie!) for the American folklorist Alan Lomax in the 'bothy country' of the North-East. I ran into him again in International House, and he broached the idea of a new Scottish poetry magazine which would complement Maurice Lindsay's *Poetry Scotland*, and maybe cast its net wider – taking in (he said temptingly) some of my own poems and ballads in the folk idiom. His problem was to find a backer, and for most of the following year he sought for one in vain. By the summer of 1952 he had decided to take the plunge and go ahead regardless, and the first number of *Lines* (later *Lines Review*) appeared, to coincide with the celebrations in honour of Hugh MacDiarmid's 60th birthday; it was on sale at the 1952 People's

Festival Ceilidh described in the last *Cencrastus* (No. 48). However, although – as related above – the mag. was more or less engendered in International House, the genteel bosses appointed by the British Council were less than helpful when Alan was trying to get if off the ground; they would not even let him sell it on the premises, let alone support it financially. I remember the lofty dismissive tones of one female termagant – she had a particularly odious high-pan Edinburgh accent, of the same genus as Malcolm Rifkind's, only worse – when she informed Alan, after he started to try to hawk *Lines* No. 1 to folk at the bar: 'Of course we don't allow that sort of thing here.'

(This episode reminded me, I need hardly say, of Burns's lines about poor Robert Fergusson:

> My curse upon your whunstane hearts,
> Ye E'enbrugh gentry!
> The tythe o' what ye waste at cartes
> Wad stow'd his pantry.)

Looking back on that period, I am convinced it would be hard to overestimate Alan's importance as a cultural catalyst: it was mainly through him that International House became a vivacious clearing house for people and movements in literary and artistic circles, reaching out far beyond our borders. As his services in this field have been largely forgotten, I reprint here a letter I wrote to *The Scotsman* on 22 March 1983, which mentions his championship of Alex Trocchi's genius:

> Sir, As James Campbell's article on Alexander Trocchi leaves the impression that he had no friends and allies in Scotland, I think it only fair to Alan Riddell, founder and first editor of *Lines Review*, to put it on record that Alan was a constant champion of Trocchi's, and that it was through him that I – and I should imagine quite a number of other people in Scotland – first learned of a major literary talent. This was long before the farcical Writers' Conference of 1962 – best remembered for the naked lady 'happening' in the McEwan Hall – to which Campbell refers.
>
> The feelings of angry revulsion which Trocchi made all too explicit in his outburst at that gathering were, of course, nothing new on the literary scene, and by no means peculiar to Scotland. In June 1951 – a year before the first number of Trocchi's *Merlin* appeared in Paris – Brendan Behan wrote a letter to the poetry editor of *Points* (a bilingual literary magazine published in the same city) giving vent to the following sentiments:
>
> > 'Cultural activity in present-day Dublin is largely agricultural. They write mostly about their hungry bogs and the great scarcity of crumpet. I am a city rat. Joyce is dead and O'Casey is in Devon. The people writing here now have as much interest for me as an epic poet in Finnish or a Lapland novelist.'

No one can read Trocchi's work, however, without realising that his relation to his Scottish background was (and no doubt is) a matter of deep concern and importance to him. A quotation from Unamuno which appears on Page 59 of *Cain's Book* is very revealing: 'Don't you suppose – since I am in a confidential and confessional vein – that when they have accused me of not being a good Spaniard I have often said to myself: I am the only Spaniard! I – not these other men who were born and live in Spain.'

A wary Joycean eye for nets flung at the soul to hold it back from flight, and a love of literature and practice of the same, were not the only things which linked Australian-born Alan Riddell and Glaswegian-born Alex Trocchi (who worked as a scow captain on the Hudson River between 1956 and 1959).

Among the papers which I inherited from Alan was a report of summer 1944 on Junior Leading Cadet A Riddell, then studying navigation at University College, Southampton. This showed that he had come first in a class of 33, and had won the prize for Best Duty Watch.

The director's remarks suggest a further link between these two intermittently nautical men of letters: 'Exceptional and outstanding work ... always maintained a high standard of efficiency and conduct in his Duty Watch. Still too many petty crimes on his conduct sheet.'

Alan was also a champion of Edwin Morgan's work, at a time when the Rose Street 'Scottish Renaissance Establishment' – Dieter Peetz's phrase – did not appear to think it was much cop. Indeed, the Milne's Bar circle seemed to be in danger, towards the end of the 1950s, of turning into a thoroughly reactionary self-congratulatory literary camorra, supporting Chris Grieve uncritically in his attacks on 'Beatniks and Beat-chicks', and on the various practitioners of Concrete Poetry. (For a brief résumé of these exchanges, see 'Teddy Boy Poetasters', a section in Alan Bold's *The Letters of Hugh MacDiarmid*, pp. 811–15).

Periodically, Chris discharged ill-tempered epistolary potshots at selected targets; in May 1962 he let fly in a pamphlet at Ian Hamilton Finlay, whose excellent poetry broadsheet *Poor. Old. Tired. Horse.* (aka P.O.T.H.) had been praised by Eddie Morgan. This tetchy lubrication of his was entitled *Ugly Birds Without Wings*.

(In a talk on Ian's work to a literary group at the Theodor Heuss Akademie at Gummersbach in the Rhineland some time later, I gave the title of the above-mentioned brochure as *Hassliche Vogel ohne Flugel*, and I could see from the expressions on the faces of the audience that it sounds even more unpleasant in German than it does in English.)

As related above, *Lines* 1 was produced without visible means of support, but after it appeared Alan had a stroke of luck – Callum Macdonald, an enterprising Lewisman who had a printing business, took an interest in it, and *Lines* 2 announced that it had been printed by M. Macdonald, 33 Marchmont Road, Edinburgh. By *Lines* 3 Callum had become Managing Editor, and he has continued ever since to exert a direct personal influence on the progress of the magazine, which has now reached its 120th number. It is no exaggeration to say that, but for him, the magazine would probably have sunk without trace long ago.

Alan continued as editor until No. 6, but it seems that Callum felt increasingly that *Lines* – now *Lines Review* – could do with a new editor, and for No. 7 Sydney Goodsir Smith – in what those not in the know could have been forgiven for 'suspecting was a 'palace *coup*' – was elevated from the Advisory Board to the editorial chair. His valedictory salute to the departing founder editor struck a note which some found not a little discordant:

> This issue sees a slight reshuffle of the editorial caucus. First, Alan Riddell, our
> founder-editor, breaks the sad news that pressure of work compels his retiral

from his high office. But we are not wholly dismayed! We are glad to assure his aghast public that they will continue to enjoy the benefits of his valuable interest, experience and what-have-you in an advisory capacity as a member of the groaning board.

'His aghast public' … 'the groaning board' … These rather petty snide phrases seemed designed to wound, and although Alan was not overly sensitive, I believe he was in fact wounded by them – as he was, indeed, by MacDiarmid's unexpectedly brusque dismissal of his poetry in the letter to *The Scotsman* of 7 December 1959 (quoted in *Cencrastus* 48).

After returning to Australia for a year or two in the mid 1950s, Alan got a job in London with the *Daily Telegraph*, and it was from London that he wrote one of the more honest-sounding poems printed in *Poems Addressed to Hugh MacDiarmid and presented to him on his 75th birthday* (Akros Publications, 1967):

FOR C M GRIEVE
(ON THE EMBANKMENT)
These Embankment afternoons,
heavy with nostalgia,
stir memories of action
in the antique frigates laid up for display,
and, to come nearer the point,
rub more than the sea's salt
into my own momentarily forgotten wounds.
Yet the situation is not without its humour,
knowing one has a full belly and almost enough
money to pay the rent for a year should that often written about
worst come to the worst.
(Quite a change from the old times!)
Yes, not without humour, knowing one has after all –
even if ingloriously –
somehow managed to survive.
The really depressing thought of course is the waste:
the slow disintegration of the personality consistent
failure seems to leave in its wake.
And not just the artistic
failure, or the 'ill starred' essays into the greater
romanticism of love, but also the simple
failures of communication between
relatives and friends, and the inability
to derive interest or sustenance from
the bread-and-butter labours each and all of us
necessarily have to endure.
As if, in itself, experience were not sufficient:
increasing awareness, for once, unable to sustain
the precarious balance between knowledge and affirmation;
resulting as it were in a kind of

emotional hysteresis, the heart lagging behind
the mind's bloody but perceptible advances.
Which is why today, in this alien environment,
and between jobs, I think of you,
Chris, and your bulldozing progress
through the debris of these years, and marvel at
the extraordinary resilience of your spirit, as freshly alive
now, as thirty years ago, to the essentially human
nature of the problems which underlie
the major political and social upheavals of our time, as to
the subtle gradations of colour which transform
the tawny surface of a Scottish bog in springtime
into a shimmering carpet of unbelievable iridescence.

(As nothing of Alan's work appears in the various anthologies in which one might expect to find it – not even, for example, in Douglas Dunn's massive *Faber Book of Twentieth Century Scottish Poetry* – I subjoin here a select list of his publications: *Beneath the Summer* (1952); *Majorcan Interlude* (1960); *The Stopped Landscape* (1968); and *Eclipse* (1972). It was the last named which earned him a place among the conspicuous exponents of 'Concrete Poetry', thus attracting more slingshots from the irascible Chris Grieve.)

Alan Riddel died prematurely in 1977, just fifty years of age.

In retrospect, the various mini-flytings referred to above seem like preliminary skirmishes before a major engagement, and when that finally erupted, it turned into a full-scale rammy about the Scottish folksong revival. However, the already famous 'muckle flyting' started on a deceptively low key on 4 March 1964, when David Craig took issue with remarks made by Norman MacCaig on the Third Programme.

Depreciation of folksong

Conan Drive, Richmond,
Yorkshire, March 4, 1964

Sir, In the recent Third Programme survey of Scottish culture compiled by David Daiches, it was disappointing to hear two of our best-known poets going in for sweeping and decidedly ignorant depreciation of folksong. Perhaps there is some excuse for their ignorance: even on the Scottish Home Service our folksongs, which are the very voice of the people, are grossly under-represented.

Scotland should be proud to have, living in Aberdeen, Jeannie Robertson, a noble singer whose huge repertoire of songs gives us in living form that great body of tales, worksongs, and irrepressible sallies of comedy with which our people have kept themselves going and nourished their imaginations from time immemorial. Yet the BBC has never given this singer one 15-minute programme to herself.

Norman MacCaig ended his Third Programme comments by saying that folksongs might be good enough for berry-pickers and steel-mill workers, but not for him – he had read Homer. The two poems we now call Homer's are believed by modern scholars to have been pieced together out of short lays chanted by minstrels at the Aegean courts.

Scotland's lays are the ballads, and it is thus no exaggeration but the sober truth to say that in Jeannie Robertson Scotland has her Homeric-type singer, whose work is the equal in quality, in beauty and truth if not in scale, to the great European epics. If she is allowed to pass her prime without being heard to the full over 'our' national radio service, it will be an irretrievable crime done to our culture. I am etc. David M Craig

On 13 March 1964, a letter from MacDiarmid appeared in *The Scotsman,* taking issue with Craig's:

Sir, Mr David Craig's letter on depreciation of folksong is altogether beside the point. In all literature, there is a vast undergrowth of doggerel and mediocre versifying, but it is a remarkable instance of 'trahison de clercs' if Dr Craig would have us believe that this is to be valued as equal to or better than acceptedly great poetry simply because, thanks to their minimal literacy and because it corresponds to their ignorant tastes and reflects the sorry condition of their lives, it is more popular among the broad masses of the people than the poems of, say, Shakespeare, Dante, Goethe, Rimbaud, Rilke, Pasternak, Montale, etc. etc.

Judged on this basis, MacGonagall must be accounted a great poet, since he keeps going into edition after edition and comes only second to Burns in this respect. So must Robert Service be accounted as a great poet, because he, too, achieved great popularity and made a fortune out of the millionfold sales of his books. No doubt he reflected the lives and dispositions of the Yukon pioneers, but that does not mean he ever wrote a line of poetry. He didn't.

Dr Craig does not hesitate to suggest that some of us who took part in the discussion on the Scottish Home Service underrated folk-song because of ignorance. The suggestion is unworthy of him. I for one have been bored to death listening to more of it, including the renderings of Jeannie Robertson, Jimmy MacBeath, and others, than I venture to suggest Dr Craig has ever suffered, and I certainly never want to hear any more of it.

Unlike Dr Craig I think the BBC has already given much more programme prominence to 'corn-kisters' than they deserve, and certainly of our great treasury of Scottish song only a small fraction has yet been broadcast. We hear the same hackneyed songs, Gaelic, Scots, or Anglo-Scottish, again and again and again, and the BBC would do well if it could induce some of its artistes to extend their repertoires. It has been estimated that of the over 200 songs of Burns the great majority are never sung at all and only about 20 are frequently (and in my view far too frequently) heard.

The demand everywhere today is for higher and higher intellectual levels. Why should we be concerned then with songs which reflect the educational limitations, the narrow lives, the poor literary abilities, of a peasantry we have happily outgrown. The study of such productions may be of some historical value, but is certainly of no literary value, in regard to which, as in every other connection in life, surely our regard and, if possible emulation, should be given to the best and not to the lowest in past literary productivity. And above all we should not allow ourselves to be bogged in nostalgia for an irrecoverable way of life, and one, I think, in every respect fortunately irrecoverable. I am etc.
Hugh MacDiarmid

The slighting reference to Jeannie Robertson naturally drew me immediately into the fray:

Sir, Hugh MacDiarmid claims to have been 'bored to death' by Jeannie Robertson's renderings of Scots ballads. This should not surprise us. Performances of high excellence are not seldom found boring by people not in sympathy with them. It has been known for members of audiences to yawn and even barrack during performances of the *Oresteia, Athalie* and *Juno and the Paycock*.

As against Mr MacDiarmid's deadly boredom, it is refreshing to recall Edwin Muir's address to the Scottish Association for the Speaking of Verse, shortly after hearing Jeannie's recordings of classic balladry in the School of Scottish Studies. He said that for the first time he had understood what the ballads were; Jeannie's renderings were 'extremely noble', and had 'wonderful dignity'. Not long after, the English folklorist A L Lloyd called her 'a singer sweet and heroic', and Alan Lomax (one of the most distinguished modern American collectors) called her 'the greatest ballad singer in the world'.

Why is Scotland often so slow to do proper justice to her first-raters? As I write, Jeannie Robertson is preparing to leave for Dublin, where she has a singing engagement at the Mansion House. Since she was discovered in 1953 she has repeatedly received invitations to visit both the United States and the Soviet Union. Her records have sold thousands of copies. And yet, as Dr David Craig has pointed out, she has never been given one single 15-minute programme to herself on the Scottish Home Service.

Among the 'accepted great' poets, Mr MacDiarmid lists Montale – and rightly so, for Montale is at least as good a poet in Italian as MacDiarmid is in Scots and English. Having introduced Mr MacDiarmid to Montale in 1947, and acted as interpreter during their conversations, I well remember how keen Mr Mac-Diarmid was to stress the fruitful interaction from which folk-song and art-poetry have always benefited in the Scots literary tradition. He assented with enthusiasm when I explained to the Italian poet that he had drawn not only the language – half-forgotten Scots, which he revivified – but also whole lines and fragments of verses from the eighteenth-century anonymns collected by Herd and others. I pointed out that Sorley Maclean, influenced by MacDiarmid, had done the same sort of thing in Scots Gaelic. Replying, Montale compared some of MacDiarmid's lyrics, which I had translated for him, to poems of Garcia Lorca.

There can be no doubt that by denigrating Scots popular poetry now, Mr MacDiarmid is trying to kick away from under his feet one of the ladders on which he rose to greatness.

He gave Scots folk-song an unwitting but no doubt sincere tribute a few weeks ago, however. In a recorded conversation with T T Kilbucho on the radio, Mr MacDiarmid mentioned 'some lesser known poems' of Burns which he regarded as much superior to those for which that poet is usually praised. He then proceeded to quote three of these, viz, 'O that I had ne'er been married', 'Scroggam' and 'Wha is that at my bower door?'

Of these the first is an old song, preserved in Herd's MSS; Burns added a stanza. 'Scroggam' is recognisable at a glance as a folk-poetry, 'redded up' by the bard; the first stanza is adapted from 'Will ye na, can ye na let me be' in the *Merry Muses,* and the third stanza (still orally current in Aberdeenshire) is in 'Blythe Will and Bessie' s Wedding' – an old song, also in the *Merry Muses.* 'Wha is that at my bower door?' is founded on a broadside ballad, 'Who but I, Quoth Finlay,' and related to a large family of international folk-songs.

Mr MacDiarmid has taken exception to the term 'ignorant' applied to his comments on folk-song by Dr Craig, but ignorant – in this case, at least – is unfortunately the 'mot juste'.

I am etc.

Hamish Henderson

In his reply, written on March 19, MacDiarmid referred to the 'present menacing form of the folk-song movement'; by now his gloves were off, and I could see that we were in for a lengthy tussle:

Sir, Mr Hamish Henderson points out that on radio I quoted three lesser-known poems of Burns which I regard as much better than those for which Burns is usually praised. I was quite aware of their debt to folk sources, but Mr Henderson is quite wrong in thinking that my praise of these poems contradicts what I wrote in reply to Dr Craig. One point is that in thinking these poems better than the others I do not thereby think them great poetry.

I cannot deny that in Scottish literary history there have been fruitful interactions between folk-song and art poetry, and that this happened in some of my own early lyrics. But that was nearly 40 years ago, and my meeting with Montale was 17 years ago. The folk-song movement I was attacking in my letter had not then assumed its present menacing form, and in my own development as a poet I have had to abandon many of my early ideas and during the past 30 years I have been writing kinds of poetry quite unindebted to any folk-song source and for the most part utterly opposed to anything of the kind.

Mr Henderson seems to have a curious idea of what constitutes a 'mot juste'. The fact that I attach a certain value to some poems of Burns, based on folk-song originals, does not invalidate my general condemnation of the folk-song cult today, and it is quite a different thing to single out what has been achieved on such a basis by a poet of standing as opposed to approving generally of the unimproved mass of such 'songs'. In any case, a tremendous change has taken place since Burns' day, and since I wrote my own early lyrics, and apart from the fact that I think poets today have far other and much more important things to do, I do not believe that folk-song sources can now supply spring-boards for significant work.

I am, etc,

Hugh MacDiarmid

David Craig, who had been silent for a while, now re-entered the fray with a hard-hitting missile:

Sir, Mr MacDiarmid remains obdurately anti-folksong. But he deals wholly in generalisation, and we must be much more specific if we are to do justice to this matter. Neither I nor, I presume, Hamish Henderson is trying to ram 'the unimproved mass of such songs' down people's throats, any more than one would recommend readers to wade through the entire library of printed poetry. What I am saying is that the folk-song tradition has thrown up a great number of gems, of superb poems-to-music, that are meaningful, moving and ageless enough to claim the attention of everyone, whether steelworker, stockbroker, or teacher of Latin and Greek.

Few art-poems convey the needless suffering of warfare more poignantly than the ballad 'Edom o' Gordon', the desolation of a forsaken woman is classically expressed in another ballad, 'Waly, Waly' and so on throughout the whole vast tradition.

Mr MacDiarmid speaks as though the literary situation can change basically in a few years – folk models were in thirty years ago, now they are out. Did anyone dream ten years ago that a New Wave was about to emerge that would find creative uses for the music hall, the folk song, the vernacular tale, the tough-guy novel, and the radio documentary? Yet that is what has happened with the work of Brendan Behan, John Osborne, and Joan Littlewood, Arnold Wesker and John Arden, Alan Sillitoe and David Storey, Charles Parker, Ewan MacColl and Peggy Seeger.

Scotland's part in this is still small, yet Ewan MacColl, a great songster, is a Scottish talent, and Hamish Henderson's 'Fareweel to Sicily' and 'The Freedom Come-all-ye' – both songs to traditional airs – seem to me among the few excellent poems to have appeared in Scotland in recent times.

Mr MacDiarmid once wrote (*Second Hymn to Lenin*, 1932):

Are my poems spoken in the factories and fields,
In the streets o' the toon?
Gin they're no', then I'm failin' to dae
What I ocht to ha' dune.

If he has abandoned this aim, then he has abandoned the attempt to bridge the modern cultural gulfs and to reach the people with his work – an appalling lapse for a Socialist.

I know what he will reply – that it is the modern poet's duty to become ever more intellectual. This is a slogan from the days of Pound, Joyce and Eliot. Yet already their work, for the most part, looks like a pedantic aberration, as does the immensely long poem Mr MacDiarmid has been piecing together since 1934, compared with the poetry and drama of Brecht (full of debts to folk-song and drama) or the cream of our New Wave. What is more, this new work, both popular and quality in its technique, has been able to reach millions in the form of songs, films and paperback novels.

If Mr MacDiarmid shuts his eyes to all this, he is not being 'advanced' – he is falling behind.

I am etc.

David M Craig

MacDiarmid now openly attacked the entire corpus of the folksong collection in the sound archives of the School of Scottish Studies, asking 'what proportion of the great collection ... is more than rubbish?'

I am very tired of the unscrupulous way in which correspondents like Dr David Craig use the few lines from my *Second Hymn to Lenin* beginning:

> Are my poems spoken in the factories and fields,

to support their anti-literary demagoguery.

In honesty, they should go on to show that my subsequent verses point out that no poet of any consequence has achieved that – not Shakespeare, Dante, Milton, Goethe, Burns – or, in fact, anyone at all worth a docken.

We all know of the great vogue and inter-traffic of European balladry. Most of it is rubbish, but in a few of our Scottish ballads it soars for a verse or two into the realm of great poetry. But all that arose out of an entirely different state of society from ours today or any ever likely to recur in 'advanced' countries.

Dr Craig knows perfectly well that I was not referring to that very small number of pieces of high literary excellence, of which, 'Waly, Waly' is one; but to the bulk of the songs sung in connection with the current folk-song movement, and in particular the 'corn-kisters'.

I have been a Socialist and active in various ways in the working-class movement for over half a century. One of the main factors by which I have been actuated has always been the realisation of the very inadequate and seriously defective character of popular education, and I have never been – and am quite incapable of being – impressed by the preferences of the great mass of people adequately characterised by Professor Kenneth Buthlay in his recently published study of my work when he says, apropos the Burns cult, that it has been, and still is, largely a matter of 'fulsome lip-service paid to his genius by people who had little but contempt for poetry in every other respect, and not even in rudiments of standards by which to judge it'.

Dr Craig attempts to dissociate himself from the promulgation of 'the unimproved mass of such songs', but his original letter was largely devoted to praise of Jeannie Robertson – and what else is she doing? And what proportion of the great collection of recordings of the School of Scottish Studies is more than rubbish? Dr Craig's tribute to the two songs he mentions by Hamish Henderson shows that he falls holus-bolus into the class defined in the final clause of my quotation from Professor Buthlay.

In any event, I have always made my position clear enough, and Dr Craig would have been fairer, if, alongside the lines he quoted, he had also quoted these (written over 30 years ago, as were those he quoted):

> I'm oot for shorter oors and higher pay
> And better conditions for a' workin' folk,
> But ken the hellish state in which they live's
> Due maistly to their ain mob ignorance.
> Yet tho' a' men were millionaires the morn,
> As they could easily be,
> They'd be nae better than maist rich folk noo
> And nocht that matters much 'ud be improved
> And micht be waur!

Accused of 'anti-literary demagoguery', David Craig defended himself with an eloquent epistle:

> Sir, Mr MacDiarmid accuses me of unscrupulously misrepresenting his *Second Hymn to Lenin*. In fact, the passage I cited – the first lyric from that long poem – can be made to mean nothing else than that the poet does want to 'win through to the man in the street'. The lines saying that no poet – not Shakespeare, Dante, Burns – had ever so won through are in inverted commas to show that they represent an imaginary objector. The poet himself replied in the magnificently downright line: 'You heard what I said.' What can this mean except that the poet reaffirms his dauntless determination to write for the people? But Mr MacDiarmid takes a care to include a second line of defence – he wrote that poem thirty years ago; and it is not for me to deny him the right to repudiate his own finest work.
>
> In any case, it is not true that no front rank poet ever had his work spoken in the fields. Alexander Somerville, author of the *Autobiography of a Working Man,* did not know what 'poem' meant (he knew some Burns as anonymous songs) until, about 1820, a fellow harvest worker recited 'Hallowe'en' to him while they waited on a stack for the next cart; and James Hogg found his own love of poetry when a 'half-daft man' came to him on the hillside while he watched his flock, and repeated to him the whole of 'Tam O' Shanter'. As for factories, Mayakovsky was spoken there after the Revolution in Russia, and two years ago a Poetry Society was set up in the EMI factory at Hayes after Christopher Logue and others had spoken poetry in the canteen during a Centre 42 show. Surely all this makes cultural defeatism inexcusable.
>
> Mr MacDiarmid goes on making his assertions about the folk-song tradition in general, 'What else is Jeannie Robertson doing,' he asks, but promulgating the 'unimproved mass of folksong?' Rhetorical questions are no substitute for argument. An outstanding thing about her versions of songs is precisely their unerring distinction of wording, which is constantly more vivid and poignant than the Child ballad texts: and Ewan MacColl recently collected from an old Perthshire woman's singing a version of 'The Cruel Mother' which ends with a series of metaphors for hell and guilt much more imaginative than the versions known hitherto. Thus the folk tradition improves itself.
>
> Of course, Mr MacDiarmid means improvement by art-poets, for whom alone he has any use. Well, Brecht improved folk-songs in this sense; so do those great recent works, the radio-ballads (e.g. the adaptation of 'Windy Old Weather' to describe the slump, in 'Singin' the Fishing'); and so did Mr MacDiarmid in some of his finest lyrics. The individual artists of our time could not produce such work if they were not lucky enough to have access to the tradition of song which has come to us solely through the mouths of hundreds of peasant and worker singers.
>
> I am etc.
>
> David Craig

At this point it seemed to me necessary to bring the basic difference between our two positions right out into the open:

Sir, Mr MacDiarmid contends that none of the great figures of world literature have also been popular poets. This is not true. Leaving aside the special case of Burns, whose world-wide popularity maintains itself in spite of the cult and not because of it, I can provide from my own experience two cogent illustrations of the position Dante holds in the life of his countrymen. In October 1944 I asked a young Tuscan partisan – an electrician from Florence – why he had joined the Garibaldini, and had elected to share all the dangers and hardships of life in the mountains; his answer was in the words of Dante:

> Libertà va cercando, ch'è si cara,
> Come sa chi per lei vita rifiuta.

> Freedom he is seeking, which is so precious
> – as they know who give up their lives for it.

A few weeks later, when another partisan was 'missing, presumed killed', one of his mates compared his fate to that of Buonconte, whose body was never found after the battle of Campaldino in 1289. Somewhat surprised by the recondite allusion, I asked for further information about the earlier casualty, and the red-neckerchiefed tommy-gun-toting bhoyo floored me completely by quoting from memory some fifteen to twenty lines of the 5th Canto of the *Purgatorio*.

As this correspondence is taking on with every letter more and more of the high mottled complexion of a Celtic flyting, let me come right out at this point and say that Mr MacDiarmid displays not the smallest comprehension of the difference between traditional song-poetry in the folk idiom and the lucubrations of minor or minimal scribblers who in every age are the dim also-rans of 'art poetry'.

If Mr MacDiarmid will take a look at Douglas Young's *Scottish Verse 1851–1951*, he will find that a large part of it consists of pieces which (one feels) might have waited till doomsday for an anthologist had not Mr Young emerged as their god from the machine. But these are not folksongs; they are as far removed from the folk idiom as Canberra is from the Hudson River.

One of the few pieces in the earlier part of the anthology which merit a second or indeed a third reading is the bothy song 'The Barnyards o' Delgaty', and Mr Young included it only because he had found it in the Carswells' *The Scots Week-End*. Any reader who is doubtful about the distinction I am making should read the text of this corn-kister, as Mr Young reprints it, and then read 'My Ain Hearthstane' (p. 34) or 'The Auld Kirk o' Scotland' (p. 36).

The irony is that Mr Young could have found, among the Greig MSS, in the Library of King's College, Aberdeen, or in the archives of the School of Scottish Studies, splendid racy gallus examples of full-blooded nineteenth-century folk-poetry, almost any one of which could have knocked for six his whole trayful of gormless Victorian bric-a-brac. Luckily, thanks to the folk-song revival, an ever-increasing number of these Scots folk-songs are becoming known to the youth of the country.

Like Dr Craig, I have no doubt that we are again in a period when folk-song and art-poetry can interact fruitfully, and that it is in and through the present movement that this will come about. Anyone who looks up *The Second Hymn to Lenin* will see that the section beginning 'Are my poems spoken in the factories and fields' is an eloquent, and even poignant statement of the artist's awareness of his isolation in modern society, and of his duty to look outwards, and to attempt to communicate across the apollyon chasms. The crucial stanzas are the following:

> Gin I canna win through to the man in the street,
> The wife by the hearth,
> A' the cleverness on earth'll no mak' up
> For the damnable dearth.
> Haud on, haud on; what poet's dune that?
> Is Shakespeare read,
> Or Dante or Milton or Goethe or Burns?
> You heard what I said.

Mr MacDiarmid is by no means the only poet who has spoken on varying occasions with two or more voices. But the meaning of these two stanzas of powerful 'direct poetry' is surely quite unequivocal.

I am, etc.

Replying, MacDiarmid quoted a passage from his essay 'Problems of Poetry Today' (1934) ... 'the interest of the masses and the real highbrow, the creative artist, are identical, for the function of the latter is the extension of human consciousness ...' and went on:

It is significant that Dr Craig accuses me of 'cultural defeatism' and sneers at the extremely long poems with which, in lieu of my early lyrics, I have been pre-occupied in the last thirty years. The trouble is that he, and other professedly Communist or Left-wing advocates of regression to the simple outpourings of illiterates and backward peasants do not know what, in fact, poets are doing in the Communist countries. Our century, our society, promotes the synthesis of the arts, synthetic thinking. The art of Communism will present us with ever more edifying artistic alloys, superior forms of Lenin's 'monumental propaganda'. Indeed, the term monumental has struck root in the theory of cinematography, the theatre, and music as well. Eisenstein's films *Battleship Potemkin, Alexander Nevski, Ivan the Terrible,* are monumental, epos-like in the highest degree.

The 'epic drama' of Bertolt Brecht, an innovator through acquiring the monu-mental traditions of Sophocles, Shakespeare, and others, possesses the same basic character. A sonata by Enescu can also be sublime: in *Oedipus,* however, 'the work of my life', as the composer called it, the fruit of a quarter of a century's creative preoccupations and ten years' labours, the sublime is specifically monumental.

After the passages about the 'monumental', MacDiarmid referred to the 'crucial stanza' I quoted from *The Second Hymn to Lenin:*

The passage from my *Second Hymn to Lenin* is, I think deliberately, misunder-stood by Messrs Craig and Henderson. The aim of all great poetry is universali-sation, but in so far from attaining it, great poetry is known only to a tiny fraction of the population. The isolated cases Messrs Craig and Henderson mention prove nothing to the contrary. We even used to have an occasional shepherd in this country taking a volume of Greek poetry with him to the hills. But one swallow does not make a summer – or even a good drink! Voicing the vain desire to get through to the people, realising that I, and all literature, were failing to do so, it is noticeable that I refer to Dante, Goethe, etc. – in other words, to the great world poets, and not to the folk-poetry broad masses of the people already know.

There is no solution to the problem via the latter: the multiplication of mediocre writers is no contribution to literature.

I do not propose to do it here, but it would be useful to consider just why Messrs Craig, Henderson, and others are so concerned with inferior stuff and so indifferent to the peaks of human achievement in the arts.

The full text of this letter will be found in Alan Bold, *The Letters of Hugh MacDiarmid* (pp. 825–27).

By this time, the argument had turned into a proper bare-knuckled contest, and I think that in the next letter I gave as good as I got:

Sir, Scottish literary controversy not infrequently provides occasion for sardonic humour, and never more so than at this stage in the present correspondence, when Hugh MacDiarmid tries to suggest that because Dr Craig and I are interested in folk-music we are therefore indifferent to 'the peaks of human achievement in the arts'.

This allegation comes at the end of a long letter in which Mr MacDiarmid extols the 'monumental' in all the arts. It is clear he feels that if one is going to beg the question, one might as well go the whole hog and beg it on a truly monumental scale.

Those who have read Mr MacDiarmid's *In Memoriam James Joyce* will recall that he refers to:

> That heroic genius, Antonio Gramsci,
> Studying comparative linguistics in prison.
> For, as he said in his 'Lettere dal Carcere',
> 'Nothing less. What could be more
> Disinterested and *für ewig.*' (p. 27)

Gramsci, friend and antagonist of Croce, was a polymath who, ranging as widely as MacDiarmid (and digging far deeper), was always ready to learn from and appreciate popular culture. He was also one of the few men in this century in connection with whom one can meaningfully use such terms a 'universalisation'. Arrested by the Fascists in 1926 and given a 20-year sentence, he spent the ten years which remained to him working on the grandiose prison notebooks, out of which were later quarried such works as 'Notes on Machiavelli, Politics and the Modern State', 'Historical Materialism and the Philosophy of Benedetto Croce', and 'Intellectuals and the Organisation of Culture'.

Thinker, man of action and Socialist martyr, Gramsci has left his mark indelibly on the largest Communist Party in Western Europe, and indeed on the whole Left in Italy. Yet, far from despising the folk arts, this universal genius devoted much of his time to their study, and some of the most perceptive remarks about folk-song in modern European criticism are to be found in *Letteratura e Vita Nazionale* and other volumes.

In the same letter which Mr MacDiarmid quotes – it was written from Milan prison on 19 March 1927 – Gramsci outlines the projects he means to work on, and one of these is a study of popular taste in literature. What binds the various subjects together, he says, is 'the creative spirit of the people in its diverse phases'. A paper by Raimondo Manelii, read at the 1958 Rome Conference of Gramsci Studies, pays tribute to the philosopher's inspiration in this field ('Studi Gramsciani' 1958, pp. 183–87).

Why does Mr MacDiarmid despise the folk arts with such vehemence? Why does one encounter in his letters patronising phrases like 'the simple outpour-ings of illiterate and backward peasants' – or even (not so long back) 'analpha-betic and ineducable farm labourers, tinkers and the like'? Why this eager disparaging of Jeannie Robertson, whose magnificent classic ballad repertoire and noble singing style combine to make her in Alan Lomax's words, 'a monu-mental figure of the world's folk song'?

Some readers may have put Mr MacDiarmid's growlings down to mere testiness, or regarded them as understandable excrescences on a flyting which in the nature of things may tend to get a bit inflamed. In my opinion it goes much deeper than that. There are unresolved contradictions in Mr MacDiarmid's whole approach to the problems of language and the folk arts, and the passages in question represent no new development, but are the logical outcome of a train of thought which has been observable in his writings for twenty years and more.

Mr William Smith puts his finger on the trouble. Mr MacDiarmid has come to despise and reject the 'people of his country's past' with all the ardour of a seventeenth-century 'saint' outlawing the folk-singing and dancing damned to outer darknesss. He has been, in fact, for years – in one of his personae, at least – the apostle of a kind of spiritual apartheid, and an acrid anti-humanist flavour in some of his writings is readily documentable.

A prime example of what I am referring to will be found in Mr MacDiarmid's 'Lewis Grassic Gibbon, James Leslie Mitchell' which appeared in *Scottish Art and Letters* No. 2 (Spring 1946). After referring to Gibbon's expulsion from the Communist Party, Mr MacDiarmid proceeds: 'As I have said, I on the other hand would sacrifice a million people any day for one immortal lyric. I am a scientific Socialist. I have no use whatever for emotional humanism.' (The reader will note that Mr MacDiarmid has unaccountably omitted the operative words from the above passage. They should be inserted after 'any day', and read: 'before breakfast').

Mr MacDiarmid's present broadsides against folk-song are only to be under-stood against the background of passages such as this. Nevertheless, the anti-humanist strain which seems to parody itself here has not always borne the gree in this complex and turbulent imagination. Towards the end of *Third Hymn to Lenin*, Hugh MacDiarmid writes: 'Our concern is with human wholeness.' It is my belief that the communally shared and developed folk arts can be valuable aspects of 'human wholeness'. However, I would need another letter to do anything like justice to this theme.

I am etc.

Hamish Henderson

By this time all the combatants were becoming breathless, and David Craig summed up his position as follows:

> Sir, Let me make one point absolutely clear in what will be my last contribution to this discussion. Mr MacDiarmid says that I am 'indifferent to the peaks of human achievement in the arts'. This is not true. My original purpose in writing to you was to publicise the BBC's neglect (since partly redeemed) of 'classical' Scottish folk-song. This meant making the case for folk-song. Obviously this does not mean depreciating other kinds of art. But it is not obvious to Mr Mac-Diarmid. He cracks up the 'monumental' – Shostakovich, Neruda, Brecht (who loathed the monumental), etc.
>
> Certainly the big, comprehensive work of art is a vital thing in our culture. But why on earth has another kind of work – the more immediate, oral, sometimes extemporised – to be cried down so as to extol the big work? This is the easiest way to argue, and the most treacherous. It puts sectarian, snobbish, unnecessary barriers between forms of culture.
>
> This is precisely what the Communist countries have not done; they have both fostered the oral side of literature (from modern, poetry-speaking in the squares of Moscow to epic singing by great peasant artists such as Jamboui of Kazakhstan and Karalayev of Kirghizia), and produced big work in modern forms such as cinema and the symphony.
>
> For my own part, two of the 'biggest' composers (Beethoven and Shosta-kovich) are two whom I listen to most. In no way is this incompatible with my absorption in the unfolding of a long ballad like 'Lord Donald', my relish at the sting and crack of 'The Blackleg Miners', my feelings of solidarity with 'The Durham Lockout' or my sheer delight in the zest of 'The Calton Weaver'.
>
> The 'big' artists (such as Britten, Shostakovich and Brecht) will never turn their backs, as Mr MacDiarmid now does, on folk-song – they feel its fertility for their own art, and value it as the voice of the common people.

MacDiarmid's last letter in the controversy contained some striking phrases, and was maybe the most thought-provoking of his contribution to this now famous jousting-match.

> Sir, How silly can Mr Hamish Henderson get? Everybody in some degree practises what he calls 'spiritual apartheid' if he or she likes one thing and dislikes another, prefers to associate with certain people and not with others, and so forth. I dislike folk-song and as far as folk-song concerts go simply ask, 'Include me out'. More generally, I prefer 'to be alone in my togetherness'.
>
> But all that has little or nothing to do with the essential argument. Mr Henderson may assert, but certainly cannot show, that most of the great (as generally regarded) writers, painters and composers of Europe have owed anything decisive to folk-song, and even if they had, what matters is not that, but what they did with the influence in question. At the present stage in human history, there are far more important things to do than bawl out folk-songs which, whatever function they may have had in the past, have little or no relevance to most people in advanced highly industrialised countries today. The arts grow, like apples, from the periphery, not from the core.

Folk-song, and other folk-arts, may be the root from which all else has sprung, but a root is best just taken for granted, if the tree or plant is flourishing; or, as André Gide quoted, 'si le grain ne meurt ...' The seed has died, we have the harvest. It does not matter one iota if we never see the seed (or root), nor would it matter if we just failed to realise there is one.

It is all too easy to bandy words like 'human' – they are the common stock of all demagogues and can mean anything or nothing. So far as Mr Henderson's attempt to prove me or my work 'anti-human' goes, the significance of the term is nil.

I am etc.

Hugh MacDiarmid

PS Your readers will have noticed that Dr Craig and Mr Henderson tried first of all to show that I had retracted from the position expressed in a passage of my *Second Hymn to Lenin*. Now Mr Henderson has just gone to the opposite extreme and tried to show that in as far from wishing to write poetry that the people would read and repeat, I have all along expressed just the opposite attitude of contempt for the working class.

If my opponents had been capable of thinking rather more deeply they would have realised that the two attitudes in question are just the two sides of the same penny. What they are really anxious to do, of course, is just to pull me down as many pegs as they can, and exalt instead Miss Robertson or some other folk-singer – in other words they are (naturally, I think) on the side of the merely interpretative artist and against the creative writer.

I don't need to labour the point that MacDiarmid's general position in this folk-song controversy was diametrically opposed to what he had said at the 1952 People's Festival Ceilidh, not much over ten years before, and indeed what he has said in his address to the Porch Club in 1953. Of course, it was not only in this particular bout of unarmed combat that he adopted a Whitmanesque posture of (slightly paraphrased) – 'I contradict myself – so what!' (In any case, people are entitled to change their minds!) The thing which really does stick in my gullet is that fact that, from a position of great prestige and eminence, he was attempting to deny access to the media to fine singers and musicians who needed the money as much as he did. And it seems incontrovertible that this was indeed the effect of much of what he wrote – certain elements in the Scottish BBC were only too pleased to have the *imprimatur* of Scotland's greatest living poet for a thoroughly reactionary policy towards the native traditional singers and musicians – all the more, perhaps, because so many of them belonged to the despised caste of travelling folk.

The single case of Jeannie Robertson says it all – she only ever got one single half-hour programme to herself on the Scottish BBC, and this had to wait until she was dead. The title of this posthumous programme – wait for it! – was *Oor Jeannie*.

The only thing to be added, if you can bear it, is that a programme of tributes to her was broadcast a month or two later, and in that MacDiarmid praised her to high heaven.

In my own last letter I asserted that the Scottish BBC had to take some of the blame for MacDiarmid's failure to grasp the fact that singers like Jeannie Robertson were creative artists:

Sir, My only purpose in adding one more letter to this correspondence is to try to get the controversy into focus.

To oppose creative art to folk 'interpretation' is a false dichotomy. The essential difference between ethnic folk-song and the commercialised folk-song of the entertainers is that the former is creative and the latter is usually a dead end. Nobody with any sensitivity who has spent any time listening to Jeannie Robertson singing, talking or story-telling would deny that she is a creative artist in her own right.

Mr MacDiarmid is not, I think, wholly to blame for his evident failure to grasp this. The Scottish BBC must bear a substantial share. of the blame for the obfuscation which obviously exists on this whole issue, and in the middle of which Mr MacDiarmid is wandering benighted. Until the present revival, the BBC relied, for 'folk-song', upon art-singers who were prepared to do some occasional slumming – 'mucking the byre in white tie and tails'. If they used any near ethnic singers, these would usually be the village concert type who could be relied on to reduce even the great tragic ballads to the scale of 'couthie wee thingies'. Alan Lomax's appearance (1951) shook things up a bit, but they soon got back to normal.

It took the BBC two whole years, after they were informed of Jeannie's existence and given samples of her performance (1953), to decide that she was good enough to be put on the radio, and it was not until after the start of the present correspondence that she was given a 15-minute ballad programme to herself.

Meanwhile, hours of BBC time had been devoted to the guitar-bashing pop-folk performers who emerged in the wake of the revival. These entertainers were interpreting folk-song with an eye to the appealing gimmick, some of them quite effectively, others pretty dimly. The uniforms had changed, but the people singing Scots folk-song on the radio were still not the folk-singers. These latter had to be content with American LPs, invitations to sing at Cecil Sharp House, and their modest niche in the archives of the School of Scottish Studies.

There are, needless to say, many reasons, other than literary ones, why a department such as ours assembles ethnographic material to document the folk-arts and folk-life of a country or community. Not all the singers with interesting material have good voices or singing styles, and vice versa. What impelled Dr Craig (in his original letter) to acclaim Jeannie Robertson was precisely his realisation that Scotland possesses a major folk-singer whose talents cut across all such academic considerations, and whose merits warrant the sort of recognition from her native land which she has never so far received.

Mr MacDiarmid's comments on the phrase 'spiritual apartheid' are transparently disingenuous. To me, it signifies a great deal more than just preferring one pub to another, or one companion to another. It is a malady which used to be very rife among the 'justified sinners' of old-style Scots Calvinism, and it still bedevils some of their descendants. It never did us, or the world, any good.

And what on earth is one to say of Mr MacDiarmid's charge that because I drew attention to the anti-humanist flavour of certain of his writings, I was calling him and his work 'anti-human'? A person who can argue like this may not impress the readers of a newspaper controversy, but at least he would never find any difficulty earning a living as a professional contortionist. Is Mr

MacDiarmid trying to emulate that other MacD., whose Parliamentary performances earned him the title of 'the boneless wonder'?
I am etc.
Hamish Henderson

After this letter of mine, all three combatants retired to their tents. It seemed, both to me and to David Craig, that MacDiarmid was wilfully trying to blur the distinction between the real traditional singers – whom he had praised in 1952 and '53 – and the pop-folk performers who were cashing in on the success of the revival.

I must admit that I did have a certain sympathy for MacDiarmid's dislike of the nascent American-influenced commercial folk scene, although it was hardly as 'menacing' as he suggested. A thoughtful, level-headed approach to this genuinely thorny problem was apparent in a letter of March 14, written by Maurice Fleming, who had done valuable collecting work in Blairgowrie among the Perthshire travellers:

> For many of us in Scotland it has been a heartening, even astonishing, experience to watch the upsurge of enthusiasm for and pride in our folk culture, and in particular our folk-songs. This is a sign of a healthy, vigorous nation, and as a nationalist Mr MacDiarmid should welcome it.
>
> As a Communist too, he must know that the broad mass of every people express their loves, hates, desires, dreams and experiences in songs, stories and music that have nothing to do with 'literary values' but everything to do with life. Fortunately, there are other values besides literary ones.
>
> Instead of condemning our folk-song revival Mr MacDiarmid would be serving the country better if he were to attack those who, by commercialisation, are prostituting our culture. It is the jazzing up of folk-songs for entertainment purposes that is the most disturbing aspect of this whole matter.
> I am etc.
> M R Fleming

Anyone wishing to look into the background of this particular problem should read *The Ballad Mongers* by Oscar Brand, which was published by Minerva Press in the USA in 1962, two years before *The Scotsman* controversy got under way. Chapter 6 ('The Music Business') and Chapter 13 ('The Legal Tangle') are especially illuminating.

This argy-bargy about the folk-song revival was not the last flyting I enjoyed with Chris Grieve, but it was the one in which the issues became most clear cut – and the one which actually did serve some purpose in clarifying what we were trying to do on the folk-song front in the School of Scottish Studies. The final rammy (February–March 1968) centred round Scotland's 'self-elected elect', MacDiarmid's early fascination with Mussolini's Fascism, and the sad history of my translation of Gramsci's *Prison Letters*, which had to wait 25 years before it achieved publication (in the *New Edinburgh Review*). However, this final rammy belongs in a different theme park.

*   *   *

> Drums in the Walligate, pipes in the air.
> Come and hear the cryin' o the Fair.
>
> A' as it used to be, when I was a loon
> On Common-Ridin Day in the Muckle Toon.

For me the Common-Riding Day in Chris's birthplace Langholm has always been a red-letter day in the Scottish calendar. I've been there as often as possible for this great event since the early 1960s, and in 1979 I collaborated with Tim Neat in making a film about it called *Tig! For* the *Morn's the Fair Day.* In this we used quite a lot of Mac-Diarmid's poetry.

Some years before, in 1962 or 1963, I had taken a tape-recorder down there, to make a sound-picture of the proceedings, and quite early in the morning of the great day, after the flute band had made its 5 a.m. perambulation of the town, I found myself alone in the little square, outside the Eskdale Hotel – (in these ceremonies there is always a quiescent lull, in which everything seems to relax, before all heiven is let loose). And who suddenly shows up, coming up the road from the Esk, but Hugh MacDiarmid! We had a coffee in the little café on the corner, and I told him that the night before I had recorded old John Elliot ('Popple'), the hereditary Crier of the Fair, speaking the whole 17th-century text of the Crying, in order to get all the words clear.

After this, John had volunteered to recite a MacDiarmid poem, and had declaimed, with jocular panache:

> My grave's no bad. They've put intill't
> Twa o' the Sassenachs I Killt.
> And I'll kill them again, as sune's the horn
> Toots on the Resurrection morn.

Chris was obviously delighted with this information, and I treasure that moment as a real high point in a relationship which consisted of so many highs and lows.

Remembering this, and many other things, I decided early in 1977 to write an Open Letter to the little Border burgh which Chris had called his touch-stone in all things creative.

Open Letter to the Muckle Toun o' the Langholm

Dear Muckle Toun – Last year I had, once again, the pleasure and privilege of attending your Common Riding – as ever, one of the truly prodigious events of the Scottish calendar. I have often told visitors from the South (and other airts) that if they are desirous of witnessing what is just about the proudest manifestation of 'ingenium perfervidum Scotorum' that the country can offer, they have no need to proceed farther than a mere eight miles this side of the Border.

All that's necessary, usually, is to play them a few tape recordings made over the years – the flute band playing reveille by the Esk in the early morning; the wild gallop of the Cornet and hundreds of horsemen up the steep brae of Kirk Wynd; the crying of the Fair (by a crier standing on horseback), and the marching and counter marching of pipe, flute and brass bands – and the date duly goes down in their diaries. In 1976 a Swedish television team joined the column as well, and added a valuable film record to the archives.

However, the experience itself invariably surpasses memories and anticipations. For me, the most thrilling moment is always when the Cornet and his mounted followers appear once again at the top of Kirk Wynd, after climbing to the summit of Whita Hill and performing the ceremonial ride-around of its landmark monument. The pipe-major gives the word of command to his men, when he sees the horsemen, and the children who have formed up behind the band lift their heather besoms with the roses entwined in them, and cheer as they march forward into the square.

Then there's the moment when the walloping outsize thistle, with its prickly tentacles capering in the air, joins the procession of emblems. First comes the 'bannock and saut herrin', its escort linking arms and singing 'The Bonnie Wood o' Craigielea'; then there's the spade, decorated with heather 'lately pulled frae Whitaside', which has been used for cutting sods on the common land by men able and willing 'to gang oot in defence of their property': then there's the Crown of Roses bobbing in the lift; and last of all, the 'breenging growth' itself, the contumacious camsteerie national symbol, greeted all along the route with a special cheer.

Last year a small boy of nine or ten was sitting on a window ledge, just behind where I was standing, and I heard him exclaim 'the thistle!' as those great jigging green antlers hove into view. Any lucky spectator witnessing that incident would have learned a lot in a moment about the Borders, and about Scotland – the old Scotland, and the renascent new.

'The aucht-fit thistle wallops on hie'... and that reminds me, Muckle Toun, why I am writing you this open letter today.

Your Common Riding is indeed a noble occasion, but you possess another and, some would say, greater glory than the Common Riding, although you've aye been gey sweir to admit it. I refer, of course, to Christopher Murray Grieve, alias Hugh MacDiarmid, who is now universally acknowledged to be one of the greatest poets we have ever had in this country, and also one of the foremost poets now living in the world.

Muckle Toun o' the Langholm, I'm hardly revealing any secrets when I say that this particular prophet has been all too long without honour in his own home town. There have been attempts, off and on, to give him the 'Freedom', but they never got anywhere. And although I know Chris Grieve was given a presentation by your citizens on his eightieth birthday, I gather that all the subscriptions barring a very few came from outwith your boundaries.

I'm not contending, of course, that in this troubled relationship the fault has aye been on your side. In the rammies of life Chris Grieve has given at least as many blows as he has taken, and seeing that he would not wish us, in mim-mou'd Southron style, to be 'nice' with him, let us freely admit that he can be a rale coorse carnaptious auld blellum when the mood takes him. I, too, have had my share of flytings with him over the years, and I am quite sure that he would be game for another one right now, at the drop of a hat.

However, this alters nocht of the undoubted fact that he is one of the splendours of our literature, a man of rare genius, and (like Johnnie Armstrong o' Gilnockie) a true hero of Border history. He deserves better of you than he has got.

So, Muckle Toun – what about it? I know that the reorganisation of local government has robbed you of the power to make Chris a Freeman of Langholm. However, this is of no account. (I very much doubt, anyway, if Chris would wish to be accommodated in the same galère as a mere astronaut.) May I, with respect, offer a suggestion? Every year, for the last twenty-five years, Chris has visited Langholm as a private visitor on the occasion of the Common Riding. Why not make him a guest of honour in 1977? Alternatively, you could invite him to a birthday celebration on August 11, when he will be 85, and do him proud in traditional Border style.

It would be very appropriate, let alone the anniversary, that this should happen in 1977, for this is undoubtedly the year that Scotland will make a major step forward towards independence – the goal that Christopher Murray Grieve has devoted his life to help bring about. And, Muckle Toun, when he thought of Scotland, and Scotland's potential, it's plain he often thought of you.

> Are you equal to life as to the loom?
> Turning' oot shoddy or what? ...
> Lenin and Rilke baith gied still mair skill.
> Coopers o' Stobo, to a greater concern
> Than you devote to claith in the mill.
> Wad it be ill to learn
> To keep a bit eye on their looms as weel.
> And no' be hailly ta'en up wi' your 'tweel'?

Muckle Toun, I have to admit that I got the idea of writing you this letter on another birthday that came up for celebration recently – namely that of the 'bon sansculotte Jesus', around whose mystery so many of Chris Grieve's own poems dip and circle like seabirds. I'd like, therefore, to end with some lines written by Chris's old friend and benefactor, the late Helen B Cruikshank – who was not only a marvellous person, but also a much better poet than the lazy anthologist, repeating and repeating 'Shy Geordie', would ever have you believe. Here are the concluding lines of the epistle she wrote for C M Grieve (whom she described as 'chief pillydacus o' the haill clanjamfrie') when he reached the age of 75:

> I mind o' ane that bore in wind and weather
> A sacred load thro cataracts o' thocht.
> Na, Christopher, yer faither an yer mither
> They didna wale that wechty name for nocht.

I am, Muckle Toun, your maist leal, devoted and obleeged servitour.
Hamish Henderson

(I would like to express my indebtedness to Sonia Senatore, who kindly made available to me her complete collection of the *Scotsman* flyting correpondence.)

Zeus as Curly Snake:
The Chthonian Image

In 1974 the Publication Committee of the School of Scottish Studies decided to produce a double album of selected tape recordings of Scots traditional (or 'Child') ballads, to be called The *Muckle Sangs,* and I was asked to provide an introductory essay for the booklet which was to accompany these. It was just over ten years since I had enjoyed the 'muckle flyting' with Hugh MacDiarmid as to the aesthetic value of the folk-song recordings in our sound archive, and I had no reason to believe that he had changed his opinion on the subject. Nevertheless, it had increasingly seemed to me that much of his own work belied the stance he had taken at that time and, accordingly, I decided to preface this introductory essay with a quotation from what I regarded as one of his finest poems, 'Depth and the Chthonian Image' which is subtitled 'On looking at a ruined mill and thinking of the greatest':

> As life to death, as man to God, sae stands
> This ruined mill to your great aumrie then,
> This mined mill – and every rinnin' mill?

I subjoin the text of the introductory essay, and will endeavour to explain why I regarded that quotation as almost preternaturally apt.

Nobody familiar with the history of Scots balladry will find it strange that we set at the head of our introductory remarks a quotation from the greatest living Scots art-poet – who is also, by general consent, one of our best poets ever. There has for centuries been a constant fruitful cross-fertilisation in the fields of literary and 'folk' poetry in Scottish cultural tradition; one has the impression that many ballads which now exist in numerous variants must have stemmed from original versions composed by craftsmen-balladeers who took the inherited skills of their art very seriously indeed. By the same token, art-poets have often operated like folk-poets, appropriating opening lines or even whole stanzas from earlier or contemporary authors or from popular tradition – and using them as a basis for their own productions. The best known example is, of course, Robert Burns, who on one occasion borrowed two lines which he thought were old, but which were actually the work of a poet (John Mayne) who survived him by close on forty years.

These interactions can be observed at their most revealing when one examines the narrative songs which are 'true ballads' for the historian as well as for the folk-singer – i.e. those which, like The Laird o' Drum, The Fire o' Frendraught and Mill o' Tifty's Annie (Andrew Lammie) can be tethered fairly confidently to an actual historical incident something which can be documented from contemporary records as well as from oral tradition. Here it is maybe not too sanguine to postulate an original song-poem composed by an unknown folk-singer who was a virtuoso in the techniques of his craft and also, in some cases at least, a literate man, with a certain amount of knowledge of his country's written poetry. In the ballads connected with actual events, particularly those of the 17th and 18th centuries, we find consequently a mélange of various kinds of poetic and musical experience: on the one hand we encounter unmistakably ancient folk motifs and images which are the common patrimony of orally created and transmitted poetry everywhere, and on the other, not seldom, a sensibility more usually associated with art-poetry. Clear evidence that techniques of composition more proper to non-literate composers survived among the literate or semi-literate, has to be balanced against just as definite manifestations of organisation and management which bespeak a tutored and lettered intelligence – often a quite sophisticated one, at that. Viewed in this light, the phenomenon of Mrs Brown of Falkland – the Professor's daughter who read Ossian, wrote verses and was also source-singer of ballad versions which have been described as priceless examples of orally transmitted (and orally recreated) folksong – becomes much more comprehensible. Far from being unique, Mrs Brown seems to me to have been merely an outstanding exemplar of a type of creative literate folk-singer which is one of the most characteristic types of folk-singer on the Scottish scene, and one which certainly did not die out during the course of the 19th century. Few will be surprised to learn that in the 25 years that the School of Scottish Studies has been prospecting for songs in Lowland (or Scots-speaking Scotland) we have been encountering this type of folk-singer all the time.

The first traditional singer to record his entire repertoire for the School was Willie Mathieson, a septuagenarian retired farm servant who had devoted much spare time throughout his life to collecting songs. In his kist, which he transported from farm to farm when he got a new fee, were three large ledger books full to overflowing with songs of all kinds, from classic ballads through lyric lovesongs to place-name rhymes and bairn songs. Willie had either collected songs on the spot from his fellow plough-men, or had diligently followed up his informants by correspondence. He had also tried his hand at versifying, and one of the poems which he wrote down alongside ballads and bothy songs was a moving elegy for his dead wife. Willie Mathieson was quite capable of discoursing knowledgeably about different 'weys' of a ballad, and he would often quote 'what Gavin thocht aboot it' – giving the great collector his first name, in familiar Scots style – but the ballads, especially the tragic love ballads, were closer to him (and 'truer') than they could possibly be to the mere scholar; when he referred to Barbara Allan's callous cruelty to her luckless lover on his death-bed, he would shed tears.

What I am trying to bring out is that the Scottish ballad scene – the ambience of the makars of the 'Muckle Sangs' – has a quite different atmosphere from the English scene. Who can imagine one of the folk-singers from whom Cecil Sharp collected – or a later singer from the same area of Somerset – referring to him as' 'Cecil'? The distinction is reinforced when we read such valuable documentaries relating to English rural life as Flora Thompson's *Lark Rise to Candleford*. This delicious book, which is a mine of information on the mores of the late 19th-century English countryside, has a chapter called 'At the Wagon and Horses' which presents a picture of the village folk scene of the 1880s. After 'The Barleymow' and 'I wish, I wish' and 'Have you ever been on the Penin-su-lah', the cry comes 'Let's give the old uns a turn', and there follow the two ballads in the Lark Rise folk-singers' repertoire, viz. Lord Lovel (Child 75) and The Outlandish Knight (Child 4) then, as now, among the most frequently sung ballads in the south country.

'What's old Master Tuffrey up to, over in his corner there? Ain't heard him strike up tonight' ... So David would have his turn. He only knew the one ballad, and that, he said, his grandfather had sung, and had said that he had heard his own grandfather sing it. Probably a long chain of grandfathers had sung it: but David was fated to be the last of them. It was out of date, even then, and only tolerated on account of his age. It ran:

> An outlandish knight, all from the north lands,
> A-wooing came to me ...

As this last song was piped out in the aged voice, women at their cottage doors on summer evenings would say: 'They'll soon be out now. Poor old Dave's just singing his Outlandish Knight.'

One way of looking at all this, of course, would be to say that the Scottish ballad scene we discovered was – like the acting techniques of the Abbey Theatre in Dublin at the beginning of this century – so far back that it was forward. Certainly, the balladeer as singer and makar was still a familiar figure when we explored rural Perthshire and Aberdeenshire in search of songs, and – meeting people like Jeannie Robertson, the Stewarts of Blair, Jimmie MacBeath and John Strachan – one could easily recreate in one's mind the roisterous 18th-century folk scene of David Herd, Robert Ferguson and their fellow knights of the Cape, and enter a goliardic world of the imagination not unlike that smoky Anchor Close Howff in Auld Reekie which housed the Crochallan Fencibles.

In the long run to us it was the singers themselves who could elucidate best some still resistant problems of ballad scholarship – so here, on these two LPs, you are presented with Scots classic balladry as over twenty virtuosos have inherited it and recreated it. The language, the music, the atmosphere, the personality of Scots folksong can best be got straight from them. What are you listening in on, played back from recordings made in Jeannie Robertson's tiny house in Causewayend, John Strachan's substantial farmhouse at new Fyvie and the Standing Stones berryfield on the road to Essendy is this wonderful fluid thing, representing the actual world of the ballad singers, a shared sensibility still artistically vital and fertile. Singers who are singers remake their own version, which may gel for themselves and others, or may dissipate again ... the greatest thrill is to hear one's own songs sung in new variants by singers who feel themselves totally free to re-make them in any old way – or in any new way – that seems good to them.

One cannot forget, moreover, when one listens to the singers on these discs, that their art is in some sense the culmination of the reshaping and re-singing which has gone on over the centuries by countless singer ancestors: a whole hierarchy of shades, unknown and now unknowable, who in their time 'bore the gree'. It is only fair to add that the present-day singers are nearly always clearly – and sometimes even poignantly – conscious of this, at least in so far as the immediate background is concerned. 'It's a real pity ye couldna hae listened tae auld Andra' is the sort of remark we frequently heard after the singer's own interpretation of a song. Indeed, it is no exaggeration to say that, the better the singer, the more likely was he or she to adopt a stance of dignified humility when talking about the tradition. Hugh MacDiarmid might have been thinking of singers like Jeannie when he wrote (in *First Hymn to Lenin*):

> Descendant o' the unkent bards wha made
> Sangs peerless through a' post-anonymous days,
> I glimpse again in you that mightier poo'er
> Than fashes wi' the laurels and the bays
> But kens that it is shared by ilka man
> Since time began.

The curious thing is that this way of looking at and operating within the popularly shared culture is not peculiar to the folk-singers. Many Scottish art-poets have had it too, and consequently with us it is never easy to draw a hard and fast line between the 'popular' arts and the 'élite' arts of individual excellence. The pseudonymous 'MacAlias' (a character invented by the late Moray McLaren) is the type figure in this somewhat ambiguous set-up, and one is often faced with the sort of situation in which no one can say for sure where MacAlias ends and Anon begins. A sort of friendly free-for-all cannibalisation has therefore been the rule rather than the exception in Scottish literature. Art-poets forage in the communal bin just like folk-poets – and, as often as not, silently pass off such acquisitions as their own work. One need only mention Byron, 'born half a Scot, and bred a whole one', who appropriated the 'We'll gang nae mair a-rovin' chorus of one version of the Jolly Beggar (Child 279) and used it in one of his most famous poems. (Then, of course, you get people like 'Ossian' Macpherson who, having written original works of literature, try to palm them off on someone else; also modest characters who seek to hide their well-proportioned identities under bulging fig-leaves like 'The Author of Waverley'.)

It is, indeed, in certain of Scott's novels – as G M Trevelyan once remarked – that one finds passages which reveal and illuminate this by-ordinar and distinctively Scottish egalitarian feeling which comes into its fine flower artistically in the world of the popular ballad. The listener can learn more about what we are discussing from *Old Mortality* and *The Heart of Midlothian* than from many works on the ballads themselves. Hugh MacDiarmid, too, really goes to the heart of the matter when he writes (in the same poem we quoted at the start):

> Ein Mann aus dem Volke – well I ken
> Nan man or movement's worth a damn unless
> The movement 'ud gang on withoot him if
> He deed the morn. Wherefore in you I bless
> My sense of the greatest man can typify
> And universalise himself maist fully by.

For this reason, in the notes to individual ballads, we will try to give due prominence to the personality and artistic achievements of the individual singers; and, as far as the notes on the music are concerned, we want to emphasise as strongly as possible that the note refers to one person's singing of the ballad, and furthermore, it refers to one performance – the performance you are actually listening to – of the ballad by the person in question. For the thousands of variants which have been collected all over the English-speaking world, and for massive monumental commentary and explication, you are referred, in the first instance, to F J Child's *English and Scottish Popular Ballads*, and to Bertrand H Bronson's *Traditional Tunes of the Child Ballads*.

Also, at the risk of seeming to labour unnecessarily an often-stated truism, we point out again that the ballads are folksongs, linked by countless ties to others of the species. Many of them are also living and evolving folksongs. David C Fowler puts it well when he writes (at the conclusion of his *A Literary History of the Popular Ballads*):

> A earlier generation looked upon modern times as an era of decline and fall for the ballad tradition. But those of us who have been privileged to live through the singing sixties know better. Thanks to the artistry and dedication of modern minstrels like Pete Seeger, a new vitality has been restored to ballad and folksong. Even the element of radical social protest, largely dormant since the rhymes of Robin Hood in the fifteenth century, has made a strong comeback. The current revival, aided enormously by the electronic revolution, has been sketched by Josh Dunson in *Freedom in the Air* (New York 1965). I continue to hope, however, that a scholar of sufficiently catholic taste will be found who can chronicle the evolution of balladry from Sir Walter Scott to Bob Dylan.

It is with a mixture of pride and diffidence, therefore, that we dedicate these records of Scottish popular ballads to the memory of Francis James Child himself. All our work has been done under his formidable shadow. Surveying his life's work, and listening again to our own present offering, we cannot help feeling that the lines which we set at the beginning of this prefatory note are more than ordinarily apposite. These lines are from a long philosophical poem which is subtitled: 'On looking at a ruined mill and thinking of the greatest'. (Aumrie – the French *armoire* – means cupboard; it is one of the many words we have inherited from the 'Auld Alliance').

> As life to death, as man to God, sae stands
> This ruined mill to your great aumrie then.
> This ruined mill – and every rinning' mill?

*   *   *

As soon as the double album came out – it contained, incidentally, such five-star performances as Jeannie Robertson's 'The Gypsy Laddies', Sheila Stewart's 'The Twa Brothers', Lizzie Higgins's 'The Knight and the Shepherd's Daughter' and Betsy Johnston's 'Tam Lin' – I sent a copy to MacDiarmid, and was delighted to receive the following acknowledgement a few days later:

Brownsbank
13/3/75

Dear Hamish

Many thanks for the Muckle Sangs record and accompanying material. The various quotations from my poems are very relevant, and no matter how what I've said on occasions may have been interpreted, I of course stand by what I wrote in these quotations.

The record is a splendid one, and the whole programme of records to come represents a great achievement.

With every kind regard to Mrs Henderson and yourself.

Yours,
Chris

Depth and the Chthonian Image – originally entitled *Alone with the Alone* – was published in 1932 by Aeneas Mackay of Stirling, in a volume entitled *Scots Unbound*. That the poet himself thought very highly of it is obvious from what he wrote to Helen B Cruikshank on 10 August 1932:

> I note what you say about Mr MacNicoll, and his asking what my 'message', my philosophy was. One of the poems in this new book – one of the longest I have every written, and one which F G Scott regards as one of my very best – is called 'Depth and the Chthonian Image', and is designed as a perfectly clear and comprehensive expression of my whole aesthetic, political and general position – a complete statement of 'the faith that is in me'. Perhaps that'll help. It is in ten verses of 24 lines each – 240 in all with an elaborate rhyme scheme and little difficult Scots, and only odd words of Latin, German and Greek.
> (Alan Bold, *The Letters of Hugh MacDiarmid*, p. 116)

Seven years later, in a letter to W M Burt from Whalsay, he wrote:

> I read with keen interest what you say about the 'Depth and the Chthonian Image' poem. You – and F G at the time it was written – are the only two who seem to have spotted it at all. I personally think it is one of my best things.
> (Alan Bold, *The Letters of Hugh MacDiarmid*, p. 855)

In his *MacDiarmid: A Critical Biography,* Alan Bold provides the following summary of the thought underlying this extraordinary poem:

> His philosophical debt in this poem is to Plotinus who envisaged the Divine Being as an eternal triad comprising the One (the supreme absolute, the source) from which emanated Intelligence (*Nous*, uniting the one and the many) from which emanates the Soul (the creative force forming the material universe). Illuminated by the Soul, the individual reaches the One by contemplation, achieving the mystical flight of the alone to the Alone. (p. 271)

A close reading of the poem, however, leads one to detect at least two other major strands in it – the second of which is quite startling. First, MacDiarmid had obviously been dipping into one or two of the books of the 'Grecian anthropologist' Jane Ellen Harrison – and particularly chapter I of *Prolegomena to the Study of Greek Religion* which is entitled 'Olympian and Chthonic Ritual'. Of this and other chapters, Professor Gilbert Murray has written: 'It would be hard to overestimate the effect on the whole study of Greek religion of the first chapters of *Prolegomena*, with her analysis of the Great Attic festivals. They showed once and for all how the base of any sound study of Greek religion must no longer be the fictional, largely artificial figures of the Olympian gods, but the actual rites in which religion expressed itself, and so far as we can divine them, the implications of these rites.'

Murry regarded *Prolegomena* as 'a work of genius' – an epoch-making book, clearing away preconceptions from the approach to Greek religion, and focusing attention on *Ritual*, and what the actual practices were of the Greeks at their festivals: 'What a people does in relation to its god is the safest guide to what religion is.' The *thing done*, the rite, is before the *myth* which explains it – ritual before theology – and literature last of all.

Referring to her student days at Cambridge, Jane wrote: 'We Hellenists were in truth at that time a people that sat in darkness, but we were soon to see a great light, two great lights – archaeology and anthropology. The classics were turning in their long sleep: old men began to see visions and young men to dream dreams.'

Comparative religion thus played an historic role in the revolution of ideas which was undermining the *eidola* of the Victorian Age – a revolution in which Jane was a potent St Just-like Jacobin. Prince D S Mirsky, in his appreciation of her work – *Jane Ellen Harrison and Russia*, a Memorial Lecture given at Newham College, Cambridge in 1930 – even suggested that while *The Golden Bough* and Sir James Frazer's immense learning would remain a landmark in the history of science, 'the real salt and zest of the great age of English anthropology resided in the heterodox and unacademic Miss Harrison rather than in her more famous, canonised fellow workers.'

In the same lecture Prince Mirsky paid her this striking memorable tribute: 'She was a *contemporary* living her age.'

Jane's great service was to explore the dark underworld of Greek religion – the Chthonian deities who still lurked under and behind the shining figures of the Olympian gods. Indeed, as Jessie Stewart has written, her lifelong antipathy to these two perfect, magnified humans became a standing joke in classical circles in Cambridge. The super-imposing of the official cults on the primitive Chthonian nature-cults was the central theme of *Prolegomena*, and her sympathy was always with the superseded underdog.

One of the instances she quotes of the persistence of the gloomy worship of the underworld is the *Diasia*, which did not originally belong to Zeus but to a being called Meilichios, which – as readers of *Cencrastus* will be intrigued to know – was wor-shipped in the guise of a large curly snake! Jane wrote 'We are brought face to face with the astounding fact that Zeus, father of gods and men, is figured by his worshippers as a snake ... It is these rites of purification, belonging to the lower stratum – primitive and barbarous as they often are – that furnished ultimately the material out of which "Mysteries" are made: mysteries which, when informed by the new spirit of the religion of Dionysus and Orpheus, lent to Greece its deepest and most enduring religious impulse.'

It seemed to me, reading passages like these, that this whole theme bore a certain similarity to the curious dualities in Scottish literary tradition: 'Olympians' being the established 'greats' like Dunbar, Henryson and Gavin Douglas – plus Burns, Scott, Fergusson and Garioch – and the 'underworld' being the vast anonymous treasure-house of balladry and folksong – with all the manifold possibilities that existed and exist of constant interfusion. As Roderick Watson writes in his introduction to *The Poetry of Scotland* (1995): 'I believe that Scottish literature shows a long-standing and unique intercourse between "scholars" and "people" – for our "high art" has seldom lost touch with the expressive figure of the vernacular and folk tradition, and its utterance has been constantly refreshed by this forceful contact.'

I felt very much the same about the best work – in my opinion – of Hugh Mac-Diarmid, and that is why I prefaced the introductory essay already quoted with lines from *Depth and the Chthonian Image*. When I got his letter of March 1975, I was naturally very pleased to hear that he thought these lines were relevant in that context.

So much for Plotinus and Zeus Meilichios (the Curly Snake). But what of that other source – as I suggested above, an exceedingly surprising, even startling source – for part of this wonderful poem. It is none other than Wyndham Lewis's book *Hitler* (1931) and I have to admit I was somewhat shaken when I discovered the source of *Ein Mann aus dem Volke* ('A man of – or out of – the people') section of the poem. Here are 13 lines of this section:

> *Ein Mann aus dem Volke* weel I ken
> Nae man or movement's worth a damn unless
> The movement 'ud gang on withoot him if
> He de'ed the morn. Wherefore in you I bless
> My sense o' the greatest man can tipify
> And iniversalise himsel' maist fully by.
> Nocht ta'en at second-hand and nocht let drift,
> Nae bull owre big tae tackle by the horns,
> Nae chance owre sma' for freedom's sake he scorns,
> But a' creation through himsel' maun sift
> Even as you, nor possible defeat confess,
> Forever poised and apt in his address;
> Save at this pitch nae man can truly live.

Here are some passages from Lewis's book:

> Hitler is just a very typical *Mann aus dem Volke* ... one feels, should he fall tomorrow, the movement could still proceed without him ... I myself am content to regard him as an expression of current German manhood – resolved with that admirable tenacity, hardihood and intellectual acumen of the Teuton, not to take their politics at second-hand, not also to drift, but to seize the big bull of Finance by the horns, and to take a chance for the sake of Freedom.

Even remembering that MacDiarmid had contributed 'A Plea for a Scottish Fascism' and 'Programme for a Scottish Fascism' to the *Scottish Nation* in 1923, and that he had written in a letter to Compton Mackenzie, dated 11/4/29, 'All the young people are coming round to the realisation for the need of – and readiness to institute – a species of Scottish Fascism,' these borrowings from a monstrously inept book eulogising Hitler in a revoltingly gushing manner are undoubtedly hard to stomach. Nevertheless, re-reading the *Ein Mann aus dem Volke* section, I am convinced that in the context of my general argument the quotation in the introductory essay was not at all inappropriate.

The 'movement' to which these words apply with supreme force was, for me, the great carrying stream of folk poetry and balladry, which survives and burgeons irrespective of the life or death of its foremost practitioners, and has achieved maybe its highest apogee in the work of

unkent Bards wha made
Sangs peerless through a' post-anonymous days.

MacDiarmid himself, the best-kent Bard of the century, had composed immortal poetry, some of which was swept irresistibly into the carrying stream and my feeling – on receiving that already quoted letter of thanks, of March 197 5 – was that it represented at least a partial intellectual – as well as personal – reconciliation.

Cencrastus, 52, 1995

Alias MacAlias
The Uncanny Scot:
A Selection of Prose
by Hugh MacDiarmid

Edited with an Introduction by Kenneth Buthlay
(MacGibbon & Kee, 1968)

'And tell us,' Hynes said, 'do you know that fellow in the, fellow was over there in the ...'

He looked around.

'Macintosh. Yes I saw him. Where is he now?'

M'Intosh,' Hynes said, scribbling. 'I don't know who he is. Is that his name?' He moved away, looking about him.

'No,' Mr Bloom began, turning and stopping, 'I say, Hynes!'

Didn't hear. What? Where has he disappeared to? Not a sign. Well of all the. Has anyone here seen? Kay ee double ell. Become invisible. Good Lord, what became of him?

– James Joyce, *Ulysses* ('Hades' episode)

The Man in the Macintosh: Don't you believe a word he says. That man is Leopold M'Intosh, the notorious fireraiser. His real name is Higgins.

– *Ulysses* ('Circe' episode)

A lot of young Americans come to Scotland nowadays. Some look for ancestors, and there is no doubt that many can be aided to find them. Others are after live prey, such as literary notabilities, and in no time their attention is drawn to a venerable standing stone in the middle distance. A native guide is easily procured, and in no time they are taking part in a sort of in-group neolithic rite, well saturated in mountain dew.

The more computer-minded man becomes, the more is he likely to go a-whoring after the 'numinous'. The title which Mr Buthlay has chosen for his admirable selection of prose pieces by Hugh MacDiarmid has, therefore, a peculiar aptness and reverberation – an aptness, indeed, which quite transcends the mildly joco word-play which probably suggested it in the first place. MacDiarmid is not only one of the best living European poets; he is also, for better or for worse, the above-mentioned standing stone – or (better maybe) a sort of glorified totem-pole of the tribe, a new and in many ways more potent cult-figure than Scotland's superannuated 'Loved One', poor stuffed, cosmeticised and mummified Rabbie, now far gone in cairneyfaction. It would be a macabre 'Scotch joke' of precisely the kind that MacDiarmid himself so keenly appreciates – see 'The Dour Drinkers of Glasgow' – if the dead weight mantle of Burns-cult Burns were to fall in the latter end on his own shoulders.

The only other character who would be in the running for this dubious honour is, of course, none other than the Great McGonagall himself, about whom MacDiarmid has an essay in *The Uncanny Scot*. For MacDiarmid, McGonagall is not 'a good bad poet'. He is just 'not a poet at all'. Here I am convinced MacDiarmid is doing McGonagall an injustice. The Bard of Dundee is certainly a *kind* of poet, and his work (to quote Flecker's *Hassan*) 'has a monstrous beauty, like the backside of an elephant'. The fall with a thickening sud, the sustained belly-flop which is the distinguishing feature of McGonagall's verse, has much in common with the compulsive grotesquerie of many of the pedestrian Irish come-all-ye's brought across to Scotland in their hundreds in the last century by immigrant Irish workers like McGonagall's father. These contain, in degenerate form, a whole battery of motifs and techniques which descend ultimately from Gaelic poetry. In any case, the Langholm byspale seems to me to have much more in common with McGonagall than he himself probably realises, or would care to admit. I do not only mean that he has written a lot of 'belly-flop' poetry over the years, although even his most fervent admirers would admit that he has done so. I mean that his customary poetic stance, 'at a slight angle to the Universe' is often reminiscent of the attitudes and predilections of an off-beat Scoto-Irish popular tradition of which McGonagall's work – there is no use denying it – does form part. In quite a number of didactic poems in which MacDiarmid parades gew-gaws of learning, acquired jackdaw-wise, he makes a convincing impression of a sort of babu McGonagall.

As he would not wish us to be 'nice' with him – see 'The Dour Drinkers' again – let us put it even more bluntly. Chris Grieve, in one of his personae at least, appears very like the old gangrel 'bard of no regard' in Burns's song; appears, indeed, like a broadside hack of genius who ransacks everything from the folk idiom to the latest edition of the encyclopaedia, and turns all to his own purpose. One of his favourite parts is Autolycus, and no poet in either hemisphere can hold a candle to him as a 'snapper-up of unconsidered trifles'.

There is, in fact, a curious protean quality about Grieve's work; he can change into many characters, and is just as capable of writing bad poetry as of writing good. Sometimes these characters take on new names – *noms de guerre* rather than *noms de plume*, as Buthlay has himself judiciously noted elsewhere. One recalls, in this connection, an article by Moray McLaren which appeared in the *New Statesman* two or three years ago; it was entitled 'MacAlias', and it drew attention to the well-known penchant of Scottish poets and writers for operating under cover of pseudonyms. A surprising number have chosen and still choose to adopt a new moniker, and by the same token an alter ego. It sometimes appears as if they feel a definite *need* to do so. We are here on the edge of a gey debatable land, and must walk warily.

It is never easy to draw a hard and fast line between the 'popular' arts and the 'élite' arts of individual excellence. Owing to the constant fruitful interaction of folk-song and art literature in our tradition, we're often faced with the sort of set-up in which no one can say for sure where MacAlias ends and Anon begins. A sort of friendly communal cannibalisation has therefore been the rule rather than the exception in Scottish literature. 'Art' poets have operated like 'folk' poets in appropriating lines or even whole stanzas from earlier or contemporary authors – or, of course, from Anon – and using them as a basis for their own productions.

(It can work the other way too, naturally. You get people like 'Ossian' MacPherson, who, having written original works of literature, try to palm them off on someone else;

also modest characters who seek to hide their well-proportioned identities under bulging fig-leaves like 'The Author of Waverley'.)

The situation occasionally allows two or more turns of the screw, as when the disguised poet not only calls himself something else, but actually turns out to *be* someone else, into the bargain. A classic example of this came to light in 1964 during the correspondence in the *TLS* about the much praised and anthologised poem, 'Perfect' ('I found a pigeon's skull on the machair'). Here it transpired that, in the case of this poem at least, Hugh MacDiarmid was the pseudonym not only of Christopher Murray Grieve but also of a Welsh novelist and short story writer who had actually written the words to which MacDiarmid gave poetic shape – thus affording them a new and more permanent habitation, and a name. This is a phenomenon for which we need to invent a designation, and I'd like to suggest 'Alias MacAlias' as an appropriate name for the two-headed bard. Alternatively, we might identify him with the thoroughly waterproof but even so somewhat uncanny figure 'M'Intosh', the thirteenth mourner at Paddy Dignam's funeral in Joyce's *Ulysses*. If ever there is a MacAlias Supper, I look forward with relish to proposing The Immortal Memory.

As John Sparrow pointed out during the *TLS* controversy, the best single comment on this whole imbroglio was provided years ago by MacDiarmid himself, in a drama-tised sketch in Scots (reprinted in *The Uncanny Scot*) called 'The Purple Patch'. A new minister has included 'a maist peculiar utterance' in his sermon which 'made threads and stour o' a' the rest o't'. As the congregation skails, three groups of parishioners discuss the whys and wherefores of this unaccountable visitation. It is left to Heb Duncan, the veteran beadle, to provide the solution at the end of the sketch:

> Ye ken that muckle purple passage in the middle o't. Weel, when Dr Gilruth was writin't he found yin o' his bit sheets o' paper half-fu' to start wi' – wi' a passage he'd been copyin' frae that fantastical divine, Dr Donne – a great Yankee revivalist, if I remember rightly! – an' absent-minded-like, thocht that he'd juist written it as pairt o's sermon. So he tacked on the rest to the end o't. He never noticed it the first time he delivered it; but I spotted the cuckoo i' the nest, an' when he gied it a second time, I spiered why he keepit in a passage that had nae connection wi' the rest o' the sermon ava! 'Man, I never noticed it,' he said, an' then he tell't me hoo it must ha'e happened. 'But I'll juist leave it there,' he added. It may be an accident, or it may be the hand o' God. It'll no' dae ony ill in either case. Them that comes to the kirk i' the richt frame o' mind'll never notice that onything's amiss, an' them that dae notice'll be puzzled to death to ken what to mak' on't ...

Irony is heaped on irony, and compounded, when one recollects that in 1962, before the *TLS* storm broke, Walter Keir ended an article in MacDiarmid's seventieth birthday Festschrift by quoting 'Perfect' and remarking, 'There is really nothing to add to that'. Where the MacAlias of MacAlias is concerned, these are always likely to be famous last words. Indeed, in Grieve's later work 'Hugh MacDiarmid' is not so much a pseudonym as a trade mark which appears stamped on such items as the poet considers worthy of being displayed to the public in the trundling top-heavy co-op pantechnicon which transports his productions. Borrowing one of MacDiarmid's own titles, we can express the thing succinctly in one short formula:

The Kind of Poetry I Want –
= The Kind of Poetry I Take.

Lewis Grassic Gibbon (another MacAlias) evidently had much the same approach to the subject when – as Oliver Brown has convincingly shown – he took the stuffing out of a clumsy German mattress in order to produce a much superior article of his own. Nobody who reads the two books (*Jörn Uhl* and *Sunset Song*) can doubt for an instant that he was absolutely justified in so doing. Plagiarists of genius are the justified sinners of literature. If the operation is aesthetically successful, we need not worry about conventional proprieties. Here, again, MacDiarmid has the most telling comment to offer: it will be found in the sixth stanza of the 'First Hymn to Lenin'. The poet was addressing Lenin, of course, but he might just as well have been addressing Gibbon:

> Descendant o' the unkent Bards wha made
> Sangs peerless through a' post-anonymous days
> I glimpse again in you that mightier poo'er
> Than fashes wi' the laurels and the bays
> But kens that it is shared by ilka man
> Since time began

One or two of the seven vernacular sketches included in *The Uncanny Scot* provide evidence that when he was on form, and in the mood, MacDiarmid could write a Scots prose every bit as rich, vivid and evocative as the best of Scott, Galt, and the Ettrick Shepherd – and much better, in my opinion, than the *Scots Quair* lingo of Gibbon, whose strange hybrid Scots-English has been one thing about his work which has always left me unsatisfied. I prefer the wine of the country neat, and a full-flavoured local malt at that; the sort we get in the following passage from the best Scots sketch in the present selection:

> In front o' the Waterside hooses the bed o' the river was fu' o' muckle flat shelfs o' rock they ca'd the Factory Gullets that cut up the water into a' kinds o' loups, and scours, and slithers and gushes, wi' two-three deep channels in atween them through which the main flows gaed solid as wa's ... Sae, in the simmer time, or bricht winter days, the hooses alang the Waterside were aye fu' o' a licht and life that made the ongauns o' their inhabitants o' as little consequence as the ongauns o' the rats in the cellars were to them, and the dunt and dirl o' the river was in them like the hert in a man, and they had shoals o' licht and the crazy castin' o' the cloods and the endless squabble o' the gulls in them faur mair even than the folk talkin' and the bairns playin'. ... Alang the Waterside they were windy, thriftless, flee-aboot craturs. The sense was clean washed oot o' them. A' the sense – and a' the stupidity tae. It's only some kinds o' birds that ha'e een like what theirs becam' – cauld and clear and wi' nae humanity in them ava.

This is first-rate, and deserves to be better known, but not all the vernacular sketches are up to that standard. MacDiarmid's prose is as unequal as his verse. Apart from 'The Last Great Burns Discovery', a gorgeous comic send-up of the 'Cult' the pre-1939 pieces in English would hardly merit a second reading if one did not have prior knowledge that they were by the author of *A Drunk Man*, the *Hymns to Lenin*, and *Stony Limits*. 'Five Bits of Miller' (1934) is an uncomfortable curiosity; it reads in places like an anticipatory parody of Spike Milligan's *Puckoon* – especially the bit about the blackhead, and Miller's clock-face dropping off and disclosing the works. The best single essay in the book, in my opinion, is 'The Dour Drinkers of Glasgow' which subjects the barbaric black humour of Calvinistic Scotland – 'the recalcitrant, the sinister, the malignant, the sarcastic, the saturnine, the cross-grained, and the cankered' – to a surgical going-over, as it were from the inside. This piece, beautifully written and constructed, and operating on several different levels of irony, is a five-star example of that sustained gaze directed at the bridge of the nose which (as MacDiarmid has observed elsewhere) is 'the most exacerbating form of regard'.

A swatch of polemical prose which I missed, and which might well have rated inclusion in preference to some of the items chosen, is 'A Soldier's Farewell to Maurice Lindsay' (published in the *National Weekly* in 1952 or thereabouts). If this is not the most devastating *Arsch-tritt* in literary history, we may allow it to hold the title meantime – until a new champ appears, to the sound of the trump.

Scottish International, 1969.

At Langholm, September 13, 1992

Nothing was more characteristic of the great Chris Grieve than to flyte; and I was honoured to be his opponent on more than one occasion. In the book *The Age of MacDiarmid*, edited by P H Scott and A C Davies, and reprinted recently, there's an imaginary dialogue between Roy Campbell and Hugh MacDiarmid. At the end of this dialogue, which takes place (needless to say) in Heaven, they both have a drink of excellent malt whisky, in the best bar in Heaven. (This must surely be the bar the blessed damozel leaned out from!)

At the very end, after a number of curious and not-so-curious exchanges, Chris takes a glass of excellent malt and says to Roy Campbell 'In this I bury all unkindness.' Now of all the most unlikely imaginary dialogues in world history, that must take the biscuit! For I cannot imagine exchanging a drink or two with Chris Grieve beyond that Gulf, in that great bar of Heaven, and expect him to to say something like that about me!

I first met him not long after coming out of the army, and it was a privilege, naturally, for a bloke who had loved his poetry for a long time, to meet this being of bright genius, who descended on the Muckle Toon o' Langholm 100 years ago. He's not only a world poet, a poet of huge significance everywhere, but he's also a strongly *local* poet. He loved Langholm, and said that Langholm was his touchstone in all things creative. I first saw a poem by Chris Grieve – you've just heard it read by Tom Fleming – 'Mars is braw in crammasy'; it was included by John Buchan in an anthology called *The Northern Muse*. I was at school in England at the time, and opening this book and seeing in a collection of poems this astounding poem, which was quite unlike anything else in the anthology, I wondered who this C M Grieve was – it was signed not 'Hugh MacDiarmid' but 'C M Grieve'. So after a little while I ferreted out that Hugh MacDiarmid and C M Grieve were one man, and eventually I succeeded in picking up copies of *Sangschaw*, *Penny Wheep*, and above all, *A Drunk Man Looks at the Thistle*, which changed my life. Lots of people have said this, and I just add it to the other expressions of appreciation of that amazing goliardic book. I carried it with me, incidentally, throughout the war, took it out to Africa, and had it with me in the desert, and through Libya and Tunisia, and into Italy. The only other poetry I had with me all the way was *17 Poems for Sixpence*, a wee bookie containing work by Robert Garioch and Somhairle MacLean. These were my poetic companions throughout the campaign – and not bad company, you must admit!

But earlier on, when I returned as a teenager to Scotland from school, after reading this poem in *The Northern Muse*, I found to my astonishment that contemporaries of mine, teenagers like me, kent naethin aboot him! The very existence of MacDiarmid was unknown to them. Now, you know what's happened to him in the meantime, and this amazing transformation in the cultural life of the country is above all due to the magnificent, single-minded spadework of Hugh MacDiarmid himself. He did what he once said might happen in a little poem called 'Glasgow 1960' when a great crowd making for Ibrox is not going to see a football match, but is going to hear an intellectual debate, or a Turkish poet's 'abstruse new song'. Anyway, Chris made it – he did it.

As I say, I was astonished that none of my contemporaries, aged around 15–16, knew about MacDiarmid, and when eventually I read the *Festschrift* published in 1962 for Chris's 70th birthday by K D Duval and Sydney Goodsir Smith, there was a contribution by Maurice Lindsay in which, with admirable candour, he admitted he had not heard of MacDiarmid's existence until he was already an officer in the army. He'd been through a Glasgow education and he'd come across *A Drunk Man Looks at the Thistle* in a second-hand bookshop. That excellent, candid statement throws into high relief the achievement of MacDiarmid in the intervening years. Nowadays it is different, and I know from occasionally judging competitions like the one we've just heard the results of, that MacDiarmid is actually a popular poet among young folk now – an amazing development.

Now to go back to these flytings. MacDiarmid thought, wrongly in my opinion, that the folk song revival was a kind of resumption of the kailyard. He thought that the people interested in the old ballads, and some of the magnificent bothy songs which reflect the life of the north-east farm servants, excellent folk poetry; that in some way all this was connected with the sort of petit-bourgeois Victorian poems that you associate with the kailyard. How wrong can you get? Now, I put it to you that this was a great error on Chris Grieve's part. In fact he should have welcomed the folk-song revival. (Why should I renege now on my position of then?) Nevertheless, as I say, I give all credit to him for being what he called 'the catfish in the aquarium' – this tremendous stimulus to intellectual life in Scotland. And may I add, not exactly in the tone of John Wain's imaginary dialogue, with a glass of malt whisky exchanged in a bar, that eventually, near the end of his life, he actually told me he liked one of my own songs! And as far as the flytings are concerned, I think it should be pointed out that one of the characteristics of Chris Grieve was the old Border Riever spirit he shared with countless ancestors. He *had* to have flytings. It was in his nature. I just happened to be the fall guy in all this at one particular point in his history. Anyway we went at each other hammer and tongs, and I personally don't regret it: I don't think if we ever exchange that glass of malt whisky in the best bar in Heaven, that we will ever do anything else than resume the flyting.

Who are the characters in European or world history that resemble Chris Grieve the most? People have compared him to many poets, but I'm going to suggest a person that might not come first and foremost into your mind. It is the Bedford tinker John Bunyan, author of the *Pilgrim's Progress*. He was a man who also enjoyed his own rammies. He was a remorseless fighter, was John Bunyan, in his own way, for what he thought was the right; and in one of his famous songs he says

> There's no discouragement
> Shall make him once relent

> His first avowed intent
> To be a pilgrim.

Well, MacDiarmid took his pilgrimage into the Communist Party of Great Britain. And many folk may consider that he made a wrong political choice. But I would put it to you that in view of his temperament, and in view of his own indomitable nature – 'aye gaun whaur extremes meet' – there was nowhere that he could land up except in a Stalinist Communist party. Now this, needless to say (in my opinion), didn't do Scotland any good. I belong, as you might say, to the Dubcek wing in all this; and consequently that's another reason why I would have to have flytings with him. If I concentrate on these antagonistic things, incidentally, it's because I feel it's part and parcel of the whole nature of Chris Grieve, and in fact I would almost like to say that without this particular vein he wouldn't have been the man he was.

So may I, at the very end, quote one of the poems he made out of Scottish folk poetry – this folk poetry he claimed to despise. It is 'Empty Vessel'. He went, as we all know, to Jamieson's dictionary and found some of these amazing words. At one time he said 'it is out of words that you create poetry' and of course so it is, but the words in Jamieson's dictionary led him on inevitably to the folk poetry, out of which these words had come. Out of David Herd's great collection, for example. And it was in Herd's collection that he found a poem, which is a roch randy poem, called 'Jenny Nettles'. This is the opening of the second verse:

> I met her on the kairney
> Jennie Nettles, Jennie Nettles,
> singing to her bairnie
> Robin Rattles Bastard …

'Unpromising material' was George Bruce's rather tight-lipped comment in the 1962 *Festschrift* I have already mentioned. But out of it MacDiarmid made this truly magical poem 'Empty Vessel' which many of you probably know by heart:

> I met ayont the cairney
> A lass wi' tousie hair
> Singin' til a bairnie
> That was nae langer there.

> Wunds wi' warlds to swing
> Dinna sing sae sweet.
> The licht that bends owre a'thing
> Is less ta'en up wi't.

Langholm byspale, we salute you!

Chapman, 69–70, The MacDiarmid Centenary Issue.

'There's A Fine Poet In Gaelic'
Sorley MacLean

Readers who saw the film *Whisky Galore!* will remember hearing a number of rousing songs in a strange lingo. This may have puzzled the English a bit, but the Scots in the audience will have recognised it as Gaelic, the most ancient language of their country.

For about 200 years it has been the fashion to call Gaelic a 'dying' tongue, and it's true that a number of attempts have been made to hustle it into its death-bed. Gaelic has been discriminated against in exactly the same way as the minority languages of the Soviet Union used to be, in the days when the Tsarist Empire was a prison house of nations. To this day it is allowed no place in administration and commerce, and next to no place in education. However, it's still kicking, and on the whole has stood up to persecution with astonishing resilience. Some may consider it impossible that poetry of a high order could still be written in such a language. I suggest that not only is it quite possible, but that some of the finest Marxist poetry in modern European literature has been written in this despised minority language.

Sorley MacLean, the poet concerned, is a Hebridean. He was born in 1911 on the island of Raasay, which lies between Skye and the mainland of Wester Ross. After a brilliant career at Edinburgh University he returned to the West Highlands and wrote much of his best work while schoolmastering in Portree and Tobermory. During the Second World War he fought in the desert as a signaller with the 1st Royal Horse Artillery and was blown up on a land-mine on 2 November 1942 during the break-through at El Alamein. After being invalided out of the Army he went back to teaching, and is now a master at Boroughmuir High School in Edinburgh. When Sorley started writing he was in the familiar state of disorientation induced by an orthodox Anglo-Scottish education.

However, he mustered up the courage to look twentieth-century Scotland in the face, and the sight daunted him. In the Highlands, depopulation and decay: in the cities, unemployment, overcrowding and disease. No cultural focal point for the nation, no political focal point either. Worst of all, the old culture of which he was a rightful inheritor seemed likely to be eroded and blown away, like soil from the dust-bowl. Luckily for him he soon came on the writings of a Marxist poet who was to have an incalculable effect on his development.

Once in Italy I was in the basement of a house which received a direct hit from a shell. It was like receiving a giant's blow between the eyes, and still retaining conscious-ness. This was exactly the sort of impact that Hugh MacDiarmid's *Hymns to Lenin* made on all the young Scottish poets of MacLean's generation. Another turning-point was the outbreak of the Spanish Civil War, which aroused in the young Gael a passionate hatred of Fascism.

Some of his most forcible blows have been against the Kirk; reacting violently against the Scots paraphrases, with their 'crude frontal assault on Zion', he wrote:

> My eyes are not on Calvary,
> nor on Bethlehem the Blessed,
> but on a shitten backland in Glasgow,
> where growing life decays;
> and on a room in Edinburgh,
> a room of poverty and pain,
> where a poor sickly bairn
> writhes and wallows to its death.

In his *History of the Working Classes in Scotland* Tom Johnstone writes that under the Presbyterian zealots the catalogue of sins and offences grew to such a length 'that it covered almost every human activity, except praying, fasting and toiling for the lairds and merchants'.

MacLean is clearly thinking along these lines when he writes in his 'Ban-Ghaidheal' ('A Highland Woman'):

> Have ye seen her, great Jew,
> that are called the One Son of God?
> Have ye seen the like of her on your road,
> at labour in the distant vineyard?
>
> Ye havena seen her, son of the carpenter,
> that are called the King of Glory,
> among the rugged western shores
> in the sweat of her food's creel.
>
> This Spring and last,
> and every twenty Springs from the beginning,
> she's carried the cold sea-weed,
> for her children's food and the castle's reward.
>
> And your couthie Kirk has spoken
> of the lost state of her immortal soul...
> The hard black-labour was her inheritance.
> Grey is her sleep tonight.

This indignation generated in MacLean a desire to rediscover the militant traditions of the Highland people, and of Scotland as a whole. How many readers know that in the 1880s, when ruthless evictions were still the order of the day, the crofters of the North and West rose against the landlords and their agents? Few, I'm afraid, even in Scotland, have heard the names of MacPherson the 'Martyr', of Donald Beaton, and the Land Leaguers who fought the Battle of the Braes. Fewer still know that in 1882 warships were sent to Skye and marines landed in Uig Bay.

MacLean steeped himself in these traditions and gave eloquent tongue to them in his greatest poem *The Cuillin*, which runs to over 2000 lines.(The Cuillin - or Cuillins is a mountain range in Skye, well known to rock-climbers and photographers.) Readers who have seen translations of Pablo Neruda may remember his tremendous evocation of Andean scenery in a cycle of poems. MacLean does much the same thing in his *Cuillin*, which not only evokes with splendid verve the heroic landscape of the Hebrides, but also makes it a symbol of man's achievement in shaping his own history. The indomitable spirit of the great revolutionaries Lenin, Liebknecht, Dimitrov and John Maclean is found in 'heights beyond thought on the mountains', among the chasms and pinnacles of the proud sierra:

> The lyric Cuillin of the free,
> The ardent Cuillin of the heroic.

All around them is the eternal sea-surge of human struggle, made stone in the ramparts of the Cuillin:

> Summit wall
> Of man's spirit:
> Dangerous rocks
> For the élan of desires.
> Glorious Cuillin
> Of the luminous bare summits.
> Noble precipice,
> Head of lovetalk's ecstasy!

This poem, which ensures MacLean's place in European literature, ends in an affirmation of the 'courage of the many' - and a vision of their ultimate triumph.

> Beyond poverty, consumption,
> fever, agony;
> Beyond hardship, wrong,
> tyranny, distress;
> Beyond misery, despair, hatred,
> treachery;
> Beyond guilt and defilement –
> watchfully,
> Heroically is seen the Cuillin
> Rising on the other side of
> sorrow.

Daily Worker, 24 November 1949.

At Glasgow Cross

The first poems of Freddy Anderson's I came across were in the 1949 Clyde Group collection *Fowrsome Reel;* this 'slim volume', now a collector's piece, also contained striking work by the late Morris Blythman ('Thurso Berwick'), John Kincaid and George Todd. The poems of the three latter were nearly all in Scots, and bore impressive witness to the invigorating ideological and linguistic influence of Hugh MacDiarmid. Freddy's poems, on the other hand, were magical atmospheric evocations of his Irish childhood, written in a distinctive Monaghan-accented English, and for that reason they rather stood apart, and caught the eye. It was evident, however, that all four poets were 'fellow-countrymen of the mind' and that their alliance was no fortuitous one: the Clyde Group represented a genuine innovatory poetic movement, inspired by the memory and political heritage of John Maclean, and it was single-mindedly committed to the cause of Scottish Republicanism.

Re-reading Freddy's contributions, I am struck again by their seemingly artless but actually highly accomplished artistry. The landscape and the 'props' are those of Patrick Kavanagh's early poetry – he also was a Co. Monaghan man – but the voice and the rhythm are quite individual. 'The Blackberry Man', 'The Connolly Ballad' and above all 'The Love Ballad' are poems that have stuck in my mind ever since I first read them.

> Come gently round me, town bred folk
> and listen to my tale
> I was born in Monaghan of the little hills and vales
> My mother kept a fruit shop, my father he ran wild
> and I became in a village street an anxious daring child.

It seemed to me that the man who had written these lines had learned to good effect from Yeats's later ballad style.

Another very obvious characteristic of these lyrics of Freddy's was their 'oral' quality – and this was something they definitely did share with the Scots poems in the same collection, particularly Morris's. I well remember the spontaneous applause which interrupted one of the latter's poems, at the John Maclean Memorial Meeting of 1948, when he reached the line -

> A Maclean is at yuir banquet!

This vigorous spoken poetry of *Fowrsome Reel,* a potent agent in the contemporary folk-song revival, reappears to superb advantage in one of Freddy's finest poems

'Bonnymuir'. By the time he wrote this splendid ballad, which never fails to gain warm applause when he declaims it, Freddy had mastered the 'feel' and the rhythms of Scots traditional ballad-poetry; this means that he had effectively bridged the idiomatic divide between his Ulster poetry and the kindred but separate literary tradition of his adopted country.

Another 'bridge poem' is Glen Masson, written after Freddy heard of the tragic fate of an orphaned boy from Mull whose bones were found in an Argyll glen. Glen Masson is in Cowal; like Glen Etive and Glendaruel it is mentioned in the Irish tale of 'The Sons of Uisneach' of which the well known Gaelic song 'Deidre's Farewell to Scotland' forms a part. The very name, therefore, recalls this old Scottish-Irish connection; using it as a springboard, Freddy has written a poem which encompasses the closely-related, but non-identical twin tradition. Indeed, it's a poem which could easily have been composed on either side of the Moyle.

Another idea that springs to mind is that Glen Masson lies not far from the Holy Loch, and that brings us by a leap to Freddy's political poetry. Like many other young writers in the West of Scotland, he threw himself whole-heartedly in the early 1960s into the struggle against Polaris and the unwanted American bases on the Clyde. Responding to Morris Blythman's appeal for songs and singers, he came up trumps with, 'The Polis of Argyll'. This was much sung, and it appeared in several of Morris's anti-Polaris songbooks, including 'Ding Dong Dollar'.

Since then he has written many other hard-hitting political poems, with the same target in his sights, and nobody reading them can doubt either his unflinching commitment to international Socialism, or his ability to deliver formidable propaganda broadsides. Some may consider his world-view too perfervid to take in, and put into focus, all the deep paradoxical complexities of our present human situation on this beleaguered planet, but no one (I am quite sure) would question the deeply felt 'savage indignation' which animates his political poetry. It is anti-Fascist engagement, without fear or compromise; in his hatred of cant, hypocrisy and craven self-interest he belongs to a long line of courageous radical poets whose most famous members include Byron and Burns - not forgetting Woody Guthrie.

In this long rebellious line Freddy has earned an honourable place.

Foreword to *At Glasgow Cross* by Freddy Anderson, Fat Cat, 1987.

The Poet Speaks

Peter Orr: Mr Henderson, let me start by asking you about your upbringing. You are a pure Scot, aren't you?

Henderson: Yes. I am a Scot on both sides. I was born in Perthshire, in the little burgh of Blairgowrie, and I spent my childhood years there. I was educated at Blairgowrie High School, and without any doubt my poetry and my songs owe a good deal to the speech habits, and the singing habits, of the people in that part.

Orr: How early did you come to poetry?

Henderson: Well, I was always very interested in folk poetry, without knowing that it was folk poetry or balladry or anything like that. Lots of people in the area were singers: 'The Bonnie Hoose o' Airlie' and 'Lord Randal' and the big ballads like that were sung by a whole lot of people in and around Blairgowrie, and up in Glenshee where I spent part of my childhood too. Without a doubt they did play a very big part in my feeling for poetry, and most of my life has been devoted to an interest in them and research work about them. For the last fifteen years, nearly, I have been working in Scotland on the Scots folk poetry, and this is the sort of poetry that I like best.

Orr: Tell me, do you find this an advantage or a handicap, being a poet yourself and also having an occupation which has to do with poetry? Do you believe, as Eliot has advised, that young poets should not have anything to do with poetry in their daily lives, that they should go out and be postmen and milkmen and butchers and things like that?

Henderson: Well, I think that the job that I have isn't the sort of job that Eliot means when he says that people should go out and do something else. He is thinking there of the sort of intermediate or hermaphroditic jobs with literature like Autumn Supplement critics, and that sort of thing, whereas I think that my own work in the School of Scottish Studies is not this same sort of job at all. Most of what I am doing is, in so far as I am capable of it, pretty hard intellectual analysis of what goes to the ticking of this particular thing. I have got to find out, for example, how it fits into the mental climate of the places that make it, and I have got to analyse all sorts of intricate variants between one ballad and another, one version and another, and this is an academic work which is far removed from the light industry of poetry or literature.

Orr: Now, whom do you regard as your poetic ancestors? Since you are a Scots poet, presumably your poetic ancestors would be the Scottish Chaucerians, Dunbar, perhaps Burns, rather than Shakespeare, Wordsworth and Tennyson?

Henderson: That's true, but no Scottish poet, of course, has ever been able to ignore, even if he wanted to, the enormous literature lying over against him. The Scots

Chaucerians, so called, couldn't do it; they knew perfectly well who had preceded them, and Scottish literature, therefore, has always been under the shadow of this big ben, as you might say, across the way. And needless to say, like every other Scottish poet, I have read the great English poets, and it would be idle and stupid and ridiculous of me to deny that all the major English poets that I have read have to a certain extent influenced me.

Orr: Which have been the strongest influences?

Henderson: Well, I think in many ways the modern English poets. Without any doubt as far as the *Elegies* are concerned, Wilfred Owen influenced me greatly. I read him when I was a schoolboy, and I have gone on reading his poetry ever since. I think it is the most wonderful English poetry of this century. Eliot, too, has undoubtedly influenced me very greatly. And I love the later poetry of Yeats. I carried with me, throughout the war, the little Cuala Press *Last Poems* of Yeats that was published in 1939, and I was continually reading poems like 'The Circus Animals' Desertion' and 'Under Bare Ben Bulben's Head' and the two plays, *Purgatory* and *The Death of Cuchulain*.

Orr: Can we try and define, before you go on, just what we mean when we say you are influenced by a poet. Does this mean you are influenced in terms of what the poet thinks about, what he has to say, or the mechanics of how he sets it down on paper? How does an influence really work?

Henderson: Well, that is one of the almost unanswerable questions. I mean, a poet and the influence of a poet works at every level, surely. One can't possibly listen to what he has got to say without taking some account of how he says it, and I should imagine that if one were to isolate, for example, the influence of Eliot in my poems, 'the way he says it' is undoubtedly there. 'The way he says it' is more important, in this case, I suppose, than what he had to say. I don't think that my poems, these *Elegies* anyway, are really *like* Eliot's poetry, though I know one or two critics have said so. I think the intellectual background is completely different, and also the influences upon the *Elegies* that I think most important are the ones which, to a certain extent, liberated me from too great a bondage to Eliot. I read a tremendous amount of German poetry, and I was absolutely dumbfounded when I read the poems of Friedrich Hölderlin. If any poems have directly influenced my *Elegies,* I think it is the poems of Hölderlin, and especially the later poems, the poems of his madness. In a time of tremendous suffering and war, small wonder that poems of a poet's personal suffering, horror, ecstasy and extreme agony should influence another poet. The last poems of Hölderlin are amazingly modern too, as Michael Hamburger was pointing out in a recent number of *Stand* I was reading the other day. I was reading the originals of Holderlin's later poetry and these translations of Michael Hamburger, some of which are quite good, but I was more interested in what he had to say about them. And there is no doubt in my mind whatsoever that Hölderlin is one of those poets whose influence has never completely come to the fore as far as the 1930s and indeed the 1940s are concerned in English or Scots poetry, for the obvious reason that he is a foreign poet, and the number of people who really can appreciate his influence is going to be smaller than in the case of an English poet.

Orr: Let's look now at the themes which attract you in poetry. You've mentioned suffering: is this the one all-pervasive theme that you feel driven to write about?

Henderson: Oh no. It certainly is a main theme in my *Elegies*. They are poems of passive suffering. They are poems of stoicism, which is undoubtedly a virtue in the times that we have gone through, and to a certain extent I think my own *Elegies* prefigure the greater threat of annihilation which stands over everybody now. And not to think of suffering in such a period would condemn one, I think; at any rate would condemn me, because of the sort of person I am.

Orr: What other themes do you feel drawn to write about, then?

Henderson: Well, in many Scottish writers you get the strong swing of the pendulum between the strong, deep, heavy notes of the lament as, for example, in Dunbar's 'Lament for the Makars', and something different altogether, which can be the wildest ecstasy of the dance. This always seems to me to be much more possible for a Scottish poet in music than in poetry. Well, I don't say for every poet, but when I swing to the other extreme I move into music, and because I love Scottish folk-music generally, I find that when I begin writing in a 'Crazy Jane' mood, not only the words but the tunes suggest themselves to me, and I finish up by not publishing the poem in a magazine but singing it in a folk-song club. And then people begin listening to it and they begin repeating it. For example, my song, 'Farewell to Sicily', The Highland Division's Farewell to Sicily, was beginning to get sung by people here and there almost as soon as I had written it. And only today I got an airmail letter from the States giving me the text of a version of this particular song which is quite a distance away from the way I wrote it, sung by a group in the States.

Orr: Do you see yourself then more nearly as a troubadour, a minstrel, than an intellectual poet sitting down and wanting to have his words regarded on the printed page?

Henderson: I think that is a false antithesis. They talk of the 'Scottish Schizophrenia', but I don't think it is possible for a Scottish poet to make this sort of schizophrenic split. I don't think of myself as a troubadour or anything as airy-fairy as that: I think of myself as a lyric poet, a satiric poet, a ribald poet, at times a bawdy poet, who thinks not only in terms of words but in terms of music. If at the present moment lyricism, ribaldry, bawdry have been separated from music, it is a passing phenomenon. We are in the preliminary stages of an enormous revival of oral tradition. Everyone knows that. A lot of people don't *like* it, but everyone can see it, and in so far as my poems are part of the beginning of this, I am pleased at the idea.

Orr: Do you feel attracted to writing poetic drama?

Henderson: I have written poetic drama, but I am not very sure if I have been successful. Years ago when Joan Littlewood used to come to Scotland with Theatre Workshop I worked for a time upon a play which was mainly in prose, but the sort of O'Casey prose that was, as you might say, a half-way house between prose and poetry. I was immensely attracted to it, but I eventually decided that I would not permit it to go forward. I didn't think that I had been successful with it. I may have a go at it again.

Orr: Do you want to write novels and essays?

Henderson: Essays yes, but essays about my own subject of folk poetry and of folk tales. I have written one which has got certain, I think, literary merits, apart from the purely academic merits. On the academic side it has not been challenged yet: I don't know whether it will be, although it contains a whole lot of different ideas in it. It's a long note upon a particular folk tale in Scots, 'The Green Man of Knowledge,' a version of an international folk tale, Aarne/Thompson Märchen-type 313, 'The Magic Flight' — the tale of which the Jason and Medea legend is the archetype — which I recorded in Aberdeenshire in 1954. It brings together the Irish and the Scottish Gaelic versions of the 313 tale type, a gypsy version from Wales, and many of the other versions. It is one of the basic folk tales that you find in nearly every country under the sun, and consequently, one of the perennially fascinating folk tales. I have also brought in 'Sir Gawain and the Green Knight', this puzzling, wonderful and beautiful poem which so many people have barked their shins on, and no doubt I have barked mine. As I say, it is a literary essay as well as an academic one.

Orr: Do you feel drawn to writing about contemporary problems about the world as it is around us today?

Henderson: Well, in so far as I have written about the most pressing problems of all, namely those of continuing existence and the bomb or what have you, I have felt in this case too that song is the thing that expresses my feeling best. I have written, for example, a song which I call 'The Freedom Come-All-Ye' which is written under this tremendous shadow of the Bomb. It's a song which tries to gather together a number of the problems that face us in Scotland and the world. It faces the tremendous problem of race, for example, and it faces the tremendous problem of human brotherhood and the threat of annihilation and as I say, I don't make any barrier at all between poetry and song now. I think that the two have got to go together. I intend to go on writing in this way. To a certain extent, the poem 'The Cell' is already a sort of appendix; something that no longer really has much point in my own creation. I hope to complete the long poem. I think it has got some passages that are of merit, and I would like to complete it.

Orr: Do you feel yourself cut off from, or do you feel very strongly part of, English contemporary poetry, the poetry of the 1960s? I am thinking of people like Ted Hughes and Thom Gunn, Edward Lucie-Smith, Peter Porter and so on.

Henderson: Oh, I should suppose I am undoubtedly cut off from them. I like their stuff; I mean, I still read poetry for pleasure, which is a thing that I know not all poets do. But I think that I am doing something different, and it is this thing which I'm trying to describe. As far as Scottish poets are concerned, I think that the ones that are nearest me, at any rate in the attempt to heal the gap between song and poetry, are Sydney Goodsir Smith, who is in many ways the most successful writer of poems in the folk idiom, an extraordinary poet; also MacDiarmid, when he was writing in Scots in his first two or three books, in *Sangschaw*, in *Penny Wheep*, in *A Drunk Man Looks at the Thistle*. He draws on this particular folk tradition in the most marvellous fashion. These are the poets that I feel are much closer to me than these modern English poets that you mention.

Orr: Are you a severe critic of your own work? Can you stand back and look at it quite dispassionately?

Henderson: Yes, I think I can. So dispassionately and so critically, in fact, that I have jettisoned a great deal of stuff that I might not have jettisoned, I suppose; but I went through a period of extreme critical strictness, especially in the early 1950s when I was working on the long poem that I have mentioned, and I ditched a great deal of it because I felt that in the long run it just didn't say what I wanted to say, and then I left it at that.

Orr: Is the satisfaction you get from writing poetry (presuming that there is a satisfaction) the satisfaction of actually *doing* the thing, of working it out like a crossword puzzle, if I can put it at that level, or is the satisfaction rather in having created a piece of work to look back on?

Henderson: Oh, that is a very difficult question indeed. I think that what Wilde wrote in *De Profundis* has got some bearing upon this question when he says that the object of love is to love. To feel itself in the joy of its own being. To a certain extent this is poetry too: one shouldn't divide it between the moment of creation and the created completed thing. Its joy is the joy of itself, to feel itself in being. I certainly have felt that, whether I have published a thing or not, or whether I have come in contact with people to whom I can read stuff or anything like that. Periods when one actually feels that one has got something and that it's moving. And that, I suppose, to every poet is the most important thing. To have this sensation of the thing moving and being and in existence, and not dead and failing.

Orr: And is the idea of communicating what you have to say to an audience important to you?

Henderson: It is, but of late, as I say, this has always with me taken the shape of direct communication, not so much communication via the printed page, although I have published things here and there. I have preferred to read poetry out, and if it is a song, to sing it. I am quite conscious of the fact that this immediate communication has got its own strong drawbacks. The audience cannot often grasp a thing immediately. But nevertheless, this immediate communication, this immediate aural communication, has been to me personally of enormous interest.

13 October 1964

Interview by Peter Orr in *The Poet Speaks*, Routledge, 1966.

Pipes, Goatskin & Bones:
The Songs and Poems of Hamish Henderson
cassette tape sleeve notes, 1992

Side One

The songs and poems spoken and sung here represent a sort of fusion of two of my greatest loves: the anonymous song poetry of Scotland, which I was lucky enough to hear quite a lot of from my mother when I was a child, and the comradely solidarity of the anti-Fascist struggle which dominated much of my early manhood. I soon found the music of the one love merging with the music of the other.

That is the reason I have included two traditional songs quite early on: the bawdy 'mouth tune' 'Tail Toddle', heard in Glenshee when I was a bairn, and here collated with Burns' version in 'The Merry Muses', and 'Rhynie', first sung to me by the Aberdeenshire farmer John Strachan. A tale about a clan feud, also heard in childhood, finds an echo in 'Glasclune & Drumlochy', which was 'workshopped' at an Edinburgh folk club in the early days of the Scottish folk revival. The two 'place' poems – 'Auldearn' and 'Inverey' – are rooted in the same early experiences.

In 1972 the poet and novelist Stuart MacGregor, who as a student had been a vital driving force in the early days of the revival, left Edinburgh for Jamaica, where he was to take up a temporary medical post. Memories of Robert Burns' Jamaican project of 1786 (fortunately stymied by the runaway success of the Kilmarnock edition of his poems) suggested a valedictory poem for Stuart; its background melody is, of course, 'The Silver Tassle'.

John MacLean, socialist hero and martyr of the First World War period, must surely be reckoned one of the noblest Scots in our history; the refrain of the March I wrote in his honour was suggested by Sorley MacLean's poem about his clan in which he acclaims 'great John MacLean' as *ceann is fèitheam ar sgeula* (the top anthem of our story).

Among the messages of fraternal good wishes exchanged between former allies at the height of the Cold War was one 'from the Blacksmiths of Leith to the Blacksmiths of Kiev'. 'The Song of the Gillie More' was written in honour of this event. Eric Winter, writing in the *Melody Maker,* said of the song 'It deals with the legendary fellow, larger than life, and strong as John Hendry or as the elements themselves.'

In the winter of 1944/5 verses to the tune of 'Lilli Marlene' began to circulate among the swaddies of the 8th Army; the verse most frequently heard was a gibe at Lady Astor, who was supposed to have called the troops in Italy 'D-Day Dodgers'. I put together a version of my own, which is now the one generally sung. After the war in

Italy ended I composed a 'Victory Hoedown' to the tune of 'Kate Dairymple'.

'The Ballad of the Speaking Heart' is based on a 19th-century French song by Jean Richepin. 'Under the Earth I Go' was specially written for Tim Neat's film *Journey to a Kingdom*. The background to the poem is the May Day festival in the Cornish fishing village of Padstow, during which twin 'Obby Osses' dance through the streets all day long.

Side Two

The tune of 'Rivonia' is 'Viva la Quince Brigada', a Spanish Civil War song. The refrain suggested to me the sound of African drums. According to contacts in the ANC, the song was actually heard by Nelson Mandela on Robben Island.

The sight of the devastation of German cities after World War II prompted a series of poems, of which 'A Picture in St Sebaldus Church, Nuremberg' was the first. These poems were eventually incorporated into 'Freedom Becomes People', a sequence which took its inspiration from words of Heine: 'Freedom, which has hitherto only become man here and there, must pass into the mass itself, into the lowest strata of society, and become people.'

These poems also celebrate the martyrs who endured long terms of prison and even death in the cause of freedom and social justice. The two parts of 'The Cell' also grieve for the tragic political victims who got lost in the doom-laden petrified forest of Stalinism.

Just before the outbreak of World War II, I came on a short anonymous German poem called 'Streitlied zwischen Leben und Tod' (battle song between life and death). Years later I turned it into the much longer 'Flyting o' Life and Daith', using the ballad-Scots I had become familiar with in the singing of Jeannie Robertson and other tradition-bearers.

'The Taxi Driver's Cap' developed, in the desert, out of a political squib written by the Irish poet Maurice James Craig. News of the heroic resistance put up by the Red Army against the Germans greatly encouraged swaddies in Egypt, and the figure of the unflappable pipe-smoking Uncle Joe was naturally an exceedingly popular one. However, Tom Crawford was no doubt right when he observed, in 1977, that 'the song radiates a decided irony today'.

The three parts of 'Ballad of the Simeto' are an evocation of the mood of the troops during the crossing to Sicily, the landing, and the advance which led up to the battle for the plain of Catania. The song 'Banks of Sicily', to the tune 'Farewell to the Creeks', was composed immediately after the campaign ended, and it was immediately taken up by Scots troops, becoming in effect a kind of folksong.

All these poems belong, to a greater or lesser extent, to the general category 'oral poetry', and this certainly applies to 'So Long', which was written in 1943 immediately after the fall of Tunis. It became a favourite of the late Michael Croft, founder of the National Youth Theatre, and his voice can be heard speaking it on the cassette *Return to Oasis,* a companion to the book of the same name.

The 'Freedom Come All Ye' to the pipe tune 'The Bloody Fields of Flanders', is a product of the folk revival: it was written for CND demonstrators in 1960. In it I have tried to express my hopes for Scotland, and for the survival of humanity on this beleaguered planet.

JAMES (HAMISH) SCOTT HENDERSON was born on 11 November 1919 in Blairgowrie. He was educated there and at Dulwich College, London, and studied modern languages at Cambridge. As a visiting student in Germany he acted as a courier for a Quaker network which helped refugees to escape the Nazi regime. He left Germany just before the outbreak of World War II.

He served as an intelligence officer in Europe and North Africa. From this experience of war came his poem sequence *Elegies for the Dead in Cyrenaica*, which received the Somerset Maugham Award in 1947. A lifelong socialist, he used the prize money to travel to Italy to work on his translation of the Prison Letters of Antonio Gramsci, the philosopher and founder of the Italian Communist Party.

In 1951 he accompanied the American folklorist Alan Lomax on a collecting tour in Scotland, at the beginning of an upsurge of interest in Scottish folk material and tradition. Henderson became a collector, and later a permanent member of staff with the newly-founded School of Scottish Studies in the University of Edinburgh. One of his greatest achievements was his discovery of the singer/storyteller Jeannie Robertson.

Henderson was closely involved with the Scottish folk revival, which began with the Edinburgh People's Festivals in the early 1950s: one of his most notable songs was 'The Freedom Come-All-Ye'.

Henderson held several honorary degrees and after his retirement became an honorary fellow of the School of Scottish Studies. In 1983 he refused an OBE in protest at the nuclear arms policy of the Thatcher government. He died in Edinburgh on 8 March 2002, survived by his wife Kätzel and their two daughters.

ALEC FINLAY is an artist, poet and publisher-editor of Morning Star publications and the Pocketbook series. As well as *Alias MacAlias* he edited Henderson's Selected Letters, *The Armstrong Nose*, and a selection of translations from Italian poets, *The Obscure Voice*. He lives in Byker, Newcastle, and is currently artist in residence at Yorkshire Sculpture Park.